PRACTICAL
ELECTRICAL WIRING

PRACTICAL ELECTRICAL WIRING

Residential, Farm, and Industrial

BASED ON THE 1947
NATIONAL ELECTRICAL CODE

by

H. P. RICHTER

*Member, International Association of Electrical
Inspectors, American Society of
Agricultural Engineers*

THIRD EDITION
FIFTH IMPRESSION

McGRAW-HILL BOOK COMPANY, INC.
NEW YORK AND LONDON
1947

PRACTICAL ELECTRICAL WIRING

Copyright, 1939, 1941, 1947, by the
McGraw-Hill Book Company, Inc.

Printed in the United States of America

*All rights reserved. This book, or
parts thereof, may not be reproduced
in any form without permission of
the publishers.*

THE MAPLE PRESS COMPANY, YORK, PA.

PREFACE TO THE THIRD EDITION

The wide acceptance and the continued popularity of the first two editions of this book, as well as its translation into foreign languages, have encouraged the preparation of the third edition. The appearance of a new National Electrical Code likewise urges a new edition.

While ordinarily a new Code appears every two years, this practice was not followed during the years of wartime upheaval. The latest Code was that for 1940, probably the most complicated of all Codes in practical application. During the war many interim amendments to cope with wartime emergencies and shortages were issued and repealed, making interpretation still more difficult. The new 1947 Code, the first complete revision in seven years, happily marks a sensible return to simpler tables, simpler wording, and good horse-sense application.

The science or principles of electricity do not change; the art or method of application does. That portion of this book having to do with *principles* has been revised to present such principles more clearly; that portion concerned with *methods* has been revised as required by Code changes and also to outline the methods more clearly.

The author will appreciate suggestions for improvement of the content or the presentation of this book.

H. P. RICHTER

MINNEAPOLIS, MINN.,
   August, 1947.

PREFACE TO THE FIRST EDITION

In preparing this book it has been the author's aim to make it simple enough for the beginner, yet complete enough so that it will be of value also to those already engaged in electrical work. It is intended to be, not a manual that merely recites the methods used in wiring buildings for the use of electricity, but rather a book that explains the subject in such fashion that the reader will learn both the *way* things are done and *why* they are done in that particular way. Only in this manner can the student master the subject so that he can solve his own problems as they arise in actual practice, for no book can possibly cover all the different problems that are likely to arise.

Since this book is not intended to include the subject of electrical engineering, only so many basic engineering data as are essential have been included, and these so far as possible have been boiled down to ABC proportions.

All methods shown are in strict accordance with the National Electrical Code, but no attempt has been made to include a detailed explanation of *all* subjects covered by the Code. The Code is written to include any and all cases that might arise in wiring every type of structure from the smallest cottage to the largest skyscraper; it covers ordinary wiring as well as those things that come up only very rarely. The scope of this book has been limited to the wiring of structures of limited size and at ordinary voltages, under 600 volts. Skyscrapers and steel mills and projects of similar size involve problems that the student will not meet until long after he has mastered the contents of this book.

The book consists of three parts:

Part 1 presents the fundamentals of electrical work; terminology; basic principles; the theory behind general practices. Part 2 deals with the actual wiring of residential buildings and farms. Part 3 covers the actual wiring of nonresidential buildings, such as stores, factories, schools, and similar structures.

The author acknowledges with appreciation permission to quote from "The Science of Seeing" by Matthew Luckiesh and Frank K. Moss. Other books that he has found helpful are listed in the Bibliography appearing at the end of the text.

H. P. RICHTER

EVANSTON, ILL.,
  November, 1939.

CONTENTS

	PAGE
Preface to the Third Edition	v
Preface to the First Edition	vii

Part 1. Theory and Basic Principles

CHAPTER
1. Underwriters and Codes 3
2. Electricity: Basic Principles and Measurements . . . 14
3. Types of Current; Power Factor; Transformers . . . 31
4. Basic Devices and Circuits 54
5. Overcurrent Devices 73
6. Types and Sizes of Wires 84
7. Selection of Proper Wire Sizes 101
8. Wire Connections and Joints 112
9. Theory of Grounding 127
10. Outlet and Switch Boxes 134
11. Different Wiring Methods 149
12. Branch Circuits and Service Entrance 176
13. Adequacy 203
14. Good Lighting 213
15. Residential and Farm Motors 248

Part 2. Actual Wiring: Residential and Farm

16. Planning an Installation 261
17. Installation of Service Entrance and Ground . . . 269
18. Installation of Specific Outlets 286
19. Finishing: Installation of Switches and Other Devices 315
20. Miscellaneous Wiring 324
21. Old Work 344
22. Farm Wiring 362
23. Isolated Lighting Plants 377

Part 3. Actual Wiring: Nonresidential Projects

CHAPTER	PAGE
24. Wiring Apartment Houses	385
25. 1947 Code Requirements with Respect to Wire	400
26. Planning Nonresidential Installations	415
27. Miscellaneous Problems in Nonresidential Wiring	438
28. Nonresidential Lighting	450
29. Wiring for Motors	462
30. Wiring Schools and Churches	490
31. Wiring Offices	499
32. Wiring Stores	502
33. Wiring Miscellaneous Occupancies	508
Appendix (Code Tables)	519
Bibliography	565
Index	567

PART 1
THEORY AND BASIC PRINCIPLES

Part 1 of this book is the introduction to practical electrical work, the ABC of the science and the art of electrical wiring. In order to master the art, obviously the principles involved must be clearly understood. The terms used in the measurement of electricity, the names of the devices used in wiring, must be at the student's finger tips.

For that reason a considerable portion of the material presented in Part 1 covers the "how *and why*," rather than a mere presentation of the facts as such. The "how *and why*" are more important than the facts; master both, and Parts 2 and 3 will be relatively simple.

CHAPTER 1

UNDERWRITERS AND CODES

This book will cover the ordinary methods used in installing electrical devices necessary to make up a complete system, permitting advantage to be taken of all that electricity has to offer.

In any discussion of electrical subjects, the reader will with great regularity meet with the terms "Underwriters" and "Code." It is therefore important to understand clearly just who the Underwriters are and what the Code is.

Electricity performs an endless variety of work; still, if the various parts that make up an electrical system are of questionable quality or installed in haphazard fashion, great damage may follow. Buildings may be set on fire, people may be killed, and other lesser evils follow. Individuals will be the greatest sufferers, but insurance companies will also be subject to substantial losses, with the result that insurance rates must be adjusted accordingly. It is natural therefore that insurance companies have led the way in establishing minimum standards of quality in electrical merchandise as well as uniform methods of installation—standards and methods that experience and experiment have shown lead to maximum utility with minimum hazard.

Underwriters' Laboratories.—The National Board of Fire Underwriters has established a testing organization known as Underwriters' Laboratories, Inc., with testing stations in Chicago, New York, and San Francisco. To these laboratories manufacturers who wish to do so submit samples of their product before going into production. In the laboratories the product is given exhaustive tests in accordance with established standards, and if it in every way comes up to the minimum requirements, it is listed in the Underwriters' Official published list and is then known as "Listed by Underwriters' Laboratories, Inc.," or as most people say, "Approved by Underwriters."

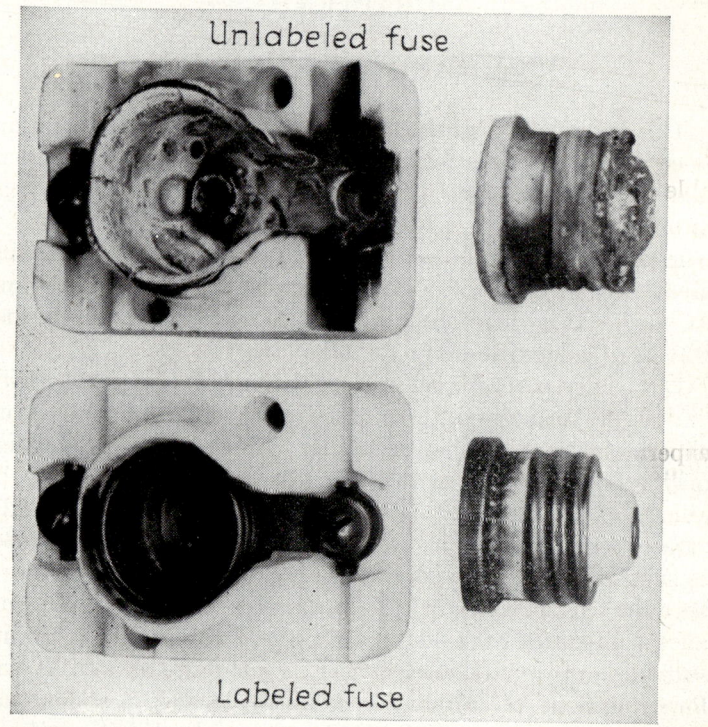

Underwriters' Laboratories, Inc.

FIG. 1-1.—After testing both fuses, the Underwriters approved the one at the bottom. The fuse at the top didn't have a chance of becoming a listed item.

It should be interesting to know that the tests by the Underwriters, and frequently also the test that the manufacturers are required to make, are many times more severe than any conditions that will be imposed upon the merchandise in actual use. For example, one of the tests required of manufacturers by the Underwriters for every foot of rubber-covered wire designed for use at not over 600 volts, most of which is never used at voltages in excess of 230, is to submerge it in water for at least 12 hr. At the end of that time it is tested against breakdown at 1,500 volts. Only after it meets this test is the wire put up into coils and labeled with the Underwriters' label.

An example of the extreme severity of tests at the Underwriters' Laboratories is that applied to all plug fuses when submitted by manufacturers for approval. Such fuses are never rated at more than 30 amp. In the laboratory test, the fuse is short-circuited across a circuit capable of delivering 5,000 amp. The fuse will naturally blow, but it must cause no damage external to itself. See Fig. 1-1, which shows two fuses after test. The one shown at the bottom of the picture passed the test successfully; the one at the top did not. In the case of the former, both fuse and fuse holder are in good condition, except that the fuse is blown; in the case of the other, both fuse and fuse holder are demolished. Used in a home, such a fuse could easily cause a fire or an injury.

In order that the product may stay on the approved list, the quality must remain at least as high as the Underwriters' minimum specifications. To make sure that it does, the Underwriters send traveling inspectors to the factory from time to time to see that the required factory tests are made and that every effort is made to preserve uniform quality. Inspectors are more or less permanently stationed at some of the larger factories. The Underwriters also regularly buy samples in the open market from merchants stocking the item and repeat the original test. If the quality is not maintained, the listing is withdrawn. There are two types of listing service by the Underwriters: reexamination and label.

Reexamination Service.—This type of service is applicable to products where it is relatively simple to maintain the quality of the original sample. Many devices fall into this classification: sockets, receptacles, outlet boxes, porcelain insulators, most appliances, etc. On such merchandise it is not necessary to test and inspect a large percentage of merchandise manufactured.

It is not essential that items falling into the reexamination classification be individually labeled to the effect that they are listed or approved, although practically all manufacturers are anxious to state this fact so that the purchasing public will not overlook it. For this purpose the uniform markers shown in

Fig. 1-2.—The markers above on merchandise or container indicate that the material is approved by Underwriters.

Fig. 1-3.—Many items have an individual label on each piece of merchandise. Above are shown a few examples.

Fig. 1-2 have been developed and are in general use, both on the merchandise and on containers.

Label Service.—This type of service is applicable to products where each piece of merchandise is individually labeled with a label that reads "Underwriters' Laboratories Inspected," or an abbreviation like "Und. Lab. Insp." Under the label service, representatives of the Underwriters' Laboratories make frequent inspections at the factory to examine and test samples of the labeled product. Into this classification fall wire and cable of all kinds, conduit, switches of all kinds,

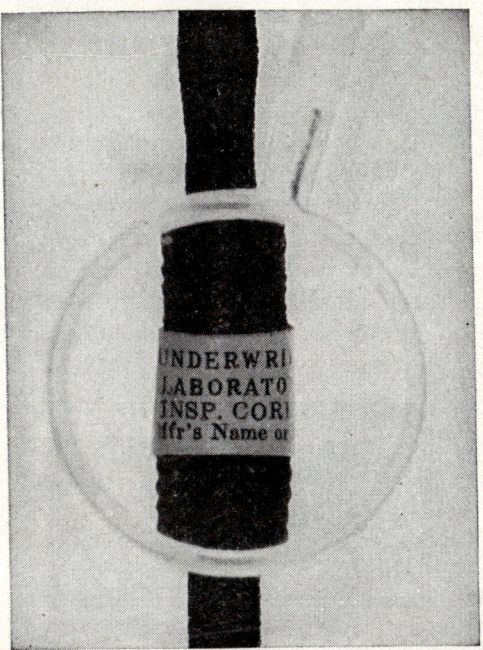

International Assn. of Elec. Inspectors.
FIG. 1-4.—Lamp cords have a bracelet label every 5 ft.

lighting fixtures, and similar devices. Examples of the labels used on the merchandise are seen in Fig. 1-3.

Lamp cords receive a special label which is applied in bracelet fashion every 5 ft. on the cord, so that, when it is sold over the counter, the purchaser definitely knows that he is buying safe, sound merchandise (see Fig. 1-4). The bracelet label likewise is of great value when devices such as floor lamps, for example, are sold. The presence of the label on the cord testifies that the cord is approved.

The presence of such a bracelet label on the cord used in an assembly, such as an appliance cord or extension cord, indicates only that the lamp cord used in the assembly is approved; the devices used on the ends of the cord may still be unapproved. Today every assembly if it is approved must bear, slipped over the cord, a "doughnut" label of the type illustrated in Fig. 1-5, indicating that the complete assembly is approved. The bracelet is used mostly on lamp cords sold by the foot over the counter.

Fig. 1-5.—Cord assemblies bear "doughnut" labels slipped over the lamp cord of which they are made.

In certain classes of devices—such as toggle switches—the words "Und. Lab. Insp." are molded or stamped or otherwise made an integral part of the merchandise and constitute the label. Look for these words molded or stamped into bakelite, steel, or porcelain parts of such devices.

Underwriters' Laboratories, Inc.

Fig. 1-6.—Merchandise which is only tentatively approved bears the "trial-installation" label.

Trial Installations.—From time to time new types of wire or other electrical devices are developed. Laboratory tests may show the new product to be in every way practical and suitable for general use, yet it may be deemed desirable to give the new product the benefit of practical field tests in actual use before giving it final approval for general use. In that case the product is classified as "trial-installation" material—the product is listed or approved, but only for limited use in trial installations. Figure 1-6 shows a label for this class of merchandise, approved temporarily for experimental purposes only. Under this label the item may be used only with the approval of the local electrical inspector and under such conditions as he may direct. Installations are kept under close observation to gain as much experience as possible, and if over a period of some years the new product lives up to expectations in every way, it may then be given full-fledged listing or approval for general use.

How Underwriters Are Supported.—Underwriters' Laboratories being a nonprofit organization, their cost of operation is absorbed by the manufacturers who submit merchandise. There is a fee for testing merchandise, and when a manufacturer buys from the Underwriters the labels for his product, he pays more than the bare cost of the label, the difference being a service charge which pays for inspectors' expenses in checking at the factories and also supports the laboratories in general.

Purpose of Underwriters.—What good is accomplished by all this? The public is assured that the products bought, if listed or approved, have at least a minimum of safety, quality, and utility. As far as manufacturers are concerned, they know that competitors' goods automatically meet the minimum requirements of the Underwriters, that no one is skimping on quality. As far as the insurance companies are concerned, they are assured of smaller losses than would be the case if merchandise of substandard quality were used. This is obviously an arrangement by which everybody benefits.

"Approved by Underwriters" does not mean that all approved products are of equal quality. It merely means that those approved do meet the *minimum* requirements of the Underwriters. For example, one approved toggle switch may outlast another approved switch by five times, although both meet the minimum safety requirements.

"Approved by Underwriters" means that the material in question is approved for the purpose for which it was designed, but not for other purposes. For example, flexible lamp cord is intended for use in connecting lamps, clocks, and similar portable devices consuming nominal amperages, to plug-in receptacles. It is not designed for or intended for use in adding wiring to an existing installation. Figure 1-7 shows the result of misusing it for a purpose for which it was not intended. A serious fire could easily have occurred, even if the material was approved; it was approved for a purpose other than that for which it was used.

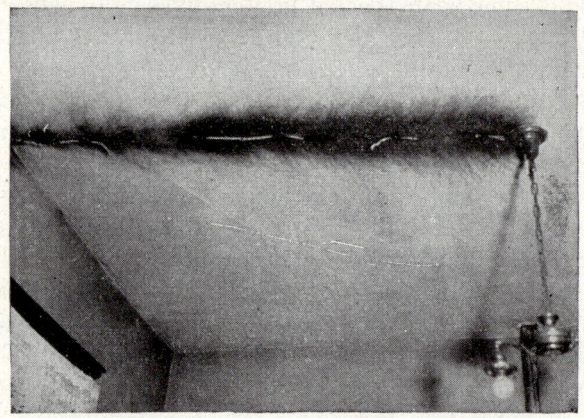

International Assn. of Elec. Inspectors.

Fig. 1-7.—Misuse of extension cord here could easily have caused a fire far more serious than the picture shows. Do not use materials for purposes for which they were not intended.

Identification.—In any event, regardless of whether a product is listed under reexamination or label service, it must always be identified by the manufacturer's name or trade-mark, by a number that has been assigned by the Underwriters, or by some arbitrary symbol, and in addition by a type or catalogue description, or by an "Inspected" label, so that it may be recognized as approved merchandise.

How to Recognize Approved Merchandise.—How is the public to recognize approved merchandise when they see it? If the merchandise is labeled "Underwriters' Laboratories Inspected" or with an abbreviation indicating the same, it is approved. If the merchandise or its carton bears the UL insignia of Fig. 1-2, it is approved. If it does not bear the manufacturer's marking or other designation which will identify it, it is not a listed item. Reference to the Underwriters' list of approved devices will establish in any event whether the merchandise is approved or not. The safest policy is to buy electrical merchandise only from concerns that have a reputation to maintain and that cannot afford to jeopardize it by selling unapproved merchandise.

It does not follow that just because an item is not approved it cannot be good merchandise, as some manufacturers have an exaggerated idea of the cost of having an item approved, and others just do not care; for these reasons they do not submit their merchandise for approval. The presumption, however, is against merchandise that is not approved.

In fairness it must be stated that the Underwriters do not concern themselves at all with certain devices on which it is a simple matter to maintain good quality, or which present no hazard whatever. In this class are, for example, low-voltage devices, such as doorbell wires and doorbells. Strangely, electric motors, except those of the explosion-proof type, are not listed.

National Electrical Code.—If electrical devices of high quality are used, but installed in a haphazard fashion and with no regard to the relation of one device to the other or the total load they may be called upon to carry, the complete installation may still be of a hazardous nature. It is necessary therefore that standardized methods be set up which have been found in practice to present no hazard.

These standardized methods that experiment and experience have shown to be correct are set down in a form which has come to be known as the National Electrical Code. Whenever in this book the word "Code" is used, it refers to this National Electrical Code, abbreviated N.E.C. Its purpose is admirably outlined in a paragraph of a pamphlet on the subject by the International Association of Electrical Inspectors, which reads as follows:

The National Electrical Code is a collection of rules and regulations governing the installation, and, to a certain extent, the use of electrical equipment. Its purpose is to reduce the hazard from electrical fires and electrical accidents, and it does this by specifying the exact manner in which electrical materials, devices, fittings and appliances shall be both originally installed and later maintained. A strict compliance with the requirements of the National Electrical Code will produce an electrical installation which may be deemed reasonably safe from electrical fires or accidents at the time of its installation and which, with proper maintenance, should remain in a safe condition over a period of years.

The purpose of the Code will be better understood by reading the following paragraph from the Code itself:

The provisions of this Code constitute a minimum standard. Compliance therewith and proper ma'ntenance will result in an installation reasonably free from hazard but not necessarily efficient or convenient. This Code is to be regarded neither as a design specification nor an instruction manual for untrained persons. Good service and satisfactory results will often require larger sizes of wire, more branch circuits, and better types of equipment than the minimum which is here specified.

The National Electrical Code is ordinarily revised every two years or so. During the war, however, no new Code was issued between 1940 and 1947 (see Preface to third edition). The wiring methods shown in this book are in accordance with the new 1947 Code.

The Code is not written by one man or by just a few people. Each phase of the work is handled by those in the industry who are most competent. The exact procedure is outlined in the following paragraphs, quoting again from the same pamphlet of the International Association of Electrical Inspectors:

The preparation of the National Electrical Code is now under the supervision of the Electrical Committee, a technical committee of the National Fire Protection Association and a sectional committee, according to the procedure of the American Standards Association.

The National Fire Protection Association is a group which includes a wide variety of interests concerned with, or directly connected with, fire prevention. The membership represents federal, state and city governments, consumers, engineering societies, insurance and inspection groups, public utilities, electrical dealers, contractors, manufacturers and others.

The American Standards Association is the recognized organization through which industrial standards are promulgated . . . .

The Electrical Committee at the present time consists of a Chairman, a Secretary, 44 members and 40 Alternates.

Enforcement of the Code.—The question should by this time logically arise as to what jurisdiction insurance companies or their laboratories or a group of manufacturers may have over individuals—why one should not be allowed to use such merchandise as he pleases and in such fashion as he pleases. The answer is that these bodies have no jurisdiction whatever and that so far as they are concerned the individual may do as he pleases. However, he is still obligated to obey the laws of the state, or city, or other municipality, and with few exceptions, these lawmaking bodies pass laws or ordinances which require that the provisions of the National Electrical Code must be observed in the territory involved. Another important consideration is that fire insurance companies may refuse to issue policies covering premises that are not properly wired.

Aside from all legal requirements, common sense suggests that the individual take advantage of the experience of those who know more about the subject than he does—such experience of experts collectively comprising the National Electrical Code.

Local Codes.—The National Electrical Code defines in a broad way what may and may not be done in the line of wiring, the different methods that are permitted, and so on. Frequently the local ordinances limit the National Code, so that only a portion of what it permits is then permitted locally. For example, the National Code specifies that under certain conditions a conduit system, an armored cable system, a nonmetallic system, or one of several other systems may be used in wiring a house. The local code or ordinance may specify that all these systems may be used locally, except armored cable. It is therefore important that the student and the contractor be familiar not only with the National Electrical Code[1] but also with the local codes or ordinances that apply in their locality.

[1] A copy of the National Electrical Code may be obtained by sending 15 cts. for postage to the National Board of Fire Underwriters, 85 John St., New York, N.Y., 222 W. Adams St., Chicago, Ill., or 1014 Merchants Exchange, San Francisco, Calif.

CHAPTER 2

ELECTRICITY: BASIC PRINCIPLES AND MEASUREMENTS

Many terms are used in the study of electricity. Here will be explained only those necessary to understand clearly the problems that come up in ordinary electrical installations.

Volts.—In blowing up a toy balloon, very little work is involved, for the volume is small and the pressure involved is low, probably 1 lb. per square inch or less. In a bicycle tire the pressure is about 20 lb. per square inch. In automobile and truck tires the pressures range from 30 to 60 lb. per square inch, while in the compressor that inflates them it may be 150 lb. per square inch. Many torpedoes fired from the Navy's submarines are powered by compressed-air motors, and the pressure in the tanks in the torpedo may be 3,000 lb. or more per square inch.

If a bicycle tire is pumped up by hand, it is more work to pump it up to 20 lb. pressure than it is to pump it to only 10 lb. pressure. If a pressure tank were involved, having the same number of cubic inches capacity as the bicycle tire, and it were required to pump it to 500 lb. pressure, it would obviously take much longer and would be more work than to inflate the bicycle tire to the same pressure. *The work involved is proportionate to the pressure involved, so long as* **the volume** *of the inflated vessel remains the same.*

Similarly, there are differences of *electrical* pressure, only instead of being measured in pounds per square inch, they are measured in volts. One volt[1] is not a very great pressure, so

---

[1] The volt is named after Count Alessandro Volta (1745–1827), one of the great pioneer scientists who had much to do with the early development of electricity. For example, he discovered that when two dissimilar metals are immersed in an acid an electric current will flow through a wire that connects the two metals.

for commercial purposes, higher pressures or voltages are used. An ordinary flashlight cell (regardless of size) or an ordinary dry cell battery develops 1½ volts (approximately) when new and fresh. Four of them connected in series as in the battery commonly known as a "hot-shot" produce 6 volts; 30 of them make a 45-volt B battery such as used in non-electric radios. A single cell of a storage battery develops 2 volts when fully charged; three of them in series develop 6 volts as in an automobile battery; 16 of them develop 32 volts as in the case of a farm-lighting-plant battery.

Kilovolts.—The Greek word "kilo" means "thousand." Therefore 1 kilovolt is 1,000 volts; 20 kilovolts is 20,000 volts. It is much simpler when speaking of high voltages to say "50 kv." than to say "50,000 volts."

Amperes.—Voltage alone defines only what the pressure of an electric current is; it does not define the quantity of electrical energy involved. Go back to the comparison with air. Assume that there are two rubber tires to be inflated *to the same pressure in pounds per square inch:* one a small bicycle tire, the other a much larger automobile tire. Everybody knows that it is much more work to pump up the larger tire by hand than it is to pump up the smaller tire, even if the pressure is the same. If both are pumped to 20 lb. per square inch *in the same number of minutes,* more work must be done per minute. If the pumper works only as hard to inflate the larger tire as when inflating the smaller tire, he must work a longer time. *The work is proportionate to the number of cubic feet of air pumped, so long as* **the final pressure** *remains the same.*

Electricity is not measured in quarts or pounds or cubic feet, but the rate at which it flows is measured in amperes. The ampere[1,2] measures the rate at which electricity is flowing,

[1] The ampere is named after André Marie Ampère, another great scientist of the early nineteenth century, who discovered many of the fundamental laws concerning the flow of electrical current.

[2] In these days of electronics and atom bombs, a word may be in order to those who are interested in the purely scientific aspect of the subject. A current of 1 ampere is said to flow when 1 coulomb of electricity flows

just as water is measured in gallons per minute, or air in cubic feet per minute. Note that the term is not "amperes per minute" but just "amperes." Pounds and gallons and cubic feet each denote a quantity, but an ampere is not a quantity of electricity; it is merely a term describing the *rate* at which electricity flows, the quantity itself being measured in coulombs or electrons. The term "ampere" might be compared in air flow to a nonexistent term that would express the *rate* at which air must uniformly flow so that at the end of one minute exactly one cubic foot has flowed.

Ampere-hour.—If electricity has flowed at the rate of one ampere for one hour, the total is called an ampere-hour. The term is little used except in storage battery work.

Watts.—Just as it requires more work to deliver a quantity of air at 25 lb. pressure than it does to deliver the same quantity at 10 lb. pressure (or to deliver 25 cu. ft. at any given pressure than to deliver 10 cu. ft. at the same pressure), so also does it require more energy or work to deliver 10 amp. or any other amperage at 115 volts than it does to deliver the same amperage at, say, 6 volts pressure. In any given case, multiply the volts by the amperes; the result is the *watts* flowing in a circuit. The watt[1] measures the total energy or power flowing in a circuit *at any particular moment*, just as horsepower denotes the energy developed by an engine. Indeed, horsepower and watts are merely two different ways of measuring or expressing

---

past a given point in 1 second. That is equivalent to a flow of 6,280,-000,000,000,000,000 electrons per second past a given point. However, it is entirely safe to forget all about coulombs and electrons per second, except for those who intend to delve very thoroughly into basic electrical engineering—and even for those the exact figure is of more academic than practical interest. For those who are interested in comparing numbers as such, it may be interesting to note that the big number shown above, representing the number of electrons moving past a given point when a current of one ampere flows, is approximately two million times greater than the number that represents the number of seconds that have elapsed in the 1947 years since the beginning of the Christian era.

[1] The watt is named after one of the eighteenth century scientists, James Watt, the Englishman who invented the steam engine and originally defined the horsepower.

rate of work or power; for 746 watts are always equal to 1 horsepower.

If a light bulb consumes 746 watts, it would be entirely correct to call it a 1-hp. bulb, although that method of designating bulbs is never used. Likewise it would be entirely correct to state that a motor which has an output of 1 hp. has an output of 746 watts, although that method of designating power of motors is not used (except in the case of "flea-power" motors which are sometimes rated, for example, "approximately $1\frac{1}{2}$ watts output," instead of being rated as "$\frac{1}{500}$ hp."). It should be noted however that a motor which delivers 1 hp. or 746 watts of power actually consumes more nearly 1,000 watts from the power line. The difference between the 1,000 watts consumed and the 746 watts delivered as useful power is consumed as heat in the motor, to overcome bearing friction, to overcome wind resistance of the moving parts, and similar factors.

Again it should be noted that the electrical term is just "watts," not "watts *per hour.*" One would not say that the engine in an automobile delivers 80 hp. *per hour;* at any given moment it delivers 80 hp., the power that 80 horses would or could deliver at any one moment if working simultaneously. Both watts and horsepower denote a *rate* at which work is being done, not a *quantity* of work being done in a given time.

From the above it should be evident that a given wattage may be a combination of any voltage whatsoever and the correspondingly correct amperage. For example:

$$3 \text{ volts} \times 120 \text{ amp.} = 360 \text{ watts}$$
$$6 \text{ volts} \times 60 \text{ amp.} = 360 \text{ watts}$$
$$12 \text{ volts} \times 30 \text{ amp.} = 360 \text{ watts}$$
$$60 \text{ volts} \times 6 \text{ amp.} = 360 \text{ watts}$$
$$120 \text{ volts} \times 3 \text{ amp.} = 360 \text{ watts}$$
$$360 \text{ volts} \times 1 \text{ amp.} = 360 \text{ watts}$$

Carrying the illustration farther, a bulb in an automobile headlight consuming 10 amp. from a 6-volt battery consumes a total of 10×6, or 60 watts; a bulb consuming $\frac{1}{2}$ amp. from a 120-volt lighting circuit in a home consumes a total of

½ × 120, or 60 watts. The voltages and the amperages differ widely, but the wattages of the two bulbs are the same.

This simple formula is not correct under all circumstances; the exceptions will be covered in a later chapter.

Kilowatts.—Since a watt is a very small amount of energy, large quantities of power measured and stated in watts lead to rather unwieldy figures. Therefore the Greek word "kilo" is again used, one kilowatt (abbreviated "kw.") being 1,000 watts, 10 kw. being 10,000 watts, and so on.

Watt-hours.—The watt merely indicates the total amount of electrical energy that is flowing at a given moment; it tells us nothing about the total quantity of electrical energy that has flowed during a period of time, just as knowing how hard a man is working at any given time is a useful bit of information, but of no value in establishing what the man should be paid for a day's work, if he did not work at a uniform rate during the entire day. Multiplying the watts flowing at one time by the number of hours during which this number of watts flowed gives us *watt-hours*, which definitely measures the total amount of electrical energy consumed or flowing during a given time. For example:

$$10 \text{ watts} \times 1{,}000 \text{ hours} = 10{,}000 \text{ watt-hours}$$
$$100 \text{ watts} \times 100 \text{ hours} = 10{,}000 \text{ watt-hours}$$
$$1{,}000 \text{ watts} \times 10 \text{ hours} = 10{,}000 \text{ watt-hours}$$
$$5{,}000 \text{ watts} \times 2 \text{ hours} = 10{,}000 \text{ watt-hours}$$
$$20{,}000 \text{ watts} \times \tfrac{1}{2} \text{ hour} = 10{,}000 \text{ watt-hours}$$

Kilowatt-hours.—Once more the Greek "kilo" is used, so that 1 kilowatt-hour (kw.-hr.) is 1,000 watt-hours, 20 kilowatt-hours is 20,000 watt-hours, etc. Power is paid for by the kilowatt-hour.

Reading Meters.—Reading meters of the type shown in Fig. 2-1 needs no explanation. The most modern kilowatt-hour meters have a cyclometer dial, as shown in Fig. 2-2, and they are the most easily read. Older meters, like that shown in Fig. 2-3, have a register, shown in approximately full size in Figs. 2-4 and 2-5, with two different readings. There are four dials, on two of which the figures read from left to right in clockwise fashion, on the other two in the opposite or counterclockwise fashion. Simply write down the last number the pointer has *passed* on each dial, considering the direction in which the pointer moves.

Refer to Fig. 2-4, and write down the proper numbers, as indicated by the pointers. The first (left-hand) pointer is between 2 and 3, so write down 2; the second is between 7 and 8, so write down 7; the third is between 4 and 5, so write down 4; the last is between 6 and 7, so write down 6. This makes 2,746 and indicates that 2,746 kw.-hr. of energy have been used since the meter was put into use.

Weston Elec. Inst. Co.

Fig. 2-1.—Meters of this type are simple to read.

Now write down the readings in Fig. 2-5, which represents the same meter a month later. The first pointer presents no problem; write down 3. The second pointer, however, points directly at 2; shall one write down 2 or 1? If a watch had no minute hand but only an hour hand and that pointed to 4, how

Westinghouse Elec. & Mfg. Co.

Fig. 2-2.—This type of dial is found on the most modern kilowatt-hour meter.

Westinghouse Elec. & Mfg. Co.

Fig. 2-3.—The ordinary meter formerly produced is a little harder to read.

would one know whether the time was 3:58 or 4:02? There would be no way of knowing. However, the watch does have a minute hand, and if it points to 2 min. before 12, it is 3:58; but if it points to 2 min. after 12, it is 4:02. In other words, the minute hand tells whether the hour hand has not reached 4 or is a little after 4. Similarly on the watt-hour meter, look at the pointer on the dial to the right of the one that points

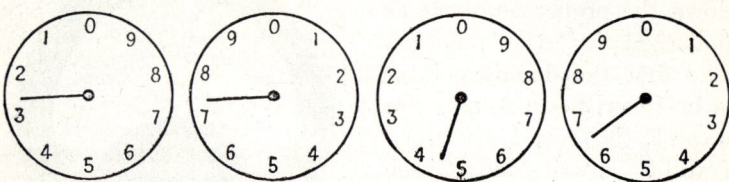

Fig. 2-4.—Enlarged register of a kilowatt-hour meter. Read the figure the pointer has passed. The reading above is 2,746 kw.-hr.

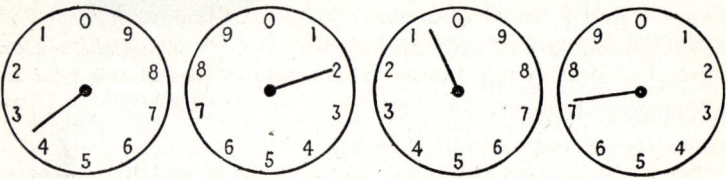

Fig. 2-5.—The meter now reads 3,207 kw.-hr.

directly to a figure. If it has not reached 0, the pointer to the left has not reached the figure to which it apparently points. In this particular case, the second pointer points directly at 2, but since the third pointer is between 0 and 1, the second one must point a little after the 2, so write down 2. The third and fourth pointers present no difficulty; write down 0, 7, making 3,207 kw.-hr. The difference between 3,207 and 2,746, or 461, obviously represents the kilowatt-hours used since the previous reading.

Some meters used for measuring very large quantities of power may have a notation on the dials "multiply by 10" or "multiply by 100," in which case the indicated kilowatt-hours must be multiplied by 10 or 100, as the case may be, to arrive at the correct number of kilowatt-hours used.

Power Consumed by Various Devices.—It will be well to know the approximate power consumed by common everyday devices used in homes. These wattages are as follows:

Lamp bulbs	7½	to	300
Radios	50	to	150
Heating pads	10	to	35
Refrigerators	200	to	275
Vacuum cleaners	150	to	400
Food mixers	150	to	250
Fans	25	to	100
Sewing machines	40	to	75
Electric clocks	1	to	3
Christmas-tree lights (per string)	25	to	50
Flatirons, toasters	600	to	1,000
Waffle irons	500	to	660
Roasters	600	to	1,500
Portable heaters	600	to	1,500
Hotplates, per burner	500	to	1,000
Ranges (maximum heat, all burners)	4,500	to	12,500
Hot-water heater	2,000	to	4,000
Mangles	1,000	to	1,500
Sun lamps	250	to	600
Motors, ¼ hp	250	to	300
Motors, ½ hp	450	to	500

Figuring an Electric Bill.—The cost of electricity varies a great deal between localities, and also with the amount used per month. For residential and farm use it seldom falls below 1 ct. and seldom rises over 10 cts. per kilowatt-hour. The average for the United States is well under 5 cts. per kilowatt-hour. Usually there is a step rate; the more power that is used per month, the lower the cost per kilowatt-hour. For example, a typical rate is as follows:

First 60 kw.-hr	6 cts. per kilowatt-hour
Next 40 kw.-hr	3 cts. per kilowatt-hour
Over 100 kw.-hr	2 cts. per kilowatt-hour

Assuming a monthly consumption of 461 kw.-hr., the total bill would be

60 kw.-hr. @ 6 cts	$ 3.60
40 kw.-hr. @ 3 cts	1.20
361 kw.-hr. @ 2 cts	7.22
Total 461 kw.-hr	$12.02
Average per kilowatt-hour	$2\frac{7}{10}$¢ (approx.)

To determine the cost of operating any electrical device for 1 hr., multiply the watts consumed by the rate in cents per kilowatt-hour and point off five decimal places, giving the cost directly in dollars per hour. For example, assume a 1,000-watt flatiron at a rate of 5 cts. $1,000 \times 5 = 5,000$; pointing off five decimals gives 0.05000, or 5 cts. per hour. For a 40-watt bulb the figures are $40 \times 5 = 200$; pointing off five

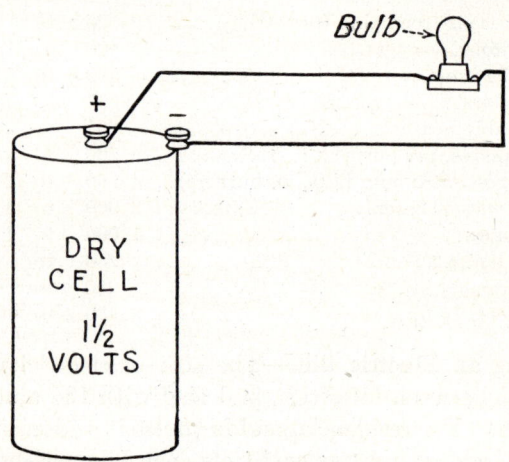

Fig. 2-6.—Dry cells, no matter how large or small, develop $1\frac{1}{2}$ volts when new.

places gives 0.00200, or $\frac{2}{10}$ cts. per hour, 5 hr. for 1 ct. The oven on a range may consume 1,800 watts, and at 2 cts. per kilowatt-hour the figures are $1,800 \times 2 = 3,600$; pointing off five decimals gives 0.03600, or a little over $3\frac{1}{2}$ cts. per hour.

To determine the number of hours any device can be operated to consume 1 kw.-hr., simply divide 1,000 by the wattage of the device. Obviously a 1,000-watt bulb can be used just 1 hr.; a 50-watt bulb, 20 hr.; a large motor consuming 2,000 watts, $\frac{1}{2}$ hr.; and so on.

Conductors and Nonconductors.—When a bulb is connected through a piece of wire across the two terminals of a dry cell, as shown in Fig. 2-6, current flows for the bulb lights. Yet no current flows through the wax that is poured over the top of the dry cell, nor does it flow through the paper carton that makes contact with the terminals of the cell during shipment. If a material will permit current to flow through it, it is known as a "conductor"; if it will not permit current to flow, it is a "nonconductor" or "insulator."

Resistance.—Experiment has shown that, if the two ends of a piece of No. 10 wire (which happens to be 0.1019 in. in diameter), made of copper and exactly 1,003 ft. long, are connected to a source of electricity delivering exactly 1 volt, exactly 1 amp. of current will flow.

If, however, a wire of *exactly the same diameter and length* but made of aluminum is substituted, then only $6/10$ amp. flows. Substitute iron, and the current drops still more, to about $1/6$ amp. Substitute a column of mercury, and the current drops to a very small fraction of its original value, about $1/60$ amp. In other words, different metals under identical circumstances permit different amperages to flow, or, stating it in a different way, different metals resist the flow of current to different degrees. The resistance is measured in ohms. A given length of wire or other conductor is said to have a resistance of one ohm[1] if it permits exactly one ampere to flow when connected to a source of electricity delivering exactly one volt.

Ohm's Law.—In a preceding paragraph it was shown that 1 volt forces exactly 1 amp. to flow through different lengths of wire each made of different materials, but each with exactly 1 ohm of resistance. Experiment shows further that, if the voltage is doubled, 2 amp. will flow; if it is 5 volts instead of 1 volt, 5 amp. will flow. *So long as other conditions remain constant, the amperage is in direct proportion to the voltage.*

Still further experiment shows that, if the voltage remains constant and the material in the wire is not changed but its cross-sectional area (not its diameter) is doubled, twice the amperage will flow. If the wire is increased to 5 times its original cross-sectional area, 5 times the amperage will flow. *So long as other conditions remain constant, the amperage is in*

---

[1] The ohm is named after Georg Simon Ohm, a German scientist of the early nineteenth century, who discovered the basic laws concerning resistance.

direct proportion to the cross-sectional area of the wire. Remembering that doubling the diameter of a circle increases its area 4 times, tripling the diameter increases the area 9 times, it is evident that, so long as other conditions do not change, doubling the diameter of a wire increases the amperage 4 times, increasing the diameter 3 times increases the amperage 9 times etc.

The data given above pertain only when the wire in question is connected directly across a source of electricity. The conclusion should not be reached that doubling the cross-sectional area of the wire used to connect a motor, for example, will double the amperage flowing through the motor. The wire used for connections is only a small portion of the total wire in the circuit; the wire inside the motor must also be taken into consideration.

The basic principles and definitions outlined in the preceding paragraphs make it easy to recreate the well-known formula, known as Ohm's law, for calculating resistance, voltage, and amperage. If two of these factors are known, it is easy to calculate the missing one. The formula is

$$\frac{\text{Volts}}{\text{Amperes}} = \text{ohms.}$$

For brevity, it is customary to use the standard symbols for these three factors:

E for voltage.
I for amperes.
R for ohms.

The same formula then becomes $\frac{E}{I} = R$. If by measurement the voltage is 10 and the amperage is 2, the resistance must be 5 ohms. Likewise, if the voltage is 110 and the amperage is 22, the resistance is 5 ohms.

The formula can be transposed easily so that instead of

$$\frac{E}{I} = R,$$

ELECTRICITY: PRINCIPLES AND MEASUREMENTS

it becomes
$$\frac{E}{R} = I,$$
or the third form
$$E = I \times R.$$

Divide the voltage by the amperes to find the ohms. Divide the voltage by the ohms to find the amperes. Multiply the amperes by the ohms to find the volts.

Careful inspection of the formula will confirm the facts pointed out in the previous paragraphs:

Voltage being constant, reduce resistance (increase size of wire) to increase the amperage.

Resistance (size and length of wire) being constant, increase voltage to increase amperage.

Amperage being constant, reduce resistance (increase size of wire) to permit lower voltage to be used.

Dangerous Voltages.—Whether any given voltage is dangerous to human life depends on a great many factors. Sometimes a voltage as low as 115 is fatal, yet at other times individuals come in contact with much higher voltages and survive. The sensible course to follow is *safety first*—assume that any voltage of 115 and upward is dangerous. In specific cases, everything depends on such factors as the health of the individual, whether he is in contact with a grounded object, the amperage available along with the voltage, and many other factors. For example, the voltage involved when one touches a spark plug in a car is of the order of several thousand volts, yet results only in an unpleasant shock. It is a very brief shock; if the current were continued, it would perhaps be fatal for at least some individuals.

Voltage Drop.—All conductors have resistance; it requires energy to force a current through them. Assume a motor connected through a *long* length of wire to a source of electricity. Connecting a voltmeter directly across the circuit of Fig. 2-7 will indicate the full voltage, probably 115 volts. The same meter connected directly across the motor will indicate a lower figure, probably 110 volts. The difference of 5 volts has been consumed in forcing the current through the wire.

The voltage that is lost in forcing current through the wire is known as "voltage drop." It is wasted power so far as useful purpose is concerned; it merely heats the wires. Excessive voltage drop also is responsible for many other bad effects, which will be discussed in Chap. 7.

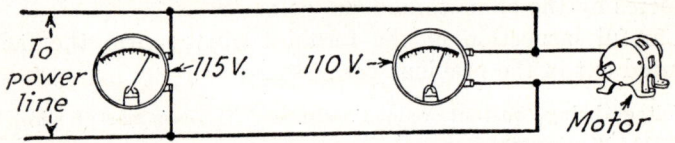

FIG. 2-7.—This circuit illustrates voltage drop.

Voltage drop is like lost pressure in a water hose. If a short hose is attached to a water faucet at the side of a house, water can be squirted, say, 50 ft. If a long length of hose is attached to the same faucet, one will be able to squirt only a lesser distance, say 35 ft. A pressure gauge might indicate 35 lb. pressure at the faucet but at the end of the hose only 20 lb. pressure. The difference is expended in forcing water through the hose, and it corresponds to voltage drop in a wire.

The actual amount of voltage drop is easily calculated if the resistance of the wire and the amperage are known, using Ohm's law, $E = I \times R$. For example, if the amperage is $7\frac{1}{2}$ and the resistance is 2 ohms, the voltage drop is $7\frac{1}{2}$ amp. $\times$ 2 ohms, or 15 volts.

From this it is equally simple to calculate the amount of power wasted. Remembering that watts = volts $\times$ amperes, the loss in the example of the previous paragraph is 15 volts $\times$ $7\frac{1}{2}$ amp., or $112\frac{1}{2}$ watts.

Assume now that in the same example the amperage is doubled so that 15 amp. flow instead of $7\frac{1}{2}$. The voltage drop now is 15 amp. $\times$ 2 ohms, or 30 volts. *Doubling the amperage doubled the voltage drop.* Calculating the wattage loss involved, 30 volts $\times$ 15 amp., gives 450 watts. *Doubling the amperage increased the wattage loss 4 times.* The wattage loss in a circuit is proportional to the *square* of the amperage. Current cannot be made to pass through a wire without some loss; but doubling the amperage of the load (which is the same as doubling the wattage so long as the starting voltage does not change) increases the wasted watts by 4 times; tripling the amperage increases the wasted watts by 9 times; etc.

The formula for wattage loss has already been given as

Wattage loss = amperes × voltage drop.

However, since voltage drop = amperes × ohms, substituting "amperes × ohms" for "voltage drop" in the first formula gives this new formula:

Wattage loss = amperes × amperes × ohms = I^2R.

This merely puts into formula form the statement of the previous paragraph that the wattage loss is proportional to the *square* of the amperage.

Operating Voltage.—Previous paragraphs explained the fact that the greater the amperage in a wire, the greater the voltage drop, and the greater the wattage lost in the form of heat. From this it should be obvious that, in order to carry high amperages without undue loss, large sizes of wire are required. The greater the distance, the heavier the wire must be. Therefore it is distinctly advantageous to keep amperages as low as is practical.

This, at least in theory, is simple, for any given wattage may consist of a low voltage with high amperage, or a high voltage with low amperage. Therefore relatively high voltages must be used, automatically giving correspondingly low amperages.

In practice, the actual voltage depends on the amount of power to be transmitted and the distance. In an automobile, while the wattage is fairly heavy at times, a battery of only 6 volts is used, even if the amperage flowing through the starting motor when it is cranking the engine is as much as 250 amp.; this is practical only because the distance is so short.

On a farm lighting plant usually a battery of 32 volts is

used. The distances are seldom over a few hundred feet, and the amperages are reasonable.

For ordinary city residential lighting the voltage is usually 115,[1] while for ranges and water heaters it is 230 volts. For industrial purposes, where the wattages are great, voltages of 440 and 550 are usually used.

The distribution lines that run down the city alleys are usually 2,300 volts, but the main distribution lines are at still higher voltages, until, for long-distance cross-country distribution, the voltages are over 100,000 volts.

Three-wire Systems.—Since it is advantageous to keep amperages as low as possible in order to reduce voltage and wattage losses in the wires and to do away with the necessity of buying large size wire when a smaller size will do, and since this can be done by making the voltage higher, it would appear entirely logical to use a high voltage for all purposes. One might ask: "Why not use, for ordinary house wiring, 230 volts or 500 volts, or higher?"

First of all, the higher voltages require heavier insulation, so that wire becomes more expensive; the higher voltages are more dangerous in case of accidental contact. Another important consideration is the fact that in the manufacture of devices consuming relatively low wattage, under 100 watts, the wire used inside the device is often of almost microscopic dimensions, even when the device is for a voltage as low as 115 volts. For example, the tungsten wire in the filament of a 60-watt 115-volt bulb as manufactured today is only 0.0018 in. in diameter; in a 3-watt bulb it is about 0.00033 in.[2] in diameter. If the device were for 230-volt use or for an even higher voltage, the wire would have to be still smaller, making factory production and uniformity decidedly difficult. The

[1] The voltage is often referred to as 110 volts, although today actually it is usually either 115 or 120 volts, with the trend toward 120 volts. Throughout this book, whenever the terms "115 volts" and "230 volts" are used, they will mean the common voltages, whether they happen to be 110 and 220, 115 and 230, or 120 and 240.

[2] To cover a space of 1 in., 3,000 such filaments would have to be laid side by side.

device would also be more fragile, and it would burn out more easily. The present common level of 115 volts is a compromise for lowest over-all cost of installation, operation, and purchase of devices to be operated.

However, since the same home may use small devices consuming from 5 to 500 watts, also appliances like electric ranges which may consume over 10,000 watts, it would be desirable to have available two different voltages, one relatively low for the low-wattage devices, and one relatively high for the high-wattage devices. Fortunately this can be simply done by using the 3-wire system, which provides both 115 and

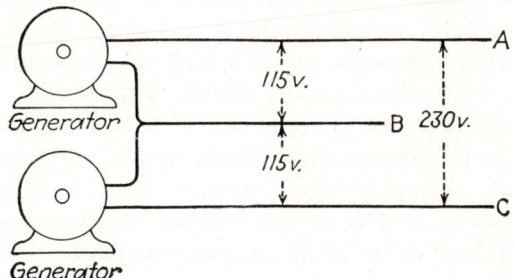

Fig. 2-8.—With only three wires, two separate voltages are available.

230 volts. Only three incoming wires are used and only a single meter. The 3-wire 115/230-volt system constitutes the ordinary system as installed in practically all houses and farms. The higher voltage is usually used for any single device consuming over 1,650 watts.

Figure 2-8 shows two generators, each delivering 115 volts; the two combined deliver 230 volts. Any device connected to either wires A and B or wires B and C will be connected to 115 volts. Any device connected to wires A and C will be connected to 230 volts. In actual use the center or neutral wire B is usually white; the outer two or "hot" wires are black. Connect any device operating on 115 volts to one black and one white wire, and any device operating on 230 volts to the two black wires. (These colors are correct only on grounded-neutral systems; this will be explained in the chapter on grounding. Practically all installations today have a grounded neutral.)

Effects of Electricity.—The endless assortment of things that electricity does can, in great part, be broken down into forms or combinations of three basic effects: thermal, magnetic, chemical.

The thermal effect of electricity is simply heat. A current cannot flow without causing some heat. Sometimes heat is not desired, as, for example, in the case of the unavoidable wattage loss referred to in the examples in the first part of this chapter. In an ordinary light bulb over 90 per cent of the current is wasted as heat, and less than 10 per cent is converted into light, but the light is not possible without the heat. In a toaster or flatiron the heat only is desired.

The magnetic effect can be stated very simply. When a current flows through a wire, the wire is surrounded by a magnetic field—the area immediately around the wire becomes magnetized. Bring a small compass near a wire that is carrying current and the needle will move just as it will when you bring it near an ordinary horseshoe magnet. Wrap a wire a number of times around a piece of soft iron that is not in the least magnetic; during the time that a current flows through the wire, the soft iron becomes a magnet, weak or powerful depending upon such factors as the number of turns of wire and the number of amperes flowing. The moment the current stops flowing, the iron ceases to be magnetic. It is this property that causes doorbells to ring, motors to run, and telephones and radio loud-speakers to operate.

The chemical effects are of great variety, including the electroplating of metals, the charging of storage batteries, and the electrolytic refinement of metals.

CHAPTER 3

TYPES OF CURRENT; POWER FACTOR; TRANSFORMERS

As the student reads about electrical subjects, he will frequently meet the words "direct current" and "alternating current," also "cycles"; he will read about "single-phase," "2-phase," "3-phase," and "polyphase." These terms, while at first formidable and not at all understood by many people, really are fairly simple and easily understood, if only close attention is paid to their explanation.

Direct Current.—If the ordinary direct-current voltmeter which was shown in Fig. 2-1 (such as is used for testing dry cells or radio B batteries) is connected to a battery, the pointer will swing sometimes to the right, sometimes to the left, depending on how the two terminals on the meter are connected to the corresponding terminals of the battery. Inspection will show that the two terminals of the meter are marked " $+$ " and " $-$," "P" and "N," or "pos." and "neg.," all indicating positive and negative; the battery terminals are similarly marked. Only when the positive terminal of the meter is connected to the positive terminal of the battery will the pointer swing in the right direction. If on any source of electricity, whether battery or generator or other device, one terminal is positive, the other negative, and they never change, the current is known as "direct current," or "D.C." Current from any type of battery is *always* direct current.

Alternating Current.—Instead of the meter of Fig. 2-1, which has the 0 at one end of the scale, a zero-center voltmeter of the type shown in Fig. 3-1 may be used. This meter is the same as the first except that the terminals are not marked "pos." and "neg." If connected to the two terminals of a battery in one way, the pointer will swing to the left; if connected the other way, with the terminals reversed, the pointer will swing to the right. The meter is equally easy to read whether the pointer swings to the right or to the left, and it provides the additional convenience that it is not necessary, before connection is made, to investigate carefully which is the positive and which is the negative terminal.

Weston Elec. Inst. Co.
FIG. 3-1.—The voltmeter above is the same as that in Fig. 2-1, except that the zero is in the center of the scale.

Assume that such a zero-center voltmeter is connected to a pair of wires of unknown voltage and type of current. Observe the pointer carefully; it never comes to rest but swings from left to right, then back to left, and keeps on going through the cycle. Follow the pointer starting from the 0 at the center.

It starts swinging toward the right, first rapidly, then more slowly, until it reaches a maximum of about $162\frac{1}{2}$ volts, in exactly 15 sec. Then it starts dropping back toward 0, first slowly, then rapidly, until in 15 sec. more it is back at 0. It does not stay there but keeps on swinging toward the left, and in 15 sec. more it reaches the extreme left at $162\frac{1}{2}$ volts, the same relative position as it originally had at the right. Again it swings back toward the right, and in 15 sec. more, 1 min. from the starting point, it is back where it started from—the 0.

It performs this same procedure indefinitely, every minute. The voltage is never constant, is always changing, from 0 to a maximum of $162\frac{1}{2}$ volts, first on the positive side, then on the negative. Current in which any given wire regularly changes from positive to negative, not suddenly but gradually as outlined above, is known as "alternating current," or "A.C." If the data just observed are plotted, the actual voltage against the time, they will produce a chart such as is shown in Fig. 3-2. This portrays one cycle of alternating current.

Alternating current if considered at any fixed moment, rather then over an interval of time, is still direct current. *Alternating current may be defined as a current of regularly fluctuating voltage and regularly reversing polarity.*

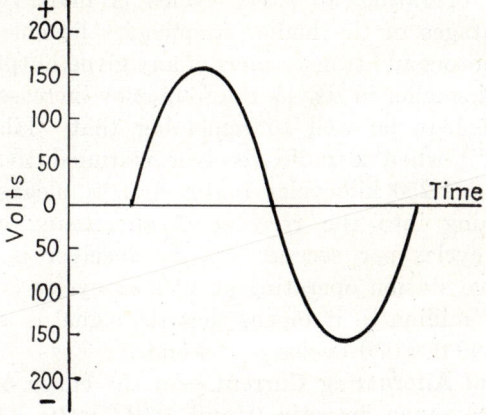

Fig. 3-2.—This represents one cycle of alternating current. The voltage fluctuates regularly from zero to maximum to zero, and each wire alternates regularly and continuously between positive and negative.

Frequency.—Alternating current which takes a full minute to go through the entire cycle (from no voltage to maximum voltage on positive side, back to 0, to maximum voltage on negative side, back to 0) would be known as "1 cycle *per minute.*" There is no such current in actual practice; actually in ordinary 60-cycle alternating current, as used in perhaps 98 per cent of all wired American homes and industrial establishments, all this change takes place at the rate of 60 times *per second*, much too fast to be observed by an ordinary voltmeter. Such current is then said to have a frequency of 60 cycles, the "per second" being understood. In the United States practically all current is 60-cycle, and the few remaining 25-, 40-, and 50-cycle installations are rapidly being changed over to 60-cycle. In foreign countries, 50-cycle current is more common, but various other frequencies are also in commercial use, some as high as 133 cycles. In the United States, 180-cycle current is in common use in some industries, for special applications, and 400-cycle current for operating portable electric tools is coming into use. During World War II much military equipment was operated on frequencies of 400, 500, and 800 cycles per second. Metal-hardening equipment operating at 9,600 cycles is under discussion. The advantages of the higher frequencies lie chiefly in the fact that motors and transformers of any given output become smaller and smaller in size as the frequency increases.

It might here be well to remember that "kilo" means "thousand"; when a radio receiver is tuned to a station operating at 1,250 kilocycles (abbr. kc.), it means that the signal coming into the receiver is alternating current of 1,250,000 cycles per second. If the receiver is tuned to a short-wave station operating at 40 megacycles ("mega" is Greek for "million"), it means that the signal is alternating current of 40,000,000 cycles per second.

Voltage of Alternating Current.—In the curve of Fig. 3-2 the voltages range between 0 and $162\frac{1}{2}$ volts. If a light bulb rated at 115 volts is connected to a circuit of such varying voltage (1 cycle per *minute*), it will burn far more brightly than normal while the voltage is above 115 volts, less brightly than normal while the voltage is under 115, and part of the time the bulb will not light at all, because the voltage is very low, or even zero twice during the cycle. Flickering would be extreme and unendurable. However, in the case of the ordinary 60-cycle alternating current, all this change of voltage takes place twice per cycle, 120 times every *second*. The filament of a light bulb does not have time to cool off during the very short periods of time when no voltage is impressed on it, which is the chief reason for lack of observable flicker. In the case of very small bulbs which have very thin filaments that can cool off quickly, operated on 25-cycle current which is still found in a few localities, a noticeable and annoying flicker is present.

The rated voltage of an alternating-current circuit is an

averaged value between 0 and the peak voltage and in the case under discussion is 115 volts.[1] An alternating-current voltmeter connected to the circuit will read 115 volts. A circuit fed by a 115-volt alternating-current source will light a 115-volt bulb to the same brilliancy as a circuit fed by a 115-volt direct-current source.

Alternating Current and Motors.—Alternating current as discussed up to this point is "single-phase" alternating

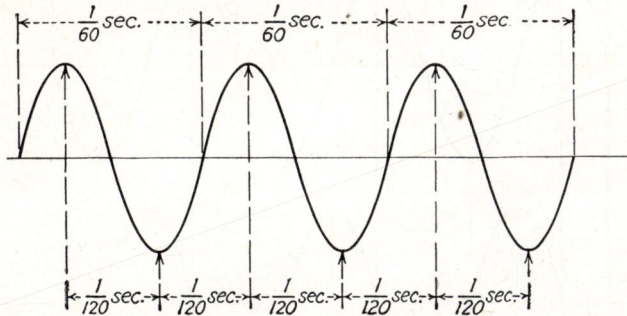

FIG. 3-3.—Three cycles of alternating current. All the changes shown take place in $3/60$ or $1/20$ sec.

current. In foreign countries it is frequently designated "monophasic" current. When applied to a motor, remember that it magnetizes the steel poles of the motor every time it builds up from zero to peak voltage, or in other words 120 times per second, as shown in Fig. 3-3, which shows three consecutive cycles of 60-cycle current. At the top is indicated the duration between cycles, or $1/60$ sec. At the bottom is indicated the time between alternations, or $1/120$ sec. One might say that the motor is given a push 120 times a second, just as a gasoline engine is given a push every time there is an explosion in the cylinder. Offhand, 120 times per second may seem fast enough for any purpose, but remember that an ordinary motor runs at 1,800 r.p.m., which means that the rotor (the rotating part) makes 30 revolutions every

[1] The rated voltage is 0.707 of the peak voltage; the student will recognize 0.707 as $\frac{1}{2}\sqrt{2}$. From this it is evident that the peak voltage is rated voltage times $\sqrt{2}$.

second. In turn this means that the 120 pushes per second become only 4 pushes per revolution; if the motor is a large one the rotor or armature may be 12 in. in diameter, over 36 in. in circumference, which in turn means that the rotor has to turn about 9 in. between pushes.

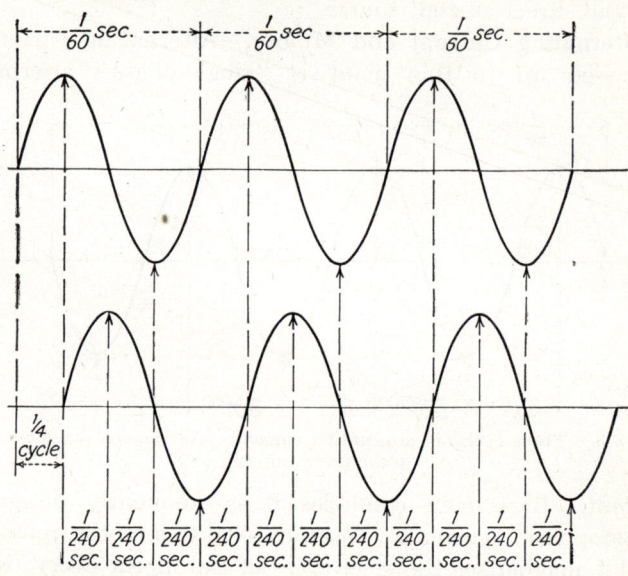

Fig. 3-4.—Two-phase alternating current is merely two separate circuits of single-phase current, but the maximum voltage in one comes when there is zero voltage in the other.

In an ordinary 1-cylinder 4-cycle gasoline engine, running at 1,800 r.p.m., there is an explosion in the cylinder every other revolution, or 900 times every minute, or 15 times every second. The crankshaft gets a push 15 times every second. If more pushes are needed every second to secure smoother operation, or more power, it is simply done by using more cylinders: two or four, or as many as needed. How is this to be done in the case of an electric motor? Fortunately it is rather simple.

Two-phase Alternating Current.—It can be done by putting into the motor two separate windings not connected to each other in any way, but each connected to a separate source of single-phase alternating current. The two separate sources of current must be so designed that the peak voltage of one comes when there is no voltage in the other; then the motor will receive twice as many pushes as before. Figure 3-4 shows the voltage curves of the two separate sources. At the top again is indicated the duration between cycles *in each separate source:* $\frac{1}{60}$ sec. At the bottom again is indicated the time between pushes *from the two separate sources combined,* now

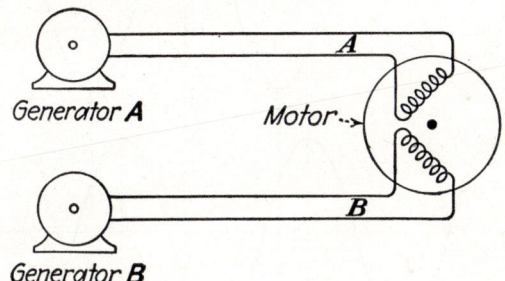

FIG. 3-5.—Two-phase generator connected to 2-phase motor.

$\frac{1}{240}$ sec. That is 2-phase current, and it is nothing more or less than two separate sources of single-phase alternating current so arranged that the peak voltage of one comes when there is minimum or zero voltage in the other.

Figure 3-5 shows this diagrammatically—generator A and inside the motor winding A, and also generator B and inside the motor winding B. In practice it would be impossible to make two separate generators run at such a precisely uniform rate that the peak voltage of one would always coincide with the zero voltage of the other; instead a single generator is used with two separate windings so that automatically the peak and zero voltage of each winding come at precisely the right moment.

Each phase is carried on separate wires although in practice two of the wires may be combined; more will be said about this later.

Three-phase Current.—Instead of the 2-phase current just described, which doubles the number of pushes the motor of the foregoing example receives every second, 3-phase current, which triples the number of pushes, can be used. It boils

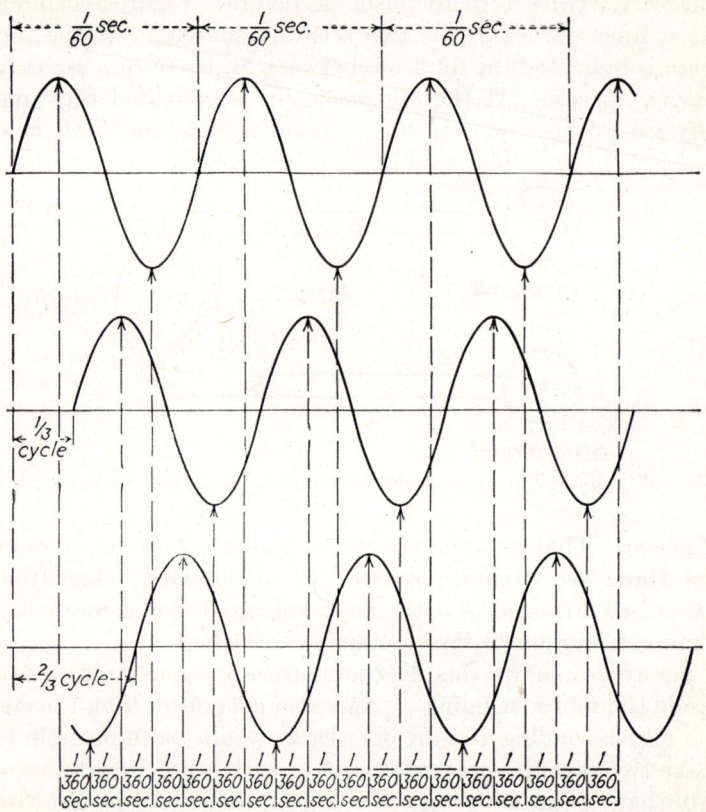

FIG. 3-6.—Three separate single-phase circuits combine to form 3-phase current.

down to three different windings in a generator so designed that the peak voltages in the three windings come equally spaced, as indicated in Fig. 3-6.

Here again the time per cycle is $\frac{1}{60}$ sec. *in any one winding,* but looking at the bottom of the diagram one sees that the

TYPES OF CURRENT; POWER FACTOR 39

pushes *from the three windings combined* are only $\frac{1}{360}$ sec. apart. Note that the pushes are imparted by each of the three windings in turn, at the moments of peak voltage, as shown by the dotted lines from the peaks to the bottom of the diagram. It should not be imagined that these pushes are abrupt impacts; rather they are gradual pushes that start slowly and build to a maximum as the voltage builds up.

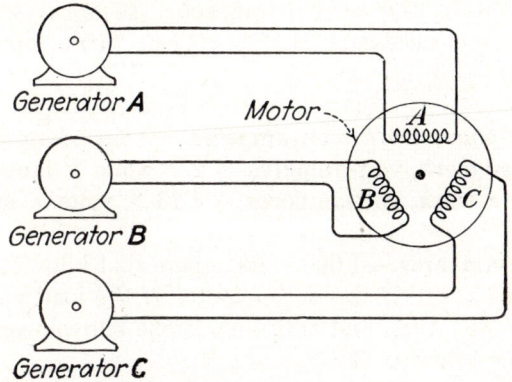

FIG. 3-7.—Three-phase generator connected to 3-phase motor.

Figure 3-7 shows a pictorial presentation of a 3-phase motor connected to three single-phase generators, which in combination become one 3-phase generator. The diagram shows three pairs of wires, but in practice these become only three wires, sometimes with the addition of a fourth grounded wire. This will be discussed in more detail later.

Polyphase Current.—When a current is either 2-phase or 3-phase, it is known as "polyphase" current (from the Greek word "poly" meaning "many"). It is also known as "multiphase" current. With a few rare exceptions, polyphase current is never found in homes, but it is the general type of current employed for commercial and industrial uses for operating motors and similar devices. Even in those establishments, single-phase current is also found for lighting purposes and operating small miscellaneous devices. The

3-phase current is common; the 2-phase is used in only a few cities.

Abbreviation.—The word "phase" is usually abbreviated ϕ, the Greek letter *phi*.

Volt-amperes.—The previous chapter contained the formula volts × amperes = watts. That formula is always correct in connection with direct current, but in connection with alternating current it is not correct because of power factor, which will be discussed in the next paragraph. Before that can be discussed, it is necessary that the term "volt-amperes" be understood.

In *single-phase work*, volt-amperes = volts × amperes.
In *2-phase work*, volt-amperes = 2 × volts × amperes.
In *3-phase work*, volt-amperes = 1.73 × volts × amperes.

Kilovolt-amperes.—1,000 volt-amperes is 1 kilovolt-ampere, abbreviated kva. If the power factor of the load happens to be 100 per cent, then and only then is one kilovolt-ampere the same as one kilowatt (kw.).

Power Factor.—To explain just what power factor is must be left to any good book on electrical engineering. An explanation of how to measure it and a general idea of its importance are simple enough to be covered here.

When any device whatever is connected to a direct-current line, together with an ammeter, a voltmeter, and a wattmeter, the product of the volts and the amperes is *without exception* equal to the reading of the wattmeter. If, however, the same experiment is made on an alternating-current circuit, sometimes the same is true, sometimes not.

Whenever on an alternating-current circuit measurements show that the product of the volts and the amperes *is exactly equal to* the wattmeter reading, the device that constitutes the load is said to have a power factor of 100 per cent. Into this classification fall lamp bulbs, most appliances that generate only heat, and in general all noninductive devices, that is, those that do not involve windings of wire around a steel core.

TYPES OF CURRENT; POWER FACTOR

If the product of volts times amperes *is greater than* the reading of the wattmeter, then the power factor is less than 100 per cent.

Power factor is abbreviated P.F.; it is referred to also as "cos ϕ."[1] It is defined as the proportion between the real or measured watts (also known as "effective power") and the volt-amperes (also known as "apparent watts"). The formula is simply

$$\text{Power factor} = \frac{\text{watts}}{\text{volt-amperes}}.$$

Measuring Power Factor.—To measure power factor we need only a voltmeter, ammeter, and wattmeter. Assume a small single-phase motor on a circuit of 115 volts, consuming 5 amp. as indicated by the ammeter and 345 watts as indicated by the wattmeter. The formula then becomes

$$\text{Power factor} = \frac{345}{5 \times 115} \text{ or } \frac{345}{575} \text{ or 60 per cent.}$$

In the case of a 3-phase 230-volt motor consuming 12 amp., the volt-amperes are $1.73 \times 230 \times 12$, or 4,775. If the wattage as indicated by the wattmeter is 3,950,

$$\text{Power factor} = \frac{3,950}{4,775} \text{ or 82.3 per cent.}$$

Generally speaking, the power factor of a motor improves (increases in percentage) with the increase in horsepower of the motor and also varies considerably with the type and quality of the motor in question. It may be as low as 50 per cent for small fractional-horsepower motors, and over 90 per cent for a 25-hp. motor.

Watts in Alternating-current Work.—The correct formula for use in connection with alternating-current work is

Watts = volt-amperes × power factor.

In using this formula do not overlook the fact that, if the power

---

[1] Cosine phi.

is 2- or 3-phase, the product of the voltmeter and ammeter readings must be multiplied by 2 and 1.73, respectively.

Desirability of High Power Factor.—Assume that a factory is using 100 amp. of single-phase power at 230 volts, a total of 23,000 volt-amp., or 23 kva. If the power factor is 100 per cent, this is equivalent to 23 kw. At 5 cts. per kilowatt-hour, the power company receives $1.15 per hour for the total power.

Now assume a second factory also using 100 amp. at 230 volts, but with a power factor of only 50 per cent. That is still 23 kva. but only 11.5 kw., and at 5 cts. per kilowatt-hour the power company now receives only $57\frac{1}{2}$ cts. per hour.

Since it is the kilovolt-ampere load that determines wire size, transformer and generator size, and similar factors, and since each factory uses the same 23 kva., the power company must furnish wires just as big for the factory where they are paid $57\frac{1}{2}$ cts. per hour as for the one where they are paid $1.15 per hour; they tie up just as much transformer capacity, generator capacity, and all other equipment for the one as they do for the other.

It is natural, therefore, that power companies, when furnishing power to establishments where the power factor is low, not only charge for the kilowatt-hours consumed, but also make an extra charge based on the kilovolt-amperes used during the month or other period in question, as compared with the kilowatt-hours used. Since with a constant load in watts the volt-amperes decrease as the power factor increases, it is definitely in order to watch the power factor very carefully. Few installations attain 100 per cent power factor, and few fall as low as 50 per cent. The over-all power factor in an industrial establishment is generally determined by the electric motors in use, although other devices also contribute their share.

Power-factor Correction.—The theory covering power-factor correction is entirely beyond the scope of this book but can be found in any good book on electrical engineering. The actual correction is accomplished by means of capacitors or synchronous motors; the required calculations should be made

TYPES OF CURRENT; POWER FACTOR

by one thoroughly familiar with the subject. Correcting the power factor not only reduces the charges for power consumed, but carries with it many other advantages, including, usually, higher efficiency of electrical machinery because of reduced voltage drop.

Transformers.—When it is necessary to transmit thousands of horsepower of electrical energy over a considerable distance, wire large enough to transmit it at, say, 115 or even 230 volts would have to be so big that the cost would be entirely prohibitive. If a relatively small wire and a much higher voltage are used, the voltage will be so high as to be dangerous in the final consumption and there will be many other disadvantages.

It would be most convenient, therefore, to have a way of changing current from one voltage to another as required. In the case of direct current there is no simple, efficient device available, but for alternating current there is fortunately available a simple and efficient device that does just that—the transformer.

If an electric current flows through a wire that is wrapped around a soft iron rod or core, the core becomes a magnet as long as the current flows. The experiment can be simply made by wrapping a couple of dozen turns of insulated wire around an iron bolt; connect a dry cell to the two ends of the wire, and the bolt becomes a magnet as long as the dry cell is connected (see Fig. 3-8). Magnetic lines of force surround the wire and build up in the iron core. The moment the dry cell is disconnected, the bolt loses practically all its magnetism.

With a good galvanometer (which is a *very* sensitive direct-current voltmeter), this next experiment is simply made. Discard the dry cell, and connect the two ends of a coil with at least several hundred turns of wire to the two terminals of the galvanometer (see Fig. 3-9). Push the iron bolt suddenly into the coil, or pull it suddenly out; nothing happens. Then use a permanent magnet of any type; a 10-ct. horseshoe magnet will serve the purpose. The more powerful the magnet, the easier it will be to make this demonstration. Push one leg of the magnet suddenly into the coil, and the needle on the galvanometer, if sufficiently sensitive, will move, then drop back to zero. As long as the magnet is stationary inside the coil, nothing happens. Pull the magnet out suddenly, and the galvanometer needle will again move, but in a direction opposite to that taken when the magnet was pushed into the

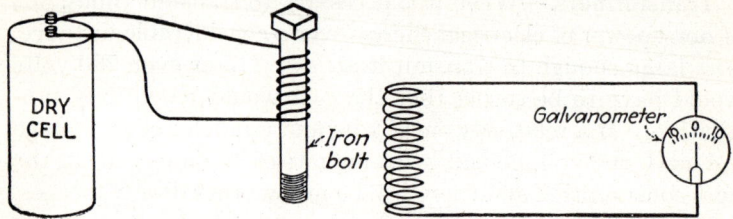

Fig. 3-8.—When current flows through a wire wrapped around an iron bolt, the bolt becomes a magnet.

Fig. 3-9.—Pushing a magnet into the coil generates a current indicated by the voltmeter. This is the simplest possible electrical generator.

coil. The more turns of wire in the coil, the easier it will be to perform this experiment.

This demonstrates that, whenever there is a *change* in the magnetism in the space occupied by a coil of wire, electricity flows in the wire; if magnetism of a constant nature is there, nothing happens.

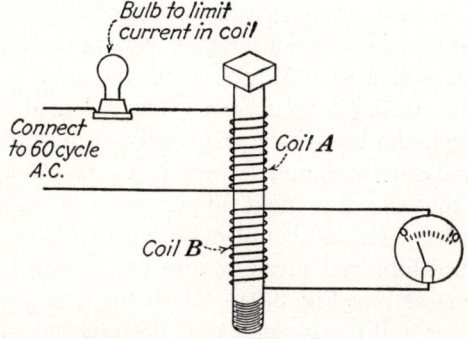

Fig. 3-10.—A very crude transformer.

Consider now what will happen if 60-cycle alternating current is connected to the two ends of the coil of wire around the bolt. The voltage in the alternating current applied to

TYPES OF CURRENT; POWER FACTOR   45

the coil changes 120 times every second from zero to maximum to zero. Therefore 120 times every second the bolt becomes a magnet, and 120 times every second it loses its magnetic power, as the voltage in the circuit builds up from zero to maximum and then drops back to zero. Consider now a contraption like that in Fig. 3-10, where again an iron bolt is used and on it two coils of wire, A and B, not connected to each other in any way. To coil A is connected a source delivering 60-cycle alternating current; a bulb is connected in series with it to limit the current. The other coil is connected to a very sensitive *alternating-current* voltmeter.

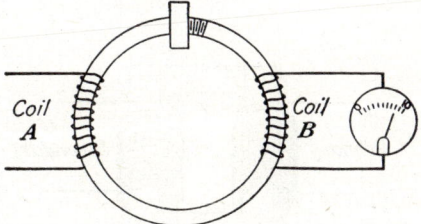

Fig. 3-11.—Still a crude transformer, but much more efficient than the one shown in Fig. 3-10.

Remember that, whenever a magnet was moved inside the coil in the first experiment, electricity flowed in the coil. Remember also that, with 60-cycle current flowing through coil A, the bolt becomes a magnet, then becomes just a plain iron bolt, 120 times every second. That is exactly the same as inserting and removing a magnet into coil B 60 times per second; accordingly, alternating current will flow in coil B, and the voltmeter, if it is sensitive enough, will show it. The device is a transformer, which transfers current from one coil to another coil not connected to it.

The device described is exceedingly crude. If a longer bolt is used, and bent into the form of a complete circle, as shown in Fig. 3-11, it will be much more efficient and more current will flow in coil B.

In commercial use, solid cores like the bolt would be impractical because solid cores heat excessively. Instead, thin sheets of a special grade of iron are used, cut in U sections, which can later be stacked into a core, usually of rectangular shape, generally with the two coils over opposite legs. Many variations are possible, but for showing the principle, the type shown in Fig. 3-12 will serve the purpose. The coil to which the power is applied is called the "primary"; the other coil from which the power is taken is called the "secondary."

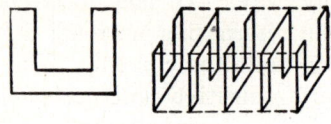

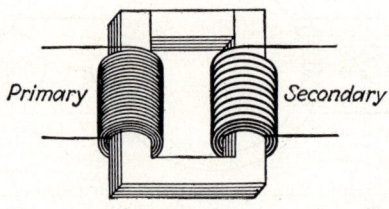

Fig. 3-12.—This shows the general construction of transformers.

An interesting demonstration transformer is described in the June, 1946, issue of *Electricity on the Farm* magazine, and illustrated in Fig. 3-13. Wind 150 turns of insulated bell wire or similar wire, about No. 18 in size, around one end of a heavy iron bar or bolt. This is the secondary; connect the ends of this winding to an ordinary flashlight bulb. On the other end of the bar, wind 50 turns of the same wire, this constituting the primary. Connect one end of the primary to a coarse file, the other end to one terminal of an ordinary dry cell. Connect a length of wire to the other terminal of the dry cell, and bare the opposite end of the wire but do not connect it to anything. Rub the bared end of this wire rapidly along the file.

The flashlight bulb will light, even if there is no connection between the two coils of wire. The dry cell is direct current, and direct current cannot be used ordinarily to operate transformers. However, rubbing the bare end of the wire along the teeth of the file causes the direct current to be frequently interrupted, so that there will flow in the primary an interrupted direct current, approximating one-half of an alternating current. Such a circuit would be impractical for handling any substantial amount of power, but it does demonstrate the principle of the transformer.

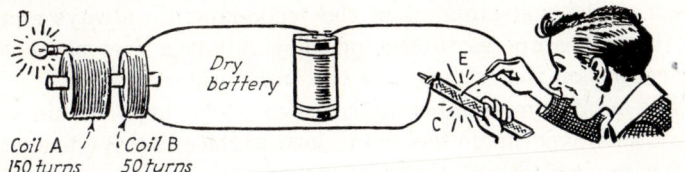

FIG. 3-13.—This circuit demonstrates further the principle of the transformer.

Transformer Ratios.—If the primary of a properly designed transformer is connected to a source of alternating current of the voltage for which the primary was designed, and of practically unlimited power, but if the two ends of the secondary winding are *not* connected to anything or to each other, practically no current will flow in the primary. If however a load (lamp bulbs, appliances, motors, etc.) is connected to the secondary, then just as much current will flow in the primary as is required to deliver the required wattage to the secondary, but no more (assuming of course that the capacity of the transformer is adequate to the load connected to it).

Experiment shows that, if the primary has as many turns of wire as the secondary, the voltage and the amperage that can be made to flow in the secondary will be exactly the same as the voltage and the amperage in the primary, minus a small percentage because a transformer is not 100 per cent efficient. It would be more correct to say that the voltage of the primary and the secondary will be the same, and the amperage flowing in the primary from the power line adjusts itself to the amperage demanded in the secondary by the nature of the particular load connected to it.

If the secondary has twice as many turns as the primary, the voltage in the secondary will be twice that of the primary,

48 THEORY AND BASIC PRINCIPLES

but the amperage will be only half as great. If the secondary has 10 times as many turns as the primary, the voltage in the secondary will be 10 times that of the primary, but the amperage will be only one-tenth as great. By reversing the proportions and having fewer turns in the secondary than in the primary, it is equally simple to step the voltage down, instead of up; the amperage, of course, will go up as the voltage goes down. The volt-amperes in the secondary are always equal to the volt-amperes in the primary minus a few per cent, depending on the efficiency of the transformer.

The minimum number of turns must be kept within the limits that experiment has shown lead to the greatest efficiency, and wire sizes in both primary and secondary must be chosen to carry the amperages involved. The smallest transformer usually found is the ordinary doorbell type, costing under a dollar, which steps 115-volt alternating current down to about 8 volts for operating doorbells and similar equipment; the largest are so big that there is difficulty finding railway cars sturdy enough to transport them.

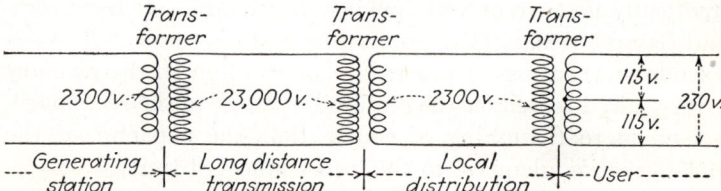

FIG. 3-14.—Power is generated at a reasonable voltage, stepped up to a higher voltage for transmission over a distance, and then stepped down to the working voltages.

Well-built transformers are very efficient, and, generally speaking, the larger the transformer, the greater the efficiency. In very large transformers it is possible to recover from the secondary over 99 per cent of the power applied to the primary.

Practical Use of Transformers.—In a large generating station, power is generated at, say, 2,300 volts. Then it is fed through transformers and stepped up to, say, 23,000 volts for transmission over a distance. At the point where it is to be distributed, it is again fed through a transformer and stepped down to a more reasonable figure, often 2,300 volts, which is usually the voltage at which it is transmitted in the lines running down city alleys. At strategic spots it is stepped down by another transformer to 115/230 volts, at which figure it is used (see Fig. 3-14). Actually the voltage at which the power is generated varies a great deal, as does the maximum voltage to which it is stepped up, this depending upon the amount of power involved, the distance over which it is to be transmitted, etc. Frequently, voltages considerably in excess of 100,000 volts are used.

Series-parallel Connections.—It is the usual practice in power and lighting transformers to have both the primary and the secondary consist each of two separate coils. When the two primary coils are connected in series, as shown in A of Fig. 3-15, the primary will be suitable for connection to a 4,600-volt line; reconnected in parallel, as shown in B, the transformer becomes suitable for 2,300 volts. Likewise, the two secondary sections may be connected in parallel to deliver 115 volts, as shown in A, or in series to deliver 230 volts. More usually the secondary coils are connected in series, with a tap at the mid-point, forming the common 3-wire 115/230-volt system, as shown in B. Any given transformer, when the secondaries are connected in parallel to deliver 115 volts, will deliver twice the amperage that it will on 230 volts.

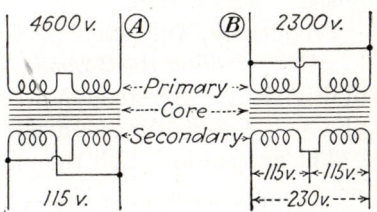

Fig. 3-15.—By connecting the windings of transformers in series or parallel, the same transformer serves for two different voltages.

Use on Alternating Current Only.—Considering the discussion in the first paragraphs on the subject, it should be superfluous to state this, but let it be repeated: a transformer operates only on alternating current.

Two-phase Transformers.—A 2-phase transformer bank consists simply of two separate single-phase transformers. If a total of 20 kva. of 2-phase power is needed, two single-phase 10-kva. transformers are used. They may be connected simply as two separate transformers not connected to each other in any way, as shown in Fig. 3-16 (secondaries only are shown for simplicity in this and the next four figures).

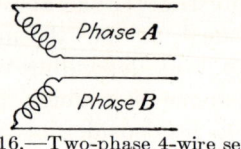 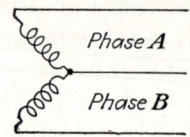

FIG. 3-16.—Two-phase 4-wire separate-phases method of connecting 2-phase transformers.

FIG. 3-17.—Two-phase 3-wire method of connecting 2-phase transformers.

This makes what is known as the "2-phase 4-wire separate-phases" installation.

Frequently, the ends of the two secondaries are joined together, making the 2-phase 3-wire system. This is pictured in Fig. 3-17. The common wire that carries wire for both phases is frequently grounded.

The system in which the mid-points of the two secondaries are joined together, making the 2-phase 4-wire system, is also used. It is pictured in Fig. 3-18. Note that if the words "separate phases" are not included but the designation is simply "2-phase 4-wire," the system of Fig. 3-18 and not that of Fig. 3-16 is described. Often a fifth wire is brought out from the mid-point of the secondaries and run to the various 2-phase devices operated, as shown by the dotted line in Fig. 3-18. This then becomes the 2-phase 5-wire system. The fifth wire is usually grounded.

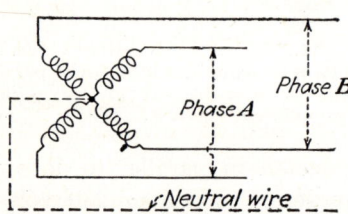

FIG. 3-18.—Two-phase 4-wire method of connecting 2-phase transformers. Adding the wire shown in dotted lines makes it the 2-phase 5-wire system.

Three-phase Transformers.—A 3-phase transformer bank consists of three separate single-phase transformers. The secondaries of these transformers, one for each phase, may be connected in a variety of ways. The delta scheme shown in

TYPES OF CURRENT; POWER FACTOR

Fig. 3-19 formerly was the most common; frequently one of the wires is grounded. In new power lines today the star or Y scheme, as shown in Fig. 3-20, is more frequently used; usually there is a fourth wire, the grounded neutral as shown in dotted lines. This system has many advantages, the detailed discussion of which belongs in a textbook of electrical engineering.

There is one point of comparison that should be noted. First of all, in any 3-phase system, single-phase current is

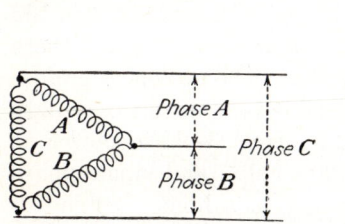
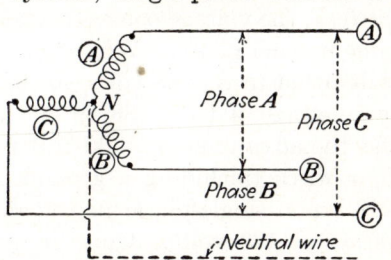

Fig. 3-19.—Delta method of connecting 3-phase transformers.

Fig. 3-20.—Star or Y method of connecting 3-phase transformers.

available by simply connecting across any two wires. In the delta system, if the 3-phase voltage is 230, the single-phase voltage is also 230. By leading a fourth wire back to the midpoint of that transformer secondary which serves the two wires to be used for single-phase current, 115-volt single-phase is also made available. However, the middle one of the three wires of such a 115/230-volt system is usually grounded. Sometimes in a 3-wire 3-phase system one of the wires of the system is already grounded. If there is one grounded wire at the *end* of one of the transformer secondaries and the fourth wire which leads to the *mid-point* of the same transformer secondary is also grounded, one-half of that secondary is short-circuited. A delta system providing both 3-phase and single-phase power may therefore provide a distinct grounding problem. Consult the power company or your inspector in case of doubt.

In the star or Y system already described, and shown in Fig. 3-20, the 3-phase voltage instead of being 230 volts is usually 208 volts. The single-phase current available across any two of the wires (not including the neutral wire) is also 208 volts. However, the single-phase voltage between the neutral wire and any of the other three wires is 120 volts.

At first glance this may seem all wrong for, if the voltage between wires A and B in Fig. 3-20 is 208 volts, the voltage between the neutral wire and either A or B might be expected to be one-half of 208, or 104 volts, instead of 120 volts as previously stated. Remember, however, that in 3-phase current, the voltage comes to a peak or maximum at a different time in each phase. While the voltage in secondary A is 120 volts, that in B is 88 volts, so that across wires A and B there is a voltage of $120 + 88$, or 208 volts. The system therefore has the advantage of making it possible to transmit over only four wires (including a grounded neutral) 3-phase power at 208 volts, single-phase power at 208 volts, and single-phase power at 120 volts. Quite frequently in a home, instead of providing the usual 115/230-volt 3-wire system, three wires of the star-connected system (the neutral and any other two wires of Fig. 3-20) are provided, thus furnishing 120 volts for lighting and 208 volts (instead of the usual 230 volts) for water heaters and similar large loads.

Autotransformers.—An autotransformer can be defined as a transformer in which a portion of the turns are common to

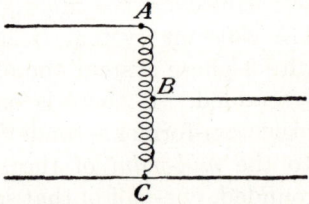

FIG. 3-21.—In an autotransformer some of the turns are common to both primary and secondary.

both primary and secondary (see Fig. 3-21). Let there be a tap at the mid-point of the coil so that, although there are, for example, 1,000 turns of wire between A and C, there are only 500 between B and C. The entire coil A to C may then be considered the primary, those turns from B to C the secondary.

TYPES OF CURRENT; POWER FACTOR

Whatever the voltage across A to C, the voltage across B to C will be exactly half. The tap may be at any point in the coil. The voltage across B to C, as compared with the total voltage across A to C, will always be proportional to the number of turns from B to C, as compared with the total number of turns from A to C. This type of construction is somewhat less expensive than the usual two-coil type, but it is rarely employed as its use in general is prohibited by the Code with certain exceptions, notably in connection with motor-starting devices.

CHAPTER 4

BASIC DEVICES AND CIRCUITS

In order to assemble properly and intelligently the great number of available electrical devices to form a complete wiring system, it is necessary to understand the basic principles regarding electrical devices and electrical circuits.

In order that the electric current produce an effect, it is not enough that the current merely flow up to the device that is to be operated; the current must flow *through* it. In other words, there must be two wires from the starting point to the device. The electric current can be compared to a series of messengers who start from some given point (the generator of an electrical system), make a trip to their destination (the device to be operated), and return to the starting point before their errand is completed. The wires can be considered the streets over which they travel, only they must be considered one-way streets; the messengers must go out on one, return over a different street (wire), because there are millions of them. As a matter of fact, an electric current can be considered as consisting of many millions of billions of such messengers per second for every ampere flowing.[1]

Bulbs.—The most common electrical device is perhaps the light bulb. According to strictly correct terminology, the device should be called a "lamp," and the glass portion only should be called the "bulb," but since almost everybody calls the complete devices bulbs, that term will be used in this book too. The bulb consists essentially of a filament which is a wire made of tungsten having a very high resistance and a very high melting point. This makes it possible to heat the wire to a very high heat and still have it last. The filament is sus-

[1] See footnote, 2 p. 15.

pended on supports inside the bulb, from which the air has been exhausted and into which, in most sizes, usually some inert gas like argon has been introduced to prolong the life. The

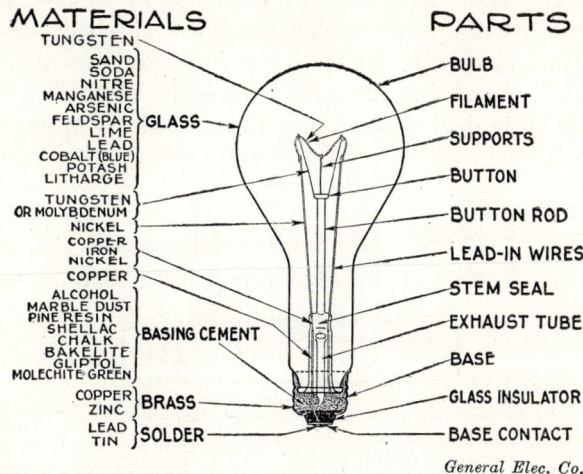

Fig. 4-1.—Cross-section of a typical bulb.

ends of the filament are brought out to a convenient base, which makes replacement simple. In the base the center contact is insulated from the outer brass part of the base, thus providing two terminals for the two wires leading up to the bulb. The cross-section of a bulb shown in Fig. 4-1 should make this clear. This picture also shows the wide variety of materials used in making lamp bulbs.

Pass & Seymour.
Fig. 4-2.—A "cleat receptacle"—the simplest form of socket.

Bulbs are held in sockets, the simplest being the screw-shell receptacle shown in Fig. 4-2; Fig. 4-3 shows a cross-section of it. One terminal A is connected to the center contact corresponding to the center contact on the bulb base; the other terminal B is connected to the screw-shell terminal (which is carefully insulated from the center contact and terminal A), corresponding to the outer shell of the base on the bulb. When a bulb is screwed into such a socket, the current will flow in at one terminal, through the filament, and out again at the other terminal.

Circuits.—Used in a general sense, as it will be in this chapter, a circuit is any combination of wires and devices which will permit electricity to do its work. Perhaps the words "hookup" or "wiring diagram" would be more descriptive. Only the basic devices necessary to make the combination of

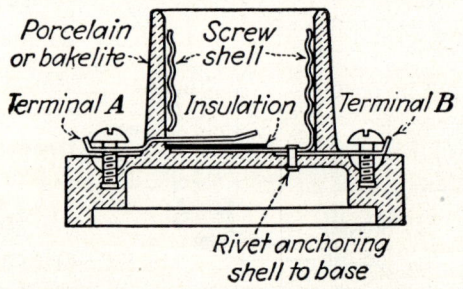

FIG. 4-3.—Cross-section of the cleat receptacle shown in Fig. 4-2.

devices work will be included in this chapter; the supplementary devices such as conduit, outlet boxes, switch plates will be deferred to a later chapter.

Outlets.—Every point where electricity is taken from the wires *and consumed* is an outlet. Receptacle (plug-in) outlets in themselves use no current, but since current-consuming devices like radios and lamps are plugged into them, they are considered outlets. A switch uses no current; therefore it is not an outlet. Sometimes the term "outlet" is loosely and improperly used to indicate any point where a device is connected to the wires, this being commonly done in contracting work, when estimating the cost of a job on a "per-outlet" basis.

Source.—In all the diagrams in this book where the word SOURCE appears, it will mean the generator, the battery, or wherever the current comes from—the SOURCE of supply. Actually, it will usually be the point where the wires enter the building, or the point where the particular circuit under discussion begins.

Basic Circuit.—Figure 4-4 shows a wire running from SOURCE to the socket with the bulb, and another wire from the socket back to SOURCE. Assume that the current flows outward

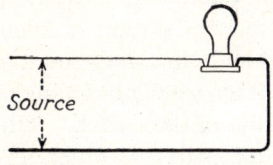 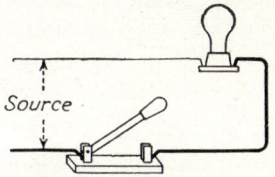

FIG. 4-4.—The most simple circuit. There is no way of turning the bulb on or off.

FIG. 4-5.—A switch has been added to the circuit at the left, to control the bulb.

through the wire, which is shown as a light line in the diagram, and back through the wire, which is shown as heavy line. This makes a complete circuit, and so long as SOURCE furnishes power, the bulb will light. It is not at all a practical circuit, since it is necessary to disconnect one of the wires from the socket, or to cut a wire, whenever the light is to be turned off. Such a circuit would not be very sensible, so a switch must be included. This has been done in Fig. 4-5, the switch being the open porcelain-base type. Opening the blade is the same as disconnecting or cutting a wire, or, comparing it with the one-way street, it is the same as opening a drawbridge in the street—no way of going ahead on that street until the bridge is again closed.

Bryant Elec. Co.
FIG. 4-6.—A toggle switch. The mechanism is completely enclosed.

Toggle Switches.—Instead of using a porcelain switch, which is clumsy, there is used, in actual wiring, a neat switch, concealed in the wall with only its handle or "toggle" protruding (see Fig. 4-6). It has two terminals just like the knife switch shown in Fig. 4-7. The mechanism is small and compact, but it does exactly what the knife switch does; in one position of the handle the switch is open, in the other position it is closed. Any switch that merely opens one wire is known as a "single-pole" switch. It is identified by its *two* terminals, *and* the words ON and OFF on the handle. The Underwriters require that all switches of this and similar types be constructed with the mechanism operating under spring tension, so that the circuit is opened and closed suddenly in a very small part of a second. This prevents arcing and prolongs the life of the switch. Obviously this style of switch is much safer than one with an exposed mechanism.

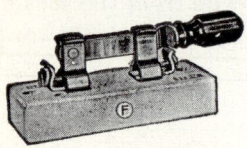

Circle F Mfg. Co.
FIG. 4-7.—The switch shown in Fig. 4-6 does exactly what this switch does—it opens one wire.

Series Wiring.—The circuit of Fig. 4-4 controls only one bulb; often one switch must control two or more bulbs. In drawing a diagram for this, most beginners will connect several sockets, as shown in Fig. 4-8. The current can be

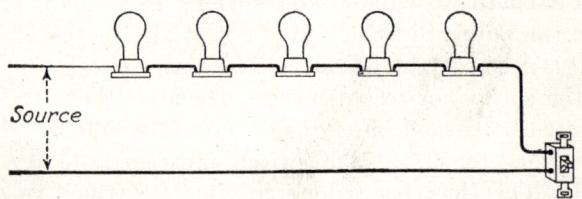

FIG. 4-8.—This type of wiring is known as "series" wiring.

traced from the SOURCE along the light one-way street (wire) to the first bulb, to the second, to the third, to the fourth, to the fifth, and then along the heavy one-way street (wire) back to the SOURCE; consequently the bulbs should light. They will light if the correct sizes are used. However, assume that each bulb is a different size; since all the current that flows through one must also flow through the others, the smallest bulbs will carry more current than they should; consequently they will burn more brightly than normal. The biggest ones will carry less current than they should and will burn less brightly than normal. Medium-size bulbs may burn at normal brilliancy. So far the scheme does not seem very practical. Burning out one bulb or removing it from its socket, as shown in Fig. 4-9, is

BASIC DEVICES AND CIRCUITS 59

equivalent to opening a switch in the circuit. All the bulbs go out. This type of wiring is known as "series" wiring and is impractical for ordinary purposes. It is used on Christmas-tree lighting outfits, where usually eight identical bulbs are

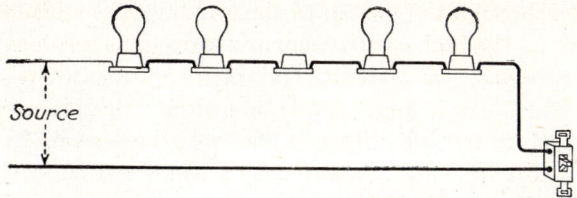

Fig. 4-9.—In series wiring, when one bulb goes out, all go out.

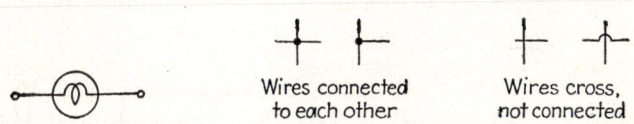

Fig. 4-10.—In illustrations from this point onward the symbol above will indicate a bulb with its socket.

Fig. 4-11.—Note carefully the designations above, which show whether crossing wires are connected to each other or not.

used and consequently all burn at the same brilliancy. Each bulb is rated at 15 volts; they can be used on a 115-volt circuit because each receives one-eighth of the total of 115 volts, or roughly 15 volts.

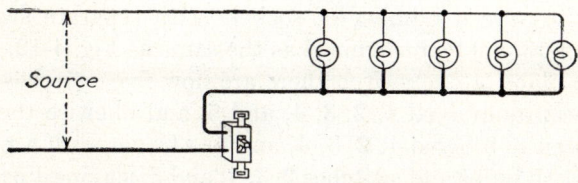

Fig. 4-12.—One switch here controls five bulbs.

Instead of using a picture of a bulb in a socket as in past diagrams, from this point onward the arbitrary symbol of Fig. 4-10 will be used to denote a bulb and its socket. Note also the diagrams of Fig. 4-11, indicating whether wires that cross each other in diagrams are connected to each other or not.

Parallel Wiring.—The scheme used in practically all wiring is known as "parallel" wiring, shown in Fig. 4-12. When one bulb burns out or is removed, the current can still be traced from the SOURCE directly to *each* of the bulbs, whether there are five as shown, or a dozen or more. From the other terminal of each bulb the current can be traced back along the wire through the switch to the SOURCE. Try it; cover one or more of the bulbs with a narrow strip of paper, leaving the wires exposed; the circuit will operate, regardless of the number of bulbs in place, and the switch will always turn all the bulbs on and off. This is the way the sockets in a five-light fixture are wired, operated by a single switch in the wall.

Using Several Switches.—The circuits covered up to this point might serve well in a one-room summer cottage, or an

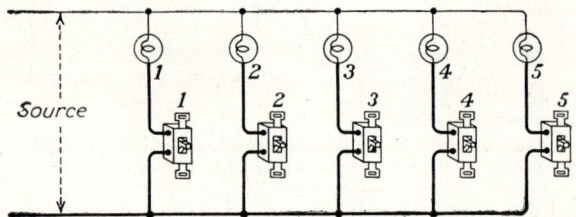

FIG. 4-13.—Now each bulb is controlled by a separate switch.

outbuilding on a farm, but all the lights in an entire home would never be controlled by one single switch. It is equally simple to wire a number of sockets with separate switches. Figure 4-13 will be recognized as the same as Fig. 4-12, except that in place of one switch there are now five switches; these have been numbered 1, 2, 3, 4, and 5, and likewise the bulbs have been numbered 1, 2, 3, 4, and 5. Cover with a piece of paper both bulbs and switches 2, 3, 4, and 5, leaving 1 exposed; immediately it becomes the simple circuit of Fig. 4-5. Cover bulbs and switches 1, 2, 3, and 4, and again it becomes Fig. 4-5. Cover *any* four switches and bulbs, and it becomes Fig. 4-5. Trace the current from the SOURCE to *any* bulb; it can be traced through the bulb to the switch for that bulb, and back to the SOURCE. This can be done whether one or two or all the switches are on; each one is independent of the others.

Turn now to Fig. 4-14, where a group of bulbs has been substituted for each single bulb, so that there are now five groups of bulbs and five switches, numbered 1, 2, 3, 4, and 5. Cover with a piece of paper groups 2, 3, 4, and 5 with their switches, and immediately the simple circuit of Fig. 4-12 appears—five bulbs controlled by a single switch. Cover any four groups, and in each case the current can be traced from SOURCE to any one of the bulbs and through the switches controlling the group (if switches are turned on) back to SOURCE.

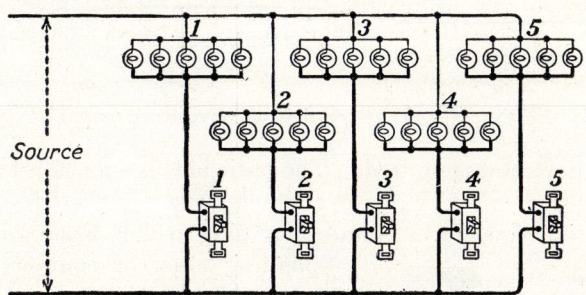

FIG. 4-14.—This is the same as Fig. 4-13 except that each switch controls five bulbs.

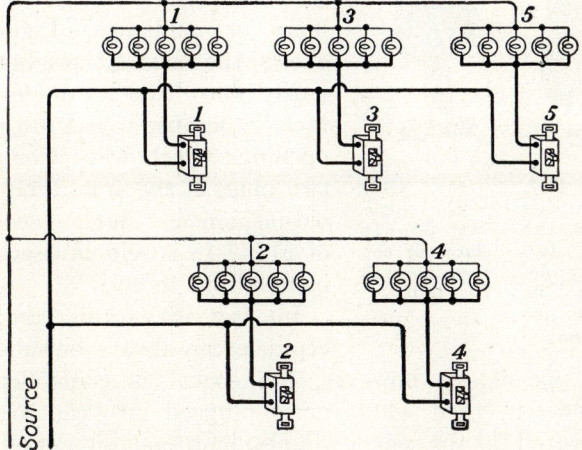

FIG. 4-15.—Same as Fig. 4-14 but rearranged.

Figure 4-14 is the basic wiring diagram for a five-room house with a five-light fixture in each room, controlled by one switch

62   THEORY AND BASIC PRINCIPLES

for each room. Actually the wires would run more as shown in Fig. 4-15, which is more pictorial, with wires coming into the basement, then running to two rooms on the first floor and three rooms on the second floor.

Receptacles.—Radios, toasters, floor lamps, and similar devices must be portable; receptacles are used to plug-in

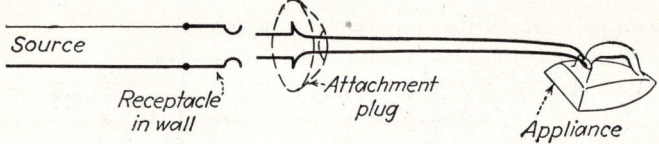

Fig. 4-16.—The principle of convenience outlets.

these devices as required. The basic idea is shown in Fig. 4-16—a pair of metal clips or contacts, one attached to each of the two wires from SOURCE; a plug which has two corre-

Pass & Seymour.

Fig. 4-17.—A duplex receptacle permits two different devices to be used at the same time.

Fig. 4-18.—The single receptacle shown is not used a great deal today.

sponding clips or contacts which can be brought into connection with the first pair, and a pair of wires leading from them to the lamp or appliance. Figure 4-17 shows the finished product ordinarily known as a "duplex receptacle" (because it has *two* pairs of openings which will accommodate two plugs at the same time). The old-fashioned "single receptacle" of Fig. 4-18 is seldom used in new installations today.

In any wiring diagram, a receptacle can always be substituted for a socket; if, however, the socket is controlled by a wall switch, then whatever is plugged into the receptacle substituted for the socket will also be turned on and off by the switch. In any diagram or circuit, connect the receptacle in such a way that, if it were a lamp bulb, it would always be on. If in doubt, go back to the one-way-street idea, and see if the messengers can go from SOURCE to the receptacle and back again to SOURCE even if all switches are in the open or off position.

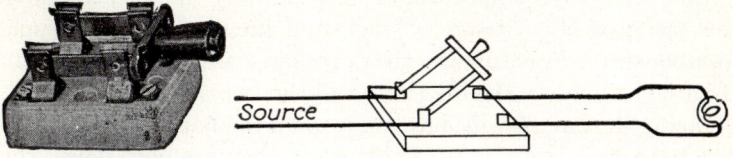

Monowatt Elec. Corp.

FIG. 4-19.—Using a double-pole single-throw switch, both wires are disconnected when a bulb is turned off.

Double-pole Switches.—While opening one of the two wires to a bulb turns it on and off, still both wires may be opened if desired, as is done in Fig. 4-19. The porcelain-base switch there shown is known as the "double-pole single-throw" type, and the corresponding flush toggle switch of the type shown in Fig. 4-6 is usually referred to simply as a "double-pole" switch. It is identified by the fact that it has *four* terminals for wires *and* the words ON and OFF on the handle.

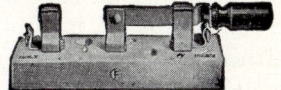

Circle F Mfg. Co.

FIG. 4-20.—A single-pole double-throw switch. It is more commonly known as a "3-way" switch.

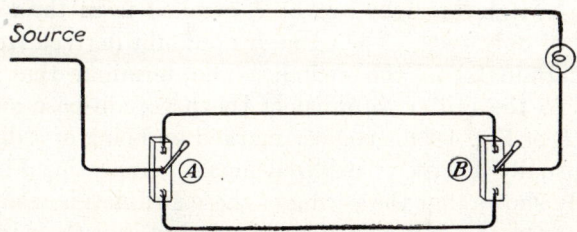

FIG. 4-21.—The basic diagram for 3-way switches which are used to control a light from two different points.

Double-pole switches are required by Code when a bulb or other device is operated on 220 volts or a higher voltage, and usually also on 115 volts in cases where one of the two conductors is not grounded—this will be explained in more detail in a later chapter.

Three-way Switches.—Often it is convenient to be able to turn a light on and off from two different places, for example, a hall light from upstairs and downstairs, or a garage light from either the house or the garage. Fortunately this is easily done by the use of switches of the type known as "single-pole double-throw," pictured in the porcelain-base type in Fig. 4-20. Figure 4-21 shows the diagram; call the two switches A and B. Tracing the circuit will show that, when the handles of A and B are both *up*, the bulb will light; when they are both *down*, the bulb will also light. If either one is up and the other down, the bulb cannot light. Careful study will show also that, if the light is on (regardless of whether the handles of the two switches are both up or down), it can be turned off by throwing the handle of either A or B to the opposite position; likewise, if the light is off, it can be turned on by throwing the handle of either A or B to the opposite position. The light can be controlled by either switch A or switch B, regardless of the position of the other switch of the pair.

In actual wiring, a switch that looks like the switch in Fig. 4-6 is used, except that it has *three* terminals instead of two and the words ON and OFF do *not* appear on the handle. Switches of this kind are known as 3-way switches, a name which is misleading because it might indicate that by the use of such switches a light can be controlled from three points instead of only two. The name is no doubt derived from the three terminals on the switch. The terminal that corresponds to the center terminal of the porcelain-base switches A and B of Fig. 4-20 is usually marked by being of a different color, usually a dark or oxidized finish. Analyzing Fig. 4-21 carefully shows that the wiring of these switches is really very simple. On one of a pair of such switches, run the wire from SOURCE to the marked or "common" terminal; on the other switch, run a wire from the bulb to the marked terminal. Then run two wires from the two remaining terminals on one switch to the two remaining terminals on the other.

The mechanical construction of 3-way wires varies among manufacturers, so that the marked terminal is sometimes alone

BASIC DEVICES AND CIRCUITS

on one end of the switch, sometimes alone on one side. Therefore the pictorial diagram will be either that of Fig. 4-22 or that of Fig. 4-23, depending on the brand of switch. Fortunately no harm is done if the wrong terminals are selected, except that the circuit will not work, and if there is any doubt as to

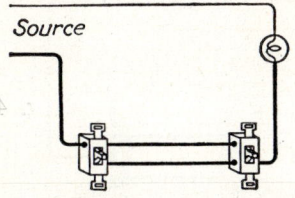

FIG. 4-22.—If the common terminal on 3-way switches is alone on one *side*, use this diagram.

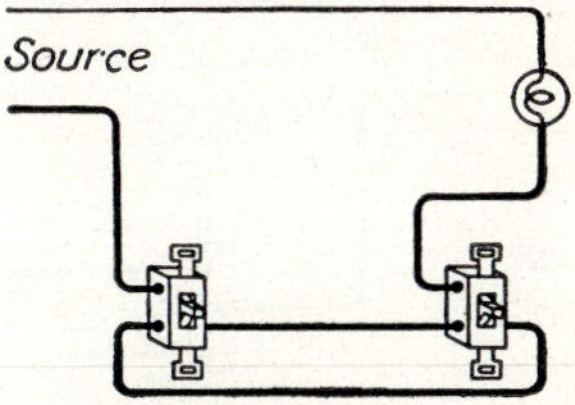

FIG. 4-23.—If the "common" terminal on 3-way switches is alone on one *end*, use this diagram.

which are the correct terminals, proceed by trial and error until a combination is found that works properly. For the purposes of this book, whenever a pictorial diagram involves 3-way switches, the terminal that is alone on one *side*, as in Fig. 4-22, is the common or marked terminal.

Four-way Switches.—The preceding paragraphs showed how to control a light from two different points. What about

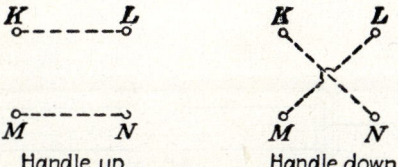

Handle up   Handle down

FIG. 4-24.—This shows what happens inside a 4-way switch when the handle is thrown from one position to the other.

three different points? Again it is relatively simple, although a bit more complicated. At the point nearest the SOURCE, and also at the point nearest the light, use the 3-way switches just described. At the in-between point use what is known as a 4-way switch, the construction of which is such that it performs the operations shown in Fig. 4-24. In one position of the handle the terminal K is connected to the terminal L; also the terminal M is connected to the terminal N. When the handle is thrown, K is connected to N, and M is connected to L, as the diagram shows.

With this operation clearly in mind, now note Fig. 4-25, which shows a light with three switches: a 3-way at A, another

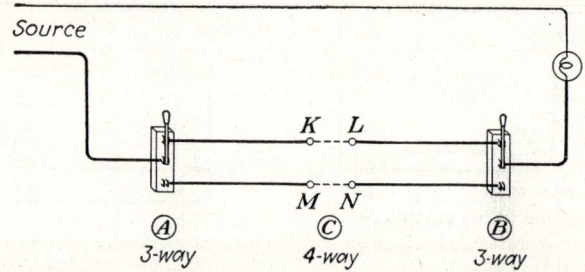

Fig. 4-25.—The basic diagram for 4-way switches, used with a pair of 3-way switches, to control a light from three different points.

at B, and a 4-way at C in the center. So long as the 4-way switch C is in the position shown, the current flows through the switch from K to L and from M to N. The wires from A to B might just as well be continuous wires without the switch C. In this picture the handles of switches A and B

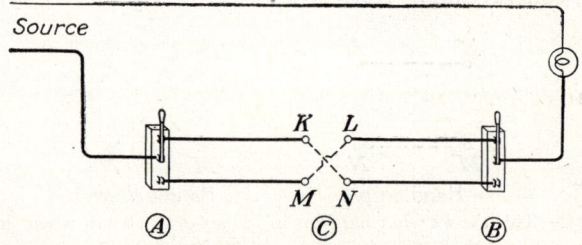

Fig. 4-26.—The same as Fig. 4-25, but with the handle of the 4-way switch thrown to the opposite position.

are both in the up position, and, of course, the light is then on. If then the wires from A to B are considered as continuous wires (forgetting for the moment that switch C is there), Fig. 4-25 becomes identical with Fig. 4-21, merely a light controlled from two points by two 3-way switches.

Now see Fig. 4-26, which is exactly the same as Fig. 4-25,

except that the handle of the 4-way switch C has been thrown to the opposite position. Trace the circuit. Chase the messengers any way at all; they cannot get through and the light is off. Draw a few diagrams similar to Fig. 4-26, but with

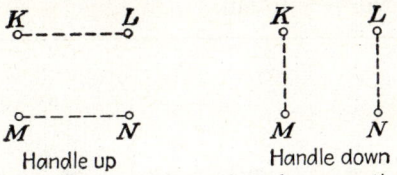

Fig. 4-27.—On some brands of 4-way switches, the connections inside change, as shown above, when the handle is thrown.

the handles of switches A, B, and C in different positions; the diagrams will show that the light can be controlled from any one of the three switches. To control a light from three positions, use two 3-way switches and one 4-way switch. The flush switch of Fig. 4-6 is in the 4-way type identified by its

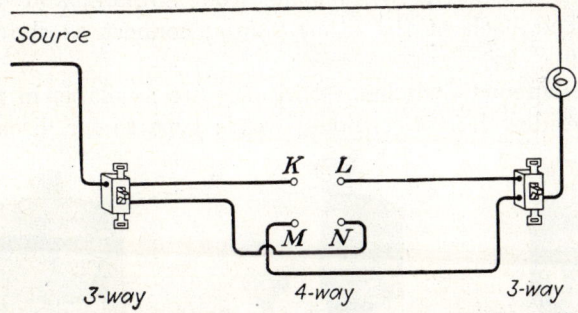

Fig. 4-28.—With 4-way switches of the type shown in Fig. 4-27, use this diagram instead of the one in Fig. 4-25.

four terminals and the fact that it does *not* have the words ON and OFF on the handle (double-pole switches also have four terminals but *do* have the words ON and OFF on the handle).

Some manufacturers make their 4-way switches so that the internal connections, when the handle is thrown, change as shown in Fig. 4-27. In that case the diagram of Fig. 4-26 becomes that of Fig. 4-28—simply cross two of the wires as shown. As in the case of 3-way switches, no harm can be done by wrong connections, except that the circuit will not work, and if there is doubt as to the internal wiring of the switch, simply proceed by trial and error, so far as the four terminals of the 4-way switch are concerned, until a combination that works is found.

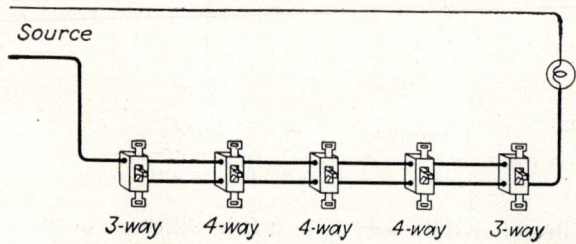

FIG. 4-29.—When a light must be controlled from more than three points, use this diagram.

To control a light from four, five, or any number of points, use a 3-way switch at the point nearest the light, another at the point where the wires come from SOURCE, and 4-way switches at each of the other points; connect as shown in Fig. 4-29.

Miscellaneous Switches.—Switches are available in many types besides the conventional toggle type so far discussed.

Arrow-Hart & Hegemann Elec. Co.

Bryant Elec. Co.

FIG. 4-30.—Push switches are little used today.

FIG. 4-31.—This type of switch requires a key to operate.

FIG. 4-32.—A surface type of switch.

The push-button type shown in Fig. 4-30 is little used today except as replacements in older installations. The lock type shown in Fig. 4-31 can be operated only by those having keys to fit. The momentary-contact type of switch looks like the ordinary toggle type, but the handle is held in one position by a spring, returning to its original position when the operator releases the handle. The surface type of Fig. 4-32 is used chiefly in exposed wiring, as in garages and farm buildings.

Ordinary switches are usually rated 10 amp. at not more than 125 volts, 5 amp. at 250 volts. If therefore the switch must break a current in excess of these values, heavier switches

 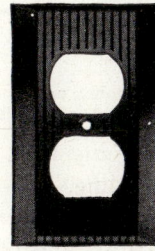 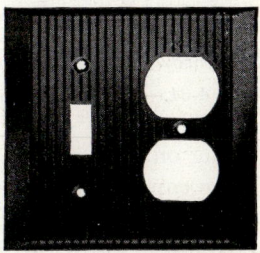

Monowatt Elec. Corp.

Fig. 4-33.—Wall plates are used to cover switches, receptacles, and similar devices. Such plates are available in a great many types and combinations of openings.

of proper amperage rating must be used instead of the ordinary ones.

Wall Plates.—Switches and receptacles cannot be mounted in walls leaving untidy openings around them, nor can the terminals be left exposed, for that would not be safe. Therefore they are covered with "wall plates" or "face plates" after installation. Figure 4-33 shows several plates. The smaller ones are used for single devices. Sometimes it is necessary to mount two or three or more devices side by side, requiring wider plates known as "2-gang," "3-gang," or "4-gang" plates, depending on how many devices the plate covers. They are available also in combinations so that switches, receptacles, and other devices may be mounted side by side, as the same figure shows.

Wall plates of 3-gang and larger types, especially those with odd combinations of openings, are difficult to find in stock. There is now available a new type of single-gang plate so constructed that if a multi-gang plate is wanted it can be quickly done by breaking off a strip at the edge of each plate and mounting the several single-gang plates side by side to produce the larger plate. Figure 4-34 should make this clear.

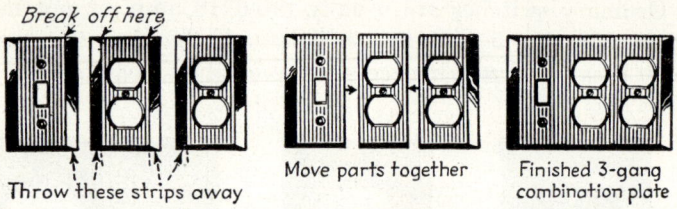

Fig. 4-34.—This new type of plate construction makes it possible to make 2-gang or larger plates in any desired combination out of single plates.

Using only single-gang plates, any kind of larger combination plate can be made in a short time.

Wall plates are made of a great variety of materials, such as bakelite in brown or ivory, brass and other metals in natural

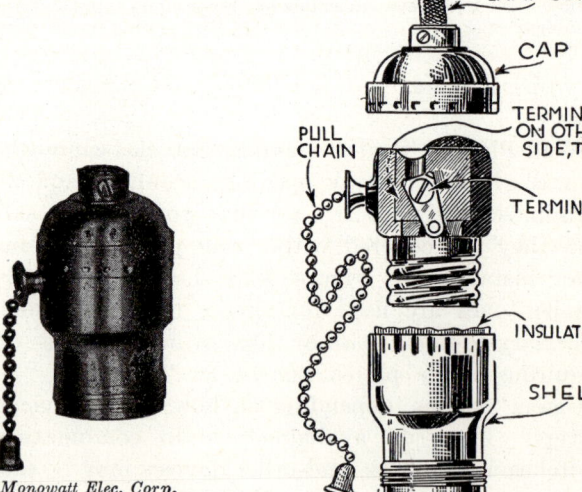

Fig. 4-35.—A typical brass-shell socket. Besides the pull-chain type shown, there are several other types.

Fig. 4-36.—Cross-section of the socket shown in Fig. 4-35.

finish or plated in chromium, oxidized, and other styles to suit the user. The nonmetal plates are generally favored.

BASIC DEVICES AND CIRCUITS

Sockets.—In the Code any device into which a bulb is inserted is called a "lampholder." Practically everybody calls these devices "sockets"; sometimes the term "receptacle" is used for certain types of sockets, although this is not correct according to the Code, for a receptacle is a device where connection is made by plugging in an attachment plug.

Sockets are available in a very great variety of types. The type that was shown in Fig. 4-2, commonly called a "cleat

Bryant Elec. Co.

FIG. 4-37.—Especially in damp locations, it is well to use sockets with an insulating shell of porcelain or bakelite instead of brass.

Circle F Mfg. Co.

FIG. 4-38.—The socket above fits directly on top of an outlet box.

receptacle," is not actually used a great deal in house wiring. The most commonly known socket is the brass-shell type; it may be either keyless or with a switching mechanism to turn the bulb on or off. There are three common types of switching mechanism: the key, the push-through, and the pull-chain type, all serving the same purpose. One of the pull-chain type is shown in Fig. 4-35. The socket consists of the brass shell with an insulating paper liner to insulate metal parts from the shell, the mechanism proper with two terminals, and the cap. The cap may have a threaded hub, used when the socket is used on a floor lamp, a fixture, or similar device, or it may have an insulating bushing, when the socket is used on the end of a piece of cord. A cross-sectional view is shown in Fig. 4-36. Instead of brass for the outer shell, bakelite or porcelain may be used as in Fig. 4-37. Other sockets are of the type shown in Fig. 4-38, used on top of outlet boxes; the weatherproof type shown in Fig. 4-39, for outdoor use; "sign receptacles" shown in Fig. 4-40, used chiefly in the manufacture of lighting fixtures.

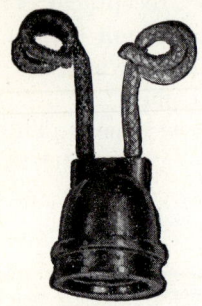

Monowatt Elec. Corp.
Fig. 4-39.—The weatherproof socket shown is intended for outdoor use.

Pass & Seymour.
Fig. 4-40.—Sign receptacles are used mostly in the manufacture of lighting fixtures and similar devices.

Other Devices.—There are dozens of other devices, and these will be described in later chapters of this book, as their use is discussed.

New Work; Old Work.—When a building is wired while it is under construction, the electrical work is known as "new work." If the building is completely finished before the wiring is started, it is known as "old work."

CHAPTER 5

OVERCURRENT DEVICES

It is impossible for an electric current to flow through a wire without heating the wire. As the current increases, the temperature of the wire also increases. The heat produced is proportional to the square of the amperage.

Need for Protective Devices.—As the temperature of a wire increases, the insulation may become damaged by the heat, leading to ultimate breakdown. With sufficient amperage the conductor itself may heat to the point where it constitutes a serious fire hazard. It is therefore most necessary that the amperage be carefully limited to a maximum value that is safe for any given size and type of wire; fortunately this is easily done. Any device that limits the current in a wire to a predetermined number of amperes is termed an "overcurrent device" by the Code. There are many different types of overcurrent devices, and all of them may be considered the safety valves of electrical circuits.

Besides being used to protect *wires* against too great amperage, overcurrent devices are frequently used also to protect electrical *devices*. For example, an electric motor may require 15 amp. to deliver the horsepower stamped on its name plate. Yet a good motor is capable of delivering, without harm, considerably in excess of that horsepower, for short periods, but it will then draw a correspondingly greater amperage. If the higher amperage is allowed to flow for an indefinite period of time, the motor probably will burn out. Therefore an overcurrent device is provided to protect the motor.

Fuses.—The most common overcurrent device is a fuse. A fuse is merely a short length of metal ribbon or wire, made of an alloy with a low melting point and of a size that will carry any given amperage indefinitely, but that will melt quickly when a larger amperage flows. When this wire inside the fuse melts, the fuse is said to "blow."

Plug Fuses.—The common plug-type fuse is shown in Fig. 5-1. The fusible link is enclosed in a sturdy housing which prevents the molten metal from spattering; there is a window through which the user can see whether the fuse has blown; there are contacts for quick replacement when required. The largest fuse approved in the plug type is the 30 amp.; smaller standard sizes are 10, 15, 20, and 25 amp. The Code requires that plug fuses rated at 15 amp. or less be of hexagonal shape, or have a window or other prominent part of hexagonal form; those rated at more than 15 amp. are round. This detail enables inspectors to see at a glance whether a circuit in a home (where generally speaking a 15-amp. fuse is the maximum permissible) is overfused or not.

Bussman Mfg. Co.
FIG. 5-1.—Plug fuses are made only in ratings up to 30 amp.

The Code limits the use of plug-type fuses to installations not exceeding 125 volts, except that they may be used on

Bussman Mfg. Co.
FIG. 5-2.—The ferrule type of cartridge fuse is made in sizes up to 60 amp.

Bussman Mfg. Co.
FIG. 5-3.—The knife-blade type of cartridge fuse is made only in sizes of 61 amp. upward.

installations with one grounded conductor with maximum voltage of 150 volts to ground. This means that they are permissible on a 230-volt circuit with grounded neutral, for, although the voltage is 230 between conductors, it is only 115 to ground (see page 127).

Cartridge Fuses.—Although the plug fuse is the common fuse for homes, the cartridge type is by far more common for industrial purposes, and is the only type that can be used when current in excess of 30 amp. is involved. There are two basic types of cartridge fuse, the ferrule contact type, shown in Fig. 5-2, and the knife-blade contact type, shown in Fig. 5-3. The ferrule construction is used only on fuses rated 60 amp. or less, the knife-blade construction on fuses rated 61 amp. or more. Ordinary cartridge fuses are approved for use on circuits not exceeding 250 volts, and a heavier, larger, sturdier construction of the same appearance is approved for use up to 600 volts.

Mechanically, cartridge fuses of different amperage and voltage ratings are of 12 different sizes, as shown in the following table:

Fuse ratings, amperes	Over-all length, inches	
	250-volt type	600-volt type
0 to 30	2	5
31 to 60	3	$5\frac{1}{2}$
61 to 100	$5\frac{7}{8}$	$7\frac{7}{8}$
101 to 200	$7\frac{1}{8}$	$9\frac{5}{8}$
201 to 400	$8\frac{5}{8}$	$11\frac{5}{8}$
401 to 600	$10\frac{3}{8}$	$13\frac{3}{8}$

From the above table it is evident that it is next to impossible to use a fuse of an amperage which differs widely from the amperage and voltage intended when the installation was first planned. This is a very desirable safety measure.

Renewable Fuses.—Cartridge fuses are further divided into renewable and nonrenewable types. The nonrenewable types, once blown, are of no further value. Since only the fusible link is destroyed when a fuse blows, renewable fuses are available that permit the fusible link to be replaced after blowing. Figure 5-4 shows a clear view of the basic construction; it is a very simple matter to replace the fusible link. In external appearance there is no basic difference between nonrenewable and renewable fuses, except that the latter are so constructed that they can be taken apart.

Time-delay Fuses.—Consider a circuit in a home, wired with No. 14 rubber-covered wire, having a maximum carrying capacity of 15 amp. and protected by 15-amp. fuses. Most of the time the wire will be carrying considerably under 15 amp.; the temperature of the wire and its insulation will be well within safe limits. If the amperage is increased to 30 amp., the fuse will blow in a very few seconds. On the other hand, 30 amp. flowing for a few seconds or even for half a minute would not heat the wire or its insulation to the danger point,

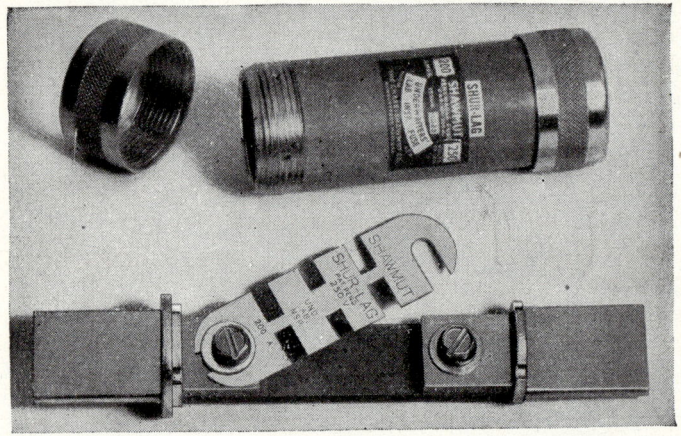

Chase-Shawmut Co.

FIG. 5-4.—The renewable type of fuse is easily disassembled for replacement of the fusible link.

especially if the amperage was very small before it was increased to 30.

In practice, there are often conditions just as described; perhaps 3 amp. are flowing in the wire, representing about 300 watts of light bulbs. Then a motor is turned on, for example, a washing machine. The motor requires in the neighborhood of 30 amp. for a few seconds, while it is starting; after that it drops to a normal of around 6 amp. Very frequently the fuse blows during this starting interval, although the wire and its insulation are in no danger whatever.

Accordingly time-delay or time-lag fuses have been developed which carry their rated amperage indefinitely and blow within a few minutes like ordinary fuses on an overload of say

50 per cent, but which carry overloads of 100 per cent for about 30 sec. and even a 200 per cent overload for about 5 sec. In other words, they do not blow like ordinary fuses on large but temporary overloads, but they do blow like ordinary fuses on *continuous* small overloads or on short circuits. Several types of such fuses are shown in Figs. 5-5 and 5-6. The use of this type of fuse is very desirable, especially when motors are used. It is entirely likely that this type of fuse will in due course of time completely replace ordinary fuses. Power companies, especially, find the use of time-delay or time-lag fuses by their customers most desirable, for it is well known that a large percentage of service calls are caused by nothing more serious than blown fuses—and usually such blown fuses could be avoided by using the time-lag type, which carries short nondangerous overloads safely without blowing.

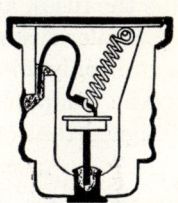

Bussman Mfg. Co.
FIG. 5-5.—A typical time-lag fuse, known as a "Fusetron." Time-lag fuses carry temporary overloads safely without blowing.

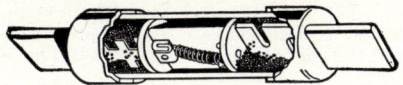

Bussman Mfg. Co.

FIG. 5-6.—Time-lag fuses are also made in cartridge type. They are especially useful in protecting motors that usually require several times as many amperes while starting as while running.

Nontamperable Fuses.—Since each size of wire has a very definite maximum safe carrying capacity in amperes, it is required by the Code that the overcurrent device selected to protect the wire be of a rating no greater than that amperage. For example, the No. 14 rubber-covered wire used for ordinary residential wiring has a carrying capacity of 15 amp. and accordingly should be protected by fuses no larger than 15 amp., yet all plug fuses up to 30 amp. are interchangeable. Nothing prevents the homeowner from substituting a 30-amp. for the 15-amp. size, completely defeating the purpose of the fuse. This led to the development of fuses of the nontamperable type, shown in Fig. 5-7; Fig. 5-8 shows a cross-section of its construction. The device consists of an adapter and the fuse proper. The adapters have amperage ratings just like the fuses, and a 15-amp. adapter will permit only 15-amp. or smaller fuses to be inserted into it; a 25-amp. adapter will permit only 25-amp. or smaller fuses to be used; and so on.

The adapters fit into ordinary fuse holders, but are so designed that once installed, they cannot be removed. Obvi-

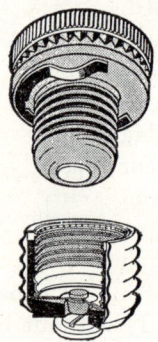

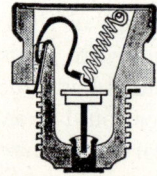

Bussman Mfg. Co.
Fig. 5-7.—This fustat is designed to resist tampering on the part of the user.

Bussman Mfg. Co.
Fig. 5-8.—Cross-section of the fuse shown in Fig. 5-7.

ously then if a contractor when wiring a home with the usual No. 14 wire (which has a carrying capacity of 15 amp.) installs 15-amp. adapters, he makes it impossible to use fuses larger than 15-amp. size, thus making it impossible on the part of those who know no better, or are inclined to take chances, to overfuse. This eliminates one of the greatest causes of electrical fires and is obviously a sensible move.

The most common of these nontamperable fuses is known as a "fustat" and besides being of the nontamperable type is also of the time-lag type, the advantages of which have already been discussed. The Code calls this type of fuse a "Type S" fuse.

The 1940 Code required that original installations made after Nov. 1, 1941, be equipped only with nontamperable fuses, but the requirement was never really enforced. The new 1947 Code in its first drafts required the use of Type S fuses, but, as finally adopted and published, the requirement was dropped. The use of nontamperable fuses is therefore optional.

Circuit Breakers.—The Code defines a circuit breaker as "a device designed to open under abnormal conditions a

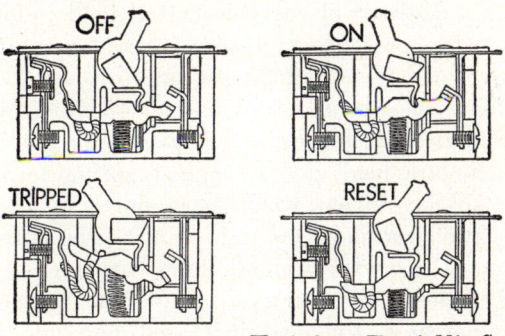

Westinghouse Elec. & Mfg. Co.

FIG. 5-9.—This circuit breaker may also be used as a switch. When it trips, reset as shown in lower right, then move handle back to ON.

current-carrying circuit without injury to itself. The term as used in this Code applies only to the automatic type designed to trip on a predetermined overload of current." Since all switches break circuits, they can be termed circuit breakers, and the above definition merely states that so far as the Code is concerned, when circuit breakers are mentioned, it refers only to the type that open the circuit when an amperage greater than that for which the unit was designed flows through it. When it opens a circuit, moving a handle, pushing a button, etc., closes the circuit again—there is nothing to replace.

A circuit breaker may be of the instantaneous type, opening the circuit instantly when more than the prescribed amperage flows. This is more or less a special-purpose type and is seldom used for circuit protection. The more usual type is of the time-delay type, functioning like the time-delay fuses described above. There are many types and brands available.

One of the most common is the type shown in Fig. 5-9. Essentially it consists of a carefully calibrated bimetallic strip, similar to that used in thermostats. As current flows through this strip, heat is created, and the bimetallic strip bends. Under sufficient heat it bends enough to release a trip that opens the contacts, interrupting the circuit just as it is interrupted when a fuse blows.

While this device will carry its rated load indefinitely, it will carry a 50 per cent overload for about a minute, a 100 per cent overload for about 20 sec., and even a 200 per cent overload for 5 sec.—usually long enough to start a motor.

Other similar devices operate on the "solder-pot" principle. The contacts are held closed, against spring tension, by a ratchet or similar device, which is anchored in a tiny pot of solder of a predetermined melting point. The current in the circuit which the device protects flows through the solder, or through a heater coil which surrounds the solder. As the amperage increases, the heat increases, and, at the critical point, the solder melts, releasing the spring which opens the contacts and the circuit. After the solder solidifies, the device is reset by pushing a button.

Determining Proper Rating of Overcurrent Device.—In general, it is never permissible to use an overcurrent device rated higher in amperes than the allowable carrying capacity of the wire in question, per Tables 1 and 2 of the Code (see Appendix). There are a number of important exceptions, particularly in connection with motors, and these will be covered in connection with related subjects in other portions of this book.

It will be well to memorize carefully the carrying capacity of the smaller sizes of ordinary rubber-covered wire; this is also the maximum rating of the overcurrent device protecting that size. The 1947 Code increases the permissible carrying capacities[1] of No. 10 and heavier sizes. The new carrying capacities are as follows:

[1] The amperages shown are for Type R or "Code" grade of rubber-covered wire, the type used for ordinary residential wiring. Some other

Wire size	Amperes	Wire size	Amperes
No. 14	15	No. 6	55
No. 12	20	No. 4	70
No. 10	30	No. 2	95
No. 8	40	No. 0	125

Joining Different Sizes of Wire.—If two different sizes of wire are joined as in Fig. 5-10, then the fuse (or other over-

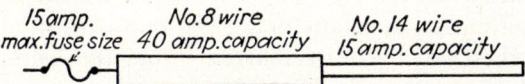

Fig. 5-10.—When two different sizes of wire are connected, the biggest fuse that may be used is the one that protects the *smaller* wire.

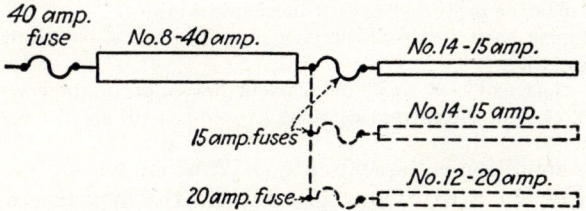

Fig. 5-11.—If fuses are used where the wire size is reduced, select an amperage rating that protects the *smaller* wire.

current protection) may be no greater than that permitted with the smaller wire. Since in this case the smaller wire has a capacity of only 15 amp., this is the maximum size fuse permitted. In practice, a condition of this kind is often met, especially in farm wiring, where a No. 8 wire is used for an overhead span to secure mechanical strength and to avoid voltage drop. Although it has a capacity of 40 amp., the circumstances may be such that more than 15 amp. is never required, and the maximum fuse permitted, 15 amp., will not in any way prove inconvenient.

---

types, not usually used for residential wiring, have higher carrying capacities and are described in Chap. 25.

On the other hand, there may be a condition, as shown in Fig. 5-11, where under similar circumstances No. 8 is again used but where more than 15 amp. is to be carried altogether; in this case a second fuse is used at the point where the wire size is reduced. A 40-amp. fuse may be used to protect the No. 8 wire, and a 15-amp. fuse to protect the No. 14 wire. Usually when these conditions are present, additional wires protected by individual fuses are used, as shown in the dotted lines.

There are a number of exceptions to these general requirements, the most important being the one permitted by Sec. 2434d of the Code. No overcurrent protection is required at the point where the wire size is reduced if the smaller wire meets *all four* of the following conditions:

1. It must be not over 25 ft. long.
2. It must be protected against mechanical injury.
3. It must have a current-carrying capacity at least one-third that of the larger wire.
4. It must end in a *single* overcurrent device of an amperage rating not greater than the current-carrying capacity of the smaller wire.

This condition is shown in Fig. 5-12, which portrays a combination of No. 8 with No. 14. Beyond the final fuse or other

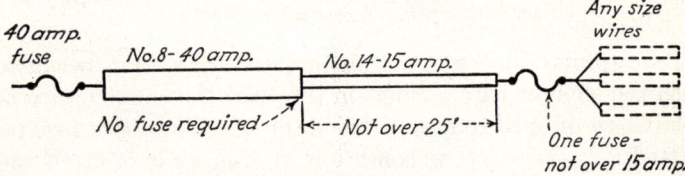

FIG. 5-12.—Under certain conditions no fuse is required at the point where the wire size is reduced.

overcurrent device at the end of the smaller wire, additional wires of any length or size (but not smaller than No. 14) may be run; they are protected by the 15-amp. protective device ahead of them.

Considering the carrying capacity of various sizes of wire and the requirements of the preceding paragraph, it will be evident that, if all those requirements are met and if ordinary Type R wire is used,

>No. 14 may be tapped to No. 8 or lighter
>No. 12 may be tapped to No. 6 or lighter
>No. 10 may be tapped to No. 3 or lighter
>No. 8 may be tapped to No. 1 or lighter

Another exception is that permitted by Sec. 2434c of the Code. In the case of switchboards, panelboards, and similar devices, it is not unusual to have wires of considerable size run through such devices, with taps taken off to feed a smaller load. In such cases no overcurrent protection is required where the smaller wire is tapped to the larger, provided it is not over 5 ft. long, provided it has a carrying capacity equivalent to the total of the carrying capacities of all the circuits it feeds, and provided it does not extend beyond panelboards or other devices in question.

An additional common-sense exception is contained in Code Sec. 2121-c-2, which permits taps not over 18 in. long to be made from circuit wires of any size, to serve an individual socket, fixture, or outlet, provided only that the short wire is heavy enough to serve its specific load, and never smaller than No. 14 (on 50-amp. circuits, No. 12). Section 2121-c-3, in turn, permits wiring inside fixtures, also portable cords, to be smaller than the circuit wires serving them, provided they are heavy enough to carry their specific loads. Sections 2403d and 2403f, in turn, authorize the omission of overcurrent protection at such points where wire sizes are reduced.

CHAPTER 6

TYPES AND SIZES OF WIRES

Electricity is conducted over wires from the point where it is generated to the point where it is used. Copper is the material used in practically all cases. The Code makes very little reference to "wire" but speaks frequently of the "conductor," which it defines as "a wire or cable or other form of metal suitable for carrying current." All wires therefore are conductors, but not all conductors are wires. Copper bus bars for example are conductors, but are not referred to as wires.

Previous chapters showed that all wire has resistance that prevents an unlimited flow of current and causes voltage drop. For any given load, a size of wire that causes only a reasonable voltage drop must be selected.

Current flowing through a wire causes heat; the heat varies as the square of the amperage. There is a limit to the degree of heat that various types of insulation will safely withstand, and even a bare wire must not be allowed to reach a temperature that might cause fire. The Code carefully and in great detail specifies the maximum amperage that is considered safe for wires of different sizes with different insulations and under different conditions. These maximum amperages will be given later.

Circular Mils.—In order to discuss intelligently the different sizes of wire, it is necessary to understand something about the scheme used in numbering these sizes. The units used are "mils" and "circular mils." A mil is one one-thousandth (0.001) in. A circular mil (abbreviated c.m.) is the area of a circle one mil in diameter. Thus a wire that is 0.001 in. or 1 mil in diameter is said to have a cross-sectional area of 1 c.m. Since the areas of two circles are always proportional to the squares of their diameters, it follows that the cross-sectional

TYPES AND SIZES OF WIRES

area of a wire 0.003 in., or 3 mils, in diameter is 9 c.m.; that of one 0.01 in., or 10 mils, in diameter is 100 c.m.; that of one 0.1 in., or 100 mils, in diameter is 10,000 c.m., etc. The cross-sectional area of any round wire in circular mils is equivalent to the diameter of the copper only, in mils or thousandths of an inch, squared or multiplied by itself.

Wire Sizes.—Instead of referring to common sizes of wire by their areas, sizes or numbers have been assigned to them. The gauge commonly used is the American Wire Gauge, abbreviated A.W.G.; it is the same as the Brown and Sharpe,

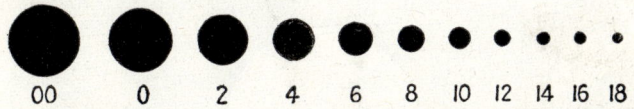

00   0   2   4   6   8   10   12   14   16   18

FIG. 6-1.—Actual diameters of typical sizes of copper wire, without insulation.

or B. & S., gauge. This gauge is not the same as that used for steel wires used for nonelectrical purposes, for example, fence wires.

Number 14 wire, which is a size most commonly used for ordinary house wiring, has a copper conductor 0.064 in., or 64 mils, in diameter. Wires smaller than this are Nos. 16, 18, 20, and so on. Number 40 has a diameter of approximately 0.003 in., as small as a hair; still finer sizes are made. Sizes larger than No. 14 are Nos. 12, 10, 8, etc. Note that the higher the number, the smaller the diameter of the wire.

In this way, sizes proceed until No. 0 is reached; the next sizes are No. 00, No. 000, and finally No. 0000, which is almost ½ in. in diameter. Numbers 0, 00, 000, and 0000 are frequently designated also as 1/0, 2/0, 3/0, and 4/0. As still heavier sizes are reached, they no longer are designated by a numerical size, but simply by their cross-sectional areas in circular mils.

Figure 6-1 shows the approximate actual sizes of typical gauge wires, without the insulation. The sizes from Nos. 40 to 20 are used mostly in manufacturing electrical devices of all kinds. Numbers 18 and 16 are used chiefly for flexible cords, for signal systems, and for similar purposes where relatively

86 THEORY AND BASIC PRINCIPLES

small amperages are involved. Numbers 14 to 4 are used in ordinary residential and farm wiring and, of course, in industrial work, where the still heavier sizes are also used. Number 14 is the lightest size permitted for ordinary wiring. The even

Brown & Sharpe Mfg. Co.

FIG. 6-2.—Typical wire gauge. Measure the wire by the slot into which it fits. The picture is actual size.

sizes of wire such as Nos. 18, 16, 14, 12, 10, 8, etc., are commonly used; the odd sizes, as Nos. 15, 13, 11, 9, are seldom used in wiring. The odd sizes, however, are commonly used in the form of magnet wire for manufacturing motors, transformers, and so on, for which purposes even fractional sizes such as No. $15\frac{1}{2}$ are not at all uncommon.

In Fig. 6-2 is shown the usual gauge used in measuring wire sizes. The wire is measured by the slot into which it will fit, not by the hole behind the slot.

Table 18 of Chap. 10 of the Code shows the commonly used sizes of wire, their areas in circular mils, their resistances in

TYPES AND SIZES OF WIRES

ohms per thousand feet, their dimensions in fractions of an inch, and their areas in fractions of a square inch. For convenience this table is reproduced in the Appendix of this book.

It is interesting to know that any wire which is three sizes heavier than another will have a cross-sectional area exactly twice that of the other. For example, No. 11 has an area exactly twice that of No. 14; No. 3 wire has an area exactly twice that of No. 6. Any wire that is six sizes heavier than another has exactly twice the diameter, four times the area, of the other. For example, No. 6 wire is exactly twice the diameter, and four times the area, of No. 12.

Stranded Wires.—When common sizes of wire are used for ordinary wiring purposes, there is usually no reason why the copper conductor should not be one single solid conductor. Where considerable flexibility is needed, as in a lamp cord, the conductor instead of being one solid wire consists of a great many strands of fine wire twisted together. The number assigned to such a conductor is determined by the total cross-sectional area of all these individual strands added together. For example, per Table 18 of the Code, the cross-sectional area of No. 16 wire is 2,583 c.m. The total cross-sectional area of 65 strands of No. 34 wire is 2,585 c.m.; the total cross-sectional area of 26 strands of No. 30 wire is a trifle above this figure. Therefore wire made up of either of these two combinations, or any other combination totaling substantially 2,583 c.m., is known simply as No. 16 wire. If it is necessary to describe such wire in more detail, the first-mentioned combination is described simply as No. 16, 65/34, and the second as No. 16, 26/30.

Wires No. 6 and heavier are usually stranded, solid wires being too stiff to be entirely practical. The stranding of these has been entirely standardized, so it is not necessary to specify the sizes of the individual strands.

Rubber-covered Wire.—Although rubber[1] is used as insulation in many different types of wire, actually only one specific

[1] According to Code definition (Sec. 3102), "rubber insulations

type is today known by the rather general name of "rubber-covered wire." It is the wire used for all ordinary electrical wiring. Its general construction is shown in Fig. 6-3; it consists of a copper conductor with a layer of rubber insulation. The copper is tinned to prevent the rubber from sticking to

U. S. Rubber Co.

Fig. 6-3.—Single-braid rubber-covered wire. This is the type wire used for most kinds of ordinary wiring.

the conductor. Over the rubber insulation is a cotton protective braid, usually saturated with a flame-retarding and moisture-resistant compound and then finished off with a wax finish for cleanliness and for facilitating pulling the wire into conduit. The thickness of the rubber insulation varies with

U. S. Rubber Co.

Fig. 6-4.—Double-braid rubber-covered stranded wire. Heavier sizes of wire have a stranded conductor and two protective braids.

the size of the conductor and is carefully standardized to specifications set up by the Underwriters' Laboratories in accordance with findings of test and usage. Ordinary rubber-covered wire is for use on voltages not over 600 volts; for use in excess of 600 volts, heavier insulation is used. This type of wire is known as "SBRC"—single-braid rubber-covered.

Sizes 6 and heavier are stranded and provided with two protective cotton braids instead of a single braid, as in the lighter sizes (the general construction is shown in Fig. 6-4). They are known as "DBRC, Str."—double-braid rubber-covered, stranded.

Grades of Rubber-covered Wire.—The 1940 Code recognized three different types of rubber-insulated building wires, as follows: *Type R*, commonly known as the "Code" grade;

---

include those made from natural and synthetic rubber, neoprene and other vulcanizable materials."

Type RP, commonly known as "performance" grade; and *Type RH*, commonly known as "heat-resisting" grade.

The 1947 Code recognizes only two of these types, as follows: *Type R*, which however as now being manufactured is equivalent to the old Type RP in quality[1] (the quality equivalent to the 1940 Type R being dropped); and *Type RH*, substantially the same as the old Type RH.

As the name implies, Type RH is more heat-resistant, less harmed by heat. Since it will stand more heat, larger amperages are permitted than with Type R, but this applies only to No. 8 and heavier wires.

For ordinary residential use, Type R is used almost exclusively. In industrial and commercial use, the Type RH has many advantages. However, although Chaps. 1 to 24 of this book deal with *principles* of wiring of all kinds, this section covers *methods* only as used in residential and farm wiring. Therefore in these chapters only Type R wire will be discussed, and Chap. 25 and the remaining chapters will cover Type RH wire, as well as wires with other kinds of insulation.

Cable.—Usually a stranded wire heavier than No. 0000 is known as a "cable." Thus one would refer to a "1,000,000 c.m. cable." The word "cable" is also used equally often as outlined in the following paragraphs.

Cables.—For many purposes, especially in residential and farm wiring, it is desirable to have two or more wires grouped together in a cable. This makes a compact assembly which may be simply installed, especially when used in a building that has been completely finished before the wiring is started, for the cable lends itself well to fishing through wall spaces.

A cable that contains two No. 14 wires is known as "14-2" (fourteen-two); if it contains three No. 12 wires, it is known as "12-3"; if it contains only one No. 8, it is known as "8-1"; etc.

---

[1] To distinguish a roll of Type R wire made to the 1947 specifications from a roll of the earlier and less desirable Type R, look at the Underwriters' label on the coil. The improved type will be overstamped "1947 Code."

Nonmetallic Sheathed Cable.—One of the most common cables is known as "nonmetallic sheathed cable" and is of the general construction shown in Fig. 6-5. It is available under a great many trade names such as Romex, Cresflex, and Loomwire. It consists of two or more rubber-covered wires practically identical with "rubber-covered wire" described in a

National Elec. Products Corp.

Fig. 6-5.—Nonmetallic sheathed cable is used for ordinary house wiring, and its popularity is rapidly growing.

previous paragraph. Over each wire is a spiral wrapping of a tough paper tape, which serves to space the wires a bit and also adds mechanical strength. Over the assembly is an outer covering of cotton thoroughly saturated with moisture-resisting and flame-retarding componds. If this outer braid were

National Elec. Products Corp.

Fig. 6-6.—Armored cable has a layer of steel armor for its final protection.

applied directly over the conductors, empty spaces would result. These are filled with a jute cord.

Armored Cable.—Another common cable is armored cable, commonly called "BX." The Code refers to it as Type AC. It is pictured in Fig. 6-6 and is available under a great variety of trade names such as "BX" and "Flexsteel." In construction it consists of two or more rubber-covered wires, wrapped with a spiral layer of tough kraft paper, and over all is a continuous galvanized steel armor. The paper affords protection against abrasion by the steel and in addition serves another useful purpose, a discussion of which will be found in a later chapter.

TYPES AND SIZES OF WIRES

Lead-covered Cable.—Ordinary rubber-covered wire may not be used except in reasonably dry locations. There are many locations where it would be entirely suitable were it not for the fact that a certain amount of moisture is continuously present. To make it possible to use rubber-covered wire in such locations, lead-sheathed cable was developed. It consists of ordinary rubber-covered wires covered with a continuous layer of lead. Figure 6-7 shows its general construction. The lead sheath is relatively thin, only $3/64$ in. on small

U. S. Rubber Co.

FIG. 6-7.—Lead-sheathed cable is used where there is too much moisture for ordinary rubber-covered wire. The lead is not intended as mechanical protection; it serves only to keep moisture out.

General Elec. Co.

FIG. 6-8.—Armored-lead cable is simply the same material shown in Fig. 6-7, plus a steel armor.

sizes, and affords very little mechanical protection. This is the reason the Code requires that lead cable be further protected mechanically. Other types of wire besides the rubber-covered type, for example, varnished-cambric, are also made in the lead-sheathed type. Lead-sheathed cable is commonly used for underground runs as well as in other locations where considerable moisture is present.

Armored-lead Cable.—Instead of running lead cable through conduit, it is permissible to use the type that has a steel armor around it, as on armored cable, and known in the Code as Type ACL. Its construction is shown in Fig. 6-8.

Type RW Rubber-covered Wire.—Since lead-sheathed cable must be given additional protection in the form of conduit or similar material, it becomes a relatively expensive method of construction, from the standpoint of material cost. Likewise, it is difficult and takes a good deal of time to pull such cable into conduit without damaging the lead sheath, especially if long runs and several bends are involved, so it becomes expensive from the labor viewpoint. These facts were responsible for the development of a special variety of rubber-covered wire, the insulation of which is especially water-resistant. It looks like ordinary rubber-covered wire and may be distinguished by the Underwriters' Type RW label. It may not be buried directly in the ground but must be protected like lead-sheathed cable. Its cost is considerably less than that of lead-sheathed cable. Its use is recommended not only for underground work, but for all other locations where moisture is apt to be continuously present.

Crescent Ins. Wire & Cable Co.

FIG. 6-9.—Wire of this type may be buried directly in the ground without further protection.

Type USE Service-entrance Cable.—There is available another type of wire, in appearance very similar to Type RW wire, but which has an even more moisture-resistant insulation and, in addition, an outer jacket of a type of rubber that is extremely strong and tough mechanically. It is illustrated in Fig. 6-9. This material is not considered a variety of rubber-covered wire, but rather as a special variety of service-entrance cable, designated by the Underwriters as Type USE (underground service entrance). It may be buried in the ground directly, without conduit or other similar protection. Common sense dictates that it be buried deeply enough so that it will not be disturbed or damaged by digging, farm implements, etc. It is recommended that a board or similar obstruction be laid on top of the wires as a warning when subsequent digging becomes necessary. The use of this cable results in the least costly of all underground installations, which probably explains its rapidly growing popularity.

Parkway Cable.—Another cable that may be buried without further protection is parkway cable. It is commonly used for suburban street-lighting purposes. It consists of one or more conductors insulated with a particularly high grade of rubber compound that is especially resistant to water. Over these wires there is a layer of moisture-resisting rubber compound to make an assembly that is round or oval as desired, and over this there is usually a layer of duck or similar material impreg-

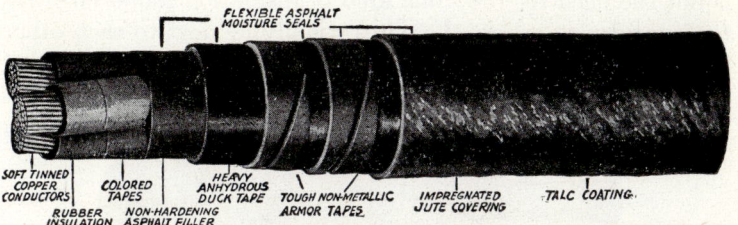

Fig. 6-10.—Nonmetallic parkway cable can be buried directly in the ground, for it is moisture-resistant and mechanically tough.

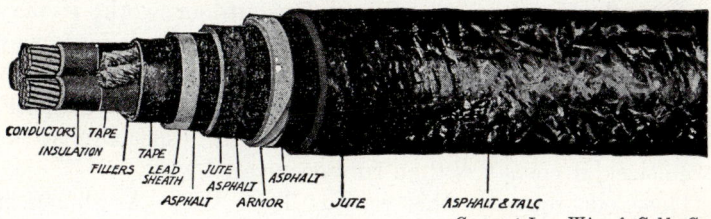

Fig. 6-11.—This armored parkway cable is similar to the nonmetallic type shown in Fig. 6-10, but has metal armor for still further mechanical protection.

nated with moisture-resistant saturants. Over these come, in turn, several layers of tough semihard rubber tapes for mechanical protection; and finally over all is a braid of fabric, usually jute, saturated with weatherproofing compound of an asphalt nature, finished with a layer of talc or mica for cleanliness. This construction, shown in Fig. 6-10, is typical of parkway cable of the nonmetallic type.

Frequently a layer of interlocking steel tape is added making the metal-armored type shown in Fig. 6-11. Often, to make the cable still more enduring, a lead sheath is applied over the filler and under the armor. There are many other variations in the exact method of construction, but the types shown in Figs. 6-10 and 6-11 are the most common.

Weatherproof Wire.—When wires are run between buildings, there is no great likelihood that anyone will ever touch them. They are usually suspended a considerable distance above the ground and not close to each other. Therefore there is not the need for the same kind of insulation found on wires for interior use, where the wires usually lie next to each other inside conduit or cable. On the other hand, wire used out-of-doors must stand exposure to the weather, a factor that need not be considered for interior use. A special wire known

U. S. Rubber Co.

FIG. 6-12.—Triple-braid weatherproof wire. It may never be used indoors.

as "weatherproof wire" is used for outdoor work; it may never be used indoors (Code Sec. 3102). The Code in no way prohibits the use of rubber-covered wire out-of-doors, but it is common practice to use weatherproof wire for that purpose; as a matter of fact, it will last longer and, especially in the large sizes, it costs less than rubber-covered wire.

The Code refers to this wire as Type WP. As shown in Fig. 6-12, there is a copper conductor, usually with three separate cotton braids; the entire assembly is saturated with weatherproofing moisture-resistant compounds, usually of an asphaltic nature, and is finished off with an application of flake mica for cleanliness. Most of the wire of this type made today is manufactured to the specifications of the Utilities' Research Commission and is known as Type URC.

Since weatherproof wire is installed outdoors, any heat developed is easily radiated; extra heat does not create a fire hazard, as in the case of wires installed indoors. For these reasons any given size of weatherproof wire is permitted to carry more amperes than the same size of rubber-covered wire. The carrying capacities will be found in Code Table 2 (see Appendix); those of the smaller sizes are as follows:

TYPES AND SIZES OF WIRES   95

No. 14................	30 amp.	No. 6................	100 amp.
No. 12................	40 amp.	No. 4................	130 amp.
No. 10................	55 amp.	No. 2................	175 amp.
No. 8................	70 amp.	No. 0................	235 amp.

Service Entrance Cable.—There are several types of cable known as "service entrance cable." These will be described in Chap. 12.

Lamp Cords.—When wires are installed permanently, they need be only sufficiently flexible to permit reasonably easy installation. If the wires must be moved about, as on a floor lamp, a vacuum cleaner, or a portable motor, they must be

U. S. *Rubber Co.*

FIG. 6-13.—Type PO lamp cord is commonly used on floor lamps and similar devices.

very flexible. This is necessary first of all for convenience and secondly to prevent the conductors from breaking, which would be likely if they were solid copper of considerable diameter. Flexible wires of this type are called "flexible cords" in the Code and have come to be known usually as "lamp cords." There are a great many different kinds, the more common of which will be described here.

Type PO.—This is the familiar cord used on floor lamps and similar devices which is commonly called "silk cord." Like all lamp cords it begins with a conductor made of many strands of fine copper, over which there is a layer of cotton which prevents the rubber insulation from sticking to the copper. If this were not done, it would be practically impossible to clean off the rubber sufficiently well to make a good electrical connection. Over the rubber comes a loose braid of cotton, completing the single conductor. Two of these are laid parallel side by side, and a final braid of rayon completes the assembly. The detailed construction is shown in Fig. 6-13.

The thickness of the insulation varies with the size of the conductor. If the insulation is $\frac{1}{64}$ in., it may be used only in No. 18, and the resultant wire is known as "PO-64." If the insulation is $\frac{1}{32}$ in., it may be used on sizes 18 and 16, and the resultant wire is known as "PO-32." If the insulation is $3/64$ in., it may be used on No. 14 and heavier, and the wire is known simply as "PO."

Type POSJ.—The Type PO described in the preceding paragraph is fast being replaced by the Type POSJ shown in Fig. 6-14. It consists of the two basic stranded conductors, as

U. S. Rubber Co.

Fig. 6-14.—Type POSJ lamp cord is very tough and stands more mechanical abuse than the Type PO.

in Type PO, each covered with a serving of cotton to prevent the insulation from sticking to the copper, but the two conductors are imbedded in a solid mass of rubber insulation which is built up to the full of the finished wire, with no further protection. For this reason the rubber is of a much higher grade than is required for ordinary insulation, making it very much tougher mechanically. The two conductors are

U. S. Rubber Co.

Fig. 6-15.—Type C lamp cord is a good all-around knockabout cord.

usually made with a slit between them, or with a depression on either side of the assembly, to make it easy later to separate the two conductors at the point where a connection is to be made. This Type of wire is usually made only in Nos. 18 and 16.

Type C.—Where appearance is not a great factor and durability is more important, Type C cord is frequently used. It is shown in Fig. 6-15 and is usually known by the name "Green and Yellow." It consists of two basic conductors as used on Type PO, each conductor finished off with a serving of tough cotton, usually green and yellow in color, from which it derives its popular name. Two of these conductors twisted together form the completed cord. It is made in sizes from Nos. 18 to 8. The insulation is never lighter than $\frac{1}{32}$ in.

Types S and SJ.—The types of lamp cord described have relatively little resistance to moisture and will not stand a great deal of mechanical wear and tear. For motors, garage equipment, and similar devices, it is necessary to have a cord that is strong mechanically and that is also resistant to moisture. Type S, pictured in Fig. 6-16, is usually used for this purpose. The foundation consists of two or more stranded insulated conductors, as in other types of lamp cords, twisted together and the open spaces filled with cotton, jute, or

U. S. Rubber Co.

FIG. 6-16.—Type S lamp cord has more mechanical strength and is very tough.

twisted paper so that the complete assembly is round. Over this is usually a very loose cotton braid to hold the assembly together. Then comes a final layer of a very high-grade rubber, which is very tough mechanically. This makes the complete assembly pictured.

Type SJ is identical except that the outer layer of rubber is not so thick, making an assembly of a smaller diameter.

Either type comes in two styles—stationary and constant service. In the constant-service style the conductor is made of a greater number of strands of copper, each smaller in diameter than in the stationary style. For example, No. 18 stationary style consists of 16 strands of No. 30, whereas the constant-service style consists of 41 strands of No. 34. The total cross-section area of copper of each assembly is the same.

Type S cord is made in sizes from 18 up to as heavy a size as is needed, some of the cords being over an inch in diameter. Type SJ is made only in sizes 18 and 16.

Type SV.—This is practically identical with Type SJ but is of a smaller over-all diameter. It is approved only for use on vacuum cleaners and is made only in No. 18.

Type PWP.—A cord that is sturdier than Type PO, C, or POSJ, yet not so heavy and durable as Type SJ or S, is the Type PWP shown in Fig. 6-17. It consists of two basic conductors, as in Type C, twisted together, plus a rubber filler which is added to make the assembly round, finished off with an outer jacket of cotton impregnated with a moisture-

U. S. Rubber Co.

FIG. 6-17.—Type PWP lamp cord is relatively little used; it is tougher than ordinary Type C but serves approximately the same purposes.

resistant compound. It is often known simply as "reinforced cord."

Type K.—This type of cord is very similar to the Type PWP just described, except that the rubber filler is omitted and the spaces between the individual conductors are filled with jute or similar material. Its construction is shown in

U. S. Rubber Co.

FIG. 6-18.—Type K lamp cord is usually made only in fairly heavy sizes and is used where Type S is sturdier than required and other types are not sturdy enough.

Fig. 6-18, and it is known also as "brewery cord" or "stage cable."

Heater Cord.—Cords that are used on heating devices such as flatirons, toasters, and portable heaters fall into the classification known as "heater cords." The basic stranded conductor has the usual serving of cotton to prevent the rubber insulation from sticking to the copper, but over the rubber there is a layer of asbestos to withstand the heat developed should there be accidental contact with the hot surface of the appliance. Moreover, in this particular type of construction the Code permits a carrying capacity of 10 amp. for No. 18 and 15 amp. for No. 16, as compared with 5 and 7 amp., respectively, for the same sizes of ordinary lamp cords. This higher amperage causes more heat, and the asbestos layer is a safety measure. The asbestos is applied in various ways but in any event must cover each conductor completely before twisting. Over all comes a layer of rayon or cotton which makes a compact assembly and gives a neat appearance. The type described is HPD and is shown in Fig. 6-19; if the outer layer is rubber instead of cotton or rayon, it is Type HSJ; if each conductor is given an outer layer of cotton over the asbestos, before the two conductors are twisted together, it becomes Type HC.

Cycles.—The smaller the size of the individual strands in a cord, the greater the flexibility of the cord. Depending on the stranding, heater cords are known as "3,000 cycle" or "10,000 cycle," the latter being the more flexible.

U. S. Rubber Co.

Fig. 6-19.—Heater cords have a layer of asbestos over the rubber insulation. They are used on toasters, flatirons, and similar appliances.

Fixture Wire.—For the internal wiring of lighting fixtures, special wire known as "fixture" wire is used. There are many types of fixture wire, and the particular type used depends to

U. S. Rubber Co.

Fig. 6-20.—Fixture wire is used only in the internal wiring of lighting fixtures. Above is shown one of several approved constructions.

a great extent on the temperature that exists in the wire in use. Those with rubber insulation may be used only if the temperature does not exceed 122°F. (50°C.), but the most common is the Type CF pictured in Fig. 6-20, which employs no rubber in the insulation. It may be used at temperatures not exceeding 194°F. (90°C.). At higher temperatures, Type AF using asbestos for insulation must be used.

Identification of Conductors.—Whenever two or more wires are assembled in a cable or in lamp cord, one of them is always white. Of the other wires the second is black, the third red, etc., each one different in color.

Low-voltage Wire.—Certain types of wire are intended only for low-voltage work, usually under 30 volts, such as wires for doorbells, telephones, etc. Usually the source of current for operating such devices is very limited in capacity so that ordinarily it is safe to assume that no hazard exists. Therefore the Underwriters do not concern themselves with wire for such purposes.

U. S. Rubber Co.

FIG. 6-21.—Annunciator wire has very little insulation and is used only for low-voltage work.

U. S. Rubber Co.

FIG. 6-22.—Thermostat cable consists of two or more separate annunciator wires bundled into one cable.

Annunciator Wire.—This wire is pictured in Fig. 6-21. It consists of a copper conductor over which are two layers of cotton, the two wrapped in opposite directions, then paraffined to give it some semblance of being moisture resistant. It is commonly known as "bell wire." Frequently two or more such wires are bundled together into one cable, which then receives a final outer braid of cotton, again paraffined. An assembly of this kind appears in Fig. 6-22; it is commonly known as "thermostat cable" because it is most frequently used in connection with furnaces and thermostats.

CHAPTER 7

SELECTION OF PROPER WIRE SIZES

For any given combination of volts and amperes it is necessary to select a size of wire that not only prevents the development of dangerous temperatures, but also avoids wasted power in the form of voltage drop. Regardless of the size of wire selected, it is impossible to avoid all voltage drop; nevertheless, it must be held to nominal, practical proportions.

Advantage of Low Voltage Drop.—Voltage drop is simply wasted electricity. If the drop is 5 per cent, it means that 5 per cent of the power is wasted as unwanted heat in the wires. Moreover, all electrical devices operate most efficiently on the voltage for which they were designed. If an electric motor is operated on a voltage 5 per cent below its rated voltage, its power output drops almost 10 per cent; if operated on a voltage 10 per cent below normal, its power output drops 19 per cent.

If a lamp bulb is operated on a voltage 5 per cent below its rated voltage, the amount of light it delivers drops about 16 per cent; if the voltage is 10 per cent below normal, its light drops over 30 per cent. So it is with most other electrical devices—the output drops off much faster than the reduction in voltage. It should then be readily apparent that voltage drop must be limited to as small a figure as is practical.

Practical Voltage Drops.—The 1947 Code in Sec. 2202 recommends that, for *feeders*, wire size be chosen to limit the voltage drop to 3 per cent for power loads, or 1 per cent for loads consisting of lighting or lighting and power combined. Feeders are the wires up to the branch-circuit fuses or other overcurrent protection; the branch circuits begin where the feeders end. The Code contains no recommendation regarding permissible voltage drops in branch circuits. In most house wiring the only wires that can be considered feeders are those ahead of the main switch; on farms the wires between buildings are usually considered feeders.

It seems likely that the Code Sec. 2202 was intended primarily for commercial and industrial use, but its advice is useful for all conditions; where there are no feeders, the recommended figures may well be adopted as applying to branch circuits. A happy medium, which will probably not be found unsatisfactory for general application in home and farm use, is to limit the voltage drop to a maximum of 2 per cent over the entire circuit from meter to current-consuming device.

This means that on a 115-volt circuit the voltage drop should not exceed 2.3 volts; on a 230-volt circuit it should not exceed 4.6 volts.

In residential wiring, if No. 14 wire is used for the ordinary branch circuits, the voltage drop will usually not greatly exceed the 2 per cent figure. On the other hand, the bulbs commonly used in floor lamps are getting bigger and bigger; appliances consuming 1,000 watts are becoming more and more common, and, all told, people are using more electricity every day, so that circuits are being loaded closer and closer to the limit of their carrying capacity. Therefore there is good reason for the trend today toward considering No. 12 the smallest size wire to be commonly used for residential wiring. It seems probable that some future Code will require No. 12 as the minimum size wire permitted for ordinary wiring, just as today No. 14 is the smallest permitted.

Determining Minimum Wire Sizes.—First, determine the maximum amperage the wire will be called upon to carry. Then refer to Table 1[1] of the Code (see Appendix) and determine the smallest size wire that may be used. For example, if 18 amp. is to be carried, reference to this table will show that if rubber-covered wire to be used No. 14 is too small,

---

[1] Use Table 1 for all types of wiring except the knob and tube system, for which Table 2 is used. In either case, for the purpose of illustration, it is here assumed that only Type R rubber-covered wire is used. Chapter 25 will cover other types.

SELECTION OF PROPER WIRE SIZES

No. 12 is suitable. If, however, weatherproof wire is to be used, No. 14 is sufficient. This table merely shows what the minimum size may be, considering the safe carrying capacity. The minimum size may be entirely too small when voltage drop is considered.

Calculating Voltage Drops by Ohm's Law.—The actual voltage drop in any problem may be determined by the use of Ohm's law, which was discussed in Chap. 2:

E = IR, or Voltage drop = amperes × ohms.

For example, assume that a 500-watt floodlight is to be operated at a point 500 ft. from the meter; this requires 1,000 ft. of wire. At 115 volts, 500 watts is equivalent to about 4.4 amp. Taking No. 14 wire as a random size, Table 18 in the Appendix shows that it has a resistance of 2.475 ohms per 1,000 ft. The voltage drop then is 4.4 × 2.475, or 11 volts, considerably over the limit of 2 per cent, or 2.3 volts.

Trying other sizes, No. 6 with 0.387 ohm per 1,000 ft. involves a drop of 1.703 volts, No. 8 with 0.6158 ohms per 1,000 ft., 2.709 volts. Therefore, if the floodlight is to be used a great deal, use No. 6 wire; if it is to be used relatively little, No. 8 is acceptable; and if it is to be used only in emergencies, No. 10 with 4.3 volts drop (or even No. 12) will be entirely suitable, in that the amount of power wasted per year would not begin to pay for the extra cost of the heavier wire.

If in this example the distance had been 400 ft. instead of 500 ft., the length of the wire would have been 800 ft. instead of 1,000 ft. The voltage drop would then have been 800/1,000, or 80 per cent of what is for 1,000 ft.

Now assume that the same floodlight is to be operated at the same distance of 500 ft. but at 230 volts instead of 115 volts. The amperage now becomes 2.2 instead of 4.4. Making the same calculations, No. 14 wire gives a drop of only 5.5 volts, still above the 4.6 volts (2 per cent of 230 volts) considered permissible on a 230-volt circuit. Number 12 with a resistance of 1.557 ohms per 1,000 ft. gives a drop of 2.2 × 1.557, or 3.425 volts, well under the 4.6-volt limit that has been set. This emphasizes the desirability of using higher voltages where a considerable distance is involved as well as where considerable power is involved.

Desirability of Higher Voltages.—For any given *wattage* and any given *distance*, the voltage drop *measured in volts* is on any given size of wire exactly twice as great on 115 volts as it is on 230 volts. Doubling the voltage (regardless of what the actual voltages are) reduces the voltage drop *in volts* exactly 50 per cent if the wattage, the distance, and the wire size remain the same. It is the wattage and not the amperage that must remain unchanged for this statement to be correct.

When the voltage drop *in percentage* is considered, remember that in the case of the 230-volt circuit the initial voltage is twice as large but the actual voltage drop only half as large as in the case of the 115-volt circuit. From this it should be evident that the voltage drop *in percentage* will be only one-fourth as great using 230 volts as it is using 115 volts—the wattage, the wire size, and the distance, of course, remaining unchanged during the discussion. For example, in the first instance, 500 watts, 500 ft. distance (1,000 ft. of wire), No. 14 wire on the 115-volt circuit involved a drop of 11 volts, which is 9.6 per cent of 115 volts; on the 230-volt circuit the drop was 5.5 volts, which is 2.4 per cent of 230 volts; 2.4 per cent is one-fourth of 9.6 per cent.

All the foregoing can be simply restated: any size of wire will on 230 volts carry any given wattage 4 times as far as on 115 volts, with the same *percentage* of voltage drop. This statement should not be confused with the statement made above, that any size of wire will carry any given wattage twice as far with the same *number of volts* drop.

Another Method of Calculating Voltage Drop.—Another formula that is frequently used is

$$\text{Circular mils} = \frac{\text{distance in feet} \times \text{amperage} \times 22}{\text{volts drop}}.$$

Applying this to the floodlight example, which involves a distance of 500 ft., 4.4 amp., and a voltage drop that is to be

SELECTION OF PROPER WIRE SIZES

limited to 2.3 volts, the formula becomes

$$\text{Circular mils} = \frac{500 \times 4.4 \times 22}{2.3} = \frac{48{,}400}{2.3} = 21{,}043.$$

In other words, to limit the voltage drop to exactly 2.3 volts, wire having a cross-sectional area of 21,043 c.m. must be used. Reference to Table 18 of the Code (see Appendix) shows that there is no wire having exactly this cross-sectional area, but No. 7 comes very close, with 20,820 c.m. Since the odd sizes of wire are not available, compromise on No. 6 with a little under 2.3 volts drop, or No. 8 with a little over 2.3 volts drop.

If, instead of determining the size of wire that will produce a given voltage drop, the actual voltage drop with a given size wire is to be determined, merely transpose the formula to read

$$\text{Volts drop} = \frac{\text{distance} \times \text{amperes} \times 22}{\text{circular mils}}.$$

To determine the number of feet any given size of wire will carry any amperage, transpose the formula once more to read

$$\text{Distance} = \frac{\text{volts drop} \times \text{circular mils}}{\text{amperes} \times 22}.$$

Three-phase Voltage Drop.—The formulas given above are correct for direct current as well as for single-phase and 2-phase alternating current. In the case of 3-phase current a correction factor must be applied. Calculate the drop, using the formula above; then multiply the answer by 0.865 (0.865 is one-half of the square root of 3). A simple short cut is to deduct $\frac{1}{7}$ from the answer, whether it is volts or circular mils. If preferred, the formula above may be used after substituting 19 for 22.

Voltage-drop Tables.—For most purposes there is no need of going through tedious calculations to arrive at the right size wire to use. Suitable tables are shown on pages 106 and 107, one for 115 volts, the other for 230 volts, each based on 2 per cent drop. Under each wire size is shown the *one-way* distance

Wire Table—115 Volts—2 Per Cent Voltage Drop

Amperes	Volt-amperes* at 115 volts	No. 14	No. 12	No. 10	No. 8	No. 6	No. 4	No. 2	No. 0	No. 00
1	115	450	700	1,100	1,800	2,800	4,500	7,000		
2	230	225	350	550	900	1,400	2,200	3,500		
3	345	150	240	350	600	900	1,500	2,300	3,750	
4	460	110	175	275	450	700	1,100	1,750	2,750	3,500
5	575	90	140	220	360	560	880	1,400	2,250	2,800
7½	860	60	95	150	240	375	600	950	1,500	1,900
10	1,150	45	70	110	180	280	450	700	1,100	1,400
15	1,725	30	45	70	120	180	300	475	750	950
20	2,300	**22**	35	55	90	140	225	350	550	700
25	2,875	*18*	**28**	45	70	110	180	280	450	560
30	3,450	*15*	*25*	35	60	90	150	235	340	470
35	4,025		*20*	**30**	50	80	125	200	320	400
40	4,600		*17*	**27**	45	70	110	175	280	350
45	5,175			*25*	**40**	60	100	155	250	310
50	5,750			*22*	**35**	55	90	140	225	280
60	6,900				*30*	45	75	120	185	240
70	8,050				*25*	**40**	65	100	160	200
80	9,200					**35**	55	85	140	180
90	10,350					*30*	**50**	75	125	160
100	11,500					*28*	**45**	70	115	140

* The figure in this column is also the wattage of the circuit if the power is direct current or if it is single-phase alternating current and the load has a power factor of 100 per cent, as is the case with lamp bulbs and most appliances.

In this table, the figures below each size wire represent the maximum distance which that size wire will carry the amperage in the left-hand column, with 2 per cent voltage drop. All distances are one-way; in a circuit 100 ft. long, of course 200 ft. of wire is used, but look for the figure 100 above.

If a distance appears in **boldface** type, it indicates that the amperage in the left-hand column is too great for Type R wire in conduit, but not too great for Type R wire in open air.

If a distance appears in *italics*, it indicates that the amperage in the left-hand column is too great for Type R wire under any circumstances, but not too great for weatherproof wire.

SELECTION OF PROPER WIRE SIZES

Wire Table—230 Volts—2 Per Cent Voltage Drop

Amperes	Volt-amperes* at 230 volts	No. 14	No. 12	No. 10	No. 8	No. 6	No. 4	No. 2	No. 0	No. 00
1	230	900	1,400	2,200	3,600	5,600	9,000			
2	460	450	700	1,100	1,800	2,800	4,500	7,000		
3	690	300	480	700	1,200	1,800	3,000	4,600	7,500	
4	920	220	350	550	900	1,400	2,200	3,500	5,500	7,000
5	1,150	180	280	440	720	1,020	1,750	2,800	4,500	5,600
7½	1,720	120	190	300	480	750	1,200	1,900	3,000	3,800
10	2,300	90	140	220	360	560	900	1,400	2,200	2,800
15	3,450	60	90	140	240	360	600	950	1,500	1,900
20	4,600	**45**	70	110	180	280	450	700	1,100	1,400
25	5,750	*35*	**55**	90	140	220	360	560	900	1,100
30	6,900	*30*	*50*	70	120	180	300	470	680	940
35	8,050		*40*	**60**	110	160	250	400	640	800
40	9,200		*35*	**55**	90	140	220	350	560	700
45	10,350			*50*	**80**	120	200	310	500	620
50	11,500			*45*	**70**	110	180	280	450	560
60	13,800				*60*	90	150	240	370	480
70	16,100				*50*	**80**	130	200	320	400
80	18,400					**70**	110	170	280	360
90	20,700					*60*	**100**	150	250	320
100	23,000					*55*	**90**	140	230	280

* The figure in this column is also the wattage of the circuit if the power is direct current, or if it is single-phase alternating current and the load has a power factor of 100 per cent, as is the case with lamp bulbs and most appliances.

In this table, the figures below each size wire represent the maximum distance which that size wire will carry the amperage in the left-hand column, with 2 per cent voltage drop. All distances are one-way; in a circuit 100 ft. long, of course 200 ft. of wire is used, but look for the figure 100 above.

If a distance appears in **boldface** type, it indicates that the amperage in the left-hand column is too great for Type R wire in conduit, but not too great for Type R in open air.

If a distance appears in *italics*, it indicates that the amperage in the left-hand column is too great for Type R under any circumstances, but not too great for weatherproof wire.

which that size wire will carry the amperage shown in the left-hand column. To clarify, not the number of feet of wire in any problem, but the distance from starting point to the load in question is given. When the distance appears in **boldface** type, it indicates that rubber-covered wires in open wiring, but not in conduit or cable, may be used. When the distance appears in *italics*, it indicates that only weatherproof wire will carry the corresponding amperage in the left-hand column; distances shown in ordinary type are applicable to either rubber-covered or weatherproof wire.

In the event that the tables are used for 3-phase current, increase all distances shown $\frac{1}{6}$. In the formulas above, $\frac{1}{7}$ was deducted, which is the same as multiplying by $\frac{6}{7}$; for the table add $\frac{1}{6}$, which is the same as multiplying by $\frac{7}{6}$.

Note that these tables are based on an assumed voltage drop of 2 per cent. If, under certain circumstances, other voltage drops are to be permitted, the tables are easily converted, as follows:

For a voltage drop of 1 per cent, decrease all distances by 50 per cent
For a voltage drop of 2½ per cent, increase all distances by 25 per cent
For a voltage drop of 3 per cent, increase all distances by 50 per cent
For a voltage drop of 4 per cent, increase all distances by 100 per cent
For a voltage drop of 5 per cent, increase all distances by 150 per cent

Cost of Voltage Drop.—As already discussed, voltage drop represents wasted electricity, power used to heat the wires in carrying the current to the point where it is to be used. The smaller the wire and the greater the distance, the greater the loss will be. Voltage drop cannot be eliminated, but it can be kept to reasonable figures.

It is not difficult, although a bit tedious, to calculate the money wasted in heating wires by unwanted voltage drop. On page 109 is reproduced a tabulation[1] showing exactly what price is paid per year for the wasted power when different amperages are carried by various sizes of wire over several different distances. The table is based on the assumption

[1] By J. B. Stere, *Electricity on the Farm*, April, 1946.

SELECTION OF PROPER WIRE SIZES

Wire size	Distance, feet	Load, amperes										
		10	15	20	25	30	40	50	60	70	80	90
No. 14	50	0.25	0.60									
	100	0.50	1.20									
	200	1.00	2.40									
	300	1.50	3.60									
No. 12	50	0.16	0.36	0.64								
	100	0.32	0.72	1.28								
	200	0.64	1.44	2.56								
	300	0.96	2.16	3.84								
No. 10	50	0.10	0.23	0.40	0.62	0.90						
	100	0.20	0.45	0.85	1.24	1.80						
	200	0.40	0.90	1.60	2.48	3.60						
	300	0.60	1.35	2.40	3.72	5.40						
No. 8	50	0.06	0.15	0.25	0.40	0.60	1.00					
	100	0.12	0.30	0.50	0.80	1.20	2.00					
	200	0.24	0.60	1.00	1.60	2.40	4.00					
	300	0.36	0.90	1.50	2.40	3.60	6.00					
No. 6	50	0.04	0.09	0.16	0.25	0.36	0.64	1.00				
	100	0.08	0.18	0.32	0.50	0.72	1.28	2.00				
	200	0.16	0.36	0.64	1.00	1.44	2.56	4.00				
	300	0.24	0.54	0.96	1.50	2.16	3.84	6.00				
No. 4	50	0.03	0.06	0.10	0.15	0.22	0.40	0.62	0.90	1.22		
	100	0.05	0.12	0.20	0.30	0.44	0.80	1.24	1.80	2.44		
	200	0.10	0.24	0.40	0.60	0.88	1.60	2.48	3.60	4.88		
	300	0.15	0.36	0.80	0.90	1.32	2.40	3.72	5.40	7.32		
No. 2	50	0.02	0.04	0.06	0.10	0.13	0.25	0.40	0.60	0.77	1.00	1.26
	100	0.03	0.07	0.12	0.20	0.25	0.50	0.80	1.20	1.54	2.00	2.52
	200	0.06	0.15	0.24	0.40	0.50	1.00	1.60	2.40	3.08	4.00	5.04
	300	0.09	0.22	0.36	0.60	0.75	1.50	2.40	3.60	4.62	6.00	7.56

This table shows the cost of electrical power wasted as heat in wires, in the form of voltage drop. Start with the size of wire involved, select the proper line representing the one-way length of the circuit, follow that line to the right until it intersects the column showing the amperage under consideration. The figure shown there is the cost of the wasted power over a period of 500 hr., with power costing 2 cts. per kilowatt-hour.

that power flows exactly 500 hr. per year (less than 1½ hr. per day) and that power costs 2 cts. per kilowatt-hour.

To use the table, follow the amperage column downward until it intersects with the size-and-distance line involved. The figure at the intersection represents the cost per year of the wasted power in that circuit. For example, assume a 115-volt 2-hp. motor consuming about 20 amp., operating at a distance of 200 ft. from the service switch. If No. 12 wire is used, the cost of the power wasted in the wires is $2.56 per year. The following tabulation will show the cost with other sizes of wire. It will also show the cost of the wasted power in operating the same motor over the same size wires, but operating at 230 volts, and then consuming only 10 amp.

Wire size	115 volt 20 amp.	230 volt 10 amp.
No. 12	$2.56	$0.64
No. 10	1.60	0.40
No. 8	1.00	0.24
No. 6	0.64	0.16
No. 4	0.40	0.10
No. 2	0.24	0.06

This study shows the advantage of using 230-volt devices where possible, instead of using the corresponding 115-volt type, resulting in less wasted power, more efficient operation, and much smaller initial investment in wire. It also shows, regardless of voltage, the advantage of using the heavier sizes of wire.

As Stere[1] in his article points out, the most economical electrical installation is that in which the cost of the wire is equal to the cost of the wasted electric power during the useful life of the wire. Considering obsolescence, this should not be considered to be more than 5 to 8 years. This condition is approximated when the equipment is used 500 hr. per year and power costs 2 cts. per kilowatt-hour, if the voltage drop

---

[1] J. B. Stere, *Electricity on the Farm*, April, 1946.

is limited to 2 per cent. If the equipment is operated 1,000 hr. per year, it will probably prove economical to limit the drop to 1 per cent.

Outdoor Wiring.—In outdoor wiring there is one additional factor to be considered: mechanical strength. The wires must be heavy enough to support not only their own weight, but also the strain imposed by winds, ice loads, etc. In many areas it is not unusual to see a layer of ice an inch thick around outdoor wires after a severe sleet storm. For this reason it is best to use nothing lighter than No. 12 wire for spans up to 25 ft., No. 10 up to 50 ft., No. 8 up to 100 ft., and No. 6 over 100 ft. If distances over 150 ft. are involved, use heavier wires or install extra poles for supports.

In installing outdoor overhead wires, take into consideration the expansion and contraction that takes place with changes in the temperature. A 100-ft. span of copper wire will be almost 2 in. shorter when it is 30° below zero than on a hot summer day when the thermometer stands at 100°. If, therefore, the wires are installed on a cold winter day, they may be pulled as tight as practical. If installed on a hot day, allow considerable sag in the span so that when the wires contract in the winter no damage will be done.

CHAPTER 8

WIRE CONNECTIONS AND JOINTS

Wires must be connected to switches, receptacles, and other devices. This is very simply done, yet many times such connections are poorly made. Study carefully the following points.

Removing Insulation.—Cut through the insulation down to the copper conductor, holding the knife not at a right angle but at about 60 deg. This precaution prevents nicking of the

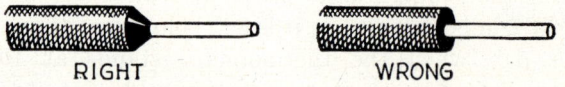

RIGHT   WRONG

FIG. 8-1.—In removing insulation from wire which is to be attached to a terminal, hold knife at an angle of about 60 deg.

conductor, which weakens it and sometimes leads to breaks. After the insulation has been severed all around, pull it off, leaving the conductor sticking out far enough to suit the purpose (see Fig. 8-1). For a good electrical connection it is necessary scrupulously to clean off traces of rubber or other insulation.

Terminals.—Wire is fastened to devices by means of terminals designed for the purpose. If the device is intended

FIG. 8-2.—Terminals for attaching wires.

for wire No. 8 or lighter, it is usually provided with ordinary screw terminals of the type shown in Fig. 8-2. The end of the terminal is bent upward to prevent the wire from slipping from under the terminal screw. This screw is often "upset" so that it cannot be removed entirely and lost.

Bend the end of the wire into a loop to fit and insert it under the terminal screw in such a way that tightening the screw tends to close rather than to open the loop. Figure 8-3 should

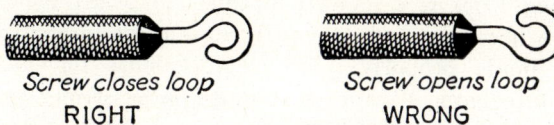

FIG. 8-3.—Bend the loop on wire so that the terminal screw tends to close the loop.

make this clear. It is best to close the loop completely with long-nosed pliers after it is inserted under the screw. Cut off any excess length of wire so that the insulation comes up close to the terminal (see Fig. 8-4).

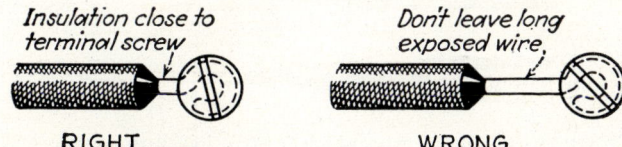

FIG. 8-4.—Do not leave exposed conductor next to terminals.

Ilsco Copper Tube & Products, Inc.
FIG. 8-5.—A typical solderless connector.

Ideal Commutator Dresser Co.
FIG. 8-6.—A typical soldering lug.

For No. 6 or heavier wire, solderless terminals of the type shown in Fig. 8-5 are commonly used. Simply insert the stripped and cleaned end of the conductor into the terminal or connector, drive home the nut or screw, and the connection is completed.

At other times soldering lugs of the type shown in Fig. 8-6

are used. In such cases it is necessary to solder the wire into the lug; the way to do this will be explained later in this chapter.

Joints.—In many cases joints between two different pieces of wire are prohibited by the Code; these will be mentioned as the related work is discussed in this book. At other times joints are necessary; consequently it is most important that they be made properly. The requirements for joints are simple. Mechanically the joint must be as strong as a con-

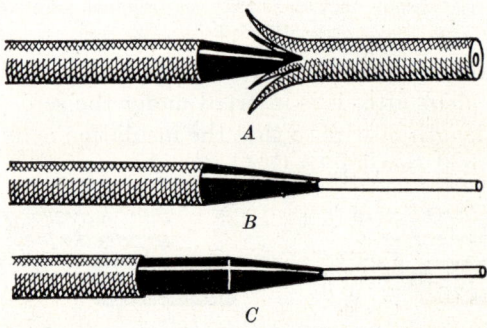

Fig. 8-7.—Preparing end of wire which is to be joined to another and later soldered.

tinuous length of the wire. Electrically it must be as good a conductor as a continuous piece of the same wire. After completion the insulation over the joint must be replaced so that it is equivalent to the original insulation on a continuous piece of the wire.

To accomplish these three things, it is necessary to remove the insulation where the wires are to be joined, make the mechanical joint, solder, and replace the insulation by means of tapes made for the purpose. Solderless connectors may also be used.

Removing Insulation.—In removing insulation for a joint, hold the knife at an angle as in sharpening a pencil, rather than at a 60-deg. angle, as in preparing wire for a terminal. When stripping stranded wires, be careful not to damage any of the individual strands. After the insulation has been cut all the way around the wire, it can often be removed to the end of the wire with one pull. In the case of rubber-covered wire it is necessary to remove also the outer braid only, for some distance back, depending on the size of the wire. Be careful to cut only through the outer braid, not into the insulation proper. All this is shown in steps in Fig. 8-7.

Making the Splice.—The simplest and most common method of joining two solid wires is shown in successive steps in Fig. 8-8 and hardly needs additional explanation.

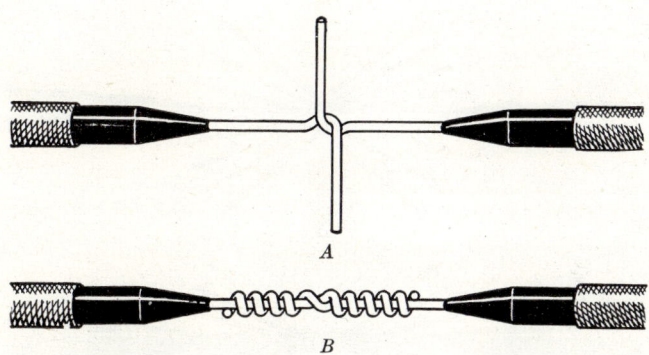

Fig. 8-8.—A simple splice; it is strong mechanically.

Small stranded wires may be spliced in the same way. If the stranded wire is of considerable size, it will be better to make the type of splice shown in successive steps in Fig. 8-9. This may appear a bit difficult but with practice becomes relatively easy. Spread the individual strands evenly, as in A. Place the two wires end to end with the several strands intersecting, as in B. Then wrap one of the strands around the assembly and repeat with one of the strands of the opposite piece, wrapping it in the opposite direction; this is shown in C. Follow through with alternate strands of each piece and continue in this fashion until each strand has been wrapped, giving the final appearance of D in Fig. 8-9. Naturally considerable practice is required to learn just how long to leave the strands for different size wires.

Taps.—The simplest and most commonly used form of tap is shown in Fig. 8-10. It is so simple that the picture should be self-explanatory.

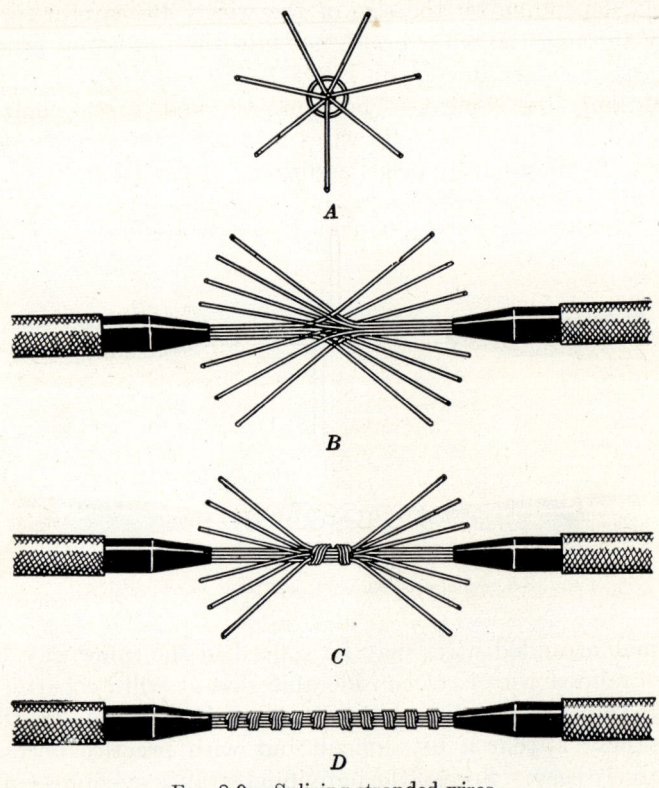

Fig. 8-9.—Splicing stranded wires.

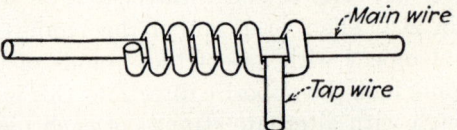

Fig. 8-10.—A simple tap.

With stranded wire the same kind of tap can be used, but, especially in heavier sizes, it is better to proceed as shown in successive steps in Fig. 8-11. First separate the strands in the main wire into two groups, as in *A*, so that the tap wire can be inserted into the opening. Divide the strands of the tap wire

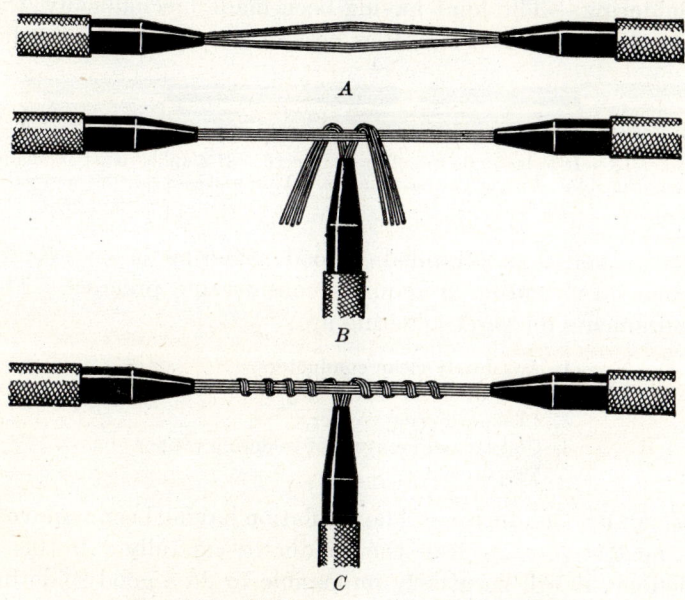

FIG. 8-11.—Making a tap with stranded wires.

into approximately equal groups, as in *B*. Next wrap each group around the main wire, one in the clockwise and the other in the counterclockwise direction, working toward opposite ends, until the tap is completed as in *C*.

Fixture Joints.—Where there is no mechanical strain whatever on the wire, usually the two ends are merely twisted together, as shown in Fig. 8-12, then soldered and taped.

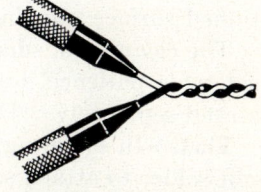

FIG. 8-12.—When there is no strain on the wires. they may be spliced by simply twisting.

Splices in Lamp Cords.—In splicing cords, splice each conductor separately, but stagger the two joints so that, when the splice is completed, they will not lie next to each other in the finished job (see Fig. 8-13). This makes a much less bulky joint in the finished job. A much better practice is never to make such a splice at all—use only continuous lengths of cord.

Soldering.—The joint having been made mechanically, the next step is to solder it. It is best to practice first on solid

FIG. 8-13.—It is best not to splice lamp cord. If a splice must be made, stagger the joints in the two conductors. This makes a smaller and safer splice.

wires rather than stranded. Good soldering is an art; to become proficient in it requires considerable practice. The requirements for good soldering are:

    1. Absolutely clean conductors.
    2. Careful use of flux.
    3. Clean soldering copper.
    4. Correct temperature of soldering copper.
    5. Proper solder.

Clean the Conductor.—The insulation having been removed, the next step is to clean the conductor carefully. If this is not done, it will be utterly impossible to do a good soldering job. The cleaning is usually done by scraping with a knife and is no great task. Most building wires have tinned conductors which make it easier to strip the insulation. If care is used in scraping off the remaining traces of insulation, the tinned surface remains intact, making soldering much easier.

The cleaning of small stranded conductors does call for considerable patience, for it is definitely necessary to clean each strand separately. Do not skimp on this detail.

Flux.—In soldering, a flux of some type is necessary to permit solder to attach solidly to the copper. For some kinds of soldering, acid is used as a flux, but under no circumstances may it be used for electrical soldering. The acid reacts with the copper to form a new compound, usually of an insulating nature, and, especially on fine stranded wires, often eats through the copper, destroying the conductor. Use any kind of noncorrosive paste, of which several excellent brands are on the market. Use it sparingly. Rosin makes a good flux, and rosin-core solder is entirely practical.

Keep Soldering Copper Clean and at Right Temperature.—If a soldering copper is used, whether it is electrically heated or heated by a blowtorch, it is necessary that it be kept clean. Applying the hot copper to a cake of sal ammoniac will clean it. The right temperature can best be learned by experience, too hot a copper being just as impractical as one that is not hot enough.

Apply the heat not to the solder but to the conductor; bring the conductor rapidly to a temperature at which the solder when touched will melt and flow into every little space. Do

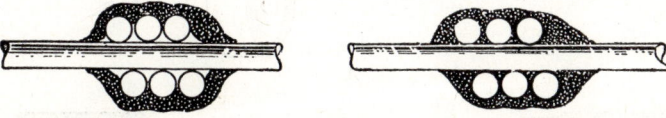

FIG. 8-14.—When hot solder is applied to cold wires, as at the left above, a poor joint results. When the hot wires melt the solder, it flows into every crevice and makes a good joint, as shown at the right above.

not touch the solder to the soldering copper at all. If the conductor is brought up to heat too slowly, the heat travels along the conductor and does little good. Especially when using a blowtorch, it is very easy to heat the conductor too much, damaging the insulation. Experience alone can show just how to proceed. When using a blowtorch for soldering, remember that the tip of the flame is the hottest spot; there is no heat in the inner cone of the flame.

Figure 8-14 shows the difference in the finished result between dropping hot solder on a cold conductor and heating the conductor sufficiently to melt the solder, which then flows into the smallest crevice.

The only exception to the rule of letting the hot wire melt the solder is in the case of relatively small wires, where the solder can be picked up in the form of a small globule on the soldering copper, if it is at just the right temperature, the globule then being applied to the joint. If the wire is small enough, the heat of the solder will heat the conductor sufficiently to permit the solder to flow, or the soldering copper can be applied to the wire after the solder has attached to it, thus heating the conductor and permitting the solder to flow evenly throughout the joint.

Splicing Compound.—After a joint has been soldered, the insulation that was removed must be replaced. Splicing compound, which has come to be known by the common name of

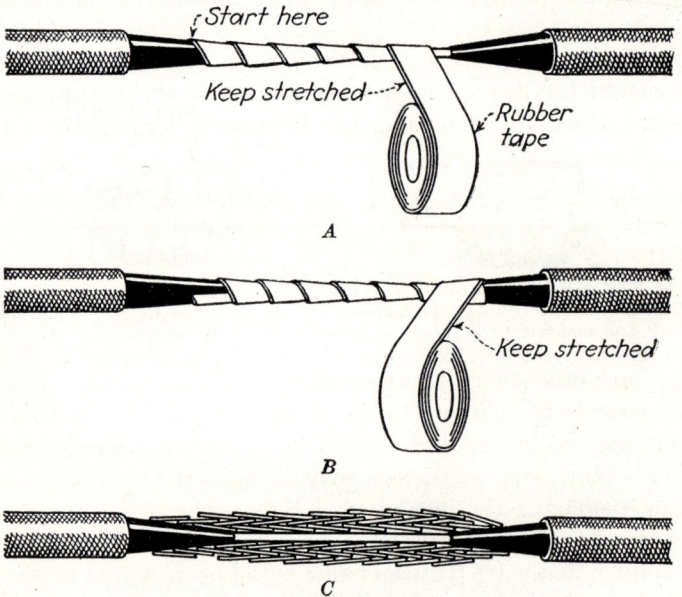

FIG. 8-15.—Applying rubber tape to a splice.

"rubber tape" (which describes it nicely), is used for the purpose. It consists of a very high grade of rubber put up in rolls. The rubber is unvulcanized and under slight pressure vulcanizes with other rubber. A layer of cloth between the successive layers of rubber in the roll prevents successive layers from sticking to each other. This layer of cloth is thrown away as the tape is used.

Wrap several layers of this tape around a pencil, one layer on top of the other, stretching the tape tightly as it is applied.

Cut through the mass of rubber with a sharp knife and, instead of the several layers of rubber that were applied, only one single mass of rubber will be found; the several layers have vulcanized into a solid mass.

In applying this tape on a joint, start at one end, laying the end of the tape over the tapered end of the rubber insulation, then winding it diagonally toward the opposite end, letting the successive turns slightly overlap (see A of Fig. 8-15). Keep the tape stretched so that, wherever the turns overlap, they will vulcanize to each other. From the opposite end, work backward toward the starting point in exactly the same manner. The individual turns of tape in successive layers will be almost at right angles to each other (see B of the same picture). Work back and forth in this fashion until the total layer of rubber applied is as thick as the original insulation on the wire. Be sure that the last application of tape covers all portions of insulation where the outer braid has been removed. Figure 8-15 at C shows in exaggerated fashion a cross-section of a finished joint; in actual practice the small openings would be filled up by the pressure caused by keeping the tape tight.

Friction Tape.—Just as the rubber insulation on wire is given mechanical protection in the form of an outer fabric braid, so the rubber tape applied on joints must be mechanically protected. Friction tape used for the purpose is made of cloth impregnated with a sticky rubber compound. This tape is applied in the same way as rubber tape. Start at one end, wrap it diagonally along the wire with turns slightly overlapping, and when finished in one direction, start over in the opposite; usually two layers are sufficient.

Weatherproof Wire.—If the joint is in weatherproof or other wire that has no rubber in the insulation, rubber tape is not required. Simply use friction tape, applying layer after layer until the tape over the conductor is as thick as the original insulation.

Soldering Lugs.—A typical soldering lug was shown in Fig. 8-6. The conductor is soldered into this lug, which then is attached to the device with bolts provided for the purpose. This sounds simple, yet it is safe to say that a goodly percentage of such soldering jobs are very poorly done, resulting in high-resistance joints which lead to arcing, overheating, and sometimes damage from the resulting heat. Figure 8-16 shows a cross-section of a poorly soldered lug. Note how most of the

Frankel Connector Co., Inc.

FIG. 8-16.—Cross-section of a poorly soldered lug.

individual strands of wire have no trace of solder. Careful study of this picture should indicate the points to watch in soldering a wire into a lug.

To solder a wire into a lug is undoubtedly more difficult than soldering, for example, a simple splice. The copper conductor first must be properly cleaned. If the wire is stranded, the individual strands must not be spread out, which would prevent a good mechanical fit in the lug. Tin the exposed end of the conductor; apply a reasonable quantity of flux; dip the end into a ladle of melted solder, making sure that it is hot enough so that it will flow freely into every crevice, every space, between individual strands. When it cools, there will be a single solid mass of metal: copper and solder. If a blowtorch is used instead of a ladle, heat the end of the conductor sufficiently so that, when solder in wire form is applied, it will melt and flow down into the space between the strands. Do not overheat the wire lest the insulation be damaged.

Tin the inside of the soldering lug in the same way; then melt sufficient solder into it so that, when the conductor is inserted, the lug, the conductor, and the solder will form a single mass of metal. Of course, heat must be applied to the lug, by means either of a soldering copper or of a blowtorch, to melt the solder previously inserted in order to permit complete fusion of the three elements.

Because it is recognized that a large percentage of soldered joints involving tubular lugs and heavy sizes of wire are poorly

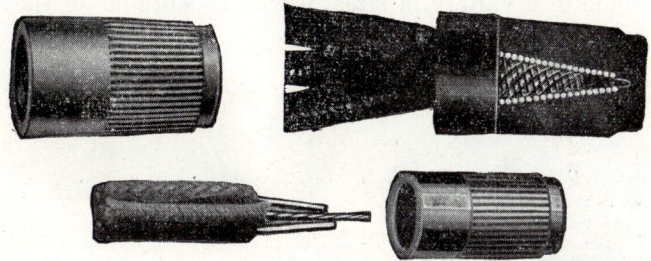

Ideal Commutator Dresser Co.

FIG. 8-17.—Solderless connectors are simply screwed on the wires to be joined.

made in the field, the 1947 Code in Sec. 2358 prohibits their use in connection with service equipment, and Sec. 2613 prohibits their use in connection with grounding conductors and clamps. Connections must be made by means of "pressure connectors," as heavy-duty solderless lugs are termed in the Code.

Solderless Connectors.—For joints of the type on which there is little mechanical strain, there are available simple solderless connectors, such as shown in Fig. 8-17, which also shows a cross-section of one joining three wires, and the simple method of installation. Hold the wires to be joined in the hand, with the stripped ends parallel. If one wire is lighter than the others, it is best to let it project a bit farther than the heavier ones (see Fig. 8-17). Place one of the connectors over the wires, and screw it on. The connector cuts its own thread as it is screwed on and makes an entirely secure joint. Strip the wires just the right distance so that there will be no bare exposed conductors outside the connector after it has been screwed on as far as it will

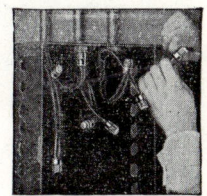

Ideal Commutator Dresser Co.

FIG. 8-18.—This shows the use of solderless connectors.

go. The connector has a bell-shaped opening which makes it possible to let the insulation extend a bit down into the body of the connector. No tape is required over the connectors. Figure 8-18 shows a number of them in use. Such connectors are made in a variety of sizes; use a size suitable for the size and number of wires to be joined.

Frankel Connector Co., Inc.

FIG. 8-19.—Typical heavy-duty solderless connector.

Frankel Connector Co., Inc.

FIG. 8-20.—Cross-section of the connector shown in Fig. 8-19.

Solderless Connectors, Heavy-duty.—The use of solderless connectors is not confined to small sizes of wire. A different type of connector is available for all sizes up to the largest of circular-mil cables. One connector of this type is shown in Fig. 8-19, and Fig. 8-20 shows a cross-sectional view. It consists essentially of a slotted body, the end of which is tapered on the outside and hollow to take a wire. Over the body goes a nut, the inner surface of which is tapered. The conductor is

WIRE CONNECTIONS AND JOINTS 125

inserted into the body, and as the nut is driven home, the bevel of the nut engages the bevel of the slotted body, pressing it inward against the conductor. Tremendous pressure is

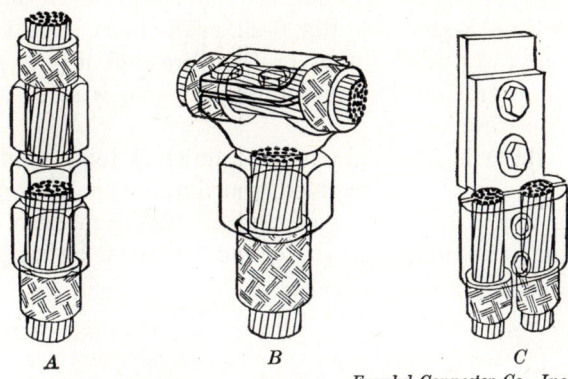

Frankel Connector Co., Inc.

FIG. 8-21.—Solderless connectors take many forms, depending on the purpose for which they are intended.

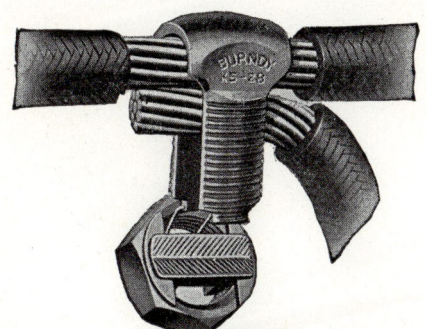

Burndy Engineering Co., Inc.

FIG. 8-22.—A connector of this type permits one wire to be tapped to another *continuous* wire.

Burndy Engineering Co., Inc.

FIG. 8-23.—Where no strain is involved in the joint, simple connectors of the type shown here may be used.

exerted this way and a good low-resistance joint quickly made. The inexperienced man can make as good a joint as the experienced man.

Additional types are shown in Fig. 8-21, where *A* illustrates the type used in joining two lengths of wire, *B* the type used in making a tap, and *C* the type used on switchboards and similar devices. Many other types are available. Such joints must all be taped unless molded insulating covers which are available are used to make the taping operation unnecessary.

A still different style of connector which is popular, especially in farm wiring, is shown in Fig. 8-22. The body has a U cross-section, and the nut slips over the threaded legs of the U, making it extremely handy for tapping one wire to another continuous wire.

When there is no strain on the finished joint, and fairly heavy sizes of wire are involved, the simple type of connector shown in Fig. 8-23 is commonly used. Being made of metal, the entire joint, including the connector, must be taped after completion.

CHAPTER 9

THEORY OF GROUNDING

The term "ground" is used with great regularity in all electrical work. Grounding simply means connecting a wire or piece of equipment to the earth, usually by connecting it to a water pipe, or in the absence of such a pipe, to an artificial ground.

When a wire is properly grounded, there is no more danger in touching that wire at any exposed point than there is in touching the kitchen faucet, or a steam pipe. The wire is already connected to the earth and therefore to all these pipes. To all intents and purposes the wire is touched every time a faucet or a pipe is touched.

Neutral Wire.—In ordinary residential wiring, there are brought into the home either three wires delivering 115 and 230 volts (as was shown in Fig. 2-8), or two wires corresponding to the middle wire and one of the two outside wires of the same drawing, and delivering 115 volts only. The middle wire is usually grounded.[1] It then becomes known as the "neutral" wire. In wiring diagrams, a connection to ground is indicated by the symbol of Fig. 9-1.

FIG. 9-1.—This symbol indicates a connection to ground.

Purpose of Grounding.—Grounds are made to promote safety both from shocks and from fire hazards. Consider the circuit of Fig. 9-2, which represents a device X connected to two ungrounded wires, one of which is, however, *accidentally* grounded at Y. The two wires are protected by fuses A and B.

[1] There are a number of exceptions to this rule especially in older installations and some industrial installations. These exceptions can always be determined by consulting the local electrical inspector or local power company.

If fuse B blows, it prevents device X from operating. The average owner in looking for his trouble will probably inspect device X. Assume that he touches one of the wires at an exposed terminal while standing on the damp floor of his basement. What happens? He completes the circuit through his own body, through the ground along the route shown in the

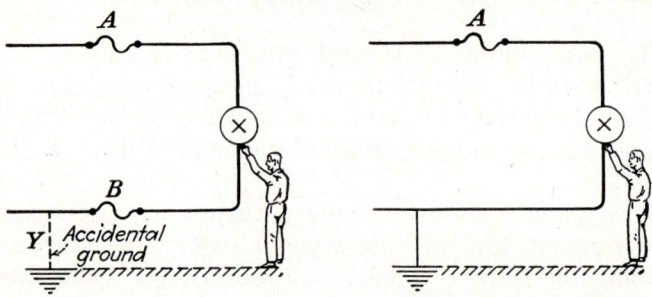

Fig. 9-2.—Ungrounded systems are dangerous. Fig. 9-3.—Grounded systems are safe.

dotted line, back through the accidental ground to the main line. He may be injured; at the least he will receive a severe shock.

Compare this with Fig. 9-3, showing the same device X connected to the same two wires, one of which has now been *deliberately* grounded and which may then never be fused. The device is then protected by a single fuse A. If this fuse blows and the owner touches any exposed wire on device X, there is no danger, even if he is standing on wet ground, because the one wire connected to X is already grounded, and the other wire from X up to fuse A is dead because that fuse is blown; it is the same as if the wire were cut at point A. A serious hazard has therefore been removed by grounding.

Consider now Fig. 9-4, which represents the same device X connected to the same two ungrounded wires and protected by fuses A and B. In this case the wires run through conduit. Assume that wire A accidentally comes in contact with the conduit and that wire B becomes accidentally grounded as at Y. Anyone touching the conduit will immediately complete the circuit through the ground and will be subject to injury or at least shock. If, however, the wire is deliberately grounded, as in Fig. 9-5, and the conduit itself is grounded, as it is in actual practice, then when wire A comes into accidental contact with the conduit, there is a short circuit and fuse A will immediately blow; thereafter all the wires except the short piece up to A are completely dead.

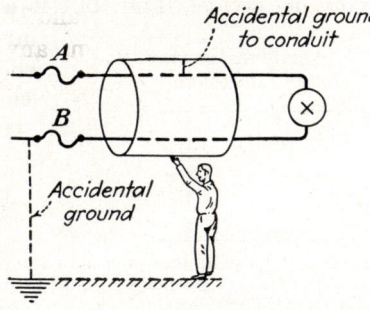
Fig. 9-4.—Ungrounded conduit or other metal raceway is dangerous.

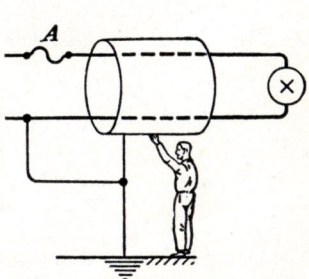
Fig. 9-5.—Grounding the conduit or other metal raceway eliminates hazard.

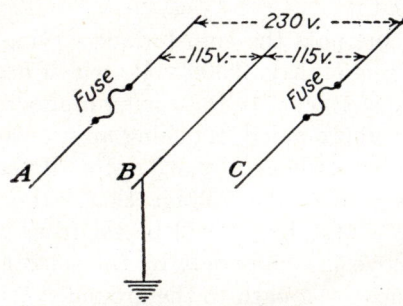
Fig. 9-6.—A 3-wire 115/230-volt system with grounded neutral greatly reduces hazards of shocks.

Figure 9-6 represents the three wires of a 3-wire 115/230-volt system. Wire B is grounded as shown and, of course, is not fused; A and C are fused. If either A or C becomes accidentally grounded, for example, to the conduit covering all three wires, immediately a fuse blows.

If wire B is *not* grounded, and A becomes accidentally

grounded, then any person standing on the ground and touching wire C will complete the connection from A to C, in other words will receive the full shock of 230 volts between A and C. If, on the other hand, B is properly grounded as shown, any one touching C and standing on the ground will bear the brunt of only 115 volts, the voltage between B and C. The difference between 230 and 115 volts may be the difference between life and death—not that 230 volts is always fatal, but it is

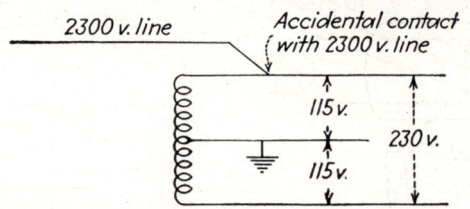

Fig. 9-7.—In an ungrounded system, if a 2,300-volt line falls across the low-voltage wires, it raises their voltage to 2,300; in a grounded system their voltage is raised only a little above the usual 115/230 volts.

decidedly more dangerous than 115 volts; even 115 volts sometimes causes death.

Figure 9-7 represents the transformer serving a house and a high-voltage line of, say, 2,300 volts which has accidentally fallen and made contact with the wires running into the house. If the wires are ungrounded, touching any of the wires in the house will involve a shock of 2,300 volts. If the neutral wire is grounded as shown, the voltage that is involved will be higher than 115 volts, but it will be far from 2,300 volts; it will increase above 115 volts only by the small amount of the voltage drop across the path to the ground.

Voltage to Ground.—In the Code this term is frequently used. If one of the wires in a circuit is grounded, the voltage to ground is the maximum voltage that exists between the grounded wire and any ungrounded wire. If no wire is grounded, then voltage to ground is the maximum voltage that exists between any two wires (Code, Art. 100).

In an installation consisting of a 3-wire 115/230-volt service, if the two ungrounded wires run to a 230-volt motor but the grounded wire does not run to the motor, the voltage to ground so far as the two wires to the motor are concerned is still only 115 volts. If an installation consists of a 2-wire service at 230 volts and no neutral or grounded wire runs into the installation at all, the voltage to ground is still only 115 volts provided there is a ground at the transformer mid-point, that is, at the point from which a grounded wire of a 3-wire circuit would be run if it were used. If there is no such ground, the voltage to ground is 230 volts.

Equipment Grounds.—Figure 9-8 represents a motor operating on 230 volts, which usually means that neither wire is

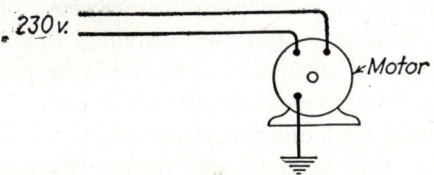

FIG. 9-8.—It is always well to ground the frames of motors and other equipment.

grounded. If a person accidentally touches one of the two wires while standing on the ground, he will be subject to shocks of 115 volts, for this is exactly the case outlined in Fig. 9-6. Assume that, while the motor is in operation, somewhere inside the motor one of the wires of the windings becomes grounded to the frame of the motor. If the motor frame is not grounded, touching the motor will impart a shock up to 115 volts. If the frame is grounded as shown, there will be no shock whatever. This illustrates the grounding of equipment as compared with the grounding of conductors.

Continuous Grounds.—When a grounded-neutral wiring system is used (and that is 99 per cent of the time), and if a *metallic* raceway or armor is used, it is customary to ground not only the neutral wire, but also this metallic raceway or armor, as well as many pieces of equipment. As will be shown in the next chapter, at every point where connections are made, an "outlet box" of metal is used. The raceway is securely fastened to every outlet box so that there is a continuously grounded enclosure, raceway, or armor for the wires throughout the entire building. In supporting lighting fixtures on outlet boxes, they usually become automatically grounded. The raceway or armor is fastened to motors and other permanently connected devices so that they in turn are grounded. In this way a completely grounded system is secured with assurance of minimum hazard.

White Wire.—As already mentioned, the grounded wire is known as the "neutral" wire. The Code in Sec. 2005 requires that *the neutral wire must always be a white or neutral gray color*. However, since No. 4 and heavier wires are seldom stocked in white, the Code permits, in these heavier sizes, black wire to be used throughout an installation provided that in each case where a white wire should be used the ends are painted white. Painting makes a white wire out of a black one. Likewise the Code requires that with one exception (which will be explained later) *white wire may never be used for any purpose other than the grounded neutral.*

For outdoor use it is not necessary to use white wire for the grounded neutral. Weatherproof wire, which is the type ordinarily used for the purpose, is available only in a black color.

The grounded-neutral wire is never interrupted by a fuse, a switch, or other device, unless the device used is so designed that in opening the grounded wire it simultaneously opens also all the ungrounded wires. The white wire, with the exception noted, always runs directly from the point where it enters the building up to the device where the current is finally consumed. This simple fundamental requirement of wiring must at all times be kept firmly in mind.

Since the neutral wire is actually grounded and there is no possible danger in touching it, why put insulation on that wire? There is no real need for it, and actually there is a trend toward using uninsulated neutral wires, but this scheme is not yet in general use; the few exceptions permitted today will be covered separately in other chapters. Unless otherwise stated, it is necessary to use the same kind of insulation, the same care to avoid accidental ground, and the same careful splices for the neutral wire as for the "hot" wires.

Polarizing.—The process of maintaining a grounded wire throughout a wiring system, always identified by its white color, is known as "polarizing." The "hot" wires may be any color other than white. In conduit wiring, usually all other wires are black, but at times, in order to aid in identifying conductors when a great many of them are in a single conduit, different colors are used. In cables of all types, each wire in the cable is of a different color.

> 2-wire circuit............ White, black
> 3-wire circuit............ White, black, red
> 4-wire circuit............ White, black, red, blue
> 5-wire circuit............ White, black, red, blue, yellow

Polarized Terminals.—Devices to which a neutral wire is to be connected have that terminal of a whitish color, usually tin, nickel, cadmium, or zinc plated. Other terminals are usually natural brass color.

Methods of Grounding.—The exact method used in making the ground will be covered in detail in Chap. 17.

CHAPTER 10

OUTLET AND SWITCH BOXES

In the early days of electrical wiring, it was the general practice to run wires on the surface of walls or inside them, without further protection, up to the devices to be connected. Fixtures were mounted directly on the ceiling, switches on the plaster walls, without any further ado. All this has been changed, and today, with few exceptions, outlet boxes are used at every point where connections are made to electrical devices.

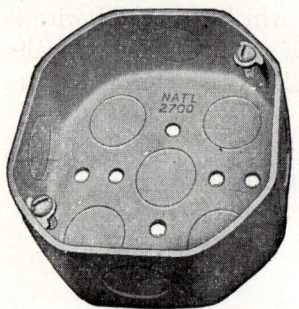

National Elec. Products Corp.
Fig. 10-1.—Typical octagon outlet box.

Purpose of Boxes.—Outlet boxes house the splices in wires at all points where the original insulation has been removed. There is little hazard in a continuous piece of wire, but a poorly made joint may lead to short circuits, grounds, or overheating at that point. Inside walls there are naturally loose dust, cobwebs, and other easily ignitible materials. Therefore there is some hazard of fire at joints; but when the joint is enclosed in a metal outlet box, this hazard is practically eliminated. Moreover, outlet boxes provide a continuity of ground, as explained in the previous chapter. The Code requires that boxes be supported in walls and ceilings according to definite standards which provide mechanical strength for supporting fixtures, switches, and other devices, eliminating the hazard of mechanical breakdown.

Common Types of Outlet Boxes.—Figure 10-1 shows a 4-in. octagon box, one of the most common boxes in use. Around

OUTLET AND SWITCH BOXES 135

the sides and in the bottom are found "knockouts"—sections of metal that can be easily knocked out to form openings for wire to enter. The metal is completely severed around these sections at one small point which serves to anchor the metal until it is to be removed. It is a simple matter to remove these knockouts—usually a stiff blow with the hand on the end of a heavy screw driver held against the knockout

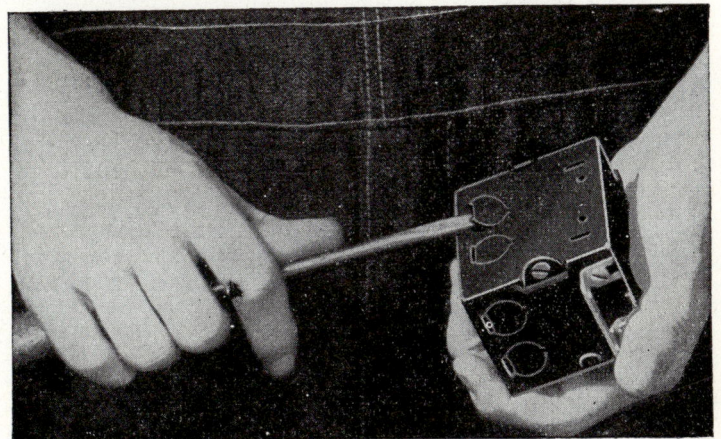

All-Steel Equip. Co.

FIG. 10-2.—On some boxes pry-outs are provided in place of the usual knockouts. They are easily removed.

will start it, and with a pair of pliers the metal disk is then easily removed. If the knockout is near the edge of a box, a pair of pliers is the only tool needed.

On many boxes the pry-out type of knockout is furnished. The pry-out is simply a small slot near or in the knockout, into which it is necessary only to insert a screw driver to pry out the metal disk, which prepares the knockout for use. Figure 10-2 should make this clear.

The outlet boxes are usually provided with ears and screws to facilitate mounting of covers, switches, or other devices used on the boxes.

There is also in common use a box similar to the one shown in Fig. 10-1 but only $3\frac{1}{4}$ in. in size. The two are more or less interchangeable, but the larger size is by far the more common because, since it is roomier, it is easier to do a good job, especially if a number of wires enter the box.

Another common box is the 4-in. square box shown in Fig. 10-3, more or less interchangeable with the octagon but decidedly roomier and handier to use. Especially when using

National Elec. Products Corp.

FIG. 10-3.—Square outlet box. This box is 4 in. square and much roomier than an octagon box.

National Elec. Products Corp.

FIG. 10-4.—A typical switch box. The sides of such boxes are always removable. Switch boxes come in a variety of depths, from $1\frac{1}{2}$ to 3 in.

conduit rather than cable, this box is used almost exclusively, for reasons that will be explained later. There is another box identical in appearance but larger, $4\frac{11}{16}$ in. square, used mostly for commercial work as distinguished from residential.

Depth of Outlet Boxes.—The Code, in Sec. 3706, requires that boxes of all descriptions be at least $1\frac{1}{2}$ in. deep, except when the use of a box of this depth "will result in injury to the building structure or is impracticable," in which case a box not less than $\frac{1}{2}$ in. deep may be used.

Switch Boxes.—For mounting switches, receptacles, and similar devices flush in the wall, switch boxes of the type shown in Fig. 10-4 are used. The sides are removable; this makes it easily possible to make a double-size, or "2-gang," box out of two single ones by simply throwing away one side on each box and joining together the two boxes. No extra parts are needed. This is shown in Fig. 10-5. In similar fashion it is possible to make boxes of any required size, to mount three or more devices side by side.

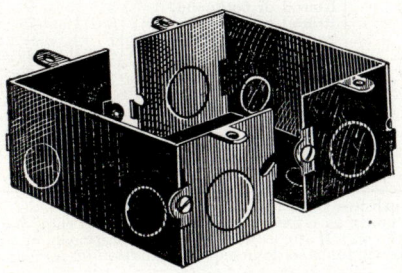

Fig. 10-5.—Two single boxes may be ganged to form one larger box of double size. Any number of boxes may be so ganged to form a box of any necessary size.

Depth of Switch Boxes.—Switch boxes range in depth from $1\frac{1}{2}$ in. to a maximum of 3 in. The $2\frac{1}{2}$-in. depth is the most popular, for it provides generous room for connectors, wire, etc., between the switch or other device and the bottom of the box. Use the $1\frac{1}{2}$-in. depth only when two boxes in two different rooms happen to come back to back in the wall, separating the two rooms; usually the wall is not thick enough to permit two deeper boxes to be used.

Material and Finish of Boxes.—The usual material of boxes is steel, with a choice of black enamel or galvanized finish. Local ordinances frequently specify that only the galvanized finish is to be used. For certain purposes outlet boxes of insulating material such as porcelain or bakelite are used; these will be discussed in Chap. 22 on farm wiring.

Number of Wires Entering Box.—The Code in Sec. 3709 limits the number of wires that may *enter* each size box, as shown in the table below. In counting wires, one that enters a box and is spliced to one running from a fixture mounted on the box is counted as one wire—in other words, the wire running *from* the fixture is disregarded. If a wire runs into a box and out again without splice or joint, as is often the case in conduit wiring, count it as only one wire.

Box		Maximum number of wires			
Size, inches	Type	No. 14	No. 12	No. 10	No. 8
1½ × 3¼	Round or octagonal	5	5	4	
1½ × 4	Round or octagonal	8	7	6	5
1½ × 4	Square	11	9	7	5
1½ × 4¹¹⁄₁₆	Square	16	12	10	8
2⅛ × 4¹¹⁄₁₆	Square	20	16	12	10
1¾ × 2¾ × 2	Rectangular	5	4	4	
1¾ × 2¾ × 2½	Rectangular	6	6	5	
1¾ × 2¾ × 3	Rectangular	7	7	6	
½* × 3¼	Round, shallow	4	4	3	
½* × 4	Round, shallow	6	6	4	
½* × 4¹¹⁄₁₆	Square, shallow	8	6	6	

* Or any other depth less than 1½ in.
NOTE: If the box contains a fixture stud and/or cable clamp, deduct 1 from the number of wires shown above. If it contains a switch, receptacle, or similar device, deduct 1 from the number shown, for each device or combination of devices mounted on a single strap.

Attaching Conduit and Cable to Boxes.—To provide a good, safe continuous ground throughout an installation, it is absolutely necessary to fasten the boxes rigidly and solidly to each piece of conduit, cable, etc., entering the box.

In the case of conduit this is very simply done by means of a locknut and bushing, both of which are shown in Fig. 10-6. Note that the locknut is not a flat piece of metal but that it is dished or bent, so that the lugs around the circumference become teeth on one side. The inside diameter of the bushing is slightly less than the inside diameter of the conduit. This causes the wire where it emerges from the conduit to rest on the rounded surface of the bushing. Slip a locknut on the threaded end of the conduit with the teeth facing the box. Slip the conduit into the knockout. Then install the bushing on the conduit inside the box, screwing it on as far as it will go. Only then tighten up the locknut on the outside, driving it home solidly so that the teeth will bite into the metal of the box, thus making a good sound ground. This construction is shown in Fig. 10-7. Detailed instructions

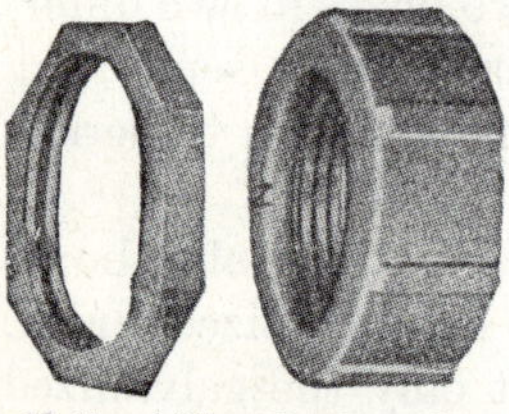

National Elec. Products Corp.

FIG. 10-6.—Locknuts and bushings are used at the ends of each run of conduit. They anchor the conduit to the box and also provide a continuous grounded raceway.

for cutting and using the conduit will be found in the next chapter.

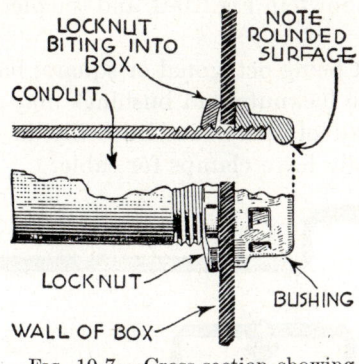

Fig. 10-7.—Cross-section showing how locknut and bushing are used at outlet boxes or other boxes.

National Elec. Products Corp.

Fig. 10-8.—Cables are attached to boxes with connectors of this type.

In the case of cable, connectors of the type shown in Fig. 10-8 are used. After the connector is fastened to the cable, slip the

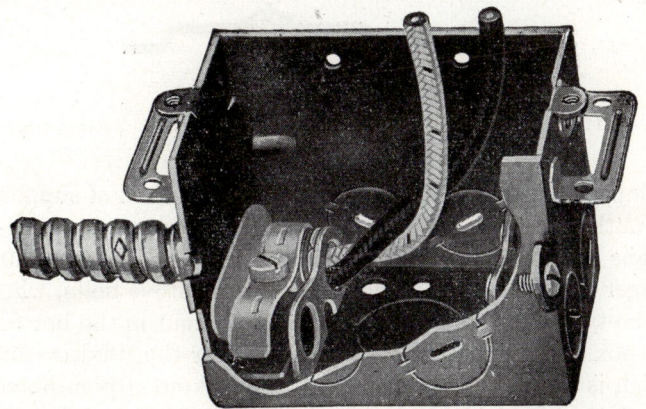

National Elec. Products Corp.

Fig. 10-9.—Often boxes are provided with clamps which serve the same purpose as separate connectors.

connector into a knockout, install the locknut on the inside of the box, and run the locknut home tightly, as in the case of conduit.

Clamps.—The use of boxes having built-in clamps which eliminate the need for special connectors for cable is common. A typical box of this type is shown in Fig. 10-9, and the picture should be self-explanatory.

Round Boxes.—Instead of being octagonal or square, boxes may be round, in which case locknuts and bushings may not be used on the rounded wall of the boxes but only in the bottom. Round boxes usually have clamps for cable.

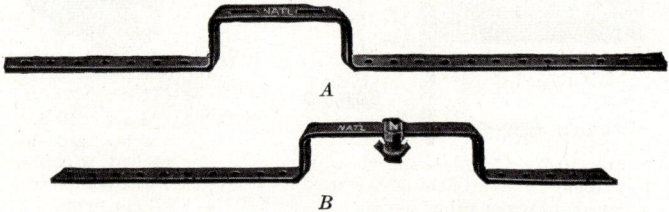

National Elec. Products Corp.

Fig. 10-10.—Outlet boxes are usually supported in buildings with the aid of offset hangers of this type.

All-Steel Equip Co.

Fig. 10-11.—Factory-assembled combinations of box and hanger are convenient.

Supporting Outlet Boxes.—The usual method of supporting an outlet box in a new building of frame construction is by means of a hanger. In the type shown at A of Fig. 10-10 the hanger is fastened to the box by means of stove bolts, whereas in the type shown at B, the middle knockout in the bottom of the box is removed, the box slipped over the "fixture stud," which is part of the hanger, and the locknut driven home on the fixture stud inside the box. The fixture stud later may be used also to support a fixture mounted on the box. There are also available factory-assembled combinations of the type shown in Fig. 10-11.

In any case the assembly is mounted between joists, as shown in Fig. 10-12. The hanger described is of the "shallow"

OUTLET AND SWITCH BOXES

type, and its depth is such that with boxes 1½ in. deep the front of the box will be flush with the plaster. The plaster must come right up to the box; there may be no open space around the box.

This shallow-type hanger is used with all wiring systems with the exception of conduit. When conduit is to be used, "deep" hangers are used instead of "shallow." The only

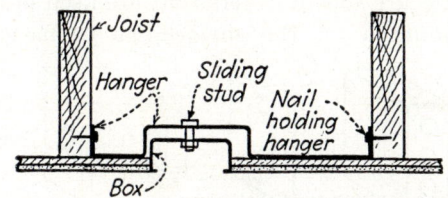

FIG. 10-12.—The mounting of boxes with hangers is very simple.

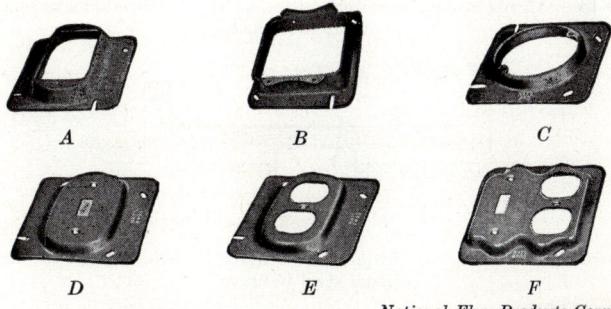

National Elec. Products Corp.

FIG. 10-13.—Typical raised covers for 4-in. square boxes.

difference is that the offset is about ½ in. deeper, which brings the front edge of the outlet box about ½ in. below the surface of the plaster but leaves sufficient room behind the plaster for the conduit, the locknut, etc. Since the Code, in Sec. 3715, requires that the front edge of the box must be not more than ¼ in. below the finished surface of the wall or ceiling (if the surface is combustible it must be flush), some expedient must be adopted to overcome the fact that the front edge is over ¼ in. below the surface. Accordingly, it is customary to use covers, the front edges of which are flush with plaster. Figure

10-13 shows an assortment of covers fitting the 4-in. square box which is usually used with conduit. Each cover serves a specific purpose, that at *A* accommodating one switch or receptacle, that at *B* two such devices. At *C* is shown a "plaster ring" which has an opening of the same size as a 3¼-in. box. When this is mounted on top of the 4-in. square box, it permits devices designed for the 3¼-in. box to be used. At *D*, *E*, and *F* are shown covers that are used only when the boxes are mounted on the surface, as in basements, fac-

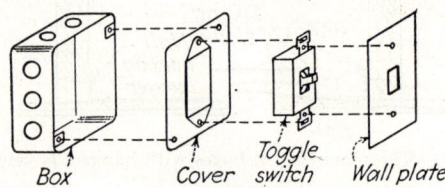

Fig. 10-14.—All parts of an electrical outlet are standardized in size so as to fit properly and easily.

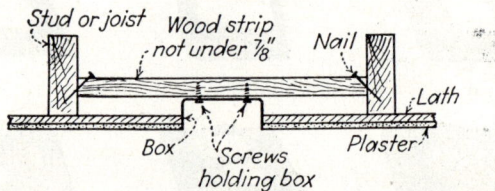

Fig. 10-15.—Mounting an outlet box on wooden strip, instead of using the usual steel hangers.

tory walls, etc. They accommodate, respectively, one toggle switch, one receptacle, and a switch and receptacle. Many other types are available. Of all these covers the types at *A*, *B*, and *C* are the most common. Figure 10-14 shows a completed installation.

Instead of requiring hangers to support boxes, the Code generally permits any other type of support which is sturdy and which becomes part of the building structure. Wooden strips may be used, provided they are at least ⅞ in. thick. This method is shown in Fig. 10-15 but is little used.

If the box is attached to a run of conduit which in turn is securely anchored, no further support is required for the box.

OUTLET AND SWITCH BOXES 143

Good judgment must be used, especially if the box is later to support a fixture. Remember that the local inspector is the final judge as to whether the spirit and intent of the Code are met by any given type of installation.

In old work (buildings wired after completion) as compared with new work (buildings wired while under construction),

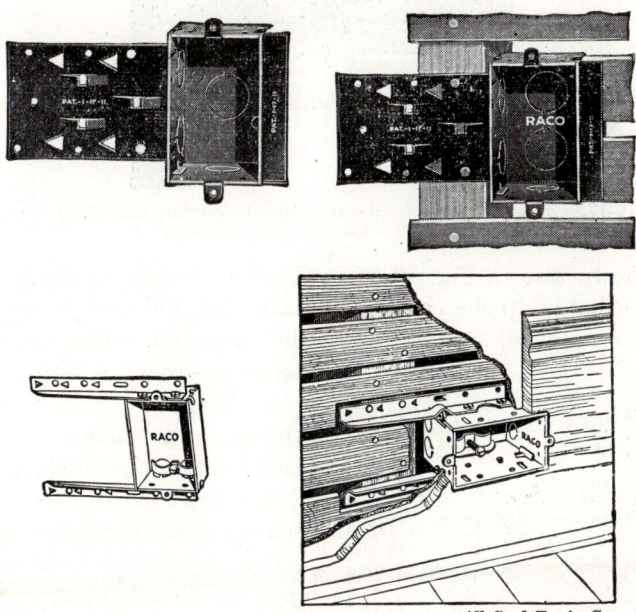

All-Steel Equip Co.

FIG. 10-16.—Switch boxes with mounting brackets may be mounted directly on the studding of a building.

different methods of support are used, and these will be discussed in the chapter on old work.

Supporting Switch Boxes.—Instead of switch boxes, 4-in. square boxes with cover are frequently used, as previously described. Usually, however, switch boxes are used, and since they are available in depths up to 3 in., there is no problem in connection with the use of conduit as there is with $1\frac{1}{2}$-in. deep outlet boxes.

144   THEORY AND BASIC PRINCIPLES

Perhaps the most common switch box for new work is the bracket type of box of which several are shown in Fig. 10-16. The bracket is merely nailed to the studding of the building,

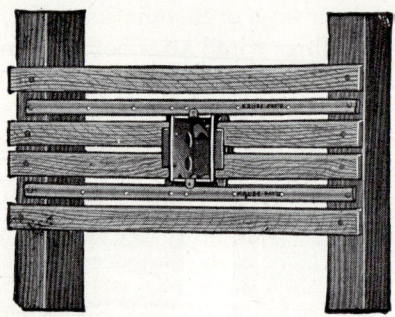

Fig. 10-17.—Switch boxes may be mounted between studding by means of special steel mounting strips.

as shown also in Fig. 10-16. Note the trough on the boxes, which holds up the ends of the lath that end at the box and that would otherwise be left unsupported. The brackets

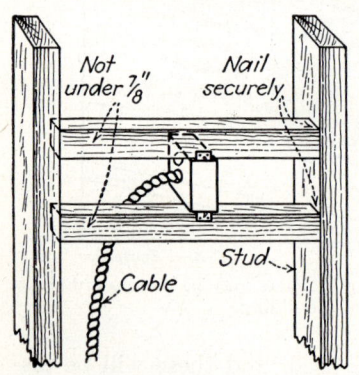

Fig. 10-18.—Using wooden strips to support switch boxes.

themselves have a number of projections that form a good support and anchor for the plaster when it is applied.

Also available and generally used are mounting strips which permit any number of switch boxes to be mounted at any point between two studs. These are shown in Fig. 10-17, and the picture will be self-explanatory.

Switch boxes may be mounted on wooden strips like outlet boxes, and a finished installation is shown in Fig. 10-18. The strips must be at least 7/8 in. thick and so mounted that the front edge of the boxes will be flush with the plaster.

Outlet Box Covers.—An outlet box may never be left uncovered. When a fixture is mounted on top of the box, no further cover is necessary. An outlet box cover must be used in every other case. Figure 10-19 shows an assortment for the conventional 3¼- or 4-in. boxes; there are corresponding ones for other styles of boxes. At A is shown a blank cover used to cover the box when it serves merely to house joints in wire. The box then is known as a "pull" box or "junction" box. Such boxes may be located only where accessible without damaging the structure of the building. At B is shown a drop cord cover used with drop cords; the hole is bushed to do away with sharp edges which might otherwise injure the insulation of the cord. At C is shown a "spider cover" on which

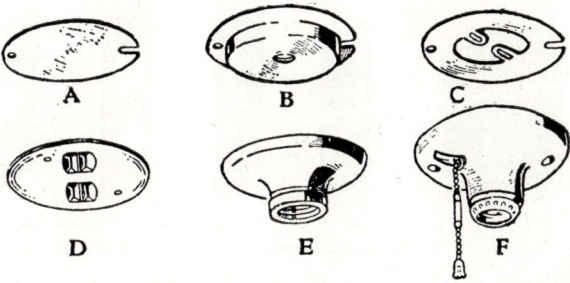

Fig. 10-19.—Outlet box covers are made in dozens of different types; the six shown here are typical.

surface style switches are mounted. At D is shown a cover with a duplex receptacle, used mostly in basements, workshops, and similar locations. E shows an outlet cover and F a similar cover provided with pull-chain control. These covers are widely used in closets, attics, basements, farm buildings, and similar locations.

The covers illustrated are the ones most commonly used; most jobs can be completed using only the ones shown. There are, however, dozens of other types, each serving a specialized purpose. For example, there are blank covers similar to that shown in A of Fig. 10-19, but with a knockout in the center, permitting an armored cable connector to be used when running the flexible cable to a stationary device like a motor. There are covers with openings to accommodate sign receptacles of the type that were shown in Fig. 4-40. For square boxes there are covers with many other combinations of openings in addition to the ones shown in Fig. 10-13.

Surface Boxes.—One style of box is used entirely for surface work, as in basements, workrooms, or any other location where flush mounting in a hollow wall space is not wanted. This surface type of box is shown in Fig. 10-20 together with covers for various purposes—blank, toggle switch, and duplex receptacle.

Boxes on Brick Walls.—When a house is of brick construction a considerable amount of labor is involved in the mounting

All-Steel Equips. Co.

FIG. 10-20.—The box shown here is used for surface mounting.

of the boxes, for the boxes must come flush with the plaster when it is applied. A space must be chiseled into the brick to receive the box. Usually 4-in. square boxes are used, together with covers of the type that were shown in Fig. 10-13. These are available in various depths so that, if the ordinary ½-in. type does not bring the cover flush with the plaster, one of a greater depth, say ¾ in., will be found suitable.

The box cannot be secured to the brick directly with screws; consequently it is necessary to use one of the many types of plugs or anchors available for the purpose. In any case it will be necessary to drill holes into the brick or masonry, using for the purpose a star drill of the general type shown in Fig. 10-21. This drill is used by simply pounding on its head with a hammer, rotating the drill a bit after each blow.

A very common mounting method is that using the well-known lead plugs or anchors which are merely inserted into

Fig. 10-21.—With a star drill it is not difficult to drill holes in brick or similar material.

Paine Co.

Fig. 10-22.—The lead expansion anchor shown at left is dropped into the hole as shown below, and forms a secure mounting for whatever is supported by it.

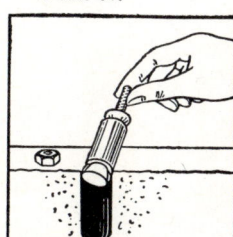 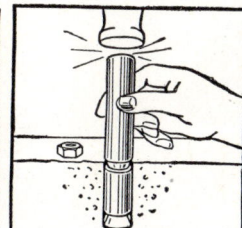 

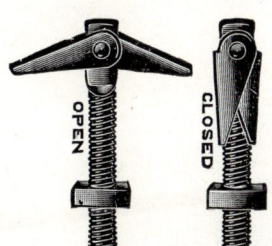

Fig. 10-23.—Toggle bolts are used in mounting devices over hollow walls or other hollow spaces.

Paine Co.

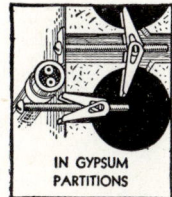 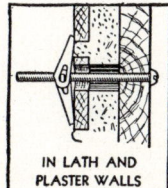 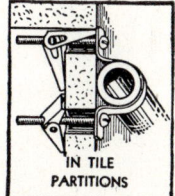

the hole in the masonry, ordinary wood screws then being used. The Code prohibits wooden plugs.

The use of lead expansion anchors of the type shown in Fig. 10-22 provides a mounting which is considerably more secure than that using ordinary lead plugs. Their use is clearly shown in steps in the same picture.

If the mounting must be over hollow areas, use toggle bolts. Typical bolts are shown in Fig. 10-23, and this picture also shows their use. Merely slip the collapsible wings through the opening in the wall or other surface; a spring opens the wings, which then provide anchorage for the bolt.

CHAPTER 11

DIFFERENT WIRING METHODS

Although the same basic materials are used in all of them, there are six different common methods or systems used in ordinary residential wiring. These systems are

1. Rigid conduit.
2. Thin-wall conduit.
3. Nonmetallic sheathed cable.
4. Armored cable.
5. Flexible conduit.
6. Knob and tube.

Detailed information applying to each system will be given in a later chapter, and only the basic principles will be found here.

Clayton Mark & Co.

FIG. 11-1.—Rigid conduit looks like water pipe but differs in many ways.

Rigid Conduit.—In this type of wiring, all wires are enclosed in steel pipe known as "conduit." Conduit differs from ordinary water pipe in that it is especially annealed to permit easy bending; the inside surface is carefully prepared so that the wires can be pulled into it with a minimum of effort and without damage to the insulation or outer braid; it has a corrosion-resisting finish so that the installation may be permanent.

It comes in 10-ft. lengths in a choice of black-enamel or galvanized finish. The galvanized is usually considered the better of the two, and the black-enameled type may be used only indoors. Rigid conduit with a galvanized finish is shown in Fig. 11-1; each length bears an Underwriters' label.

The ½-in. size is the smallest used in ordinary wiring. All sizes are identical in dimensions with the corresponding sizes of water pipe, and therefore, as in the case of water pipe, the nominal size in no way denotes the actual physical dimensions, as the following table shows:

Trade size, inches	Internal diameter, inches	Internal area, square inches	External diameter, inches
½	0.622	0.30	0.840
¾	0.824	0.53	1.050
1	1.049	0.86	1.315
1¼	1.380	1.50	1.660
1½	1.610	2.04	1.900
2	2.067	3.36	2.375
2½	2.469	4.79	2.875
3	3.068	7.38	3.500
3½	3.548	9.90	4.000
4	4.026	12.72	4.500

Since the dimensions are identical, the tools used for cutting water pipe may also be used for cutting conduit. However, the threads on conduit are not the same as the threads on water pipe. On water pipe, the threads are tapered, being slightly smaller in diameter at the end of the pipe than they are an inch from the end. On the conduit the threads are straight, not tapered, being the same diameter no matter how far they are cut. Therefore the dies used to thread water pipe must not be used for threading conduit; use special dies designed for conduit, cutting nontapered threads.

Cutting Conduit.—Conduit is cut with an ordinary pipe cutter, as used for water pipe, of the type shown in Fig. 11-2. This unfortunately leaves a sharp edge at the cut, as shown in Fig. 11-3. This sharp edge might seriously damage the insulation of the wire as it is pulled into the conduit; therefore,

DIFFERENT WIRING METHODS

common sense suggests, and the Code requires, that each cut be reamed smooth. A reamer of the type shown in Fig. 11-4 serves the purpose.

Bending Conduit.—Because the wires are pulled into conduit after it is installed, it is important that all bending be carefully done so that the internal diameter is not substantially decreased in the process. Make the bends as gradual

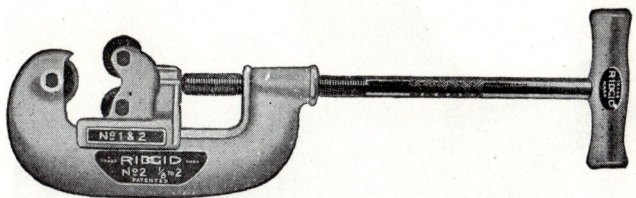

Ridge Tool Co.

FIG. 11-2.—A typical pipe cutter.

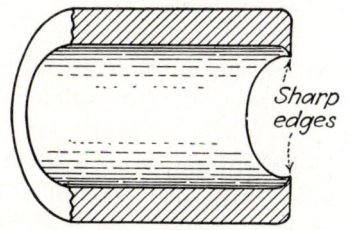

FIG. 11-3.—When pipe is cut with a pipe cutter, a sharp edge is left which must be removed before the conduit is used.

M. B. Austin Co.

FIG. 11-4.—A reamer of this type is used to remove sharp burrs from the cut end of pipe.

as possible, and remember the Code requirement (Sec. 3470) that the radius of the bend must be at least 6 times the internal diameter of the conduit. Stated another way, if the conduit were bent into a complete circle, the diameter of the circle must be at least 12 times the internal diameter of the conduit. If lead-sheathed cable is to be pulled into the conduit, then the diameter of the circle must be at least 20 times the internal diameter of the conduit.

A popular type of bending tool is shown in Fig. 11-5. The smaller sizes of conduit bend easily, but it is fairly difficult to bend the heavier sizes. Factory-bent elbows of the type shown in Fig. 11-6 are available in all sizes and are used generally on the larger sizes.

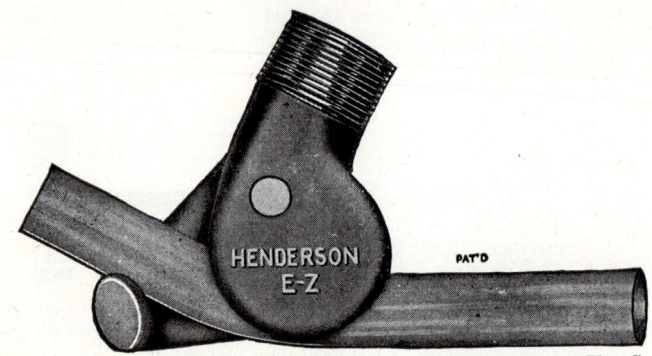

Henderson Elec. Co.

FIG. 11-5.—A typical conduit bender.

Conduit is fastened to boxes by means of locknuts and bushings as already outlined in connection with outlet boxes in Chap. 10.

Number of Wires in Conduit.—Except for special cases more than nine wires are never pulled into one conduit. The number permitted depends on the size of the conduit and the size of the wires; the information is found in the Code in Chap. 10, Table 4. Table 5 of the Code applies to lead-sheathed cables. For combinations not covered by Tables 4 and 5, use Tables 9 to 11. All these tables are given in the Appendix of this book.

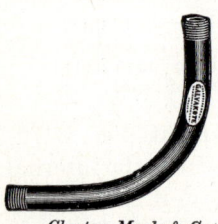

Clayton Mark & Co.

FIG. 11-6.—For large sizes, factory-bent elbows are commonly used.

Number of Bends.—The Code, in Sec. 3471, prohibits more than 4 quarter bends or their equivalent in one "run" of conduit, or the distance between outlet boxes or other openings. The fewer the bends, the easier it will be to pull the wires into the conduit.

DIFFERENT WIRING METHODS

Splices in Wires.—Wires must be continuous, without splice, throughout all conduit. Splices are permitted only at outlet boxes (Sec. 3005).

Pulling Wires into Conduit.—If the run is short and the wires occupy a relatively small portion of the area of the conduit, they can frequently be pushed in at one outlet and through the conduit up to the next outlet. If the run is of considerable length, especially if it contains bends, then "fish tape" is used. A length of ordinary galvanized steel wire will

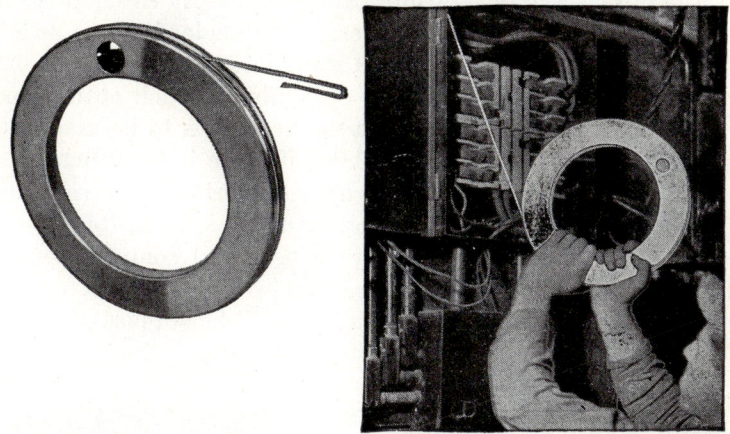

Ideal Commutator Dresser Co.

FIG. 11-7.—Fish tape is necessary to pull wires into conduit. The material is made of springy steel.

serve the purpose, but a special fish tape made of a stiff but flexible steel is more frequently used. Often it is put up in special reels (see Fig. 11-7). In size it is usually about $\frac{1}{8}$ by 0.060 in. Bend a small loop or hook on the end of the tape as the picture shows; this will permit it to go easily around bends as it is pushed into conduit. Since this tape is highly tempered, it will break if bent sharply, unless the temper is taken out; this can be done by heating it to a red heat with a blowtorch, then letting it cool.

Push the tape into the conduit through which the wires are to be pulled; when the end emerges attach all the wires which are to be pulled into the conduit, to the fish tape, taking care to leave no sharp ends which might catch at the joints in the conduit. Then pull the wires into position; this usually requires one man pulling at one end and another feeding the wires into the opening at the other end, to make sure there will be no snarls and in general to ease the wire on its way. Powdered soapstone may be used as a lubricant to make it easier to pull the wires. The Code, in Sec. 3006, requires a minimum of at least 6 in. of wire projecting at each outlet box where a connection is to be made; it is easy to cut off a few inches later if there is too much, but hard to do good work if the ends are too short to be convenient.

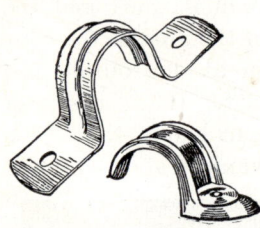

FIG. 11-8.—Either cast or stamped straps may be used for supporting conduit.

Supporting Conduit.—The Code is not specific on this point; therefore it is necessary merely to use good common sense. Pipe straps of the type shown in Fig. 11-8 are employed for the purpose. Smaller sizes of conduit should be supported every 5 ft. and the larger sizes at least every 10 ft.

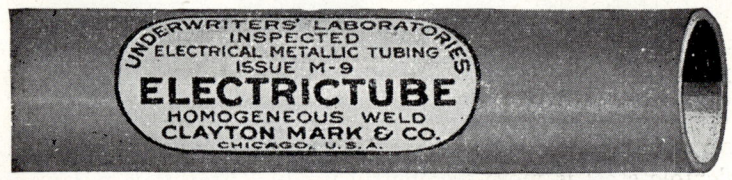

Clayton Mark & Co.

FIG. 11-9.—Thin-wall conduit is never threaded. It is lighter and easier to use than rigid conduit.

Electrical Metallic Tubing.—The material which the Code has labeled with this rather unwieldy name is commonly known by its abbreviation "EMT," or by its descriptive common name of "thin-wall conduit." It is shown in Fig. 11-9 and, as in rigid conduit, each length bears the Underwriters' label. It is available only in sizes up to and including

2 in. For residential purposes it may be used interchangeably with rigid conduit.

The internal diameter, size for size, is the same as rigid conduit, but as the name implies, the walls are thinner. For

 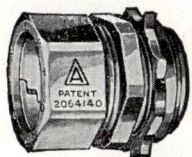

Appleton Elec. Co.

Fig. 11-10.—Connectors and couplings used in connection with thin-wall conduit.

  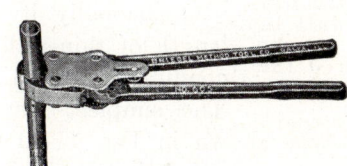

Briegel Method Tool Co.

Fig. 11-11.—With this style of fittings, the fitting and the conduit are indented with the special tool shown.

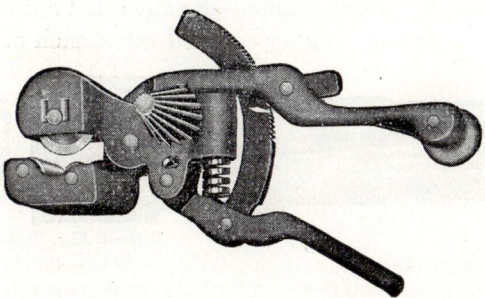

Briegel Method Tool Co.

Fig. 11-12.—A handy tool for cutting thin-wall conduit.

this reason the material is never threaded, but all joints and connections are made with special threadless fittings which hold the material through pressure. Figure 11-10 shows both a coupling and a connector; each consists of a body plus a split ring through which tremendous pressure is exerted on the conduit when the nut is forced home tightly. Another type of fitting is the "telescope" type, which requires a special tool to apply, the tool denting both fitting and tubing for good mechanical and electrical joints. The fittings and the tool are both shown in Fig. 11-11.

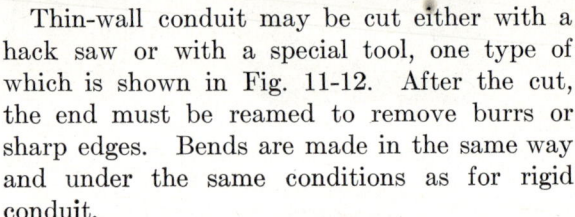

M. B. Austin Co.

FIG. 11-13.—This adapter makes it possible to use thin-wall conduit in fittings designed for rigid conduit.

Thin-wall conduit may be cut either with a hack saw or with a special tool, one type of which is shown in Fig. 11-12. After the cut, the end must be reamed to remove burrs or sharp edges. Bends are made in the same way and under the same conditions as for rigid conduit.

Occasionally it will be necessary to join a length of thin-wall conduit to a length of rigid conduit, or to a fitting designed for rigid conduit. The simplest way is to use a connector of the type shown in Fig. 11-10 for the threaded portion of the connector, for the thin-wall conduit will always fit any fitting designed for the corresponding size of rigid conduit. An adapter shown in Fig. 11-13 may also be used.

Nonmetallic Sheathed Cable.—Nonmetallic sheathed cable consists of two or more rubber-covered wires, each with a spiral

National Elec. Products Corp.

FIG. 11-14.—Nonmetallic sheathed cable is especially popular for wiring farm buildings and is also used for many other purposes.

wrapping of paper for spacing, and, to give the assembly more protection against damage by mechanical abuse, the entire assembly is enclosed in a fabric cover which is treated with moisture-resistant and flame-retardant compounds. The empty spaces which would otherwise result are filled with a twisted jute or paper filler. All of these are shown in Fig. 11-14.

DIFFERENT WIRING METHODS 157

Removing the Outer Cover.—In use, the outer covering must be removed at the ends. This can be done by slitting the braid with a knife: usually the slit is merely started; then, by pulling on the jute or paper filler mentioned before, it is possible to rip open the covering as far as desired. The unused braid is then removed with a jackknife. Extreme care is necessary so that the insulation of the wires is not injured. The use of a cable ripper, as shown in Fig. 11-15, is recommended, for it saves time and avoids damage to the insulation.

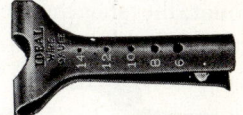

Ideal Commutator Dresser Co.

FIG. 11-15.—This cable stripper saves much time.

The cable is fastened to outlet boxes by the use of connectors, several types of which are shown in Fig. 11-16. The connector is first solidly fastened to the cable, the connector slipped into the knockout in the box, and the locknut of the connector then driven solidly home on the inside of the box. As mentioned in Chap. 10, many types of box have built-in clamps which serve the purpose of connectors.

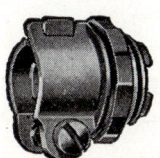  

National Elec. Products Corp.

FIG. 11-16.—An assortment of connectors used in attaching cable to outlet, switch boxes, and similar devices.

Where Used.—Nonmetallic sheathed cable is permitted only in permanently dry locations; consequently it may not be used out-of-doors. Its use is recommended (Code, Art. 300) in locations where a really good permanent ground is not found; since this condition pertains in almost 100 per cent of all cases on farms, nonmetallic sheathed cable is used to the practical exclusion of all other methods for farm work. The facts that it is very easy to handle, is light, and is relatively inexpensive, all are partly responsible for the growing popularity of this type of cable. In case of doubt, consult the local ordinances or inspector as to whether its use is permissible.

Joints.—Joints and splices are never permitted in nonmetallic sheathed cable, except at outlet boxes, where they are made as in any other type of wiring.

Fig. 11-17.—A typical strap for supporting nonmetallic cable.

Mechanical Installation.—If installed while a building is under construction, nonmetallic sheathed cable is installed inside the walls; the Code requires that it be anchored at least every 4½ ft., and in any case within 12 in. of every outlet box. Straps of the types shown in Fig. 11-17 are used for the purpose. In old work where the cable is fished through the walls, this requirement is waived. All bends in

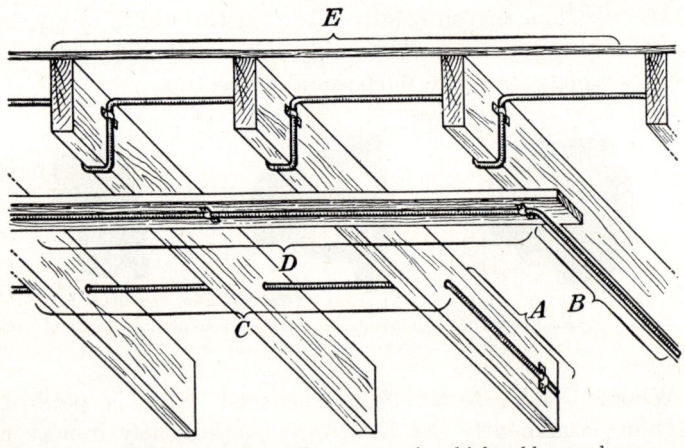

Fig. 11-18.—This shows five different ways in which cable may be run on an open ceiling. Various methods of protecting the cable are used, depending on the method of installation.

cable must be gradual so as not to injure the cable; the Code requirement of Sec. 3368 is that, if a bend were continued so as to form a complete circle, the diameter of the circle would be at least 10 times the diameter of the cable.

Where the cable is run exposed, as in basements, attics, barns, etc., it must be given reasonable protection against mechanical injury. This protection can be provided in a variety of ways (see Fig. 11-18). If the cable is run along the side of a joist, rafter, or stud as at *A*, or along the bottom edge of a timber as at *B*, no further protection is required. If it is run at an angle to the timbers, the cable may be run through bored holes as at *C*. No additional protection is required; neither are porcelain tubes, loom, or any similar materials needed where the cable goes through the bored holes.

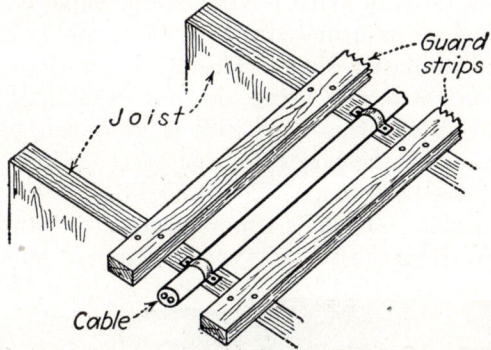

Fig. 11-19.—When cable runs crosswise of floor studs in attics, guard strips must be used.

The holes should be bored in the approximate center of the timbers. If the cable is not run through bored holes, but instead attached to the bottoms of the joists, then it must be run on substantial running boards, as shown at *D;* this requirement is waived if the cable is size 6-2, 8-3, or heavier. A final method is to let the cable follow the structure of the building as shown at *E*, when again no further protection is required. This method, however, is very wasteful of material, leads to unnecessarily long lengths of cable with consequently large voltage drops, and is therefore to be discouraged. Whichever method is used, the cable must be supported at least every $4\frac{1}{2}$ ft. and also within 12 in. of every outlet box.

In accessible attics, if the cable is run at angles across the top of floor joists, the cable must be protected by guard strips at least as high as the cable, as shown in Fig. 11-19. If run at right angles to studs or rafters, it must be protected in the same way at all points where it is within 7 ft. of the floor joists. No protection is required under other conditions. If the attic is not accessible by means of permanent stairs or ladder, this protection is required only for a distance of 6 ft. around the opening to the attic.

In any event, the cable must always follow the approximate contour of the building—never any short cuts across open space.

Cable with Ground Wire.—Nonmetallic cable is also available with one bare uninsulated wire in the assembly in addition to the usual insulated wires. This cable is required in some localities, the extra wire being used for grounding purposes. At each outlet box this bare wire is grounded to the box proper, so that all the boxes are tied together into a continuously grounded system.

Armored Cable.—Today's armored cable, as pictured in Fig. 11-20, is known as the "ABC type"—armored bushed cable.

National Elec. Products Corp.

FIG. 11-20.—Armored cable. A continuous steel armor wrapped around the wires protects them against injury and at the same time provides a continuous ground.

It consists of two or more wires of the rubber-covered type, wrapped with a spiral layer of kraft paper, and has an outer steel armor.

Cutting Cable.—A hack saw is usually used to cut armored cable. Do not hold it at a right angle to the cable, but rather at a right angle to the strip of armor as it runs around the cable, as shown in Fig. 11-21. After the cut is made, grasp the two ends of armor, give a twist as shown in Fig. 11-22, and the two ends will separate; it is then a simple matter to cut through the wires.

DIFFERENT WIRING METHODS

To use the cut end, it is necessary to remove about 6 in. of the armor. Proceed as before, holding the hack saw in the same position, being extremely careful to saw through only the armor, not touching the insulation. The paper inside the armor provides some little spacing, making this possible. Nevertheless, considerable practice is necessary to get the

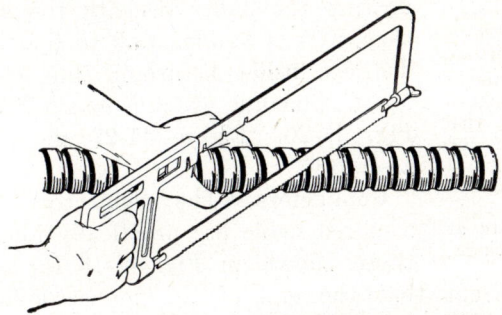

National Elec. Products Corp.

FIG. 11-21.—In sawing armored cable, hold the hack saw as shown.

National Elec. Products Corp.

FIG. 11-22.—After sawing, give the cut ends of the armor a twist to separate them.

knack of sawing through the armor without damaging the insulation. When the armor is severed, a twist will remove the short end.

Bushings.—Careful examination of the cut end of the armor will show that the hack saw has left sharp teeth on the armor, some of them quite long. These teeth point inward toward the wires and might damage the insulation, causing a short or ground. Therefore a bushing of thin but tough fiber which

162   THEORY AND BASIC PRINCIPLES

has a high insulating value is inserted between the armor and the wires. Such a bushing is shown in Fig. 11-23. Since there is little room between the paper and the armor, space is provided by removing the paper. The steps shown in Figs. 11-24 and 11-25 demonstrate how to unwrap the paper beneath the armor, and then with a sudden pull to tear it off some distance inside the armor, thus leaving room for the bushing, which is inserted as shown in Fig. 11-26. Figure 11-27 shows the final assembly.

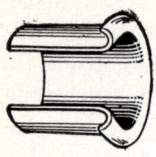

National Elec. Products Corp.

FIG. 11-23.—A bushing of tough fiber is inserted between the armor and the wires to guard against danger of grounds through sharp points at cut end of armor.

Connectors.—The connectors used with armored cable are practically identical with those shown in Fig. 11-16 for nonmetallic cable, except that the end of the connector which goes into the box has openings or peepholes through which the

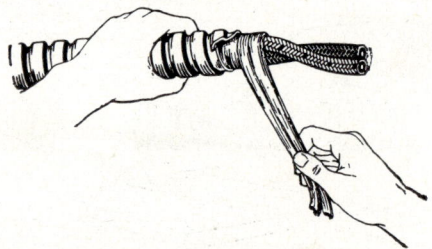

National Elec. Products Corp.

FIG. 11-24.—Unwrap the paper found over the wires up to a point some distance *within* the armor.

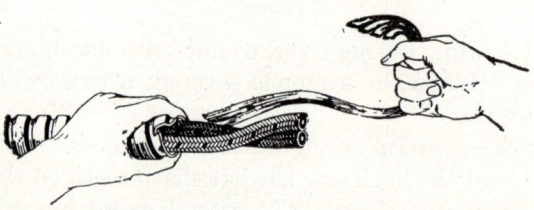

National Elec. Products Corp.

FIG. 11-25.—Yank the paper wrapper, removing it for some distance under the armor. This makes room for the fiber bushing.

antishort bushing can be seen by the inspector. Because of these peepholes, the connectors are known as the "visible type." The bushing is first properly inserted under the armor, the connector is then slipped over the cable and solidly

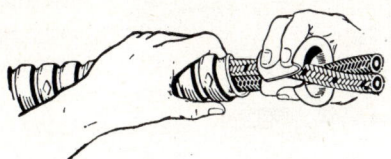

National Elec. Products Corp.
FIG. 11-26.—Inserting fiber bushing.

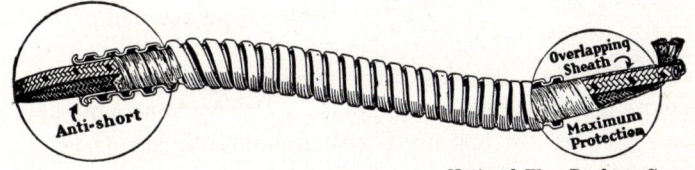

National Elec. Products Corp.
FIG. 11-27.—Cross-section of cable, showing paper removed beneath armor and fiber bushing in place.

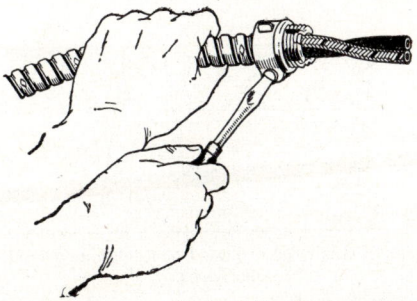

National Elec. Products Corp.
FIG. 11-28.—Attaching connector to cable.

anchored on it. The locknut is then driven solidly home inside the outlet box, as with other styles of cable (see Figs. 11-28 and 11-29). If this is carefully done, all the outlets are thereby tied together, giving the continuity of ground discussed in Chap. 9.

Where Used.—Like the nonmetallic sheathed cable, armored cable may be used only in permanently dry locations (unless it is the leaded type with lead-sheathed cable inside armor). For residential purposes it is practically interchangeable with nonmetallic sheathed cable, except that it is not recommended for farms where a good permanent ground is not available.

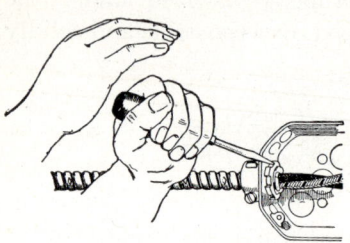

National Elec. Products Corp.
Fig. 11-29.—Driving home locknut on connector and securing it to the box.

Supporting.—Armored cable is supported and protected exactly as is nonmetallic sheathed cable. Staples of the type shown in Fig. 11-30 are perhaps a bit more convenient than the conventional straps. These staples are not used with nonmetallic sheathed cable because there is danger that they might be driven in so solidly that they would actually damage the cable. This danger does not exist with armored cable which has steel armor for protection.

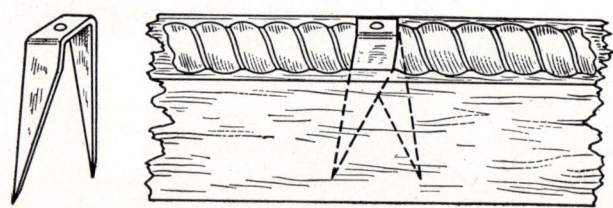

Fig. 11-30.—Staples of this type are used to anchor armored cable to wooden surfaces.

National Elec. Products Corp.
Fig. 11-31.—Flexible conduit. The wires are pulled into place after the conduit is installed.

DIFFERENT WIRING METHODS

Flexible Conduit.—This material is generally called "greenfield." It is shown in Fig. 11-31 and is neither more nor less than the empty armor of armored cable, without the wires. Except in a few scattered areas, this material is relatively little used. Where it is popular, it is used like armored cable, except that the flexible conduit is first installed and the wires are later pulled into place just as with rigid conduit or EMT. Connectors are used as in armored cable, except that the peepholes are not required since fiber bushings are not used.

Another application is in connection with installations where a certain amount of flexibility is required, for example when motors are installed with sliding bases to take up slack in belts. Obviously the wires to any motor so installed cannot be in rigid conduit because then the motor would be immovable. Similarly, a certain amount of it is used where the use of rigid conduit would involve extremely difficult or awkward bends.

Knob and Tube System.—The original method of wiring when electrical installations were first made was the knob and tube method, which today is still extremely popular in certain large areas, although it is practically unknown in others. Basically it consists merely of rubber-covered wire mounted on porcelain insulators and running through porcelain insulating tubes at points where extra insulation is needed.

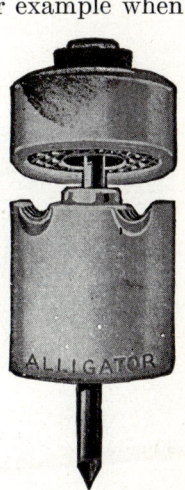

Porcelain Products, Inc.

FIG. 11-32.—Nail knobs are used to support wires in knob and tube wiring.

Where Used.—The Code places no restrictions on this type of wiring so far as residential use is concerned, except that it may not be used in garages big enough for more than two cars. It is best to check local ordinances, for in many localities it is prohibited.

Insulators.—The most common insulator is the nail knob, shown in Fig. 11-32. This consists of a body with two grooves and a head, plus a nail, with a leather washer so that the porcelain will not be fractured when the nail is driven home. This insulator is made in a variety of sizes for different size wires. The nails are usually cement coated, which causes them to hold better than plain nails. The grooves have ridges or corrugations in them so that the wires will not slip. Care should be used in driving home the nails to provide enough tension to grip the wire tightly and yet not damage the insulation.

The solid knob shown in Fig. 11-33 is not used a great deal because the wire must be tied to the knob by a separate tie

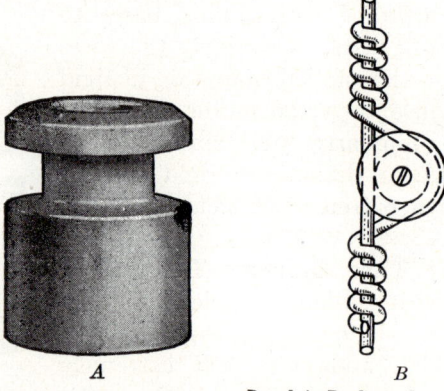

Porcelain Products, Inc.

FIG. 11-33.—Solid knobs are not as convenient as split nail knobs, for the wires must be tied to each knob.

wire, as shown in the same picture. The tie wire must not be smaller than the main wire. These solid knobs usually come without nails, and it is a nuisance to provide leather washers for the nails; if nails are used without washers, a high percentage of the insulators will be cracked. Wood screws eliminate this difficulty but take a longer time to install.

Where two wires run parallel, cleats of the type shown in Fig. 11-34 may be used. Generally these are sold unassembled, but recently they have become available with nails and leather washers, as shown in the picture, which, of course, makes them far more practical to use.

Tubes of the type shown in Fig. 11-35 are used where a wire runs through a joist, stud, or other timber. They are available in many diameters and lengths. In using them, bore the hole through the timber at a slight angle, so that when installed the tubes will not easily fall out (see Fig. 11-36).

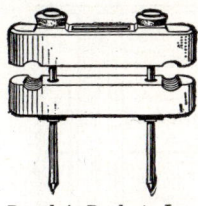

Porcelain Products, Inc.

FIG. 11-34.—Nail cleats are used like nail knobs, but support two wires instead of one. They may be used only for exposed wiring.

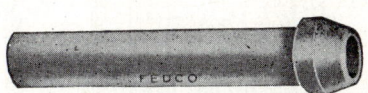

Porcelain Products, Inc.

FIG. 11-35.—Porcelain tubes are used wherever wires run through timbers, and also for several other purposes.

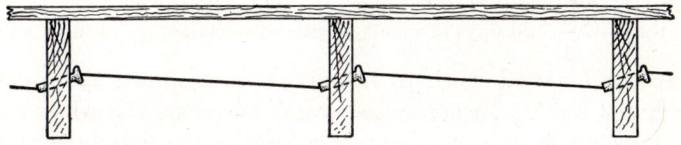

FIG. 11-36.—In boring holes through timbers, for porcelain tubes, bore them at an angle so that the tubes will not fall out of the holes.

Spacing of Wires.—Where the wires are exposed, they must be separated from each other at least 2½ in., and at least ½ in. from the surface over which they run (Code, Sec. 3205). In damp locations this is increased to 1 in. If the wires are concealed, these figures are increased, in accordance with Sec. 3245, and the wires must be kept 3 in. apart and 1 in. from the surface over which they run. Ordinary knobs keep the wires at least an inch from the surface and may therefore be used for either exposed or concealed work, but cleats separate the wires only 2½ in. and keep them only ½ in. from the surface, hence may be used only for exposed work. While split knobs have two grooves, it is not permissible to support more than one wire on a single knob, since two wires would not be separated by the required distance.

2 by 4's.—The so-called "2 by 4" timber is actually only about $3\frac{1}{2}$ in. wide. Since the ordinary 2-wire cleat is about $3\frac{1}{4}$ in. long and keeps the two wires $2\frac{1}{2}$ in. apart, it may be

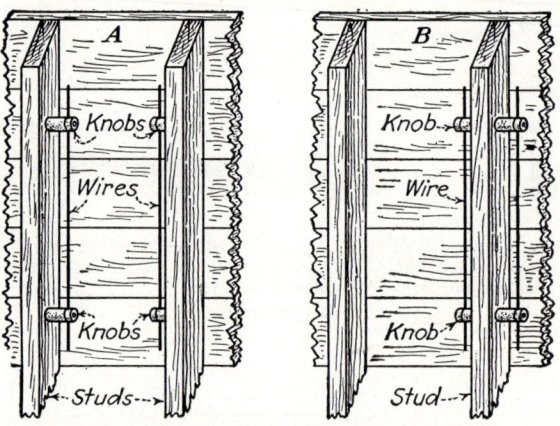

Fig. 11-37.—Two ways of running a pair of vertical wires within a wall.

used for exposed work to bring two wires down the side of such a 2 by 4. In concealed work, however, the wires must be kept at least 3 in. apart; considering the diameter of the knobs, it is evident that it will be impossible to run two

National Elec. Products, Inc.

Fig. 11-38.—Approved flexible tubing, or loom. Use it over each wire where the separation required by Code cannot be maintained.

wires on the same side of such a timber. Therefore one of the two methods shown in Fig. 11-37 must be used, that in A being the more common because it requires less boring.

Flexible Tubing.—Sometimes it is impossible to keep the wires the required distance apart or from the surface. In that case the wires are further protected by flexible tubing, as it is called in the Code. It is more commonly known as "loom." A piece of it is shown in Fig. 11-38. It comes in an assortment of sizes, the smallest of which is known as "$7/32$ in.," although its internal diameter is actually over $1/4$ in. It will in most brands accommodate No. 14, 12, or 10 wire. It is a tough material consisting of cotton and paper strands properly woven to form continuous tubing, the entire assembly impregnated with water- and fire-resistant compounds, finished off usually with wax or lacquer for the sake of cleanliness.

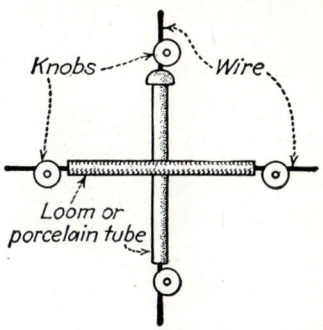

Fig. 11-39.—Where wires cross each other, give them additional protection by means of loom or porcelain tubes.

Whenever the wires come closer together than permitted by Code, slip a length of loom over each wire; two wires are never placed inside the same piece. The loom must be in one piece and must extend from insulator to insulator; a short piece might slip, leaving wires still unprotected where they most needed the extra insulation.

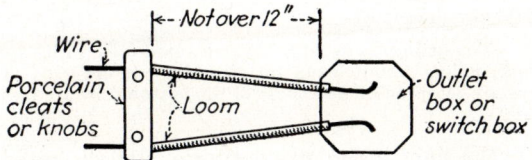

Fig. 11-40.—Typical construction at an outlet box.

Where wires cross each other, slip loom over both wires. Instead of loom, porcelain tubes are permissible. Put an insulator at each end, so that the pieces of loom or the tubes cannot slip out of place (see Fig. 11-39).

Where wires enter outlet or switch boxes, they cannot be kept the required distance apart; consequently install a piece

170 THEORY AND BASIC PRINCIPLES

of loom over each wire, making sure it extends back to the last insulator, also well into the box, as illustrated in Fig. 11-40.

Frequency of Support.—The Code requires that the wires be supported on insulators at least every $4\frac{1}{2}$ ft., with the reminder that good judgment be used and this interval shortened in places where the wiring might be disturbed. The local

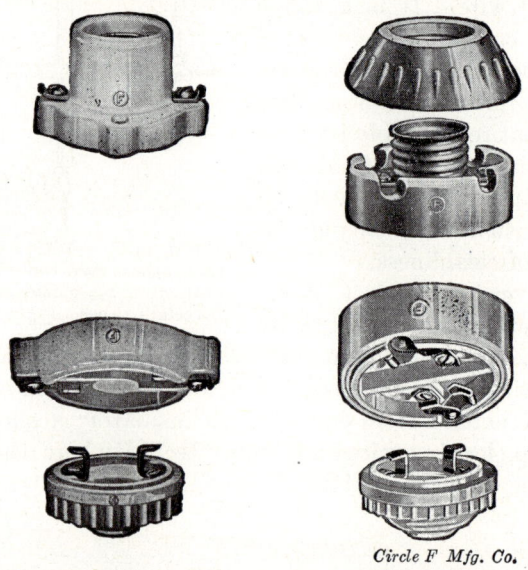

Circle F Mfg. Co.

FIG. 11-41.—The fittings here shown may be used only with exposed knob and tube work, unless mounted on top of outlet box covers. The devices in the top row are receptacles, and those in the bottom row are rosettes, used for drop cords.

inspector is the final judge of whether or not the intent of the Code has been observed.

In old work, where the wires are fished through the walls after the building is finished, obviously this requirement cannot be carried out, so for this type of work the Code permits fished wires loose within walls, except that each one must be concealed inside a continuous length of loom extending from the last support (or box) to the next. Since the cost of two lengths of rubber-covered wire, plus two lengths of loom, is usually more than the cost of one length of armored or non-metallic cable, and since cable entails much less work, knob and tube work is very little used in installations of this kind.

An insulator is required within 12 in. of every outlet, as was shown in Fig. 11-40. An outlet box is required at every out-

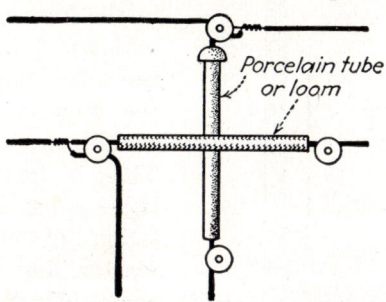

FIG. 11-42.—Typical construction where wires are tapped in knob and tube work.

let, as in other types of installations, with the exception that when the wiring is entirely exposed, fittings of the type shown in Fig. 11-41 are permitted, mounted directly on the surface over which the wires run. Nevertheless, the use of this type of fittings is to be discouraged, in favor of outlet boxes throughout; usually the receptacles, screw-shell outlets, and similar devices designed for mounting on outlet boxes are considerably more sturdy than the fittings shown in Fig. 11-41.

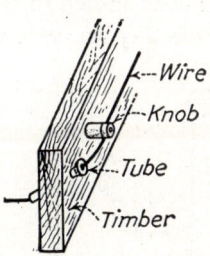

FIG. 11-43.—When a wire comes along the side of a timber and then runs through a porcelain tube, use a knob near the tube.

An insulator is required within 6 in. of every tap, as shown in Fig. 11-42. In this picture there is an apparent violation of the Code rule regarding spacing, in that two wires are shown on the same knob, closer together than Code minimum. However, one of the two wires is tapped to the other so that there is no difference of voltage between the two; it really is the same wire going through one knob twice.

Where a wire runs along the side of a timber and then goes through a porcelain tube, place a knob near the tube so that the wire will be kept the required distance from the surface. This is shown in Fig. 11-43.

In concealed work where a wire runs downward and ultimately goes through a floor sill or similar timber, additional protection must be provided in the form of another tube at least 3 in. long, besides the tube which goes through the timber. Figure 11-44 should make this clear. This is required because there is usually an accumulation of shavings, loose plaster, and other debris at this point; without the extra tube this would accumulate directly in contact with the wire.

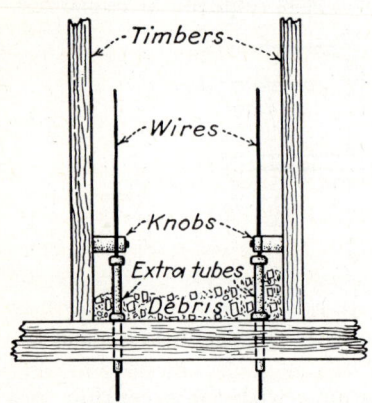

FIG. 11-44.—When a wire runs through a floor timber inside a wall, install an extra tube as shown.

Corners.—In exposed work where cleats are used, do not make the mistake of using a cleat at the corner as shown in *A* of Fig. 11-45. The cleat separates the wires 2½ in. when

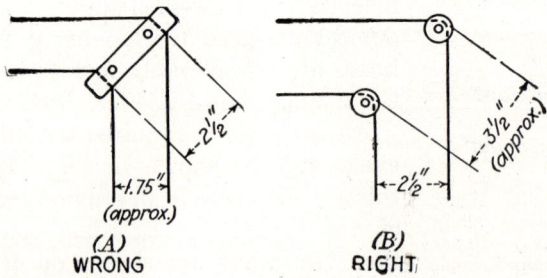

FIG. 11-45.—Where wires make a right-angle turn, cleats cannot be used even in exposed work.

measured across the cleat, but they are actually only 1¾ in. apart measured the shortest way. Two knobs, as shown in *B* of Fig. 11-45, should be used.

Separation from Metal Work.—If wires come closer than 2 in. to conduit, steam or water pipe, or other metal work, additional protection is required. Again this takes the form of loom or insulator tubes, securely fastened so they cannot slip out of place. The reason for this provision is not hard to see when it is remembered that condensed moisture often drips from water pipes. Wires should be run over, rather than under, pipes and similar metal work.

Separation from Other Wires.—The same requirements as outlined above for metal work hold for other wires, such as low-voltage doorbell wires, telephone wires, etc.

Protection against Mechanical Injury.—Exposed wires can be damaged relatively easily; therefore some rather definite requirements for protection are included in the Code. Broadly, the types of protection can be put in two groups: unfinished attics and roof spaces, and all other locations.

Unfinished Attics and Roof Spaces.—If the building is finished before the wiring is installed and if the headroom in

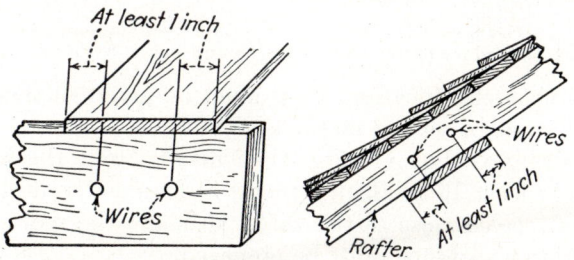

Fig. 11-46.   Fig. 11-47.
Figs. 11-46 and 11-47.—Where exposed to mechanical injury, wires must be protected by running boards, under some conditions.

the attic or roof space is less than 3 ft., such space is considered merely a hollow wall. In all other cases the requirements of the following paragraphs apply.

If the wires run along the *sides* of rafters or studs or joists, the requirements are the same as for any other location. If they run in any other direction, and are within 7 ft. of the floor or floor joists, they must go through porcelain tubes in bored holes in such timbers. They may never be run on knobs fastened to the edge of such timbers.

If the attic or roof space is accessible, that is, if it can be reached by stairs or a permanent ladder, then the wires must be further protected by substantial boards extending at least 1 in. beyond the wires, as shown in Figs. 11-46 and 11-47.

Other Locations.—In any location where the wires are within 7 ft. of the floor, they are considered subject to mechanical injury. In any given case regardless of distance from the floor, whether the wires are or are not in fact "subject to mechanical injury" is something for the local inspector to decide. If they

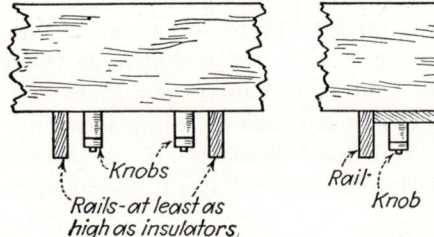

Fig. 11-48.—Rails may also be used for protection.

Fig. 11-49.—Combination of running board with rails.

fall into that classification, they must be given further protection by one of several methods.

Guard rails as shown in Fig. 11-48 may be used; the lumber must be at least $7/8$ in. thick, at least as high as the insulators used, and placed close to the wires, although the required $1/2$ in. separation distance must be observed.

A variation of this is the running board with guard rails, as shown in Fig. 11-49. The running board must be at least $1/2$ in. thick, must project not less than 1 in. and not more than 2 in. beyond the wire, and the guard strips must be at least $7/8$ by 2 in.

The wires may be completely boxed by simply putting a cover on the combination of running board with guard rails, as shown in Fig. 11-49. If this runs in a vertical position, then a cover must be provided on the top end; this may be simply another piece of board, with porcelain tubes, of course, where the wires enter. This makes concealed wiring out of the job, and the 1- by 3-in. separation must be observed as required for concealed work.

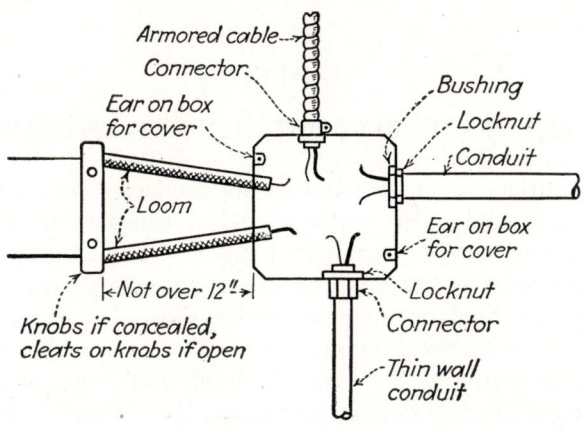

Fig. 11-50.—How to change from one wiring system to another. Four different systems here enter the same box.

Changing from One System to Another.—At times it will be necessary to change from conduit wiring to cable wiring, or from knob and tube to cable, but this presents no great problem. The simplest way is to make the change at an outlet box. Figure 11-50, for example, shows four different systems all entering the same box.

In changing from cable wiring to knob and tube, or from conduit to knob and tube, some prefer to use a fitting of the type shown in Fig. 11-51. It consists of a connector with an insulating block to separate the several wires.

Fig. 11-51.—This fitting is frequently used in changing from cable to open wiring.

CHAPTER 12

BRANCH CIRCUITS AND SERVICE ENTRANCE

The outlets[1] of an installation are connected into groups or branch circuits each protected by a separate overcurrent device, such as fuse or circuit breaker. The Code defines a branch circuit as "that portion of a wiring system extending beyond the final overcurrent device protecting the circuit."

The wires between the *main* fuse of an installation and the final fuse *protecting the circuit* beyond that fuse are feeders. Note carefully the words "protecting the circuit." An overcurrent device installed just ahead of a motor, or built into the motor, is there to protect the motor and not the circuit and, therefore, must be disregarded when determining where a circuit begins.

Advantages of Numerous Branch Circuits.—Having separate circuits for groups of lights leads to the practical result that an entire building is never in complete darkness on account of a blown fuse except on the rare occasions when a main fuse blows. There is added safety in having a considerable number of separate branch circuits. Most of the time each fuse carries but a portion of its maximum carrying capacity. However, there are times during each day when perhaps a considerable number of lights are turned on; a washing machine may be running, perhaps a flatiron is being used; other devices may also be put into service at the same time. With a considerable number of circuits, in a properly designed installation, the load will be fairly well divided among the various fuses with the result that none is overloaded and none blows. With but a few circuits, each fuse will carry a heavier load and fuses will blow far more frequently. Fuses that blow

---

[1] For definition of "outlet" see p. 56.

often tempt the owner to use a size larger than permitted with the usual No. 14 wire used in the average installation, or perhaps even to resort to substitutes which defeat the purpose of fuses entirely. Obviously, this introduces distinct fire hazards. Another practical consideration is that the greater the number of circuits, the less will be the voltage drop in each circuit, with less wasted power and higher efficiency of bulbs and appliances.

Determining Number of Circuits.—The Code in Secs. 2115 and 2116 has definite requirements concerning the minimum number of circuits that may be installed. The starting point is the floor area. For residential purposes the Code requires that this shall be computed "from the outside dimensions of the house, apartment or area involved, not including open porches, garages in connection with dwelling occupancies, nor unfinished[1] spaces in basements or attics of dwellings." **The Code for lighting purposes (including receptacle outlets into which lamps for lighting purposes are ordinarily plugged) requires a minimum of 2 watts per square foot of area so computed.**

A home that is 25×36 ft. has an area of 900 sq. ft. per floor, or 1,800 sq. ft. for two floors. Assume that it has a finished recreation room in the basement, $12\frac{1}{2} \times 16$ ft., or an area of 200 sq. ft. This makes a total of 2,000 sq. ft. and will require *for lighting* a minimum of $2 \times 2,000$, or 4,000 watts.

The average circuit is wired with No. 14 wire which has a carrying capacity of 15 amp., which at 115 volts is equivalent to 15×115, or 1,725 watts. For 4,000 watts, 4,000/1,725 or 2.3 circuits will be required. Since there cannot be a fraction[2] of a circuit, two circuits must be installed to meet the Code *minimum* for lighting only.

The same answer can be reached another way. Since each

---

[1] "Unfinished" means not suitable for living quarters. An ordinary basement is "unfinished." Any part of a basement arranged for a recreation room or similar purpose is "finished."

[2] If an answer involves a fraction smaller than $\frac{1}{2}$, drop the fraction. If the fraction is $\frac{1}{2}$ or more, use the next higher number.

circuit can carry 1,725 watts, and since 2 watts are required for each square foot, each circuit can serve 1,725/2, or 862½ sq. ft. For 2,000 sq. ft. there will then be required 2,000/862½, or 2.3, which means two circuits. The answer is the same, whichever method is used.

In addition to the circuits required for lighting, determined as above outlined, the Code in Sec. 2115b requires a minimum of one circuit for serving the "small appliance load in kitchen, laundry,[1] pantry, dining room and breakfast room." Note that no other outlets such as lighting outlets may be connected to this circuit. This special circuit must be wired with No. 12 wire, as compared with No. 14 which is acceptable for the other circuits. Being wired with No. 12, the circuit may be protected by 20-amp. fuses or other overcurrent device.

Adding this appliance circuit to the two required for lighting, results in a total of three circuits for the house in question. The Code requires this as a *minimum*. Most people will consider this minimum as entirely inadequate from the standpoint of convenience or common-sense planning; few people would be permanently satisfied with only three circuits even in a house as small as 2,000 sq. ft.

The Code in Sec. 2115a recommends, but does not require, one circuit for every 500 sq. ft. of floor area, plus one appliance circuit. Following this recommendation will in the case of the 2,000-sq. ft. house result in a total of five circuits, which would be more nearly adequate. Wise homeowners and others planning an installation will follow the recommendation of one circuit per 500 sq. ft. of area.

Note too that these determinations make no provision for range, water heater, or other appliances too large to be plugged into an ordinary receptacle. Separate circuits must be provided for such purposes. It will be well to remember that to provide a spare circuit for future use costs little at the time of original installation, as compared with the cost of adding it later.

---

[1] For details concerning the special nature of the laundry outlet, see p. 336.

Types of Branch Circuits.—As compared with the 1940 Code, the 1947 version has considerably simplified its treatment of the subject of branch circuits in general.

The 1940 Code recognized branch circuits of 15, 20, 25, 35, and 50 amp. capacity (corresponding to the carrying capacity in amperes of common sizes of wire) and "individual branch circuits" of any capacity larger than 50 amp. The 1947 Code recognizes basically two different *types* of branch circuits: The first classification is those serving *two or more* outlets such as receptacles or permanently connected current-consuming devices such as fixtures or appliances. Such circuits are rated at 15, 20, 30, and 50 amp. (based on new carrying capacities as defined in the new Code, for Nos. 14, 12, 10, and 8 wire), but never more than 50 amp. The second classification is "individual branch circuits," which may serve only a single current-consuming device and which may be of any capacity whatsoever, as determined by the load.

Branch Circuits Serving Single Outlets.—The wire size must be sufficient to carry the amperage load to be connected to it (if the circuit serves only a motor, other provisions apply; see Chap. 29). If the load is a range with a maximum capacity of $8\frac{3}{4}$ kw. or more, the smallest permissible size is No. 8, with No. 10 for the neutral. The overcurrent protection must be of a rating that may be less but never more than the carrying capacity of the wire used in the circuit, but may not exceed 150 per cent of the rating of the appliance which is the load. The types of sockets and receptacles that may be connected to any circuit are the same as are permissible on circuits of the same carrying capacity, but serving two or more outlets.

Circuits Serving Two or More Outlets.—In the 1947 Code there are only four such circuits: 15, 20, 30, and 50 amp. These ratings are based on the new carrying capacities of various sizes of wires as defined in the Code.

15-amp. Branch Circuit.—This circuit is wired with No. 14 wire and is protected by 15-amp. fuses or other overcurrent protection. The receptacles connected to it may not be rated in excess of 15 amp., which means that only the ordinary household variety of receptacle may be used. Any type of sockets for lighting may be connected to it. No *portable* appliance used on the circuit may exceed 12 amp. in rating. If the circuit serves lighting circuits and portable appliances as is usually the case, and also serves fixed or permanently connected appliances, the total rating of all the fixed appliances must not exceed $7\frac{1}{2}$ amp.

20-amp. Branch Circuit.—This is wired with No. 12 wire and protected by 20-amp. overcurrent protection. In homes it is used only for the special 20-amp. appliance circuit required by Sec. 2115b to serve appliances. Receptacles must be the ordinary 15-amp. type; lighting fixtures may not be connected to it.

30-amp. Branch Circuit.—This is wired with No. 10 wire and protected by 30-amp. overcurrent protection. It is commonly used for lighting in nonresidential occupancies. Sockets connected to it must be of the heavy-duty type, which automatically rules out the circuit for use in homes for lighting. For appliances, this circuit may be used anywhere; no portable appliance may exceed 24-amp. rating. Receptacles connected to it must be either 20- or 30-amp. rating.

50-amp. Branch Circuit.—This is wired with No. 6 wire and protected by 50-amp. overcurrent protection. For appliances, the circuit may be used anywhere; in homes it may be used for ranges, water heaters, etc. The receptacles used on the circuit must have 50-amp. rating.

For lighting it is used only in nonresidential occupancies. All sockets must be of the heavy-duty type.

"Fixed" Appliances.—Fixed appliances are those not intended to be moved about. Cord-and-plug connections are often permitted on fixed appliances; electric ranges in most cases are connected to the circuit by means of a plug and receptacle, but are nevertheless "fixed" within the Code meaning.

Appliances in General.—From these general discussions it is obvious that an electric range requires a separate circuit, except that the Code permits a water heater (but no other device) to be included on the same circuit. It is good practice to provide a separate circuit for a permanently installed bathroom heater. In suburban homes where city water is not available and individual water-pressure systems are installed, the motor deserves a separate circuit. On the other hand, in a home workshop, where perhaps half a dozen motors are installed but where it is not likely more than one will ever be used at one time, it is not necessary to install a separate circuit for each. As a matter of fact it is wise to have the motor outlets in such a shop on the lighting circuit, because, if the motors were on a separate circuit and the fuse protecting the *lighting* circuit should blow, the owner would be in a hazardous spot with machinery running at full speed in total darkness.

All appliances must be provided with disconnecting means, except fixed appliances rated less than 1,650 watts. The disconnecting means may be the usual cord and plug arrangement, or it may be an inexpensive switch such as is illustrated in Fig. 12-8 on page 188.

Balancing Circuits.—If a house is served by a 3-wire 115/230-volt service (which includes, of course, a neutral wire), the neutral wire of each branch circuit is connected to the incoming neutral. Care must be used in connecting the "hot" wires of the branch circuits so that they will be divided approximately equally between the two incoming "hot" wires. If this is not done, practically all the load may be thrown on only two of the three incoming wires, and a 2-wire service might as well have been used in the first place. Unbalanced conditions lead to frequent blowing of fuses.

Location of Branch-circuit Fuses.—The usual custom is to locate all the branch-circuit fuses or circuit breakers in one location. In the past this location all too frequently was some point in the basement, or some other equally inconvenient point. They should be located where they are easy to reach, especially in darkness. The size of the equipment, housing both the main and the branch-circuit fuses, has been reduced so that today the entire assembly is a very compact unit, designed for flush mounting if desired.

More and more it is becoming the custom to mount all this equipment, or at least the branch-circuit fuses, in the kitchen or pantry or some similar easily accessible point. The logical location is in or near the kitchen because generally speaking that is where the greatest portion of the total power is consumed. Locating the equipment there means that the heavy incoming wires can be shorter, wires to the various outlets are shorter with less voltage drop, and so on.

Branch-circuit Schemes.—The most usual scheme of locating all branch-circuit fuses at one point is shown in Fig. 12-1. So far as fusing is concerned, the wires beyond the branch-circuit fuses may be as long as desired. Note that 230-volt circuits may be run at any point by simply tapping off the two black wires. For example, the black wire of circuit No. 1 and the black wire of circuit No. 4 together would make one 230-volt circuit, the white wires, of course, being disregarded. One such 230-volt circuit is shown in dotted lines.

Especially in larger homes, some prefer to locate the branch-circuit fuses in various locations throughout the house, the fuses controlling the basement circuits, for example, being placed in the basement, those controlling the first floor being placed in the kitchen, those controlling the second floor being placed on that floor, and so on. The scheme of Fig. 12-2 is used. A pair of feeders runs from the fuse cabinet (usually located in the same cabinet with the main fuses and the entrance switch) to the location of each group of branch-circuit fuses located on the various floors.

The wires from the fuse cabinet in Fig. 12-2, to each location where a group of branch-circuit fuses is installed, are feeders, as already explained. The wires of any feeder must be of sufficient size to carry the total load of the branch circuits which that feeder serves. The ampere rating of the overcur-

BRANCH CIRCUITS AND SERVICE ENTRANCE 183

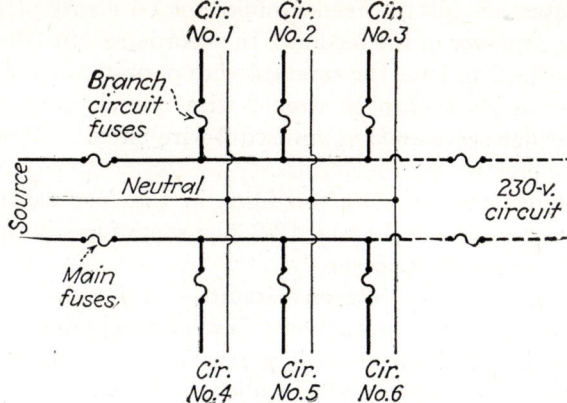

Fig. 12-1.—The most common scheme of locating all fuses at one location.

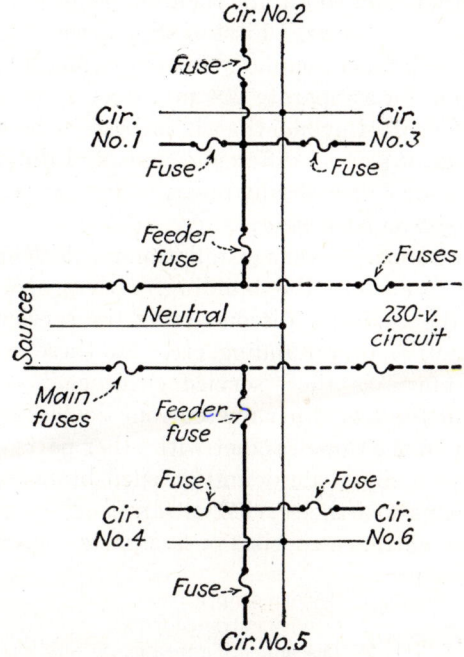

Fig. 12-2.—In this scheme branch-circuit fuses are placed in groups at various locations throughout the house. In this case fuses are required at the point where the feeders to these groups of fuses begin.

rent protection for the feeder must not be greater than the carrying capacity of the feeder. In accordance with Sec. 2201 of the Code, No. 10 is the smallest wire permitted for a 2-wire feeder that serves *two or more* 2-wire branches, or when a 3-wire feeder serves *more than* two 2-wire circuits, or when it feeds *two or more* 3-wire circuits.

Note that in Fig. 12-1 the fuses in the fuse cabinet are *branch-circuit* fuses. In Fig. 12-2, the same fuses in the same cabinet become *feeder* fuses.

Distribution of Outlets on Circuits.—If the usual scheme is used, placing all the branch-circuit overcurrent devices in one location, the question of what particular outlets to place on each circuit must be carefully studied. It is not wise to place all the first-floor outlets on one circuit, all those on the second floor on another, and so on, for then an entire floor will be in darkness if one fuse blows. First of all, place all the receptacle outlets of the kitchen, laundry, pantry, dining room, and breakfast room on a separate 20-amp. circuit, as required by Code Sec. 2115b. Beyond that it is best to have, on each circuit, outlets of several different rooms and different floors; when a fuse blows or a circuit breaker trips, there will be at least some light on each floor.

Service Entrance.—Every installation must include wires to bring the current into the building, with proper means as required in the Code for disconnecting the service, for overcurrent protection, for grounding, etc. All these related accessories are known as the "service entrance." Usually the branch-circuit fuses or other overcurrent devices are included mechanically in the same cabinet with other parts of the service entrance, but by Code definition such branch-circuit protection is not part of the service entrance.

The service entrance consists of five parts, as follows:

1. Service drop wires.
2. Service entrance wires.
3. Disconnecting means.
4. Overcurrent protection.
5. Ground.

Service Drop Wires.—The Code defines service drop wires as "that portion of overhead service conductors between the pole and the first point of attachment to the building." If the wires are not overhead, they are not classed as service drop wires but become service entrance wires, covered by the next paragraph. In general, the service drop wires are supplied and installed by the power company, although the owner or contractor furnishes the insulators by which the wires are supported at the building.

Service Entrance Wires.—The wires from the point where the wires supplied by the power company end, up to the service switch, are the service entrance wires. They may be rubber-covered wires brought in through conduit, or wires made up into special cables designed for the purpose. Wires supported on insulators as in knob and tube wiring are permitted, but seldom used. Often service entrance wires are run underground, in which case any kind of cable suitable for general underground work is used. The usual combination is lead-sheathed cable run inside conduit, parkway cable, or Style USE entrance cable (see page 92).

Uninsulated Wire in Service Entrance.—In most wiring systems the neutral conductor is grounded, which, as pointed out in an earlier chapter, means that whenever a water pipe or radiator is touched, the neutral wire is touched. This being the case, why insulate that wire? The Code in Sec. 2303a does permit uninsulated or bare wire for the grounded-neutral wire of the service entrance, but only if the voltage *to ground*[1] is not over 208 volts, which condition is met with either a 2-wire 115-volt, a 3-wire 115/230-volt or a 4-wire 120/208 volt 3-phase service.

When service entrance cable is used, to reduce the overall size of the cable, the bare neutral conductor is usually wrapped spirally around the insulated wires, as shown in Fig. 12-3, which shows the most common type of this cable. In use, the spirally wound individual conductors are grouped and twisted to form a stranded wire, as shown in Fig. 12-4.

[1] See p. 130 for definition of "voltage to ground."

Types of Service Entrance Cable.—The most common type in use was shown in Fig. 12-3; it is known as Type SE, style A. The A indicates the steel armor which is applied in the form of a flat spiral over the bare conductor for mechanical

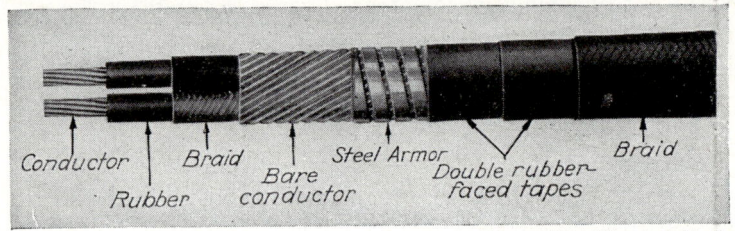

Fig. 12-3.—Service entrance cable, Type SE, style A. One of the wires is a bare wire wrapped concentrically around the insulated wires. Over all the conductors is a steel armor.

Fig. 12-4.—The concentric conductor is bunched together where it is to be attached to a terminal.

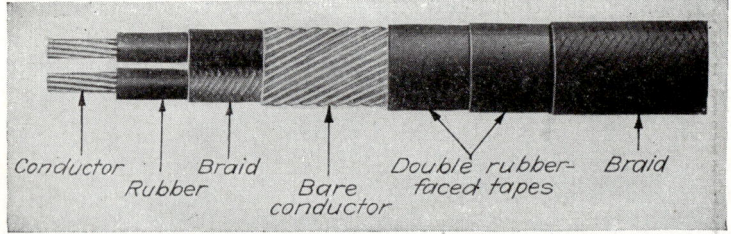

Fig. 12-5.—Service entrance cable, Type SE, style U. This cable is like that shown in Fig. 12-3 except that the steel armor is omitted.

protection. In some localities the type shown in Fig. 12-5 is more common; it differs from the first type in that it does not have the steel armor. It is known as Type SE, style U.

Figure 12-6 shows Type ASE, having all conductors insulated and a layer of interlocking steel armor for mechanical protection. It is stronger mechanically than the other types.

BRANCH CIRCUITS AND SERVICE ENTRANCE

Type SD, shown in Fig. 12-7, is also used; it is very similar to Type SE, style U, but has less protective material over the conductors. Its use is usually restricted to overhead runs. When run along a building, it must be protected by conduit, whereas other types are run exposed, merely attached to the surface over which they run.

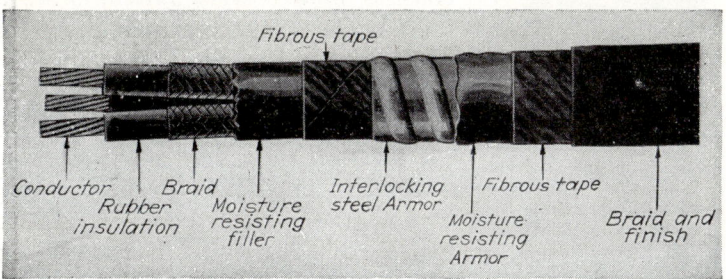

Crescent Ins. Wire & Cable Co.

FIG. 12-6.—Service entrance cable, Type ASE. All the conductors are insulated, and an armor of interlocking steel is used. This style of cable is little used today.

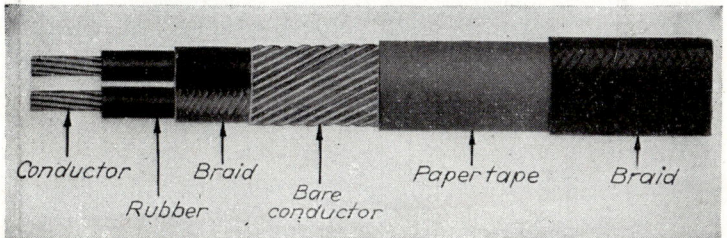

Crescent Ins. Wire & Cable Co.

FIG. 12-7.—Service entrance cable, Type SD. It is used mostly for overhead runs. When used on a building, it must be protected by conduit.

Which type to use in any given case is best determined by consulting the local power company or the local inspector.

Disconnecting Means.—A device must be provided, at or near the point where the service wires enter a building, to disconnect or isolate the entire building from its source of supply. This is a safety factor, for there are times when it is very desirable to "kill" all parts of the wiring system, for example in the case of fire or when work is being done on certain parts of the wiring system. It is customary to have the cabinet that houses the disconnecting means also hold the main fuses and branch-circuit fuses.

Square D Co.

FIG. 12-8.—The simplest type of switch. Occasionally it is used as a service switch for very small installations. It is more frequently used for other purposes.

The disconnecting means usually consists of a service switch, often a knife-blade type, the simplest form of which is shown in Fig. 12-8. This disconnects the entire wiring system. It must be "externally operable," which specification according to the Code is fulfilled if the switch can be operated without the operator being exposed to live parts. The usual method is an external handle.

Instead of a knife switch, a pull-out fuse block may be used. The clips for holding the fuses, instead of being a permanent

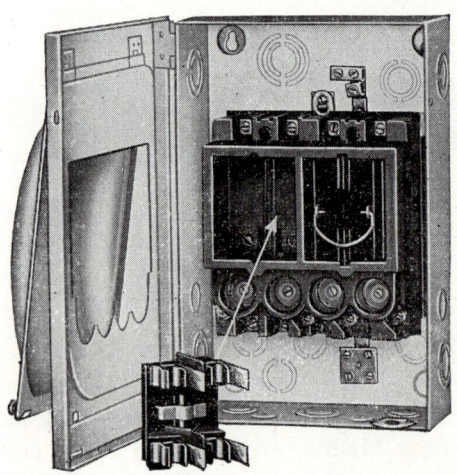

FIG. 12-9.—A pull-out type of switch. The fuses are mounted on an insulating block. When the block is pulled out, no live parts are exposed.

part of a switch, are mounted on a small separate block of porcelain, bakelite, or similar insulating material. In turn clips on this block make contact with the main mechanism through small openings in an insulating barrier, so that, when the block is pulled out, no live parts whatever are exposed. When this insulating block is inserted into the switch upside down, the switch is off. A very popular unit of this kind with branch-circuit fuses is shown in Fig. 12-9.

Very similar is the type which has jumper straps mounted on an insulating block in the door of the box, so arranged that, when the door is opened, these jumpers pull out of the main mechanism, killing all circuits. Of course, the fuse holders are completely dead while the door is open. A unit of this type is shown in Fig. 12-10.

Square D Co.
FIG. 12-10.—In this type of switch, opening the door cuts off the current. This particular switch also contains fuses for branch circuits.

Instead of a single device that disconnects the entire wiring system by a single movement, the Code, in Sec. 2351a, permits several other schemes under certain conditions. One of these involves the use of circuit breakers of the type discussed in Chap. 5; the working mechanism of one was shown in Fig. 5-8. Up to, but not more than, six such circuit breakers may be used without a separate disconnecting means ahead of them; the breakers may be either single-pole type (for a 2-wire circuit with grounded neutral) or 2-pole type (for a 2-wire circuit, usually 230 volts with or without a third grounded wire). The breakers then serve both as disconnecting means and as branch-circuit protection. Figure 12-11 shows a complete unit. A frequent combination is one with four 15-amp.

Westinghouse Electric Corp.
FIG. 12-11.—A No-Fuze type of breaker with five single-pole and one double-pole breaker. This particular unit is designed for flush mounting.

breakers for ordinary branch circuits, one 20-amp. breaker for appliance-outlet circuit, and one 35-amp. double-pole breaker for the range. For larger installations they are available with any required number of breakers above six; such units, however require a separate disconnecting means ahead of them. This may be a service switch but more usually is a main breaker, sometimes in the same cabinet as the branch-circuit breakers.

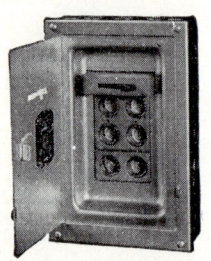

Square D Co.

FIG. 12-12.—A compact unit which takes advantage of the Code's exception: no main fuses required when six or less branch-circuit fuses are used, if an unfused switch is used ahead of the fuses. The switch shown handles six branch circuits.

Service Switches.—When the disconnecting means takes the form of a switch, it is known as a "service switch." The smallest switch for this purpose is rated at 30 amp.; larger standard ratings are 60, 100, 200, 400, 600 amp. For residential purposes they are further divided into 2-pole and 3-pole types.

The 2-pole type is used on a 2-wire service when only 115 volts is made available to the building involved. The 3-pole type is used on 3-wire service when both 115 and 230 volts are made available. Inasmuch as one of the wires in practically all cases is a grounded or neutral wire, which is never interrupted by a switch[1] or fuse, most of these switches are of the "solid neutral" type. This simply means that, if the switch is 3-pole solid neutral, it has two blades to open two of the wires and a "neutral" pole which consists merely of a strap with a number of terminals to which the incoming and outgoing neutral wires are connected. Likewise, a 2-pole solid neutral switch has only one blade, plus the neutral terminal strap. If there are main fuses in the same enclosure, naturally

---

[1] In general the grounded-neutral wire may be interrupted by a switch blade or circuit breaker (but never a fuse), provided the device is so designed that it is impossible to open the grounded wire without simultaneously opening all the ungrounded wires.

there is one for each blade of the switch, in other words, one for each pole except the neutral.

In this connection, Sec. 2351 of the Code may prove confusing to most readers. This section provides that "each set of service-entrance conductors shall be provided with a readily accessible means of disconnecting *all* conductors from the source of supply." Section 2351c reads: "if the switch or circuit breaker does not interrupt the grounded conductor, other means shall be provided . . . for disconnecting the grounded conductor." One statement apparently contradicts the other, and both may seem contrary to the statements of the previous paragraph in which it was stated that the grounded wire is rarely interrupted by a switch and usually runs directly to the neutral bar of the service switch.

The answer lies in the fact that since the grounded wire of the service entrance and those grounded wires in the feeders or branch circuits are connected to the neutral bar by means of terminals or pressure connectors, they are removable by means of ordinary tools; this satisfies Code requirements. If such wires were soldered to the terminal bar, this would not be true.

Solder Joints Prohibited.—The 1947 Code in Sec. 2358 has a new provision that prohibits the use of soldered connections on service entrance switches and circuit breakers used for that purpose. All joints must be made using solderless connectors ("pressure" connectors, clamps, and similar means).

Standardization.—Unfortunately there is a woeful lack of standardization on service switches in various parts of the country. A manufacturer wishing to service all 48 states may be required to carry in stock a dozen different switches all answering to the general description of "60-amp. 3-pole solid neutral." It is therefore necessary to consult the local power company to determine which switch in any manufacturer's line is suitable for use locally.

Two-wire or Three-wire?—This question is simply answered. If more than two circuits are involved, use the 3-wire system.

The 1947 code in Sec. 2357 provides that a 30-amp. 2-wire switch may not be used for more than two branch circuits, except by special permission. In any event the power company supplying service, or the inspector, will be glad to give advice as to their practice in a given case. If an electric range or a water heater is involved, automatically the installation will have to be 3-wire. Except for very small installations, such as cottages, few 2-wire services are being installed today.

Overcurrent Protection in Service Wires.—The Code provides that each ungrounded service entrance wire must have overcurrent protection. The overcurrent protection in each ungrounded service wire may be omitted when six or less circuit breakers are used as explained on page 189. Likewise, it may be omitted when six or less branch-circuit fuses are used, with a separate unfused switch ahead of them and in the same cabinet. A typical combination of this kind is shown in Fig. 12-12.

Determining Size of Service Entrance.—The size of service entrance wires and also the rating of the disconnecting means and the overcurrent device are all determined by methods outlined in the Code. Generally all these factors are determined by one set of calculations.

Theoretical Considerations.—Assume that, in the home used as an example in the first part of this chapter, six circuits of 15-amp. capacity each, plus perhaps a separate circuit for the oil-burner motor and one spare circuit, are to be installed. The conclusion might be reached that the service equipment must accordingly have a minimum capacity of 8×15, or 120 amp. Since there is no service entrance switch rated between 100 and 200 amp., it would then be necessary to use one of 200-amp. rating. This is absolutely not necessary, for it is not likely that all eight circuits would ever be loaded to capacity at the same time. In a home with eight circuits, it is probable that several circuits will be entirely idle, several more only very lightly loaded, at a time when one or two circuits are loaded to somewhere near their limit. Therefore the service entrance equipment need be only large enough to handle the largest *probable* total load at *any given moment*. A reserve for a possible future load is desirable.

Minimum Requirements.—If only a single circuit is involved, service entrance wires not smaller than the branch circuit wires, and in no case smaller than No. 12, may be used (Code Sec. 2304a), in which case a disconnect switch of 30 amp. capacity is used. The fuse or other overcurrent protection may not exceed the carrying capacity of the wire selected.

In all other cases the service entrance wires must be No. 8 or heavier. The overcurrent device, whether fuse or circuit breaker, may with one exception[1] never be of a rating greater than the carrying capacity of the wire involved, determined from Tables 1 and 2 of the Code (see Appendix).

A 30-amp. switch accommodates fuses up to 30 amp.; a 60-amp. switch, fuses 35 to 60 amp.; a 100-amp. switch, fuses 65 to 100 amp. In each case fuses not greater than the carrying capacity of the service entrance wires should be used.

As to the disconnecting means, a 2-pole 30-amp. switch is permitted only when there are only one or two circuits. Although the Code does not prohibit it, it is good practice to use a 3-pole *30-amp.* switch only when not over four circuits are involved. Many power companies, as well as local ordinances, establish a 3-wire 60-amp. installation as the minimum. This is only sensible because, regardless of how few lights and appliances an owner may plan to use, inevitably the load grows until the 30-amp. installation becomes hopelessly inadequate, necessitating tearing out the original installation and replacing it with heavier equipment. This is expensive, tends to discourage the owner, and, in turn, may lead to overfusing and other dangerous practices.

In calculating the various parts that make up the service entrance, it is best first to determine the rating of the entrance switch, before deciding upon the size of entrance wires to be

[1] Exception: If motors are served, with or without a lighting and appliance load, larger fuses are permitted (see Chap. 28).

used. For example the calculations for an installation may show that No. 4 wires are minimum, these having a carrying capacity of 70 amp. The nearest standard switch available has a 100-amp. rating. Use of this switch will then provide a reserve capacity of 30 amp., but it would never be possible to take advantage of it because the largest overcurrent device permissible is 70 amp., determined by the carrying capacity of the No. 4 wires. Accordingly it would be wise to use No. 2 wires, which have a carrying capacity of 95 amp., thus permitting almost the full 100 amp. capacity of the switch to be used; the larger wire will also give less voltage drop. It is in no sense contrary to Code to protect a wire with an overcurrent device rated at less than the carrying capacity of the wire.

Factors Involved.—To determine the size of entrance equipment, follow Sec. 2203 of the Code. The total load for a residential project can be broken down into four groups:

1. Lighting.
2. Small appliances.
3. Ranges.
4. Motors.

Lighting.—The *starting point* for arriving at the total wattage that the service entrance equipment must carry is outlined in Sec. 2203 of the Code: 2 watts per square foot of area, the same figure used in determining the number of circuits.

Appliances.—The Code includes in "small appliances" such things as toasters, flatirons, and similar devices ordinarily used in kitchen, laundry, pantry, etc. To allow for their use, add to the lighting wattage, as determined in the preceding paragraph, a minimum of 1,500 watts; this corresponds to the special 20-amp. circuit required by Sec. 2115b for such appliances.

Fixed appliances such as water heaters, permanently installed bathroom heaters, and so on, must be added at their full wattage. Ranges will be covered in a separate paragraph.

Demand Factor.—The larger the home, the less the likelihood that it will *all* be lighted at the same time. Considering

BRANCH CIRCUITS AND SERVICE ENTRANCE

that fact, the requirement of 2 watts per square foot plus 1,500 watts for appliances may be considered excessive for large homes, for if the computed totals were rigidly and arbitrarily enforced, it would lead to unnecessarily heavy service equipment.

Accordingly, the Code in Sec. 2203 establishes a "demand factor" of 30 per cent for that portion of the wattage which exceeds 2,500 watts, computed as above outlined for lighting and small appliances (but excluding fixed appliances). If the computed total is 2,500 watts or less, count all of it. If it is over 2,500 watts, count only 30 per cent of the portion above 2,500 watts. Examples will be given later in the chapter.

It should be remembered that this demand factor applies only in determining the service entrance equipment and not in determining the number of circuits. The individual circuits must be so planned that any *portion* of the house can be lighted to the point which requires 2 watts per square foot, but there is no likelihood that the *entire* house will ever be lighted so that the full 2 watts per square foot will be required throughout.

Range.—If a range is to be used, first determine the wattage that will be consumed if all the burners and the oven are turned on at the same time. This will vary considerably with the size, type, and brand of range involved and may be as high as 15,000 watts. Since it is not likely that all burners and the oven will ever be turned on at the same time, the Code, in Table 29, permits a demand factor of 80 per cent for an electric range. It would be better, however, to follow the fine-print recommendation of Code Sec. 2203d and assume that sooner or later a range with a maximum capacity of 12,000 watts will be installed, and allow for it (on the assumption that not all burners and the oven will be turned on at the same time) an allowance of 8,000 watts, in accordance with Col. A of Table 29 of the Code (see Appendix).

Motors.—The Code devotes considerable space to the proper installation of motors, and the subject is complex. For the purposes of calculating the service entrance equipment *for* *homes*, allow the wattages shown below, and the Code requirements will be more than met:

⅙ hp	450 watts
¼ hp	700 watts
⅓ hp	850 watts
½ hp	1,000 watts
¾ hp	1,350 watts
1 hp	1,500 watts

The wattages shown above are considerably above the actual wattages consumed by the motors, but since alternating-current motors have relatively low power factors, the amperages are considerably more than merely watts/volts. Also, motors can be overloaded to deliver considerably above their nameplate horsepower and will then consume more than their rated amperage.

If there are a number of motors but no likelihood that all will ever operate at the same time, estimate the proper demand factor. For example, if a home workshop is to have four motors, it is not likely that more than one will be used at a time. Count only the largest of them.

Calculating a 2,000-sq. ft. House.—Assuming a house of 2,000-sq. ft. area (determined in the same way as outlined for determining number of circuits), without a range and with no motors, the calculations will be as follows:

	Gross computed watts	Demand factor, per cent	Net computed watts
Lighting, 2,000 sq. ft. at 2 watts	4,000		
Small appliances (minimum)	1,500		
Total gross computed watts	5,500		
First 2,500 watts	.....	100	2,500
Remaining 3,000 watts	.....	30	900
Total net computed watts	.....	...	3,400

At 115 volts, 3,400 watts is equivalent to 3,400/115, or 29.6 amp.; hence a 30-amp. switch is sufficient. It has already

BRANCH CIRCUITS AND SERVICE ENTRANCE

been determined that this house requires three circuits, and Sec. 2357 prohibits a 2-pole 30-amp. switch when more than two circuits are involved. Accordingly a 3-pole switch must be used, which means that the service will be 115/230 volts. The amperage involved therefore will be 3,400/230, or 14.8 amp. Since No. 14 wire has a carrying capacity of 15 amp., it would appear to be heavy enough. The Code, however, in Sec. 2305a, requires a minimum of No. 8 when more than one circuit is involved. Use No. 8, which has a carrying capacity of 40 amp. The main fuses will be 30 amp., the maximum the switch will accommodate.

Circuit breakers are not generally available in 30-amp. rating but instead are rated at 15, 20, 25, 35, 50, and 70 amp. If a circuit breaker is used instead of a service switch, it will therefore be one of not over 40-amp. rating, corresponding to the carrying capacity of the No. 8 wire. More probable still, one would take advantage of the Code exception and omit the disconnecting means entirely, using a four-circuit circuit breaker of the type that was shown in Fig. 12-11. Better still, one would use wire larger than No. 8, such as No. 6 with 55 amp. capacity, to provide a reserve for future loads. In that case one would use a 60-amp. switch (with fuses not over 55-amp. rating), or if a circuit breaker is used, one of similar capacity; or one would install no main breaker at all but use instead a 4- or 6-circuit breaker panel, as was shown in Fig. 12-11.

Assume that an electric range of 7,500 watts maximum capacity is to be added to the same house and also a 1,650-watt bathroom heater. The calculation will be as shown at the top of page 198.

Since the range is a 230-volt device, a 3-wire 115/230-volt service is automatically necessary. At 230 volts, the amperage is 10,900/230, or 47.4 amp. Table 1 of the Code shows that No. 6 wire has a carrying capacity of 55 amp.; No. 4, 70 amp. Therefore No. 6 is the smallest size that may be used, and the corresponding 60-amp. service switch is also used, with 55-amp. fuses.

	Gross computed watts	Demand factor, per cent	Net computed watts
Lighting, 2,000 sq. ft. at 2 watts..........	4,000		
Small appliances (minimum)..............	1,500		
Total gross computed watts............	5,500		
First 2,500 watts.....................	.....	100	2,500
Remaining 3,000 watts................	.....	30	900
Bathroom heater........................	1,500	100	1,500
Range (maximum wattage)..............	7,500	80	6,000
Total net computed watts............	.....	...	10,900

Assuming that there are still not over six circuits, including the special range circuit and the special heater circuit, again one of the circuit-breaker cabinets shown in Fig. 12-11 could be used, dispensing with the separate disconnecting means.

Instead of figuring the range at 80 per cent of 7,500 watts, or 6,000 watts net, it would be wise to figure the range at 8,000 watts net, as recommended in Sec. 2203d. The previous calculation then becomes:

	Gross computed watts	Demand factor, per cent	Net computed watts
Lighting, 2,000 sq. ft. at 2 watts..........	4,000		
Small appliances (minimum)..............	1,500		
Total gross computed watts............	5,500		
First 2,500 watts.....................	.....	100	2,500
Remaining 3,000 watts................	.....	30	900
Bathroom heater........................	1,500	100	1,500
Range (arbitrary minimum)..............	.....	...	8,000
Total net computed watts............	.....	...	12,900

At 230 volts, the amperage is 12,900/230, or 56 amp. Therefore, No. 6 wire with 55 amp. carrying capacity is too

BRANCH CIRCUITS AND SERVICE ENTRANCE 199

small to pass as a minimum, and No. 4 with 70 amp. capacity must be used. The same 60-amp. service switch will be used, and since it will not accommodate fuses larger than the 60-amp., that rating will be used, acceptable since the load is 55 amp. It would be wiser however to install a 100-amp. switch with 70-amp. fuses to match the No. 4 wire, or to use No. 2 wire with 95 amp. capacity, then using 95-amp.[1] fuses in the switch.

Calculating a 4,400-sq. ft. House.—For the sake of practice, calculate these factors for a house having 4,400 sq. ft. If the size of the house is considered, it will probably be a pretentious home, so include not only a range but also a water heater consuming 2,500 watts, as well as a ¼-hp. oil-burner motor for which an arbitrary 700 watts will be allowed. Assuming that it is a suburban home with its own water system, allow a further 1,000 watts for a ½-hp. water-pump motor. The calculation then will be as follows:

	Gross computed watts	Demand factor, per cent	Net computed watts
Lighting, 4,400 sq. ft. at 2 watts.........	8,800		
Small appliances (minimum)............	1,500		
Total gross computed watts...........	10,300		
First 2,500 watts.....................	......	100	2,500
Remaining 7,800 watts................	......	30	2,340
Bathroom heater......................	1,500	100	1,500
Water heater.........................	2,500	100	2,500
Range (arbitrary minimum).............	......	...	8,000
¼-hp. oil-burner motor................	700	100	700
½-hp. water-pump motor..............	1,000	100	1,000
Total net computed watts...........	......	...	18,540

[1] It would probably be difficult to locate 95-amp. fuses. Therefore one would follow Sec. 2403a of the Code which specifies that, when a calculation leads to a fuse size that is not standard, the next larger size may be used. In this case, 100-amp. fuses would be used.

At 230 volts, this is equivalent to 18,540/230, or 81 amp.; so a 100-amp. service switch will be used. According to Table 1 of the Code, No. 2 entrance wires may be used. These having a carrying capacity of 95 amp., 95-amp. fuses will be used. Number 0 wire with a capacity of 125 amp. would be better, providing some reserve capacity for future use.

If circuit breakers are to be used in place of the fuses, for branch-circuit protection, a disconnecting means will still be required ahead of the breakers, because there are more than six circuits. This disconnecting means may be the same 100-amp. entrance switch already discussed, or a breaker rated at not more than the carrying capacity of the service entrance wires selected.

Separate Meter for Water Heater.—It is necessary to install a separate meter for the water heater in some localities where a special rate for water heating is offered. In that case, the wires up to the meters would still be of the same size as determined above, but at the meters they would branch out to two different disconnecting means, one for the heater and the other for the balance of the load. Accordingly, the wires from the first meter to the disconnecting means need be only large enough to carry the computed load, less the water-heater load. Deducting the 2,500 watts allowed for the water heater from the total computed load of 18,540 watts leaves a balance of 16,040 watts, or 70 amp. According to Table 1 of the Code, No. 4 wire with a carrying capacity of 70 amp. may then be used, but there would be no real object in reducing the wire size because the service switch would still have to be of 100-amp. rating (the next smallest size is 60-amp.).

From the second meter to the water-heater disconnecting means, the wire must have a carrying capacity of 2,500/230, or 10.9 amp. Since this is still part of the service entrance now serving but one circuit, No. 12 wire is the minimum permitted. Consider the requirement discussed in Chap. 5, that a tap, if it is not to be fused at the point where it branches off, must have a carrying capacity of at least one-third that of the wire off which it is tapped (in addition to other requirements there set forth). If we assume that No. 2 wire with carrying capacity of 95 amp. was selected, the wire to the disconnecting means for the heater would require a capacity of at least 31.7 amp., and No. 8 wire would be selected as the minimum. The disconnecting means for the water heater would be a 30-amp. switch.

In some localities the rate for water heating is higher during the peak-load periods than during the off-peak periods. In that case the power company installs a time switch which throws the heater on one meter during part of the day and on the other during the balance of the day. Naturally, then, the main disconnecting means must be of sufficient size, as must the main overcurrent protection, to carry the full load including the heater.

Grounding.—The details concerning grounding of service equipment will be covered in Chap. 17.

Service Entrance Cable.—In a 3-wire 115/230-volt installation, 230-volt devices connected only to the two "hot" wires impose no load whatever on the neutral wire. Such devices will operate just as well whether the neutral wire is installed or not. Therefore on a 3-wire installation, when both 115-volt devices and 230-volt devices are installed, the neutral wire carries a smaller amperage than the two "hot" wires. In such cases a neutral wire of a smaller amperage carrying capacity than the "hot" wires may be used. The size of this neutral is determined in the same way as was outlined for service entrance wires, except that in the calculation those devices which will be connected only to 230 volts are disregarded. In this connection, remember that, while a *range* is connected to 230 volts, *the neutral wire is also connected to it,* and most of the time the individual burners operate on 115 volts. Nevertheless the neutral wire to the range never carries as many amperes as either of the two "hot" wires to the range can be made to carry by certain combinations of settings of the low-medium-high switches. This is why the neutral wire to a range is usually one size smaller than the "hot" wires.

For all these reasons, service entrance cable is usually made with the neutral conductor smaller than the insulated conductors, common combinations being:

Two No. 6 insulated with one No. 8 bare
Two No. 4 insulated with one No. 6 bare
Two No. 2 insulated with one No. 4 bare

CHAPTER 13

ADEQUACY

An adequately wired home is one that has been wired in such fashion as to permit the occupant to secure a maximum of utility from the use of electricity, with a minimum of inconvenience. He must be able to plug in various floor and table lamps and radios without using extension cords, even when the arrangement of the furniture is changed. He must be able to plug in various appliances without unplugging others. He must be able to turn on the lights in any room without having to stumble through darkness to find a switch or pull chain. He must get the full utility out of appliances by having them heat quickly, without lights dimming when the appliances are turned on. Fuses must blow very rarely.

Many homes are being wired with entirely too little thought about adequacy, even though today electricity is expected to provide 10 to 50 times as much light per room as in the early days of electric and is expected to run radios, vacuum cleaners, toasters, and many other devices that were not even thought of then.

An inadequately wired home is like the automobile of 40 years ago, which furnished transportation but did not have such conveniences as spare tires, electric starters, a top, or a lighting system. Today nobody considers buying a car without all these things, which 40 years ago were luxuries but which today are considered essentials. Plan the wired home to include all those things which are today essentials.

Factors in Adequate Wiring.—In order that a home may be adequately wired, careful attention must be paid to the following details:

1. Service entrance of sufficient capacity.
2. Wires of sufficient capacity throughout the home.
3. Sufficient number of circuits.
4. Receptable (plug-in) outlets in sufficient number.
5. Lighting outlets in sufficient number.
6. Lighting fixtures of scientific design.
7. Wall switches in sufficient number for complete flexibility.
8. Miscellaneous outlets and devices for signaling, radio, and so on, in proportion to the size and pretentiousness of the house.

Service Entrance.—This general term includes all wires and equipment from the outside of the building up to and including the meter and the main switch. It must be of sufficient size so that the maximum load in use at one time will neither overload the entrance wires, causing excessive voltage drop and wasted electricity, nor blow fuses. Some provision must be made for future equipment that the owner is apt to install.

Wire Sizes.—Remember that the Code specifies only minimum sizes. While No. 14 wire may generally speaking be used throughout the average installation, the trend is entirely toward No. 12 as a minimum.

Circuits.—If all the lights in a home were protected by a single fuse, the entire house would be in darkness when the fuse blows. Accordingly, the outlets are subdivided into groups or circuits each protected by an individual fuse. The greater the number of circuits, the greater the flexibility, the less the danger of blowing fuses because it reduces the likelihood of overloading any one circuit, and the less the voltage drop, thus making for brighter lights.

Receptacle Outlets.—Sufficient receptacle or plug-in outlets do away with the need for extension cords, which are unsightly, inconvenient, and dangerous, both from the standpoint of possible injury caused by tripping over them and from the standpoint of electrical hazard caused by fraying and short circuits. The Code in Sec. 2124b requires that

Receptacle outlets shall be installed in every kitchen, dining room, breakfast room, living room, parlor, library, den, sunroom, recreation room and bedroom. One receptacle outlet shall be provided for every 20 linear feet or major fraction thereof of the total (gross) distance around the room as measured horizontally along the wall at the floor line. The receptacle outlets shall, insofar as practicable, be spaced equal distances apart. At least one receptacle outlet shall be installed for the connection of laundry[1] appliances.

Because the appliances that consume the greatest amperages are commonly used in the kitchen, pantry, dining room, breakfast room, and laundry, the 1947 Code in Sec. 2115b requires that the receptacle outlets in those rooms be on a separate circuit, serving no other outlets of any description. This circuit must be wired with No. 12 wire and protected by 20-amp. overcurrent protection, which reduces the likelihood of blown fuses and at the same time limits the voltage drop.

Lighting Outlets.—Merely one outlet in the middle of the ceiling of each room is usually not sufficient in the average home. Careful attention should be paid to lighting outlets in miscellaneous locations. It costs very little to install lights in clothes closets, halls, porches, attics; this subject will be treated at greater length later.

Lighting Fixtures.—The selection of lighting fixtures is sufficiently important to warrant a separate chapter, which will follow this chapter.

Wall Switches.—Lights that are controlled by a pull chain, or a similar switch on the fixture itself, are today inexcusable except, perhaps, in closets or other rooms so small that it is impossible to miss the cord or pull chain. Outside of this one exception, every light should be controlled by a wall switch.

If there is only a single door leading into a room, the logical location for the switch is near the door. If, however, there are two entrances, it is equally logical that there should be a switch at each so that the light can be controlled from either point; in other words, use a pair of 3-way switches. Should there be three entrances, a switch at each of the three entrances is a touch of luxury that the owner will appreciate. In a house

---

[1] See p. 336 for details concerning special type of receptacle required by the 1947 Code for laundry room.

that has been really adequately wired, one will be able to enter by any entrance and to travel from basement to attic without ever being in darkness, yet without ever having to retrace one's steps to turn off lights.

Miscellaneous Outlets.—Every home will have a minimum of at least a doorbell system which will permit signaling from either front or back door. Frequently other signaling devices are used, such as a buzzer signal in the kitchen operated by a button at the dining-room table; in the more pretentious homes there may be annunciator systems between main living quarters and servants' quarters. Special radio outlets will do away with loose wires. Pilot lights will be used at switches which control lights that cannot be seen from the location of the switch, to indicate whether the lights are on or not: common uses are in connection with basement, attic, or garage lights. Careful consideration of these details will make a home considerably more livable.

Adequacy by Rooms.—Some rooms require a great deal more light than others. Likewise the need for receptacle outlets is considerably greater in some rooms than others. Consider what is good practice in each room.

Living Rooms.—Not many years ago bulbs larger than 100 watts were not often used in floor lamps. Today 300-watt bulbs are common, and the use of the 500-watt size is perhaps not far off. This trend toward larger bulbs in floor lamps was responsible for a tendency to eliminate lighting fixtures entirely in living rooms. With white ceilings, floor lamps with large bulbs do produce very excellent lighting, but since these lamps must necessarily be used mostly in corners or at least in locations along the wall, they frequently leave dark spaces in the middle or the farther end of the room. They do not provide enough general illumination. Therefore there is a well-merited trend back to ceiling fixtures in living rooms. Provide one ceiling outlet or, if it is a very large room, two outlets.

Wall brackets may or may not be installed, in accordance with the owner's taste. These brackets are primarily decorative, and seldom provide enough light to be of great value in

ADEQUACY

general lighting, although they may contribute greatly toward making the room more livable. In well-designed installations all the brackets will be controlled by one switch.

In the living room more than in any other room, be generous with receptacle outlets. The Code ruling that there must be a receptacle for every 20 ft. of wall space is a *minimum* requirement. Place outlets in such a way that a floor lamp can be used anywhere without using an extension cord.

The ordinary duplex receptacle is so constructed that both halves are either on or off. The type in Fig. 13-1 is so con-

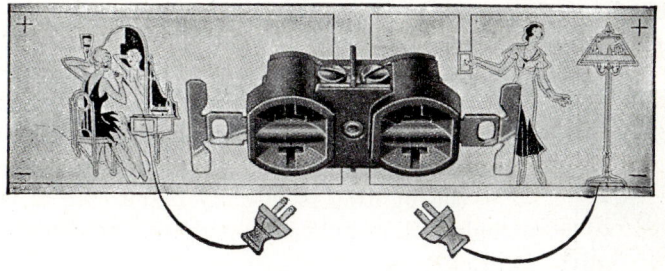

Bryant Elec. Co.

Fig. 13-1.—In this receptacle each half is independent of the other. In this way half of the outlet can be controlled by a wall switch, and the other half is always on for permanently connected devices.

structed that one of the two outlets in each device is permanently live for clocks or radios, but the other is controlled by a wall switch. Instead of having to go around to turn off each floor lamp separately, the owner can control the entire group of lamps by a single wall switch.

Outlets should be provided on mantels for use of clocks, mantel lamps, etc. A radio outlet which does away with loose aerial and ground wires should not be overlooked.

In planning the switches for the living room be sure to use 3-way and 4-way switches, so that the ceiling lights can be turned on or off both from the front entrance and from the other entrance to the room, and preferably from upstairs as well.

Sunroom.—Provide a ceiling outlet for a lighting fixture, with a wall switch and a generous supply of receptacle outlets for floor lamps, radio, or similar devices.

Dining Room.—Be sure to provide a ceiling outlet for lighting fixture, controlled by 3-way switches located at both entrances to the room. Wall brackets are a matter of choice. Receptacle outlets should be provided, not less than two, preferably three, taking into special consideration the probable location of the furniture. Too many dining-room outlets are located where it is impossible to get at them for vacuum cleaners, fans, and table appliances.

Kitchen.—So much of the housewife's time is spent in the kitchen and so much work done there that special attention should be given to this room. There are entirely too many kitchens in which many hundreds of dollars are spent for modern plumbing facilities, modern cabinets and ranges, yet the lighting is casually taken care of by a single ceiling light and perhaps one receptacle outlet.

Bryant Elec. Co.
Fig. 13-2.—This clock-hanger outlet supports the clock, and the cord on the clock is concealed from view.

Of course, a ceiling fixture will be installed for general illumination. *Be sure it is controlled by a wall switch, not a pull chain.* Better yet, install 3-way switches so that it can be controlled from the back door as well as from the usual entrance to the kitchen. Provide a good light above the sink. Again this should be controlled by a wall switch, not so much from the standpoint of convenience as from the standpoint of safety. If there is a switch on the fixture, what is more likely than that the housewife will have one hand on the water faucet, and with the other hand turn on the light? Should there be defect in the fixture, there might be a direct ground through the body to the faucet, the ideal conditions for a dangerous shock. For this reason too, fixtures in such locations should be made not of metal, but rather of porcelain or other insulating material.

In the matter of receptacle outlets, be generous. Provide one in the probable location of the refrigerator. Install a "clock hanger" outlet of the type shown in Fig. 13-2; this will support the clock and completely eliminate the unsightly cord. The modern kitchen will probably have a ventilating fan; hence locate an outlet for it at a point where the cord will be as short as possible. Then install a minimum of two outlets for general use. If there are built-in work tables, naturally the outlets should be located at convenient locations not too far above the surface of the tables. If tables are not built in, provide outlets at the probable locations of the work table and about 8 to 12 in. above the table surface.

Pantry.—Install a ceiling light. If the pantry is very small, a pull-chain cord may be sufficient; a wall switch is decidedly more convenient. A receptacle outlet should be provided if the pantry is of substantial size.

Breakfast Room.—A ceiling fixture controlled by a wall switch is necessary. A receptacle outlet at table height is practically an essential for operating a toaster or percolator.

Porches.—If the porch is a simple stoop, a ceiling or wall light illuminating the floor and steps is sufficient. Illuminated house numbers are a touch the owner and his friends will appreciate. If the porch is larger, so that it is used in summer as an outdoor living room, provide a number of receptacle outlets for radio or lamps.

Bedrooms.—Every bedroom should be provided with a ceiling light controlled by a wall switch. In addition provide a minimum of two receptacle outlets, preferably three. One at least should be located where readily accessible for the vacuum cleaner. The other two should be located on opposite sides of the room and will serve bed lamps, electric heating pad, radio, and so on. Again special attention should be paid to the location of these outlets with regard to the probable location of the furniture, so that they may be readily accessible and yet not leave the cords to the lamps unduly prominent.

Bathrooms.—For the same reasons as outlined in connection with the fixture over the sink in the kitchen, *fixtures controlled* by *pull chains or switches on the fixture should absolutely not be used in the bathroom.* Use only wall switches; likewise such bathroom fixtures should not be made of metal. There should be a ceiling light for general illumination. However, such a ceiling light seldom provides enough light for shaving or make-up, and for that reason it is best to provide additional light near the mirror, in the form either of one light above the mirror or, preferably, one light on either side. Provide an outlet near the mirror for the electric razor.

In general, the use of portable appliances in bathrooms is to be emphatically discouraged. In bathrooms, the occupant of a tub or shower is in direct contact with the ground, the ideal condition for shock. In case of a defective appliance, the person already in contact with ground, touching such an appliance, can easily receive a *fatal* shock. As a matter of fact there are on record dozens of fatal accidents *each year*, caused by people in bathrooms, especially while in tubs, touching a defective appliance, or letting some appliance such as a heater or radio (even if not defective) drop into the tub. The same fatal result can be brought about by touching defective cords, switches, or fixtures while at the same time touching a faucet or other grounded object.

FIG. 13-3. A door switch of this type turns on closet lights when the door is opened, turns them off when the door is closed.

There is real need in the bathroom for a quick-action electric heater, but it should be one built into the wall and controlled by a wall switch, and not one controlled by plugging into an outlet.

Closets.—It is most exasperating to grope around trying to find something in a dark closet. Provide a ceiling light; usually closets are so small that it is fairly easy to find the pull chain or string on the fixture. A de luxe installation will include an automatic door switch of the type shown in Fig. 13-3, which automatically turns on the light in a closet or other room as the door is opened, turns it off as the door is closed.

ADEQUACY 211

The Code in Sec. 4115 prohibits drop cords in closets and requires that fixtures must be installed on the ceiling or on the wall above the door. This is a wise provision for drop cords too often come into contact with clothes, thus leading to fires.

Basements.—First of all there should be a light that illuminates *the stairs*, controlled by a switch at the head of the stairs. If the switch is in the kitchen or some other point from which the light cannot be seen, install at the switch a pilot light which will always be on when the basement light is

Kent Metal Mfg. Co.

FIG. 13-4.—Flush ceiling fixtures are convenient when the ceiling is low.

on. Beyond this, the requirements vary, depending entirely on how elaborate the basement is.

If there is an all-purpose room which might be anything from a children's playroom to a second living room, provide as good lighting as in the living room. Since the ceilings will probably be relatively low, flush fixtures of the type shown in Fig. 13-4 may be considered. Naturally they will not provide illumination over as wide an area as the more conventional fixtures but do give most excellent light directly below, especially convenient for cards, Ping-pong, and other games. Provide receptacle outlets generously. Let the lights be controlled by wall switches.

Near the laundry tubs provide an outlet[1] for washing

[1] See p. **336** for details concerning Code requirements for the laundry receptacle.

machine, iron, or similar appliances, locating it at a convenient height. Having it controlled by a wall switch will be an added touch. Since there will be ironing done at this point, a good ceiling light will be helpful.

At other points in the basement, install ceiling lights as required. If there is a coal bin, certainly it should have a ceiling light. The storage room needs a ceiling light; surely one is needed near the furnace. Nearly every basement has at least a corner that becomes a workshop, and a good ceiling light is essential.

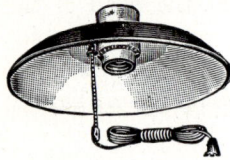

Steber Mfg. Co.

FIG. 13-5.—A reflector behind a bulb greatly increases the amount of useful light obtained from the bulb.

On all basement ceiling lights, especially if the ceiling is not plastered, it will be well to install a reflector of the general type shown in Fig. 13-5. Use of these reflectors will greatly increase the amount of useful light; dark ceilings absorb light, reflectors throw the light downward where it is wanted.

Halls.—A ceiling light controlled by wall switches will be necessary. This light should illuminate *the stairway* and should be controlled by 3-way switches so that it can be turned on from either upstairs or downstairs. Do not overlook a receptacle outlet in the hall for vacuum-cleaner use.

Attics.—If the attic is used mostly for storage, a single light, so placed that *the stairway* is illuminated, will probably be sufficient. It must be controlled by a switch at the bottom of the stairs. If it is a larger attic, provide additional lights as required; they can be controlled by the same switch as the first one.

CHAPTER 14

GOOD LIGHTING

"Better light, better sight" is the slogan of a merchandising campaign to sell better lighting equipment. It is a happy slogan for it expresses in four short words one of today's evils and at the same time suggests the remedy. Better sight, of course, implies that eyesight on the average today is not all that is should be or might be, and better light is the answer.

Extent of Defective Vision.—Broad surveys have shown that an amazing percentage of all people today have defective vision. One survey shows the percentage of defective vision to be:

Under 20 years	23 per cent
20 to 30 years	39 per cent
30 to 40 years	48 per cent
40 to 50 years	71 per cent
50 to 60 years	82 per cent
Over 60 years	95 per cent

Another survey shows that of all students in the elementary grades of school 9 per cent have defective vision, in high school 24 per cent, and in colleges the figure has risen to 31 per cent.

A different type of survey shows that the percentage of defective vision varies considerably by occupations. Those who work relatively little under artificial light, and those whose work is not of an exacting nature, suffer relatively little. For farmers and common laborers the proportion is under 20 per cent, while for carpenters and painters it has risen to between 20 per cent and 40 per cent. For machinists and printers the figure is over 40 per cent, whereas for draftsmen and stenographers it is over 80 per cent.

Of course, these figures by themselves do not prove that poor lighting is the cause of defective vision, but extensive experiment with many thousands of subjects has proved beyond doubt that proper lighting preserves healthy vision. Provide good lighting for all, and the percentage of defective vision will rapidly decrease. With better vision will come more personal comfort, for defective vision causes eyestrain and headaches; glasses are a nuisance and keep the wearer out of many kinds of more strenuous activities. With better vision will come higher efficiency, more accomplishment, more leisure. With better vision will come greater safety for all, for defective vision and poor lighting play an important part in accidents.

What Is Good Lighting?—In the early days of electrical lighting even one bulb hung in the center of a room was such an improvement over the ordinary kerosene lamp or even the gaslight then in use that apparently little time was spent in considering whether the new illuminant provided really sufficient light for good vision. This type of thinking persisted too long, and even today too little thought is given to providing good lighting. As a result, entirely too many homes and other buildings that are electrically lighted have not one-half or even one-quarter the illumination that is necessary for good seeing.

This chapter will be devoted to a discussion of the fundamentals of lighting, as well as the selection, installation, and use of lighting fixtures and the bulbs that go with them, in order to provide good lighting. Many volumes have been written on the subject, some of them covering but one single small aspect of the science, and on some points there is a good deal of disagreement among the authorities. The author does not flatter himself therefore that he can begin to cover the subject in a single chapter. He does propose, however, to set forth some of the fundamentals involved, together with what are today considered standards, so as to give some degree of working knowledge to the reader.

Dozens of factors can be enumerated that go to make up a

good lighting system. The more important ones are that the lighting system must

1. Provide sufficient quantity of light.
2. Provide light free from glare.
3. Provide light free from objectionable shadows.
4. Provide the right kind of light.

How Light Is Measured.—Inasmuch as the candle was the common method of illumination when this science was first studied, it is not surprising that standards sprang up based on candlelight, so that today there are such terms as "candle power" and "foot-candles." Since a big candle naturally gives more light than a little candle, there developed a standardized candle the definition of which, however, need not concern us here.

Candle Power.—This term does not in any way measure the total amount of light emitted by the source, for the light may be brighter in one direction than another. The standardized candle mentioned in the previous paragraph emits 1 candle power of light in a particular direction; in other directions it may emit more or less than 1 candle power. Because of this, the term "candle power" is of relatively little value because direction must always be taken into consideration when the term is used. For this reason lamp bulbs are no longer rated in candle power. However, many times the term "candle power" is still used when the term "horizontal candle power" or "mean spherical candle power" is meant.

Mean Spherical Candle Power.—If a source of light gives off 1 candle power in every direction, then it is said to have 1 mean spherical candle power; if it gives off 10 candle power in every direction, then it has 10 mean spherical candle power. If it gives off 5 candle power in one direction, 10 in another, and 12 in a third, but *averages* 10 candle power, then it has 10 mean spherical candle power. Automobile bulbs are still rated in candle power; the mean spherical candle power is meant, but this apparently is too long a term for ordinary commercial use, so that the words "mean spherical" are dropped but are usually implied.

Beam Candle Power.—When a reflector is placed behind a source of light, the emitted light rays which ordinarily go off in all directions are crowded into a relatively narrow beam. The brightness of this beam in candle power is called the "apparent beam candle power." For example, an ordinary automobile bulb of 21 candle power, if used in a good reflector, will provide an apparent beam candle power of 100,000. This simply means that there is enough candle power within the beam to produce the same intensity of light at the point of observation as would be produced at that same point by a light source of 100,000 *mean spherical* candle power, without a reflector, when located at the position of the smaller bulb and reflector.

Lumens.—The term "candle power" measures only the light in a given direction, not the total amount of light emitted. The total quantity is measured in lumens. Assume a light source producing 1 candle power in every direction, located in the center of a sphere which is exactly 2 ft. in diameter. Assume that there is an opening in the sphere and that this opening is exactly 1 sq. ft. in area (see Fig. 14-1). The lumen is defined as *the amount or quantity of light emitted through an opening of 1 sq. ft., located at a distance of 1 ft. from a light source which emits 1 candle power in every direction.*

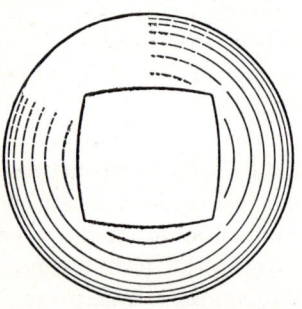

Fig. 14-1.—A bulb is in the exact center of a sphere which is 2 ft. in diameter. An opening of exactly 1 sq. ft. has been cut out of the sphere.

Note that this opening must be part of a sphere; if the opening is a hole 12 in. square in a sheet of paper, there is no way of placing the paper so that every point is exactly 1 ft. from the light source. This definition is important; study it well.

Simple geometry tells us that the total area of a sphere 2 ft. in diameter is 12.57 sq. ft. ($4\pi \cdot R^2$). Since by the definition above 1 lumen of light falls on *each* square foot of area in the sphere, the *total* light falling on the interior of the sphere must be 12.57 lumens. This was produced by a bulb of 1 mean spherical candle power. Therefore to find the lumens emitted by a bulb of which the mean spherical candle power is known, multiply by 12.57; if the lumens are known, divide by 12.57 to determine the mean spherical candle power.

Law of Inverse Squares.—The candle power and lumens of a light source are absolute or constant; other circumstances being the same, they do not change. A candle produces the same amount of light when the observer is 2 ft. away from it as when he is 5 ft. away from it. Nevertheless it is much easier to read a newspaper 2 ft. distant from the candle than it is when 5 ft. distant. Assume again a bulb of exactly 1

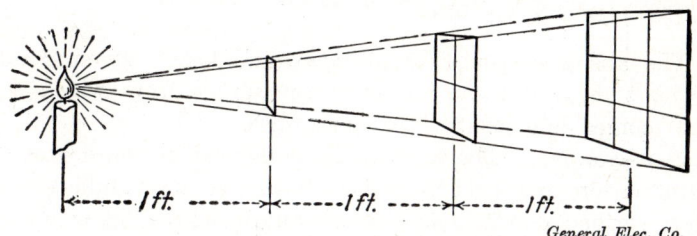

General Elec. Co.

FIG. 14-2.—The illumination on an object varies inversely as the square of its distance from the light source.

mean spherical candle power enclosed in the 2-ft. sphere with an opening exactly 1 sq. ft. in area. A newspaper placed at the opening will have 1 sq. ft. of print illuminated by the 1 lumen of light escaping through the opening. Now move the newspaper so that it is located 1 ft. from the sphere or 2 ft. from the bulb. The 1 lumen of light that escapes through the opening will now illuminate an area 2 ft. on each side, 4 sq. ft. altogether. Move it to 2 ft. from the sphere or 3 ft. from the bulb. The area illuminated will now be 3 ft. on each side, 9 sq. ft. altogether (see Fig. 14-2).

The area illuminated was first 1 sq. ft., then 4, then 9, yet the total amount of light involved remained the same, 1 lumen. Obviously it will be harder to read at the 3-ft. distance than the 1-ft. distance, because there is only one-ninth the illumination —the total amount of light has been spread 9 times as thin, if we may use the expression. *The illumination of a surface varies inversely as the square of the distance from the light source.* This is known as the "law of inverse squares." If a light source gives satisfactory illumination for a given job when it is located at a distance of 5 ft., a bulb giving 4 times as many lumens will be required if the light source is moved to a distance of 10 ft., other conditions remaining the same. To determine the relative amount of illumination, simply divide the square of one distance by the square of the other. For example, comparing the relative illumination of an object 7 ft. from a light source as compared with one 4 ft. away,

$$\frac{4 \times 4}{7 \times 7} = \frac{16}{49} = 33 \text{ per cent (approx.)}.$$

The absolute degree of illumination at any given point, without regard to the power of the source from which the light comes, is measured in foot-candles.

Foot-candles.—The foot-candle is defined as the degree of illumination produced by a light source of one candle power on a surface exactly one foot distant from the light source. Remembering the 2-ft. sphere of earlier discussions, since every point on the inside is exactly 1 ft. from the light source of 1 candle power, it should be obvious that the surface will be uniformly illuminated to the extent of 1 foot-candle.

Since this light source of 1 candle power emits a total of 12.57 lumens of light and the 2-ft. sphere has an area of exactly 12.57 sq. ft., it should be equally obvious that it requires 1 lumen of light to produce a uniform illumination of 1 foot-candle over an area of 1 sq. ft. This is a most important relation to bear in mind: *one lumen of light per square foot produces illumination of one foot-candle.* Likewise, 10 lumens per square foot produce 10 foot-candles; 100 lumens per square foot produce 100 foot-candles, and so on.

One point that often is misunderstood is the fact that the illumination in foot-candles remains the same no matter what the distance from the light source, so long as the number of lumens of light falling on each square foot does not change. This at first glance appears to be a complete contradiction of the law of inverse squares, but the following consideration should clarify it. Assume a reflector so perfect that it condenses *all* the light produced by a bulb giving, say, 100 lumens into a narrow beam so that it illuminates a spot *exactly* 1 sq. ft. *in area* on a sheet of paper 10 ft. from the bulb. The illumination on the spot will then be 100 foot-candles. If now the sheet of paper is moved to a point 20 ft. away, the beam will illuminate a spot 4 sq. ft. in area, and the illumination will be only 25 foot-candles. If, however, a different reflector is then substituted, producing a much narrower beam, so that at the new 20-ft. distance the entire 100 lumens will again illuminate a spot only 1 sq. ft. in area, the illumination on the spot will again be 100 foot-candles. So long as *all* the light produced by a source delivering 1 lumen falls on an area of 1 sq. ft., that area is illuminated to 1 foot-candle no matter what the distance. It is impossible in practice to concentrate light to this degree, for reflectors are not perfect, absorbing some light and allowing some also to spill in various directions. As a starting point, however, the relation can be considered correct. It is a most important rule, and most of this chapter up to this point has been written to help in a clear understanding of this fundamental: 1 *lumen of light on* 1 *sq. ft. of area produces* 1 *foot-candle*.

To illustrate the utility of this rule, assume that an area 12 by 12 ft. is to be lighted to 15 foot-candles. Since the total area is 144 ft., it will require 144 lumens to provide 1 foot-candle. Fifteen foot-candles will require 144 × 15, or 2,160 lumens.

The approximate lumens produced by general-purpose bulbs today are

Watts	Lumens	Watts	Lumens
15	140	150	2,600
25	260	200	3,650
40	465	300	5,900
60	835	500	10,000
75	1,100	750	14,500
100	1,580	1,000	20,700

220   THEORY AND BASIC PRINCIPLES

A 150-watt bulb delivering 2,600 lumens should therefore produce about 18 foot-candles, if all the light produced by the bulb could be directed to the floor, and none allowed to fall on the ceiling or the walls. This is entirely a theoretical figure; the actual foot-candles attained depend altogether on additional factors such as the reflector used with the bulb, the reflecting ability of ceilings and walls, the type of fixture used, and other factors which will be discussed later.

Note that brightness and foot-candles of illumination are not the same. A black sheet of paper illuminated to 10 foot-

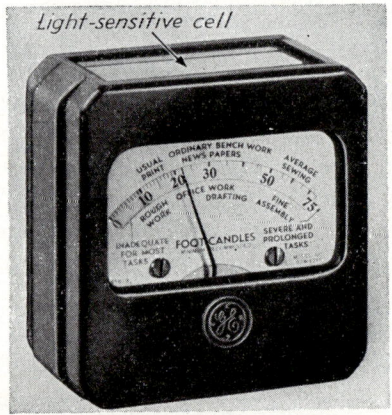

General Elec. Co.

Fig. 14-3.—This little instrument reads foot-candles of illumination directly on its scale.

candles will not seem so bright as a white one illuminated to 5 foot-candles, because the white paper *reflects* a goodly portion of the light falling upon it, while the black *absorbs* most of it.

A Few Yardsticks.—To provide some starting point of known values in foot-candles, bright sunlight on a clear day varies from 6,000 to 10,000 foot-candles. In the shade of a tree on the same day there will be somewhere in the neighborhood of 1,000 foot-candles. On the same day the light coming into a window on the shady side of a building will be of the order of 100 foot-candles, while 10 ft. back it will have dropped to something between 7 and 15 foot-candles. At a point 4 ft.

directly below a 100-watt bulb without a reflector, and backed by a black ceiling and walls which have negligible reflecting power, there will be approximately 8 foot-candles.

Measurement of Foot-candles.—Candle power and lumens are not measurable in a simple fashion. Fortunately foot-candles can be measured as easily as reading a voltmeter. In Fig. 14-3 is shown a direct-reading foot-candlemeter, commonly known as a "light-meter." Simply set the instrument at the point where the illumination is to be measured, and the foot-candles are read directly on the scale. The device consists of a photoelectric cell which is a device that generates electricity when light falls upon it. The indicating meter is simply a microammeter,[1] which measures the current generated, the scale being calibrated to read in foot-candles. The use of this instrument is invaluable, especially in commercial work, as it takes the guesswork out of many lighting problems.

Foot-candles Required for Various Jobs.—It must be remembered that there can be no absolute standard. First of all, the requirements for different individuals vary. Furthermore, what was considered adequate yesterday is insufficient today; what we by compromise accept today will be considered entirely too little tomorrow. Accordingly, all that can be given are the commonly accepted standards of today. The more critical the task, the higher the level of illumination required. The more prolonged the task, the greater the amount of light needed; for example, it is quite easy to read a paragraph of a newspaper in the relatively poor light of the dusk of evening, but almost impossible to read an entire page. Today's standards are set forth in admirable fashion in The Science of Seeing," by Luckiesh and Moss, from which volume the following table is quoted:

Conservative Footcandle Recommendation on a Rational Basis of Characteristics of the Visual Task and Requirements of Performance

100 *Footcandles or More.*—For very severe and prolonged tasks, such as fine needlework, fine engraving, fine penwork, fine assembly,

[1] A microampere is one millionth of one ampere.

sewing on dark goods and discrimination of fine details of low contrast, as in inspection.

50 *to* 100 *Footcandles.*—For severe and prolonged tasks, such as proofreading, drafting, difficult reading, watch repairing, fine machine-work, average sewing and other needlework.

20 *to* 50 *Footcandles.*—For moderately critical and prolonged tasks, such as clerical work, ordinary reading, common benchwork and average sewing and other needlework on light goods.

10 *to* 20 *Footcandles.*—For moderate and prolonged tasks of office and factory and when not prolonged, ordinary reading and sewing on light goods.

5 *to* 10 *Footcandles.*—For visually controlled work in which seeing is important, but more or less interrupted or casual, and does not involve discrimination of fine details or low contrasts.

0 *to* 5 *Footcandles.*—The danger zone for severe visual tasks and for quick and certain seeing. Satisfactory for perceiving larger objects and for casual reading.

Will these values be considered correct 10 years from today? Undoubtedly they will not. Yet illumination levels as high as those recommended above are today more often the exception than the rule; few installations meet the figures suggested.

Glare.—Because so much space has been devoted to the amount or degree of illumination, do not for a moment think that this is the one all-important factor in good lighting. It is only one of four factors. Another important factor is that the light must be free from glare.

Glare, generally speaking, is caused by a relatively bright area within an area illuminated to a lower level. An exposed bulb in the lobby of a movie is not particularly noticeable when entering because the eyes are accustomed to the outdoor brightness; upon leaving, after the eyes are accustomed to the relatively dark interior, the bulb will appear very bright, will glare and hurt the eyes. Similarly a lighted automobile headlight is barely noticeable in daylight but may be blinding at night. Harrison and Staley in their pamphlet "Fundamentals of Illumination" (from which many of the illustrations of this chapter have been borrowed) define glare as "any brightnesss within the field of vision of such a character as to cause annoyance, discomfort, interference with vision, or eye fatigue."

Glare is usually caused by exposed bulbs so placed that they can be seen while we look at the object we primarily want to see; the bulb may not be directly visible, but, even if it is so

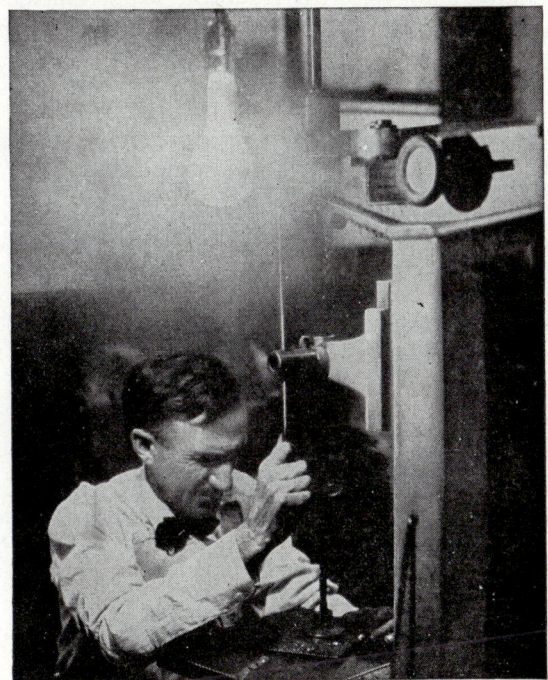

General Elec. Co.

Fig. 14-4.—Exposed bulbs cast harsh shadows and cause extreme glare. Efficient work is not possible with such lighting.

placed that it can be seen by merely moving the eyes without moving the head, it still produces glare. Bright automobile headlights constitute a good example of this type of glare, while lighting of the type shown in Fig. 14-4 is equally bad.

Glare of an equally objectionable type may be caused by reflection, for example from glass tops on desks. Glass is a good reflector, and the reflected image of a bulb may appear almost as bright as the bulb itself. For this reason glass tops are rapidly disappearing from the desks of executives. Likewise less and less highly polished and plated parts are being used on typewriters, office machinery, and other devices because manufacturers have learned that glare causes the evils recounted above, with resultant lower efficiency. For this reason, too, printers have learned to avoid papers that are extremely glossy, reflecting too much light (see the examples shown in Fig. 14-5).

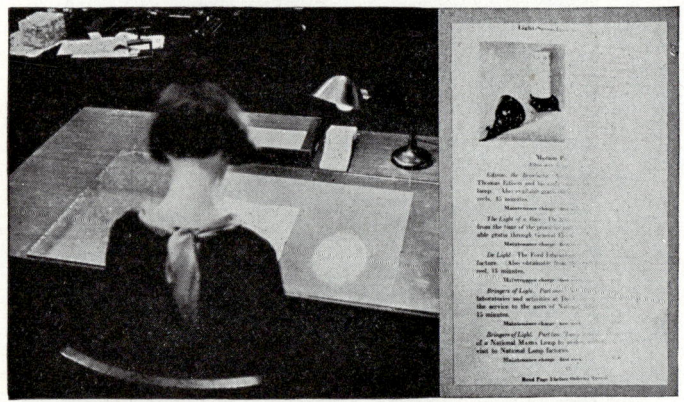

General Elec. Co.

Fig. 14-5.—Glass desk tops and glossy paper are both frequent sources of glare.

How to Avoid Glare in Lighting.—Everyone has tried reading in direct sunlight and found it difficult. Even in the early morning, reading in the direct rays of the sun is not comfortable. On the other hand it is not difficult to read in the shade of a tree on a bright day, even if there the foot-candles are higher than in the direct sunlight of early morning. Therefore the answer cannot lie only in the foot-candles of illumination prevailing at any given moment.

The answer does lie in the fact that direct sunlight comes essentially from a single point, the sun, and causes glare. In the shade of a tree the light comes from no point in particular but rather comes from every direction—north, south, east, west, and from above. Not coming from one point, it does not cause harsh shadows or glare. It is *diffused light*.

In lighting a home or office, the more the lighting can be made to duplicate the conditions of the shade of a tree, the better the lighting will be. Perhaps someday in the future there may be a way of having all the walls and ceilings of rooms give off light of low intensity but sufficient total volume to eliminate the need for lighting fixtures. Until that time such fixtures as are available must serve the purpose.

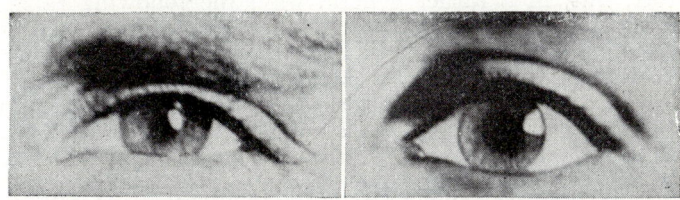

General Elec. Co.

FIG. 14-6.—The pupil of the eye adapts itself to various levels of illumination. The lower the level of illumination, the wider it opens.

Surface Brightness.—In looking at an exposed 300-watt bulb of the clear-glass type, one sees a concentrated filament not much over an inch in diameter. The bulb itself is a little over 4 in. in diameter but because the filament is so bright, the glass bulb itself is almost invisible. That is why most bulbs today are frosted—the filament is not seen, but rather the entire bulb. Since the bulb has a diameter of about 4 in., there is exposed to the eye an apparent area equivalent to the area of a circle of the same diameter, or about $12\frac{1}{2}$ sq. in. The same total amount of light, which in the case of the clear-glass bulb was concentrated in an area of about 1 sq. in., is now distributed over a much larger area of about $12\frac{1}{2}$ sq. in. Obviously then, while the total amount of light is the same, the brightness of the larger area is greatly reduced—the "surface brightness" is lower. It is still uncomfortably bright if looked at directly.

Put the bulb inside a globe of translucent, nontransparent glass about 8 in. in diameter; this has an apparent area of about 50 sq. in. altogether, instead of the 12½ sq. in. observed before. The total amount of light is still the same, but it is far more comfortable to the eye because the surface brightness of the light source has been reduced still more. For this reason the bulb size should always be matched up with the manufacturer's recommendations with respect to the enclosing globe of the fixture. It is impossible to lay down any hard and fast rule because so much depends on the shape of the glass globe, the density of the glass involved, and similar factors, but, in a rather general way, the following table is correct:

With 100-watt bulb, use glass globe not less than 8 in. diameter
With 200-watt bulb, use glass globe not less than 14 in. diameter
With 300-watt bulb, use glass globe not less than 16 in. diameter
With 500-watt bulb, use glass globe not less than 18 in. diameter

Direct, Indirect, and Semi-indirect Lighting.—Light produced by bulbs so placed that they can be seen is termed

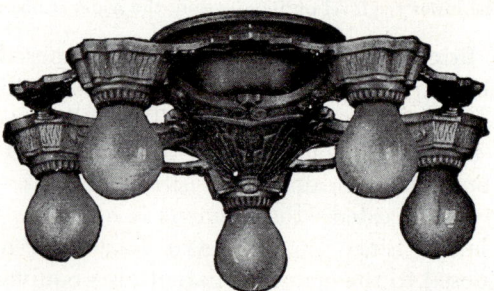

FIG. 14-7.—Fixtures with exposed bulbs may provide enough light but never provide good illumination. It is impossible to eliminate glare and harsh shadows when such fixtures are used.

"direct lighting." Light produced by bulbs in fixtures so designed that all the light is first thrown on the ceiling and then reflected back to the area below is termed "indirect lighting." If the fixture is so designed that part of the light is thrown to the ceiling and then reflected, allowing part of it to fall directly on the area underneath, through glass or plastic bowls, it is termed "semi-indirect lighting." Usually this term is applied only where upward of 50 per cent of the light is indirect.

Direct Lighting.—Direct lighting in a home usually consists of fixtures with exposed bulbs, of the type shown in Fig. 14-7. The only point in their favor is that they are inexpensive as to first cost. Using five bulbs, such fixtures are inefficient because smaller bulbs produce fewer lumens *per watt* than large ones; one 100-watt bulb produces more lumens than six 25-watt. Worst of all, because the light comes from one point, they produce glare and do not give the diffused shade-of-a-tree type of light that is so easy on the eyes. Another type of direct lighting may be the

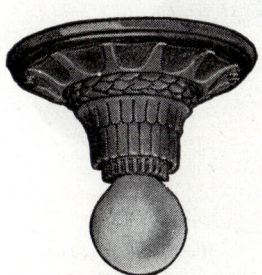
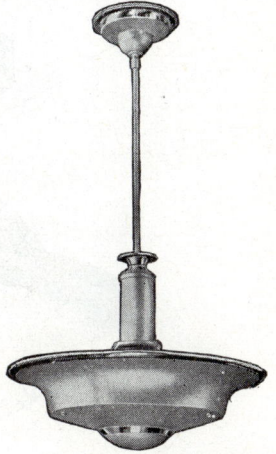

Markel Elec. Products.

Fig. 14-8.—Fixtures of this type may be acceptable in a few locations where good lighting is not necessary.

Fig. 14-9.—In an indirect fixture the light is first thrown to the ceiling, where it is diffused in being reflected.

single exposed bulb in a simple holder of the type shown in Fig. 14-8. This may justifiably be used in attics, basements, and other little-used areas. There may be times when the lighting fixture is selected more for its decorative value than as a light-producing means, in which case that factor should be considered first. The use of a beautiful crystal chandelier in a dining room may be entirely justified, especially since it undoubtedly provides much more light than the wax candles in vogue at the moment.

Indirect Lighting.—Totally indirect lighting fixtures, of which an example is shown in Fig. 14-9, are today relatively seldom used in homes. For commercial and industrial applications they are common, and more will be said about them in a later chapter.

Semi-indirect Lighting.—This type of lighting is considered by many authorities as the ideal lighting for homes. Fixtures in this classification take many forms. The simplest is per-

Markel Elec. Products.

FIG. 14-10.—A semi-indirect kitchen light. About half of the light is thrown upward against the ceiling; the other half is well-diffused direct light.

haps the "kitchen unit" of Fig. 14-10. The bulb is shielded from direct view. Some of the light goes downward through the glass and provides direct light but a goodly part of it goes upward, strikes the ceiling, and is reflected downward. Another part strikes the walls and is reflected back into the room. The light to a limited extent simulates the shade-of-the-tree condition.

Another type is shown in Fig. 14-11, where again the bulbs are concealed from direct view. A portion of the light nevertheless goes directly downward, leaving no dark spot underneath. The bulbs being farther down from the ceiling than in the "kitchen unit" style, the light strikes the ceiling at a sharper angle and thus provides better diffusion, still further

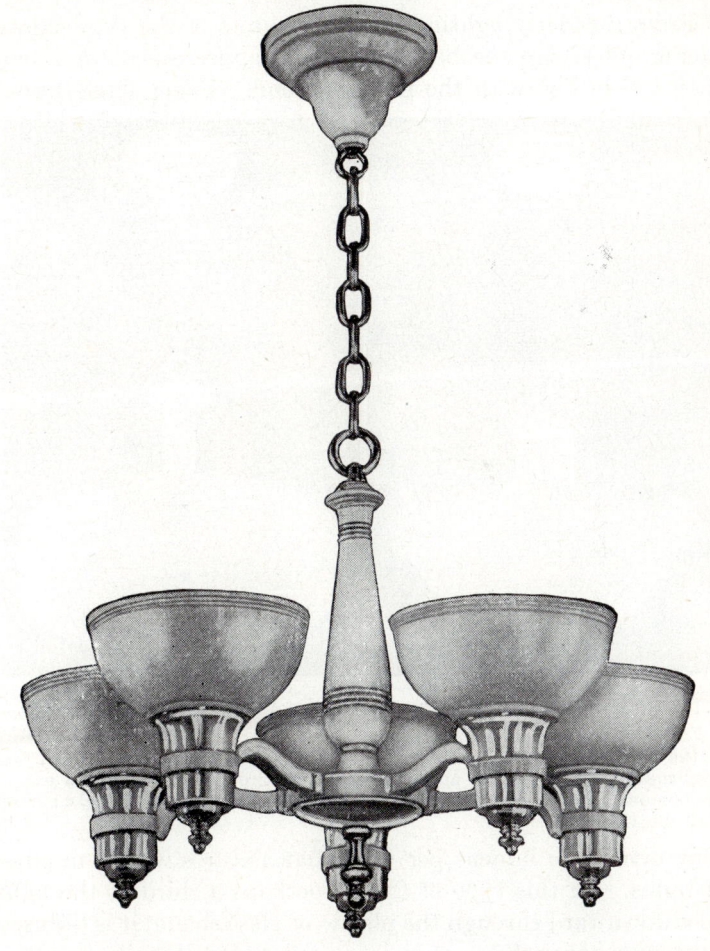

Markel Elec. Products.

Fig. 14-11.—A semi-indirect fixture which is popular. The bulbs are concealed from direct view.

approaching the shade-of-a-tree ideal. This type of fixture does have the objection that it uses five bulbs, with conse-

230   THEORY AND BASIC PRINCIPLES

quent relative inefficiency. Nevertheless it is a fair compromise for those who seek both good lighting and conventional appearance.

From a strictly lighting viewpoint units of the type shown in Fig. 14-12 are the best. From an appearance standpoint they fall in line with the modern trend. Using single bulbs,

a   *b*

Markel Elec. Products.

Fig. 14-12.—Two more examples of semi-indirect lighting. In the fixture at the left, the entire shade is translucent plastic material with low surface brightness. In the fixture at the right, the entire shade is of metal except the bottom. Louvers around the metal shade give the illusion of light emerging from the entire shade.

they give more lumens per watt than fixtures with a number of bulbs. In this type of fixture perhaps a third of the light goes downward through the plastic or glass shade; it is diffused as it goes through, so that in a well-designed unit there are no bright spots on the shade to cause glare. Instead of coming from a single point or five points, the direct light appears to come from one relatively large area: either the entire shade, if it happens to be of the plastic variety, or a large portion of the shade, if it is a combination metal-glass shade. Most of the light, however, is reflected to the ceiling, thence throughout the room in well-diffused fashion, approaching closely the desired shade-of-a-tree type of illumination. This type of fixture comes in a great variety of styles, and undoubtedly its popularity will grow rapidly. Figure 14-13 in a broad way illustrates why the light seems to fill a room rather than to come from one point. Note the path of individual rays of light: the solid lines show what their paths

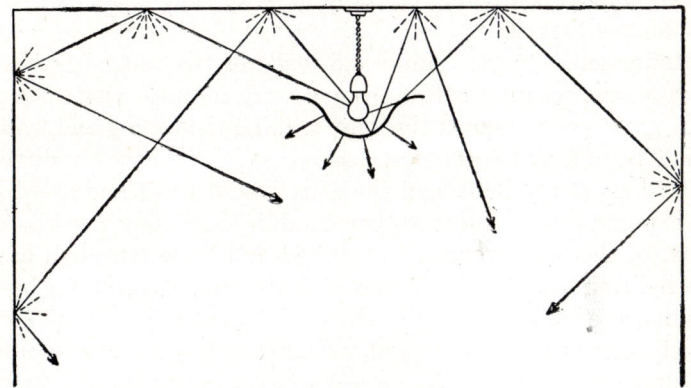

FIG. 14-13.—This diagram illustrates how light becomes diffused as it is reflected from ceiling and walls.

would be if the ceilings and walls were absolutely smooth like a mirror. While a plaster wall may seem smooth, it will, if viewed under a microscope of even low power, be found to be uneven, full of hills and dales. Therefore the rays, as they strike any one point, strike these hills and dales and are reflected in a variety of directions, so that what would otherwise be individual rays split up into a multitude of rays, in all directions (as shown in the dotted lines) giving truly diffused light.

The objection that is most frequently heard in connection with indirect or semi-indirect lighting is that "it takes too many watts." Indeed it does take more watts to produce any given foot-candle illumination below the fixture with an indirect or semi-indirect type than with a direct-lighting type, but several points must be remembered. First of all the indirect and semi-indirect, generally speaking, illuminate an entire room, especially the more remote areas, with a higher level of illumination than is provided by the direct-lighting type of fixture. Moreover, if the light is well diffused, approaching the shade-of-a-tree type, fewer foot-candles are required for comfortable seeing than if the light comes from one point, a direct-lighting style of fixture. The higher efficiency of a single bulb as compared with a number of smaller bulbs must not be overlooked.

Reflection.—If the ceiling and walls of the room in which such a semi-indirect fixture is used were mirrors, obviously a very great percentage of the light striking the ceiling and walls would be reflected downward. However, there would be direct reflections of the bulb, and the glare would be as bad as with an exposed bulb. On the other hand, if the ceiling was black, most of the light would be absorbed and little reflected, and the lighting would be inefficient indeed. Accordingly, for best results, the ceiling and walls should be a color that reflects as much light as possible, and at the same time the finish should be dull or flat rather than glossy, so as to avoid the mirror effect, with bright spots producing glare.

Experiment has shown that various colors of paint reflect light in various degrees, the percentages reflected being of the order of the following:

White	80 to 85 per cent
Ivory	70 to 80 per cent
Cream	65 to 75 per cent
Buff	55 to 65 per cent
Gray	35 to 50 per cent
Light blue	35 to 50 per cent
Light green	30 to 40 per cent
Dark green	15 to 25 per cent
Red	15 to 25 per cent
Dark blue	10 to 20 per cent
Brown	8 to 12 per cent
Black	2 to 5 per cent

Woods in natural finish seldom reflect over 50 per cent, and the darker woods may fall as low as 15 per cent. It should be evident therefore that the choice between direct, semi-indirect, and indirect lighting will be greatly dependent on the color and finish of the ceiling and, to a lesser degree, the walls.

Shadows.—When we read in direct sunlight, the extreme glare makes reading uncomfortable. Moreover, the reader's own shadow on the reading material is extremely sharp; the contrast between bright light and sharp shadow is most annoying and tiring. In the shade of a tree the foot-candle level is much lower, but reading is more comfortable: the light is diffused; shadows are soft and not objectionable. Two sources of light, for example a floor lamp and an overhead fixture, lead to greater comfort in reading. An indirect or semi-indirect fixture or lamp gives diffused light, light that seems to come from many points, as in the shade of a tree.

Color of Light.—Sunlight has come to be accepted by most people as a standard. Unfortunately it is not possible to duplicate sunlight in either quantity or color in the bulbs and fixtures available for home or ordinary commercial use. It may seem strange to speak of the "color" of sunlight, which appears colorless, yet sunlight is composed of a mixture of all colors. The rainbow is simply a breaking down of sunlight into its separate colors.

What makes one object red and another object blue when this mixture of all colors which we call sunlight hits these objects? The explanation is simple. When "white" light strikes certain objects, the component colors are all reflected equally, and we call such objects white. When white light hits other objects, the light instead of being reflected is absorbed, and we see no light; we then say that such objects are black.

Still different objects may absorb some of the colors of the spectrum, reflect the others. For example, they may absorb all except the red, and reflect that. We then see only the red part, so we say such objects are red. So with every other color: whatever the color of the object, that is the color that the object can reflect; all the other colors are absorbed and destroyed.

Ordinary bulbs produce light which has more orange and red, but less blue and green, than sunlight. It is not surprising that attempts are made to duplicate natural light; of these, daylight-blue bulbs are the most common. These bulbs have a special blue glass which absorbs some colors so that the light remaining is more nearly of the same composition as natural light. Bulbs of this type are helpful in work that involves discriminating between colors and similar tasks.

For home use the daylight-blue bulb is the only type of color-correcting lighting that is available. For industrial use other types are available, and these will be dealt with in another chapter.

Lamp Bulbs.—The life of most lamp bulbs is about 1,000 hours. It is a simple matter to make bulbs that last longer, but in so doing, the efficiency is reduced, that is, the bulb will produce less light, fewer lumens per watt. A 100-watt bulb, costing 15 cts., uses 100 kw.-hr. of energy during its normal life. At 5 cts. per kilowatt-hour the cost of the energy is therefore $5, as compared with the 15-ct. cost of the bulb itself. If then, to secure longer life in a 15-ct. bulb, we reduce the efficiency, an extra dollar may be spent for energy to produce the same amount of light, obviously an expensive scheme.

Where no great amount of light is needed and the bulb serves merely as a signal, for example in pilot lights, the bulb may be designed to last 2,000 hr. or more; on the other hand, where a great deal of light is needed and where it is important to limit the heat, for example in bulbs for movie projectors, the bulb may be designed for a relatively short life but with corresponding increase in efficiency, thus permitting smaller wattage bulbs producing less heat to be used. For example, a 1,000-hr. 1,000-watt bulb produces about 20.7 lumens per watt, but a 50-hr. bulb of the same wattage produces about 27 lumens per watt, while a Photoflood bulb of the same approximate wattage but only 10-hr. life produces roughly 34 lumens per watt.

Voltage of Lamp Bulbs.—If a lamp bulb is operated at a voltage below that for which it was designed, its life is prolonged considerably, but the watts, the lumens, and the lumens per watt drop off rapidly. If it is operated at a voltage above normal, its life is greatly reduced, although the watts, the lumens, and the lumens per watt increase. For lowest over-all cost of illumination use bulbs on the voltage for which they were designed. Careful study of the following table based on a 100-watt bulb designed for 115 volts will confirm this:

Actual voltage of circuit, volts	Total average life, hours	Total lumens output	Actual watts	Lumens per watt
100	3,900	980	81	12.1
105	2,600	1,115	87	13.3
110	1,650	1,358	93	14.6
115	**1,000**	**1,580**	**100**	**15.8**
120	600	1,815	107	16.8
125	360	2,075	114	18.2
130	220	2,370	121	19.6

Occasionally there will be applications where it is entirely in order to use bulbs on a voltage considerably above that for which they were designed. There may be conditions when a great deal of light is needed but only for short periods, for example in temporary floodlights for athletic fields. By using 115-volt bulbs on a 130-volt circuit (or 105-volt bulbs on a 120-volt circuit), the amount of light secured *per watt* is increased by about 25 per cent. The fact that the bulbs will only last about 220 hr. instead of 1,000 is immaterial when weighed against the extra cost of larger reflectors, floodlights, larger temporary power lines, to accommodate the larger bulbs.

If bulbs are located where it is extremely difficult to change them, it may be wise to burn them at less than their rated voltage in order to prolong their life.

236   THEORY AND BASIC PRINCIPLES

All bulbs blacken in use, causing their efficiency to drop off toward the end of their life. When the bulbs have burned 70 per cent of their normal life, the efficiency has usually dropped 5 to 15 per cent. Because of this, many commercial establishments make it a practice to replace bulbs after a predetermined number of hours' use, even if not burned out.

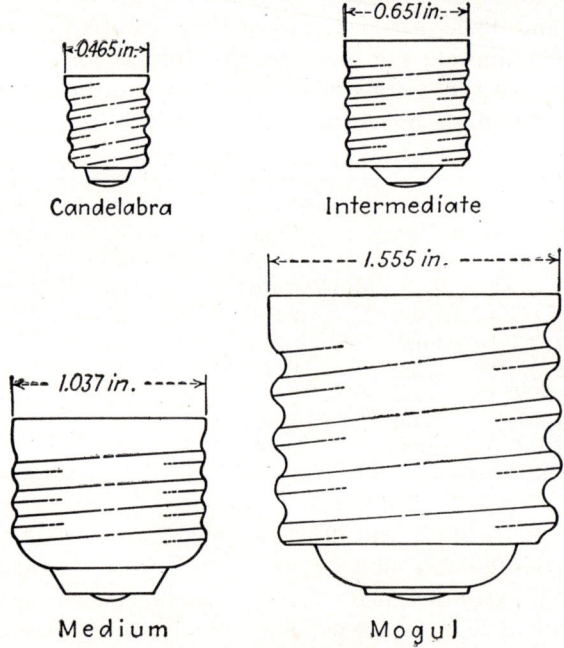

FIG. 14-14.—The screw-shell bases used on lamp bulbs are standardized to the dimensions shown.

Bases.—There are various standardized sizes of bases in use, matched to the power and size of the bulb. In the screw-shell type the largest is the mogul, used mostly on bulbs from 300 watts upward; its dimensions are shown in Fig. 14-14, together with dimensions of other standard bases. The medium is usual for ordinary household bulbs. Smaller bulbs use the intermediate and candelabra. Flashlight and similar bulbs use the miniature, which is still smaller.

Another base used on higher wattage bulbs is the bipost of Fig. 14-15. The prefocus base of Fig. 14-16 is used mostly on projection bulbs and serves to maintain the bulb in one particular position so as to give maximum light in one direction. Both of these types are available in two sizes: medium and mogul. A three-light bulb is merely a bulb with two separate filaments, say 100 watts and 200 watts, with a special base so arranged that either filament separately or both at the same time may be used,

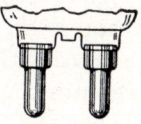

General Elec. Co.   *General Elec. Co.*

Fig. 14-15.—The bipost type of base is becoming common on larger wattage bulbs.

Fig. 14-16. The prefocus base is used on bulbs for projection purposes.

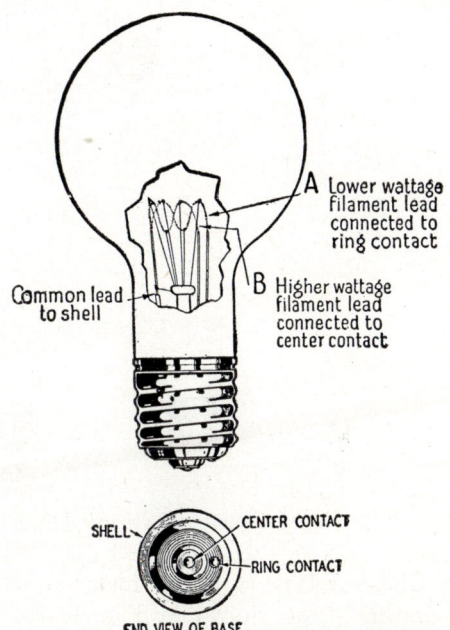

General Elec. Co.

Fig. 14-17.—Construction of 3-light bulb.

producing 100, 200, or 300 watts, as desired. The construction is shown in Fig. 14-17.

Bulb Designations.—The mechanical size and shape of a bulb are designated by standardized abbreviations such as A-19, PS-35, and F-15. The letter designates the shape of the bulb in accordance with the shapes shown in Fig. 14-18. The numeral designates the diameter in eighths of an inch. Thus an A-19 bulb has the simple A shape and is $1\frac{9}{8}$ or $2\frac{3}{8}$ in. in diameter.

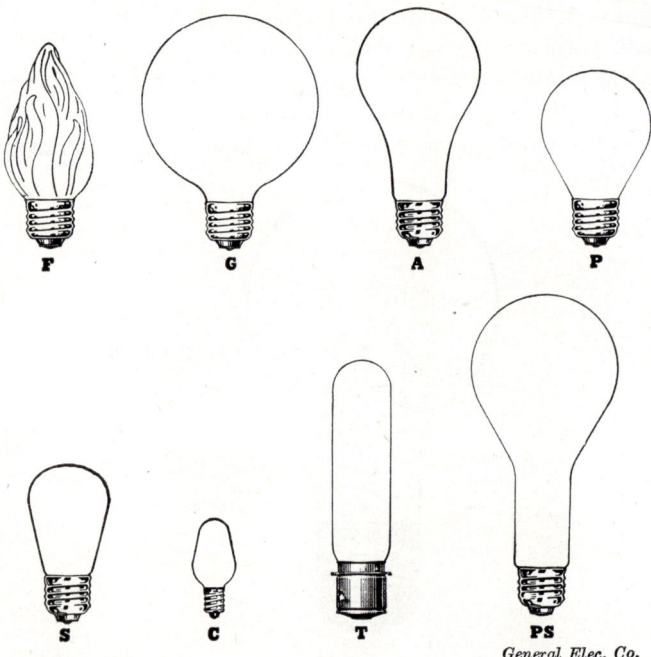

FIG. 14-18.—The shape of lamp bulbs is well standardized.

Lumiline Bulbs.—A type of bulb which is now in common use is the Lumiline type shown in Fig. 14-19. Instead of having a base with two contacts at one end, it has a single contact cap at each end, with a continuous filament from end to end. This makes the bulb usable only in a fixture designed for the purpose, for example that shown in Fig. 14-20.

Efficiency of Various Sizes of Bulbs.—Larger bulbs produce more light *per watt*, so that, generally speaking, when there is a choice, it is desirable to use one large bulb rather than several

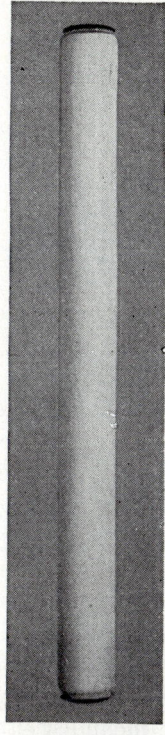

General Elec. Co.

Fig. 14-19.—The Lumiline bulb has a contact at each end.

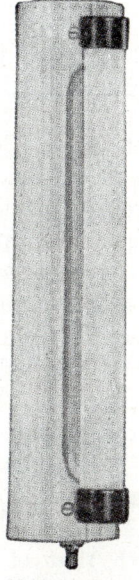

Markel Elec. Products.

Fig. 14-20. Fixture designed for Lumiline bulb.

smaller ones. Study the table on page 240, which is based on general-purpose bulbs of present manufacture.

Study of this table will show that one 150-watt bulb gives as much light as 10 of the 25-watt size; one 500-watt bulb gives almost as much light as 7 of the 100-watt size.

Size of bulb, watts	Total lumens	Lumens per watt
25	260	10.4
40	464	11.6
60	834	13.9
75	1,103	14.7
100	1,580	15.8
150	2,610	17.4
200	3,640	18.2
300	5,910	19.7
500	10,050	20.1

Efficiency of Various Colors of Bulbs.—There is no appreciable difference in efficiency between a bulb of the clear-glass type and one of the inside-frosted type. However, if the bulb is colored to produce colored light, the efficiency drops very fast. Even the popular flametint bulbs are very low in efficiency. Colored bulbs should seldom be considered except for their decorative value. The coloring material simply absorbs most of the light produced by the bulb; only that portion which matches the color of the bulb is transmitted.

Fluorescent Lighting.—This form of lighting is relatively new, having been introduced commercially in 1938. The fluorescent installation is a familiar object to all, but few understand its method of operation, which is quite complex as compared with that of an ordinary incandescent (filament type) bulb.

In the ordinary incandescent lamp, a filament made of tungsten wire is heated by an electric current flowing through it, until it reaches a high temperature, when it emits light. It operates by its terminals being connected to two wires of an electric circuit of the proper voltage.

The fluorescent lamp (or tube, as it is often called) consists essentially of a glass cylinder, with a filament at each end. The filaments are not connected to each other in the lamp. Each filament is brought out to two pins on the end, as shown in Fig. 14-21. The inside of the glass tube is coated with a whitish or grayish powder. The air has been pumped out of the tube, and a carefully determined amount of a gas called argon is introduced. A very small amount of mercury is also put into the tube. That is the basic machinery of a fluorescent tube, but if it is connected directly to the ordinary 115-volt circuit, it will not operate.

If a fluorescent lamp marked "115-volt" is connected to a source of high-voltage current, the lamp will light up, but will be quickly destroyed. If it is connected to a source of high-voltage current, and just at the instant of starting the voltage

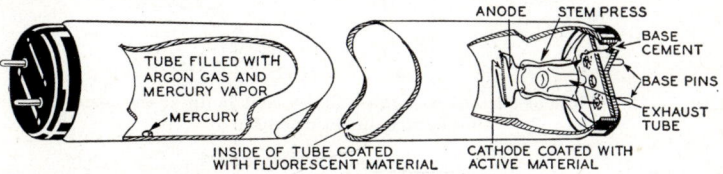

FIG. 14-21.—Construction of a fluorescent lamp.

is reduced to 115 volts, it will still be destroyed. If just at the instant of starting, it is connected to a circuit of considerably under 115 volts, the tube will continue to operate just as it does in an ordinary fluorescent fixture. Apparently then some special accessories are required to make the fluorescent lamp or tube operate.

Figure 14-22 shows the basic scheme. The secret of operation consists of two devices: a ballast or choke coil, and an automatic switch, in practice called a starter. Any coil of wire wound on an iron core has two peculiarities: (1) when connected to an alternating-current circuit, it tends to resist any change of current flowing through it; and (2) when a current flowing through it is cut off, it delivers momentarily a voltage much higher than the voltage applied to it. The ballast for a fluorescent lamp is just such a coil. The automatic switch is so designed that it is ordinarily closed (while the lamp is turned off), but when the lamp is turned on, the switch opens a fraction of a second after the current starts to flow, and then stays open until the lamp is turned off again.

Visualize then what happens. Start with Fig. 14-22, which shows the circuit just as the lamp is turned on. Current flows as indicated by the arrows, through the ballast, through one filament, or "cathode" as it is called in the case of the fluo-

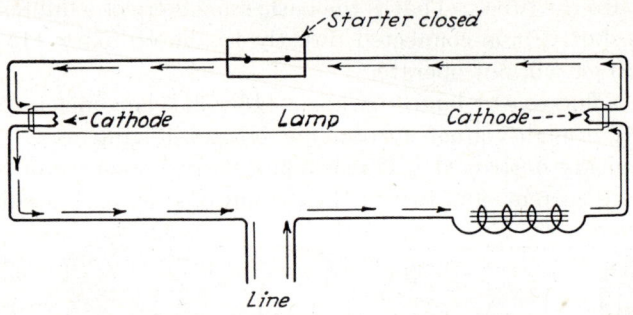

Fig. 14-22.—Flow of current through a fluorescent lamp at the instant when the light is first turned on.

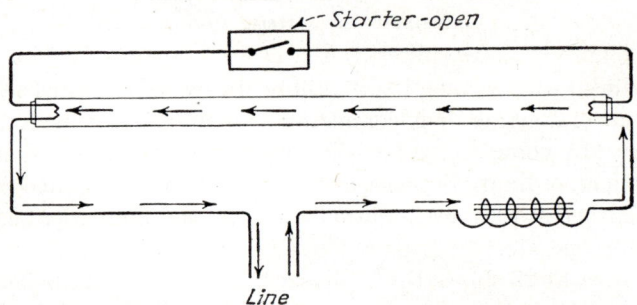

Fig. 14-23.—Flow of current through a fluorescent lamp after it has started. The automatic "starter" has now opened, and current cannot flow through it.

rescent lamp, through the automatic switch or "starter," through the other filament or cathode, and back to the line. During this period the lamp glows at each end but does not light. Then the automatic switch opens, and the ballast does its trick—it delivers a high voltage as mentioned in the previous paragraph, a voltage considerably above 115 volts, and high enough to start the lamp. The current can no longer flow through the switch because it is open; it then flows through the tube, jumping the gap and forming an arc inside the glass tube, following the arrows of Fig. 14-23 (in both Figs. 14-22 and 14-23 the current flows first in the direction indicated by the arrows, then in the opposite direction, because the current involved is alternating current). The ballast then performs its other function: it limits the current flowing through the tube to a predetermined safe value. The voltage applied to the circuit divides so that about 20 per cent of the voltage drop is across the ballast; the other 80 per cent is across the lamp. The lamp then produces light until turned off. All the above presupposes that the lamp is operated on alternating current. (When used on direct current, the control apparatus is considerably different.)

How does the current jump from one end of the tube to the other? It is a complicated story, and yet is, in some ways, simple. The filaments or cathodes of coiled tungsten wire are coated with a chemical which when heated emits electrons, particles so small that billions of them laid side by side would still be invisible, being actually basic negative charges of electricity. They shoot out into space as popcorn does in a corn popper; they travel more easily through argon gas than through a vacuum, which is the reason that gas is introduced. A stream of these particles constitutes an electrical current, which heats the argon, which heats the mercury to become mercury vapor, which then becomes the path for a heavier electric current.

If a fluorescent tube such as just described had a wall of clear glass, an insignificant amount of light would be visible, and yet the fluorescent lamp as installed produces a great deal of visible light. The answer lies in the fact that the electric arc through the mercury vapor produces only a slight amount of *visible* light, but a great deal of *invisible* ultraviolet light.

The inside of the tube is covered with a layer of chemicals that become fluorescent or light-producing when exposed to ultraviolet light. In other words, invisible ultraviolet light striking fluorescent chemicals makes the chemicals glow brightly, producing visible light. The particular chemical used determines the color of the light.

The exact scientific principles that govern the emission of electrons from a heated coated filament, the creation of the arc, the production of ultraviolet light by the arc, and the creation of visible light when invisible ultraviolet light strikes certain chemicals had best be left to the chemists and engineers.

Advantages of Fluorescent Lighting.—The greatest single advantage of fluorescent lamps lies in their efficiency. Per watt of electricity used, they produce 2 to 3[1] times as much light as ordinary incandescent lamps. Their life is much longer than that of incandescent lamps. Being more efficient, they produce much less heat, which is important when larger amounts of power are used for lighting, especially if the lighted area is air-conditioned.

Another major advantage is that the lamp or tube, being of relatively large size (in terms of area in square inches compared with the total light output), has relatively low surface brightness, which in turn leads to less glare, less shadow, all contributing to better seeing, less eyestrain. The surface brightness being low, there is no need for enclosing glassware, reducing the cost of installation and upkeep.

Life of Fluorescent Lamps.—The life of ordinary incandescent lamps is about 1,000 hr.; it does not make an appreciable difference whether the lamp is burned continuously, or turned on and off many times during its life. A fluorescent lamp that is turned on once and never turned off until the end of its useful life will probably last in excess of 3,000 hr. If it is turned on and off every 5 minutes, it may not last 500 hr. The answer lies in the fact that there is a specific amount of electron-emitting material on the filaments or cathodes; a specific part of it is consumed each time the lamp is started; when it is all gone, the lamp is inoperative. It is not possible to predict the exact number of starts the lamp will survive, and ordinary operation between starts also consumes some of the material, but the fact remains that the oftener a fluorescent lamp is

---

[1] In the case of certain colors, the fluorescent lamp produces over 100 times as much light per watt as an incandescent lamp.

turned on, the shorter its life will be. Under ordinary operation, its life will probably be twice that of the incandescent lamp.

Rating of Fluorescent Lamps.—An ordinary incandescent lamp marked "40 watts" will consume 40 watts when connected to a circuit of the proper voltage. A fluorescent lamp rated at 40 watts also will consume 40 watts within the tube, but actually an additional wattage is consumed by the ballast; this additional wattage is 15 to 30 per cent of the wattage consumed by the lamp proper and must be added to the wattage of the lamp to arrive at the total wattage of the combination.

Power Factor of Fluorescent Lamps.—Ordinary incandescent lamps have a power factor of 100 per cent. A single fluorescent lamp connected to a circuit has a power factor of somewhere between 50 and 60 per cent. Assume 100 lamps rated at 40 watts, connected singly to a 115-volt circuit. The ballast for each lamp can be expected to consume approximately 8 watts. The total for each combination is 48 watts, and for 100 such lamps, the total is 4,800 watts. The amperage consumed by these 100 lamps is however not 4,800/115, or 42 amp., as might be expected, but rather (assuming a power factor of 60%) 4,800/(115 × 0.60), or 4,800/69, or approximately 70 amp. Therefore the wiring serving this load must be capable of carrying 70 amp., rather than a theoretical 42 amp.

Fortunately this is not so serious as it sounds. The common method is to have either two or four lamps per fixture, and in addition to the usual ballast, to use power-factor-correction devices built into the same case with the ballast, which bring the power factor up to about 90 per cent or better.

Unfortunately however, not all 2- or 4-light fixtures on the market are of the high-power-factor type. The subject is introduced so that due caution may be exercised when making a purchase, to make sure the high-power-factor type are procured. This is especially important when making commercial or industrial installations, where the power company exacts an entirely justifiable penalty when the power factor of an installation is low.

Sizes of Fluorescent Lamps.—The most commonly used lamps are those listed below. Note that the wattage consumed by the ballast is *not* included in the column headed "watts."

Designation	Length, inches	Diameter, inches	Watts
T-8	18	1	15
T-12	24	1½	20
T-8	36	1	30
T-12	48	1½	40
T-17	60	2⅛	100

Other ratings are available for special purposes. Among these should be mentioned the new Circline lamp shown in Fig. 14-24, designed for floor lamps, small fixtures, and other

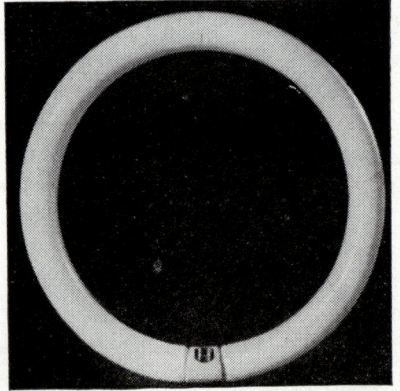

General Elec. Co.

Fig. 14-24.—The recently developed "Circline" fluorescent lamp comes in three diameters, and will find application in floor lamps and lighting fixtures for homes.

applications where a long straight lamp would not fit into the picture.

Color of Light from Fluorescent Lamps.—Everyone has noticed that colors of flowers, clothing, and so on, look differ-cnt under ordinary filament lamps than they do in natural sunlight. Ordinary lamps produce light that is rich in red.

Light from fluorescent lamps is more nearly natural light and can be controlled as to color by the selection of the chemicals that make up the powder used to coat the inside of the tube. The most ordinary color is "white," which also happens to be most efficient, producing more lumens per watt than any other color. However, where an approximation of sunlight is needed, a special color known as "daylight" is available.

Most sizes of fluorescent lamps are available also in such colors as blue, green, pink, gold, red. Their efficiency in colors is extraordinarily high; for example, the fluorescent lamp produces about 100 times as much green light per watt as is produced by incandescent or filament lamps. These colored lamps find a particular application where spectacular color effects are needed, for example, in theater lobbies, lounges, stage lighting, advertising, and similar purposes. They produce a vividness that is outstanding.

CHAPTER 15

RESIDENTIAL AND FARM MOTORS

A later chapter will cover the wiring of industrial motors; this chapter will cover only those ordinarily found in homes and farms. A brief discussion of the characteristics and limitations of the types in common use should be in order.

Types of Motors.—The split-phase type of alternating-current motor is very common; it is found on almost all washing machines. It is not practical in sizes above $\frac{1}{3}$ hp. While starting, the $\frac{1}{4}$-hp. size will usually consume up to 30 amp. and more; while running at full speed, it will consume 5 to 6 amp., which is approximately equal to the amperage consumed by other types of the same horsepower. Once running, it will handle a load as well as other types of the same horsepower, but it is incapable of *starting* heavy loads. Use it only on devices that start very easily, or where the load is thrown on after the motor is running at full speed.

Capacitor motors are similar to the split-phase type but consume a considerably lower amperage while starting and also are capable of starting heavier loads. They are commonly used in sizes up to 2 hp. Most electric refrigerators are equipped with this type.

Repulsion-induction motors consume a still lower amperage while starting and are capable of starting the heaviest kind of loads. Air compressors and water pumps are the most common applications. In size they are available up to 10 hp., but they are seldom used in sizes above 5 hp.

Three-phase Motors.—These motors, as the name implies, operate only on three-phase alternating current. Three-phase motors in sizes $\frac{1}{2}$ hp. and larger cost less than any other type, so by all means use them if 3-phase current is available. *Do* not assume that because there are 3 wires serving the premises, there is 3-phase current; more likely there is 3-wire 115/230-volt single-phase current. If in doubt, check with the power company.

Direct-current Motors.—Direct current is found in the downtown sections of some large cities like Chicago and New York and in some small towns. All 32-volt farm plants are direct current as are some of the 110-volt farm plants.

Motors for direct current are of one type only and have no special name or type. They are suitable for any general purpose work. The speed is usually around 1,800, but the speed varies considerably more than in alternating current motors, and varies considerably with the voltage. Idling, it may be as high as 2,400 rpm., unlike the alternating-current type, which never exceeds 1,800 rpm. for common types.

Universal Motors.—This type of motor operates on either direct current or single-phase alternating current of 60 or any other cycles. However, the speed cannot be kept at a predetermined figure, but varies over an extremely wide range. Idling, such a motor may run as fast as 15,000 r.p.m., while under a heavy load the same motor may slow down to 500 r.p.m. This of course makes the motor totally unsuitable for general purpose work. It is used only when built into a piece of machinery where the load is constant and definitely predetermined. For example, this type of motor is found on vacuum cleaners, sewing machines, some types of fans, electric drills, etc.

Reversing Motors.—The direction of rotation of a repulsion-induction motor can be changed only by shifting the position of the brushes. On other types of motors it is changed by reversing two of the wires coming from the inside of the motor. If a motor needs to be frequently reversed, a special switch may be installed for the purpose.

Temperature Rise.—Most motors are rated "40°C. continuous," which means that while operating at rated (nameplate) horsepower the temperature of the windings will not increase more than 40°C., or 72°F., over and above room temperature. On a hot summer day the temperature of the motor may therefore rise to 172°F., only 40° below the temperature of boiling water. This will feel decidedly uncomfortable to the hand and leads to complaints from users that their motors overheat; sometimes this is blamed on allegedly wrong wiring.

Overload Capacities.—Although most motors are capable of delivering 2 to 2½ times their rated horsepower for short periods of time, they also consume correspondingly greater amperages than normal while doing so. Their temperature then rises above normal; accordingly, motors should not be

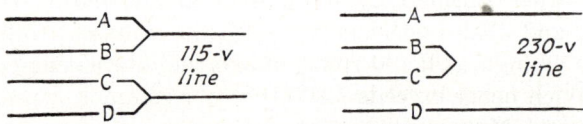

Fig. 15-1.—Many motors are so constructed that they may be operated at either 115 or 230 volts, depending upon the connection of the four leads as shown in diagram above. It is always wise to operate such motors at 230 volts, if possible.

expected to deliver continuously power in excess of their rated horsepower.

Dual-voltage Motors.—Many motors are so constructed that they can be operated on two different voltages, for example, 115 or 230 volts. Single-phase motors of this type have four leads, which connected one way permit 115-volt operation; connected differently, they permit 230-volt operation (see Fig. 15-1).

If the motor is of the dual-voltage type, that is, if it will operate on either 115 or 230 volts, two different amperages are shown on the nameplate. For example, it may be marked: "Volts 115/230 Amps 24/12." This simply indicates that, while delivering its rated power, it will consume 24 amp. if operated at 115 volts, or 12 amp. if operated at 230 volts.

Gasoline Engines vs. Electric Motors.—Because of the great amount of farm wiring in progress today many gas engines are being replaced with electric motors. Gasoline engines are usually rated at the maximum horsepower they can deliver;

there is no overload capacity as in the case of electric motors. Therefore it is frequently possible to replace a gas engine with an electric motor of a smaller horsepower rating than the engine. Good judgment must be used. If the machine in question has a reasonably constant load and the gas engine is working at the limit of its capacity, the motor must have the same horsepower as the engine it replaces. If the machine has a fluctuating load and if the engine pulls it easily and only occasionally labors at the limit of its capacity, then a motor of a smaller horsepower rating may be used.

Wiring for Motors.—The Code sections that govern the installations of motors are extremely complicated, for they cover all motors from the tiniest, to those developing hundreds of horsepower. The wiring of motors *for homes and farms*, however, can be covered by a few simple rules. Three points especially must be observed:

1. Fusing.
2. Disconnecting switch for motor.
3. Wire sizes.

Fusing.—Bear in mind the fundamental fact that any motor consumes more current while *starting* than while running. For example, an ordinary washing-machine motor may consume 25 amp. while starting, but only 5 amp. while *running* and delivering its normal horsepower. It is capable of delivering for short periods considerably more than its rated horsepower, but if it is overloaded to do so, it will consume correspondingly more current. If considerably overloaded, it may draw as much as 10 amp. It will not be harmed if it delivers normal horsepower (consuming 5 amp.) all day long, nor will it be harmed if it delivers considerably in excess of its normal horsepower (and consuming 10 amp.) for short periods, but it will burn out if it is required to deliver considerable overloads (and consuming 10 amp.) for a considerable period of time.

The wire to the motor must then be big enough to carry its *starting* current momentarily, its running current continuously, and its normal running current plus a considerable overload for short periods. Likewise it must be fused accordingly. Consider then a washing-machine motor which normally consumes about 5 amp. While starting it consumes about 25 amp. The ordinary branch circuit is wired with No. 14 wire and protected with 15-amp. fuses. This fuse will frequently blow on 25 amp. while the motor is starting. Therefore, for those circuits which serve motors, it is wise to use time-lag fuses of an amperage rating determined by the size of the wire in the branch circuit. Fuses of this type are illustrated in Figs. 5-5 and 5-6. As a matter of fact, the Code in Sec. 4332d practically requires the use of this type of fuse when motors are on the circuit.

However, the 15-amp. fuse protecting the branch circuit in no way protects the motor against overloads. Suppose the belt on a washing machine is so tight that instead of consuming its normal 5 amp. the motor consumes 10 amp. The motor will become hotter and hotter and will finally burn out. The branch-circuit fuse has not protected it at all. Therefore it is well to provide separate motor-running overcurrent protection, installed close to the motor. The Code requires it on

1. All motors larger than 1 hp.
2. All automatically started motors, 1 hp. or less.
3. All manually started motors if the motor cannot be seen from the controller, or if it is more than 50 ft. from the controller.

Even when it is not *required* by Code it is wise to provide running protection for all motors. Consider it insurance against damage to the motor.

This running protection may be a fuse or other overcurrent device rated at not more than 125 per cent of the amperage stamped on the nameplate of the motor. If this is a nonstandard rating, the next higher standard rating may be used provided that it is not more than 140 per cent of the nameplate amperage.

On devices such as refrigerators and pumps this running

RESIDENTIAL AND FARM MOTORS 253

protection is usually but not always incorporated with the machine or motor. For motors bought separately, this protection must be separately provided, although on some types and brands it is built into the motor in the form of a Thermotron or Thermoguard; in such cases no separate

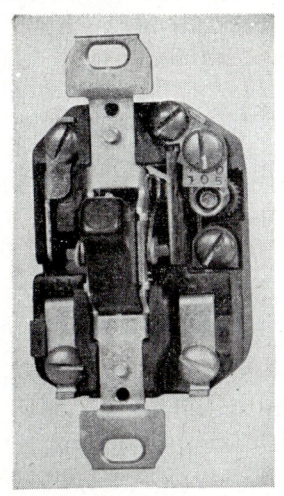 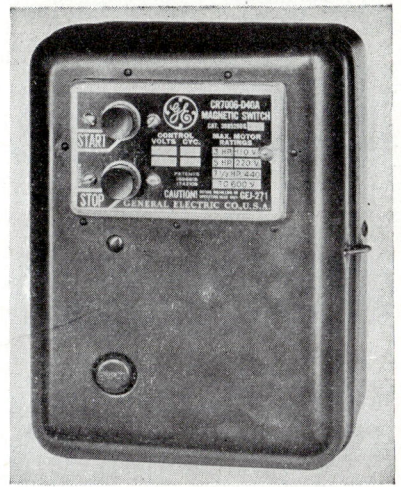

General Elec. Co.

FIG. 15-2—Controls of the type shown not only start and stop the motor, but also protect it against overloads.

protection is needed. On motors provided with cord and plug this requirement is also waived.

If ordinary fuses are used, they will blow during the starting period; consequently the time-lag type shown in Figs. 5-5 and 5-6 will have to be used, of a rating not to exceed 125 per cent (or 140 per cent) of the motor amperage, as already discussed. More usually a motor overload switch, of which several types are shown in Fig. 15-2, is used. This serves both to start and to stop the motor, as well as to protect it against overloads. It will carry substantial overloads for short periods but will disconnect the motor on short but very large overloads, as well as on continuous but small overloads. After tripping, it can be simply reset; there is nothing to replace.

Disconnecting Switch.—The motor must also be provided with a switch by which it can be completely disconnected. If an overload switch of the type shown in Fig. 15-2 is used, no additional switch is required, but if fuses are used as motor-running protection, a switch of the type shown in Fig. 15-3 should be used. The rating of the switch must be at least twice the amperage stamped on the name plate of the motor.

Square D Co.
FIG. 15-3.—A switch of this type may be used with small motors. If the switch has two fuses it is for a 230-volt motor; if it has only one fuse it is for a 115-volt motor.

Thus the 30-amp. switch illustrated in Fig. 15-3 is suitable for all motors rated not over 15 amp.

If the motor operates on 115 volts on the usual circuit with one grounded wire, a single-pole switch with one fuse must be used. If it operates on 230 volts, a 2-pole switch with two fuses must be used.

Wire Sizes.—First of all, extension cords made of ordinary No. 18 or even No. 16 lamp cord should never be used, even on small fractional horsepower motors. A short cord on the motor is in order, but if a longer extension is added, the voltage drop in the cord during the starting period while the amperage is high is apt to be so great that the motor never gets off its starting windings. A damaged motor may easily result.

The wire must be heavy enough to carry the starting amperage, and the horsepower of the motor and the distance involved must also be taken into consideration. The Code requires that the wire must have a carrying capacity equivalent to at least 125 per cent of the nameplate amperage of the motor.

For convenience the table on page 255 has been worked out. Under each wire size is given the maximum distance for which this size wire should be used if maximum efficiency is expected from the motor. This table is calculated *for single-phase alternating-current motors.* For direct-current motors the distances shown may be increased about 25 per cent above those shown (except for 32-volt, which are correct). The table is not applicable to polyphase motors.

PROPER WIRE SIZES FOR MOTORS

Motor		Wire sizes							
Horse-power	Volts	14	12	10	8	6	4	2	0	00
¼	115	85	135	230	350	520	900	1,350	2,250	2,750
⅓	115	70	110	190	280	450	700	1,100	1,850	2,300
½	115	60	100	160	250	380	620	975	1,600	2,000
¾	115	55	85	140	220	340	540	850	1,400	1,750
1	115	40	70	110	170	270	430	680	1,180	1,400
1½	115	...	45	80	120	180	300	480	750	950
2	115	...	...	55	85	135	215	340	550	700
3	115	...	...	.....	60	90	150	230	380	460
¼	230	350	500	1,000	1,400	2,000	3,600	5,400		
⅓	230	275	450	750	1,100	1,800	2,800	4,400		
½	230	250	400	650	1,000	1,500	2,500	3,900		
¾	230	200	350	550	875	1,350	2,100	3,400	5,600	7,000
1	230	160	275	450	675	1,100	1,700	2,700	4,600	5,500
1½	230	125	180	325	500	750	1,200	1,900	3,000	3,900
2	230	80	140	225	325	550	850	1,100	2,200	2,800
3	230	...	90	150	250	350	600	1,000	1,500	1,800
¼	32	30	50	80	125	200	300	500	750	1,000
⅓	32	25	40	60	100	160	240	400	600	800
½	32	15	30	45	75	120	180	300	450	600

Figures below the wire sizes indicate the one-way distances in feet that each size wire will carry the size motor indicated in the left-hand column, with 2 per cent voltage drop. A dash indicates that the wire size in question is too small to carry the current for the horsepower involved, regardless of circumstances. Figures are based on single-phase alternating-current motors, except the 32-volt type. For the 32-volt direct-current motors, a voltage drop of 5 per cent is assumed.

The table is based on a 2 per cent voltage drop. Since most motors consume about 3 times their normal current while starting, the voltage drop during that starting period will then be 3 times the percentages mentioned. If the motor is to start a machine which starts very hard, especially if it is started very frequently, use wire heavier than shown. Under no circumstances use wire lighter than the smallest shown after each horsepower rating, for this would be below the Code minimum.

Pulleys and Belts.—Even though the figuring of proper pulley ratios is not a wiring problem, a short discussion of this subject should not be amiss. In such calculations four factors are involved:

>Motor pulley diameter.
>Machine pulley diameter.
>Motor speed.
>Machine speed.

If any of the four is unknown, it is a simple matter to figure it from the three known factors, using the formulas below:

Machine pulley diameter =
$$\frac{\text{motor pulley diameter} \times \text{motor speed}}{\text{machine speed}}.$$

Machine speed = $\frac{\text{motor speed} \times \text{motor pulley diameter}}{\text{machine pulley diameter}}.$

Motor pulley diameter =
$$\frac{\text{machine pulley diameter} \times \text{machine speed}}{\text{motor speed}}.$$

Motor speed = $\frac{\text{machine speed} \times \text{machine pulley diameter}}{\text{motor pulley diameter}}.$

In making the calculations indicated above, remember that there is always some belt slippage for which allowance must be made. For motor speed use the actual speed that the motor will develop under full load.

The ratio between the diameters of the driving and the driven pulleys should be kept within reasonable limits. If one pulley is a great deal larger than the other, especially if they are close together, the belt will make contact with but a small portion of the total circumference of the smaller pulley, and slippage will be increased. The ratio should not exceed 12 to 1 in small motors; for a 1 hp., 10 to 1 is usually considered the practical limit, decreasing to 8 to 1 in the case of a 5-hp. motor, and 5 to 1 in the case of a 25-hp. motor.

Especially for small fractional-horsepower motors the use of V belts is very common. They have the advantage of being relatively inexpensive, have little slip even on small pulleys, and carry substantial loads on even the smallest size. As the load increases above ½ hp., it is often the custom to use two or more such belts side by side on multiple-groove pulleys. Avoid the use of very small diameter pulleys. Their use leads to excessive belt slippage, short belt life, and loss of power.

A common mistake is to run belts too tight. This only increases the load on the motor, causes excessive bearing wear and short belt life.

The following table should be useful in determining pulley sizes for any given machine. It is based on a motor speed of 1,750 r.p.m., and some allowance has been made for belt slippage. Figures show speed of machine with each combination of pulley diameters.

Diam. motor pulley	Diameter of pulley on machine, inches													
	1¼	1½	1¾	2	2¼	2½	3	4	5	6½	8	10	12	15	18
1¼	1,725	1,435	1,230	1,075	950	850	715	540	430	330	265	215	175	140	115
1½	2,075	1,725	1,475	1,290	1,140	1,030	850	645	515	395	320	265	215	170	140
1¾	2,400	2,000	1,725	1,500	1,340	1,200	1,000	750	600	460	375	315	250	200	165
2	2,775	2,290	1,970	1,725	1,530	1,375	1,145	850	685	530	430	345	285	230	190
2¼	3,100	2,580	2,200	1,930	1,725	1,550	1,290	965	775	595	485	385	325	255	215
2½	3,450	2,870	2,460	2,150	1,900	1,725	1,435	1,075	850	660	540	430	355	285	240
3	4,140	3,450	2,950	2,580	2,290	2,070	1,725	1,290	1,070	800	615	515	430	345	285
4	5,500	4,575	3,950	3,450	3,060	2,775	2,295	1,725	1,375	1,060	860	700	575	460	375
5	6,850	5,750	4,920	4,300	3,825	3,450	2,865	2,150	1,725	1,325	1,075	860	715	575	475
6½	8,950	7,475	6,400	5,600	4,975	4,480	3,730	2,790	2,240	1,725	1,400	1,120	930	745	620
8		9,200	7,870	6,900	6,125	5,520	4,600	3,450	2,750	2,120	1,725	1,375	1,140	915	765
10			9,850	8,620	7,670	6,900	5,750	4,300	3,450	2,650	2,150	1,725	1,430	1,140	950
12				9,200	8,280	6,900	5,160	4,130	3,180	2,580	2,075	1,725	1,375	1,140
15						8,635	6,470	5,170	3,970	3,230	2,580	2,150	1,725	1,425
18							7,750	6,200	4,770	3,880	3,100	2,580	2,070	1,725

PART 2
ACTUAL WIRING: RESIDENTIAL AND FARM

Part 2 of this book explains the actual wiring of houses and apartments, as well as farm buildings of every description. The author feels that it will be much easier for the reader to cover first these relatively simple installations, than it would be if one chapter pertaining to one particular phase of the work included everything from a simple cottage up to an elaborate project.

Practically all the fundamentals covered by Part 2 will in practice be used also in the more pretentious projects. They are the foundation for the methods to be covered by Part 3.

CHAPTER 16

PLANNING AN INSTALLATION

The plans for an electrical installation usually consist of outline drawings of the rooms involved, with indications where the various outlets for fixtures, receptacles, and other devices are to be located. Obviously a picture of a switch cannot be shown at each point on the plans where one is to be used, and so on with the different outlets. Standardized symbols are used instead.

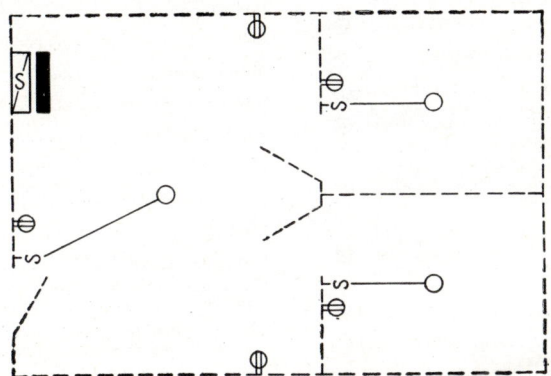

Fig. 16-1.—Layout of a simple three-room project.

Symbols.—On page 262 are shown the symbols that have been in use for many years, and on page 263 the revised symbols that have recently been adopted. It is necessary to be familiar with both, and since the differences are not great, no particular difficulty should be experienced. Each symbol must instantly indicate as much as if a picture of the device in question were shown. Throughout this book, where such symbols are required the new recommended types are used rather than the old standard.

Old Standard Symbols for Electrical Equipment of Buildings

Ceiling outlet		Pull box	
Ceiling lamp receptacle—specification to describe type such as key, keyless, or pull chain	®	Cable-supporting box	
Ceiling outlet for extensions		Meter	
Ceiling fan outlet		Branch circuit, run concealed under floor above	
Floor outlet		Branch circuit, run exposed	
Drop cord	ⒹD	Branch circuit, run concealed under floor	
Wall bracket		Feeder run, concealed under floor above	
Wall outlet for extensions		Feeder run, exposed	
Wall fan outlet		Feeder run, concealed under floor	
Wall lamp receptacle—specification to describe type such as key, keyless, or pull chain	®	Pole line	
		Push button	
Single convenience outlet		Buzzer	
Double convenience outlet		Bell	
Junction box	Ⓙ	Annunciator	
Special-purpose outlet—lighting, heating, and power as described in specification	▲	Interior telephone	
Special purpose outlet—lighting, heating, and power as described in specification	⊗	Public telephone	
Special-purpose outlet—lighting, heating, and power as described in specification		Maid's plug	Ⓜ
		Clock (secondary)	
		Electric door opener	
Exit light		Watchman station	Ⓦ
Floor elbow	Oᴱ	Watchman central station detector	Ⓦ
Floor tee	Oᵀ	Special outlet for signal system as described in specification	⊠
Pull switch	P.S.	Battery	
Local switch—single-pole	S¹	Signal wires in conduit concealed under floor	
Local switch—double-pole	S²	Signal wires in conduit concealed under floor above	
Local switch—3-way	S³	This character marked on tap circuits indicates 2 No. 14 conductors in ½-in. conduit (see note)	‖
Local switch—4-way	S⁴		
Automatic door switch	Sᴰ		
Motor	Ⓜ	3 No. 14 conductors in ½-in conduit	‖‖
Motor controller	(M.C.)	4 No. 14 conductors in ¾-in. conduit unless marked ½-in	‖ ‖
Lighting panel	▬		
Power panel	▨	5 No. 14 conductors in ¾-in. conduit	‖‖‖
Heating panel	◢		

Note.—If larger conductors than No. 14 are used, use the same symbols and mark the conductors and conduit size on the run.

PLANNING AN INSTALLATION

NEW STANDARD SYMBOLS FOR ELECTRICAL EQUIPMENT OF BUILDINGS

GENERAL OUTLETS

Ceiling	Wall	Description
○	─○	Outlet.
Ⓑ	─Ⓑ	Blanked Outlet.
Ⓓ		Drop Cord.
Ⓔ	─Ⓔ	Electrical Outlet; for use only when circle used alone might be confused with columns, plumbing symbols, etc.
Ⓕ	─Ⓕ	Fan Outlet.
Ⓙ	─Ⓙ	Junction Box.
Ⓛ	─Ⓛ	Lamp Holder.
Ⓛ$_{PS}$	─Ⓛ$_{PS}$	Lamp Holder with Pull Switch.
Ⓢ	─Ⓢ	Pull Switch.
Ⓥ	─Ⓥ	Outlet for Vapor Discharge Lamp.
Ⓧ	─Ⓧ	Exit Light Outlet.
Ⓒ	─Ⓒ	Clock Outlet. (Specify Voltage)

CONVENIENCE OUTLETS

⊖ Duplex Convenience Outlet.
⊖$_{1,3}$ Convenience Outlet other than Duplex. 1 = Single, 3 = Triplex, etc.
⊖$_{WP}$ Weatherproof Convenience Outlet.
⊖$_R$ Range Outlet.
⊖$_S$ Switch and Convenience Outlet.
⊖$_R$ Radio and Convenience Outlet.
⬤ Special Purpose Outlet. (Des. in Spec.)
⊙ Floor Outlet.

SWITCH OUTLETS

S Single Pole Switch.
S$_2$ Double Pole Switch.
S$_3$ Three Way Switch.
S$_4$ Four Way Switch.
S$_D$ Automatic Door Switch.
S$_E$ Electrolier Switch.
S$_K$ Key Operated Switch.
S$_P$ Switch and Pilot Lamp.
S$_{CB}$ Circuit Breaker.
S$_{WCB}$ Weatherproof Circuit Breaker.
S$_{MC}$ Momentary Contact Switch.
S$_{RC}$ Remote Control Switch.
S$_{WP}$ Weatherproof Switch.
S$_F$ Fused Switch.
S$_{WF}$ Weatherproof Fused Switch.

SPECIAL OUTLETS

○$_{a,b,c,etc}$
⊖$_{a,b,c,etc}$
S$_{a,b,c,etc}$
Any Standard Symbol as given above with the addition of a lower case subscript letter may be used to designate some special variation of Standard Equipment of particular interest in a specific set of Architectural Plans. When used they must be listed in the Key of Symbols on each drawing and if necessary further described in the specifications.

PANELS, CIRCUITS, AND MISCELLANEOUS

▬ Lighting Panel.
▨ Power Panel.
─── Branch Circuit; Concealed in Ceiling or Wall.
─ ─ ─ Branch Circuit; Concealed in Floor.
───── Branch Circuit; Exposed.
⟶ Home Run to Panel Board. Indicate number of Circuits by number of arrows.
Note: Any circuit without further designation indicates a two-wire circuit. For a greater number of wires indicate as follows: ─╫─ (3 wires) ─╫╫─ (4 wires), etc.
── Feeders. Note: Use heavy lines and designate by number corresponding to listing in Feeder Schedule.
▭▯▭ Underfloor Duct and Junction Box. Triple System. Note: For double or single systems eliminate one or two lines. This symbol is equally adaptable to auxiliary system layouts.
Ⓖ Generator.
Ⓜ Motor.
Ⓘ Instrument.
Ⓣ Power Transformer. (Or draw to scale.)
✉ Controller.
▭ Isolating Switch.

AUXILIARY SYSTEMS

▪ Push Button.
▯ Buzzer.
▯ Bell.
◇ Annunciator.
◀ Outside Telephone.
◁ Interconnecting Telephone.
◁ Telephone Switchboard.
Ⓣ Bell Ringing Transformer.
D Electric Door Opener.
F▯ Fire Alarm Bell.
F Fire Alarm Station.
✖ City Fire Alarm Station.
FA Fire Alarm Central Station.
FS Automatic Fire Alarm Device.
W Watchman's Station.
W Watchman's Central Station.
H Horn.
N Nurse's Signal Plug.
M Maid's Signal Plug.
R Radio Outlet.
SC Signal Central Station.
▭ Interconnection Box.
▥▥▥ Battery.
─··─ Auxiliary System Circuits.
Note: Any line without further designation indicates a 2-Wire System. For a greater number of wires designate with numerals in manner similar to ─··─12-No. 18W-3/4" C., or designate by number corresponding to listing in Schedule.
▭$_{a,b,c}$ Special Auxiliary Outlets. Subscript letters refer to notes on plans or detailed description in specifications.

Symbols in accordance with American Standards Association Standard ASA Z32.9-1943.

In plans using these symbols, wires are indicated only to connect switches with the outlets they control. Only a single line is drawn to represent all the wires that may be required. Unless otherwise specified, it is still the contractor's problem to determine which outlets go on each circuit and exactly how the different wires are to run.

Typical Plans.—Consider first a very simple plan, covering a small three-room cottage with two circuits, involving one

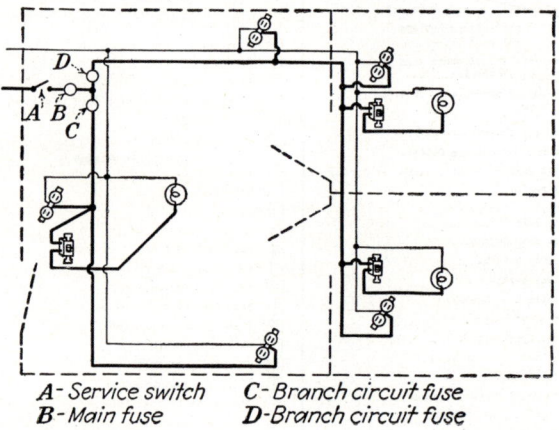

A - Service switch C - Branch circuit fuse
B - Main fuse D - Branch circuit fuse

Fig. 16-2.—The layout shown in Fig. 16-1, but here indicated in pictorial fashion.

ceiling outlet controlled by a wall switch for each of the three rooms, with three receptacle outlets for the larger room and one for each of the smaller rooms. The plan for this installation is shown in Fig. 16-1.

To make it easier to interpret this plan, Fig. 16-2 shows the same layout in pictorial fashion, with all the wires shown in detail. The neutral wire is shown as a light line, the "hot" wires as heavy lines. Note how the neutral wire runs without interruption from the point where it enters the building to each device where current is to be used. The black wires run from their fuses direct to each receptacle outlet and to each

PLANNING AN INSTALLATION

switch; an additional length runs from each switch to the light it controls, and that completes the wiring.

A represents the main switch. B represents the main fuse. C and D represent the two fuses, one for each branch circuit. The first branch circuit comprises all the wiring served by the current that flows through fuse C; the second circuit comprises all wiring served by the current that flows through fuse D.

The complete wiring plans for a larger house are shown in Figs. 16-3 to 16-6. These diagrams[1] may at first sight seem rather formidable, but with study they become simple. Such plans are supplemented by detailed specifications which give such information as size and type of service entrance, number of circuits, type of materials to be used, and similar data.

Make some plans of a similar nature of other installations, for example, your own home as it is wired and as you would like to see it wired. Do this until symbols are as clear to you as the printed words of a book. Remember that *round* symbols always denote outlets served by the full voltage of the wiring system; *square* symbols always denote outlets operating at low voltage, for example, bells, buzzers, etc. Solid lines denote wires in ceilings or walls; dotted lines denote wires under the floor.

Making Plans.—Often the electrician may be called upon to make the plans for a job instead of finding them ready-made. In that case include all those details found in plans of the type shown in Figs. 16-3 to 16-6. Likewise include in the specifications such things as the size of service entrance wires and switch, the number of circuits, the location of service switch and fuse panels, material to be used, and similar details.

In making such plans there is usually little choice except to follow the general ideas of the owner, as to the number of outlets and similar details. On the other hand, the average

---

[1] Reproduced by permission from the "Handbook of Interior Wiring Design," by the Industry Committee on Interior Wiring Design.

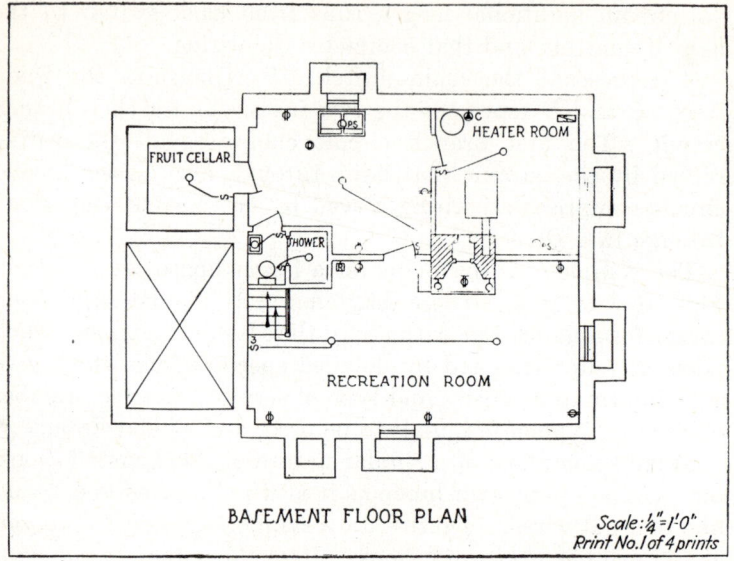

Fig. 16-3.—Typical basement plan of a residence.

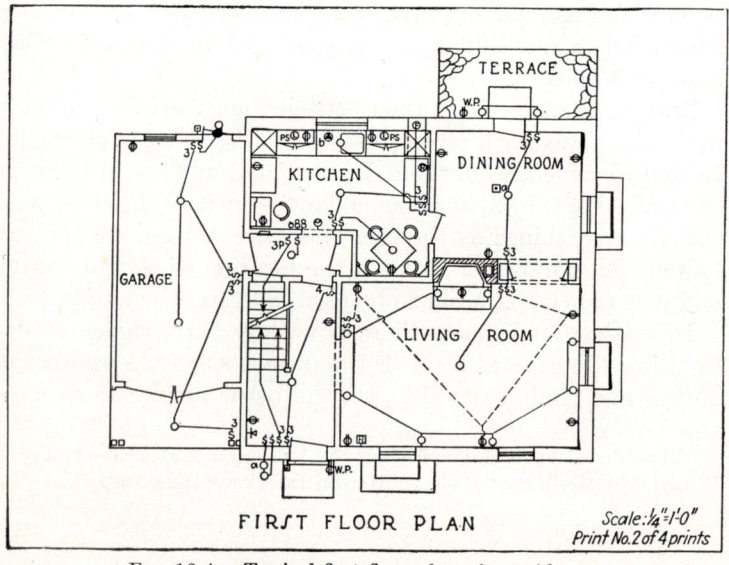

Fig. 16-4.—Typical first floor plan of a residence.

PLANNING AN INSTALLATION

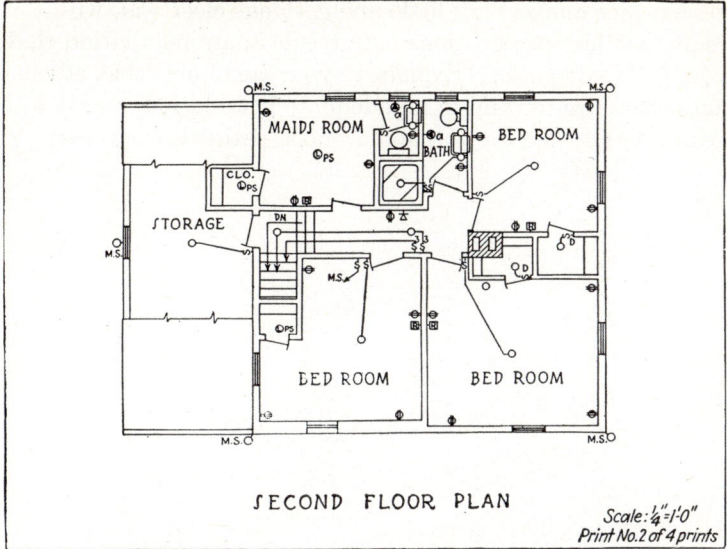

Fig. 16-5.—Typical second-floor plan of a residence.

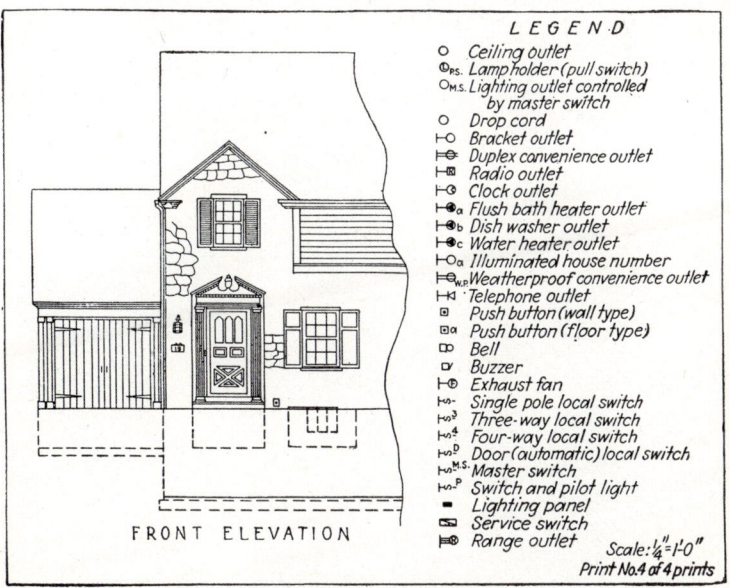

Fig. 16-6.—Typical front elevation, also legend, of plans for a residence. Note the explanations for outlets *a*, *b*, *c*.

home owner knows very little about things electrical, with the result that his specifications may result in an installation that is far from adequate. Explain to your customer what advantages there are for him in an adequate installation, and it will mean a larger sale for you and a better satisfied customer.

CHAPTER 17

INSTALLATION OF SERVICE ENTRANCE AND GROUND

Chapter 9 covered the selection of the proper service entrance wires, the rating of the service switch, and similar essentials. This chapter will cover the actual installation of the materials selected. Many variations are possible in the

Westinghouse Elec. & Mfg. Co.

FIG. 17-1.—A detachable outdoor meter and the socket on which it is mounted. Meters of this type are mounted exposed to the weather.

mechanical arrangement and selection of the different parts; the wires may come in through conduit, or in the form of service entrance cable, or underground; the meter may be outdoors or indoors; the branch-circuit overcurrent equipment may be fuses or circuit breakers; main overcurrent protection may or may not be required.

Begin with a very simple installation—a service entrance for a summer cottage which involves only two service entrance wires, a 30-amp. switch, and two branch circuits.

Meter.—The power company determines whether the meter is to be outdoors or indoors. Very likely it will be an outdoor type either as shown in Fig. 17-1, which is installed exposed to the weather, or possibly an ordinary meter housed in a weatherproof cabinet of the type shown in Fig. 17-2. In any event the power company usually furnishes the meter as well

Square D Co.
Fig. 17-2.—Ordinary indoor meters are sometimes used outdoors, mounted in weatherproof meter cabinets.

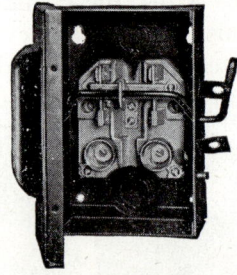

Square D Co.
Fig. 17-3.—A very simple switch is sometimes permitted as an entrance switch for very small installations.

as the socket or the weatherproof cabinet, which the contractor installs.

Service Switch.—Select either a simple switch of the type pictured in Fig. 17-3, and use with it a 2-circuit fuse cabinet of the type pictured in Fig. 17-4, or a unit which has within a single cabinet the disconnect switch, the main fuse, and the two branch-circuit fuses. Another choice is a combination of two circuit breakers.

Note that while the general description of the switch selected is merely "2-wire 30-amp. 2-pole solid neutral, with 2 branch circuits," there are often in a manufacturer's line a dozen switches that answer this general description. In some

INSTALLATION OF SERVICE ENTRANCE 271

localities the inspector and the power company will accept any switch answering this general description so long as it bears the Underwriters' label. More often the power company has definite preferences; hence it is always best on any job to consult them. Frequently they have a printed list of all brands showing the manufacturers' numbers of those switches that are acceptable.

A typical service entrance is shown in Fig. 17-5. In this case the service entrance wires

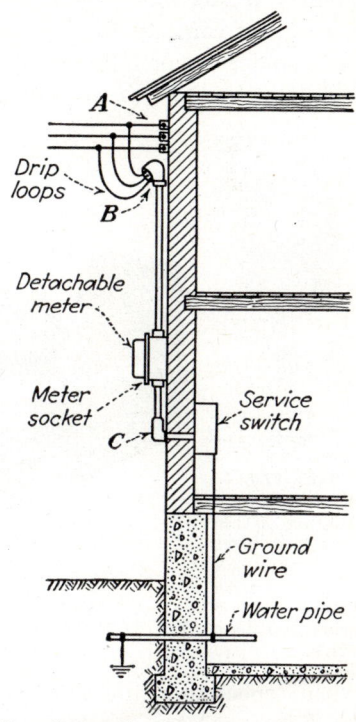

Square D Co.

FIG. 17-4.—Fuse cabinets of this type may be attached to service entrance switches to hold the branch-circuit fuses. Such cabinets are available to hold any number of fuses from two upwards.

FIG. 17-5.—Cross-section of a typical service entrance.

enter through conduit. This picture shows the service switch on the first floor; often it is located in the basement.

Solderless Connectors.—The 1947 Code has a new Sec. 2358 which prohibits the use of soldered joints in connection with the attachment of wires to service entrance switches or circuit breakers. The reason for this is not hard to understand. It is not particularly difficult to learn how to make good soldered joints or connections to terminals when using small wires; it is however quite an art to solder a joint when a heavy wire and a tubular solder lug are involved. In the finer sizes of wire, solder joints are frequently made, giving the workman much opportunity for practice; in the heavier sizes they are infrequently made, affording little opportunity for practice. In connecting wires to service equipment, use only joints made with solderless or "pressure" connectors, or similar clamp-style terminals using no solder. The same prohibition holds

Porcelain Products, Inc.

FIG. 17-6.—Screw-point insulators of this type are used to support service entrance wires or other outdoor wires.

Porcelain Products, Inc.

FIG. 17-7.—A unit which comprises two or three insulators may be used instead of separate insulators.

with respect to connections involving the ground wire, as will be discussed later.

Service Insulators.—Insulators for supporting the power company's wires where they reach the building (point A in Fig. 17-5) must be provided. These may be simple screw-point insulators, shown in Fig. 17-6; according to Code they must be kept a minimum of 6 in. apart. More frequently, however, either of the types shown in Fig. 17-7 is used; choose one with the individual knobs at least 6 in.[1] apart. These are known as "service brackets" or "secondary racks."

These insulators should be mounted as high above the

---

[1] In many localities a separation of 8 in. is required.

ground as the shape and structure of the building will permit, and per Sec. 2324, in no event less than 10 ft. above the ground, which must be increased to 18 ft. if the supported wires run over driveways, alleys, and public roads. On a farm the entire yard is more or less a "driveway," and the 18-ft. clearance should be observed.

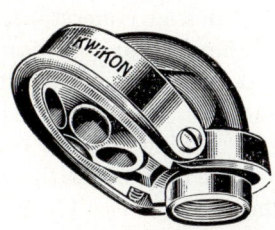 

Kwikon Co.

Fig. 17-8.—A typical service head, used at the top of the conduit through which the service entrance wires enter the building.

Kwikon Co.

Fig. 17-9.—A typical entrance ell, used at the bottom of the conduit through which the service entrance wires run, at the point where they enter the building.

Service Head.—At the top end of the service conduit (B in Fig. 17-5) the Code requires a fitting that will prevent rain from entering the conduit. A fitting of this type is shown in Fig. 17-8; it goes by various names such as "service head," "entrance cap," "weather head." It consists of three parts: the body which is attached to the service conduit, an insulating block to separate the wires where they emerge, and the cover which keeps out the rain and holds the parts together.

Entrance Ell.—At the point where the conduit enters the building (C in Fig. 17-5), it is customary to use an entrance ell of the type shown in Fig. 17-9. With the cover removed, it is a simple matter to pull wires around the right-angle corner. This device also must be raintight.

Entrance Conduit.—For this simple 30-amp. entrance, two No. 8 wires are sufficient. Table 4 of the Code (see Appendix) shows that ¾-in. conduit is sufficient; since the installation is outdoors, only the galvanized finish may be used.

First cut a length to reach from the meter socket to a point directly below the service insulators. Ream the cut end carefully and thread it. Then install the body of the service head at the top end. Thread the bottom end into the meter socket. Next cut short lengths of conduit to reach from the meter socket to the entrance ell and from the entrance ell to the service switch.

If the building is of frame construction, it is a simple matter to bore through the wall, but if it is brick or concrete, it will involve some hard labor. A star drill of the type described in Chap. 10 will serve the purpose. For an occasional job a length of pipe on one end of which teeth have been cut with a hack saw, as shown in Fig. 17-10, will answer.

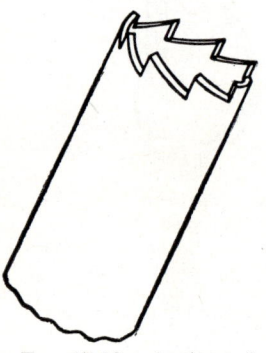

Fig. 17-10.—A piece of steel pipe with teeth cut on one end with a hack saw makes a handy tool for occasional drilling through brick walls.

The procedure in fastening together the various elements will vary with the size of the job. In small jobs simply preassemble the three lengths of conduit, the entrance ell, and the meter socket and mount the entire assembly on the wall, using the hole through the wall as the starting point.

The service switch is mounted rigidly and the conduit is fastened to it by the locknut and bushing method, which is covered in Chap. 10. The method of grounding will be covered at the end of this chapter.

Pulling Wires.—It will be no great job to pull the service entrance wires into the conduit. They must be continuous and unspliced. For a short length no fish tape will be necessary, for the wires, being of relatively large size, can be pushed through. Anchor them to the proper terminals on the meter socket; let them project out of the top of the conduit about 2 ft. Next slip the insulating block of the service head over the two wires and assemble the service head. Drip loops, as shown in Fig. 17-5, should be provided. The splices between the service entrance wires and the service drop wires are usually made by the power company. This completes the installation.

Service Entrance Cable.—If service entrance cable is used in place of conduit with separate wires, the procedure is not greatly different. The cable is secured to the building by means of one of the several types of straps shown in Fig. 11-8, or the clip of Fig. 17-11, which has no exposed screws when the

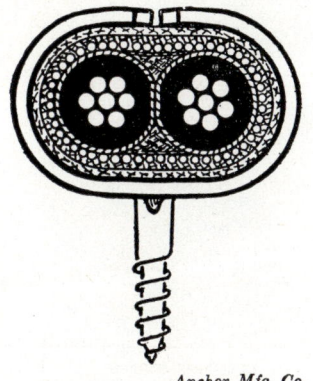

Anchor Mfg. Co.

Fig. 17-11.—Clips of this kind are handy for fastening service entrance cable to the building.

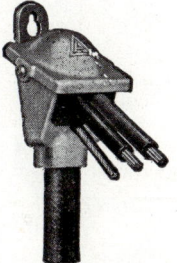

Appleton Elec. Co.

Fig. 17-12.—A typical service head for service entrance cable.

installation is finished. The service head is slightly different from the type used with conduit, in that it is fastened to the building itself, instead of being supported by the conduit (see Fig. 17-12). A new type is shown in Fig. 17-13.

Cable is attached to the meter socket by means of watertight connectors, two types of which are shown in Fig. 17-14. These connectors incorporate soft rubber glands; as the locking nut or the locking screws are tightened, the rubber is compressed, making a watertight seal around the cable. In use, the connector is screwed into the threaded opening of the meter socket, the thread being treated with waterproofing compound. Next the cable is slipped through the rubber gland and the locking screws or nut taken up, making a complete watertight connection. Inside of buildings watertight connectors are not required; armored-cable connectors of appropriate size are used instead.

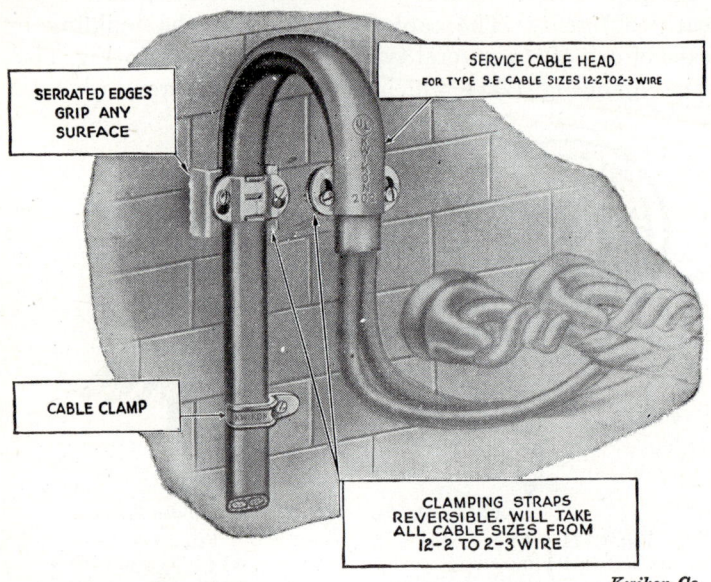

FIG. 17-13.—A new type of service head for service entrance cable.

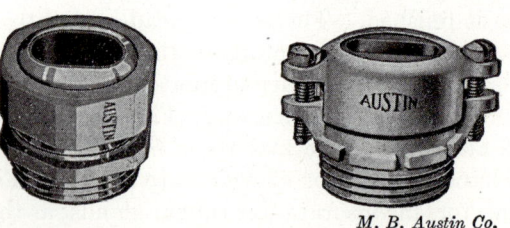

FIG. 17-14.—Watertight connectors for service entrance cable. The rubber gland inside the connector expands when the connector is tightened, making the installation watertight.

At the point where the cable enters the building, a sill plate is used to prevent the rain from following the cable into the inside of the building. One type is shown in Fig. 17-15;

INSTALLATION OF SERVICE ENTRANCE

usually a soft rubber compound is supplied with it to seal any opening that might exist.

Service entrance cable in most brands comes with a grayish paint finish, which permits painting to match the building on which it is installed.

Large Installations.—For larger installations, the work is done as just outlined, except that proportionately larger conduit, fittings, cable, etc., are used. Table 4 of the Code (see Appendix) shows the size conduit required for various combinations of wires. Do not overlook the footnote under the table, which, for the relatively short runs as used for service entrances, permits a smaller size conduit to be used with certain combinations of wire sizes than would be permitted for the same wires under other circumstances.

Indoor Meters.—When the meter is installed indoors, select a service switch which has a meter trim, or top wall, in the cabinet so designed that parts of it can be removed like knockouts, permitting the bottom of the meter to set inside the switch, thus eliminating external wires.

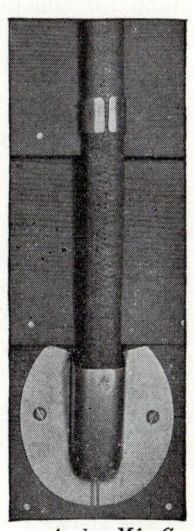

Anchor Mfg. Co.
Fig. 17-15.—A sill plate is used at the point where service entrance cable enters the building. Soft rubber compound seals openings to keep out water.

Provide a place for the power company to mount the meter; usually this consists of a board of sufficient size so that both the switch and the meter may be mounted thereon. Anchor it to the wall by one of the methods shown in Figs. 10-22 and 10-23 in connection with outlet boxes.

Wires on Side of Building.—If service conductors must run along the side of a building, service entrance cable may be used, or rubber-covered wires enclosed in conduit. Open wires may be used, supported at least every 9 ft. by insulators which separate them at least 6 in. and keep them at least 2 in. from the surface. When within 8 ft. of the ground, open wires must be run inside conduit or otherwise protected against mechanical injury.

Underground Services.—Underground wires must be suitably protected against mechanical injury. Usually the service wires consist of lead-sheathed cable protected by conduit, tile duct, or similar means. Gradually becoming more common for the purpose is Type USE service entrance cable or

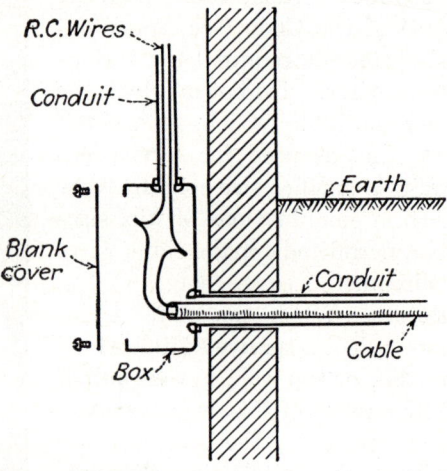

Fig. 17-16.—If underground conductors cannot be run directly to entrance switch, use the construction shown in changing over from underground cable to the usual interior wiring.

parkway cable (both described in Chap. 6), which have inherent protection against mechanical damage and need no further protection.

Usually underground conductors begin aboveground at a pole at the power company's wires. The Code requires that they be given additional protection against mechanical injury for a distance of at least 8 ft. aboveground. This is usually a length of pipe or conduit. At the top end provide a service head. If the cable is of the lead-sheathed type, seal off the end with sealing compound to prevent moisture from getting in under the lead sheath.

When the service entrance wires consist of underground

cable, there must be no underground splices, and the power company will probably insist that it continue in one piece inside the buiding up to the meter or service switch. If this is not possible, the construction shown in Fig. 17-16 may be used. In this case the underground run ends at the outlet box, separate wires being then continued up to the meter or service switch.

Grounding.—The Code differentiates between two kinds of grounds: system grounds and equipment grounds. The system ground consists of grounding the white neutral incoming wire, as well as the neutral wire as it runs out of the service switch to the branch circuits. The equipment ground consists of grounding the metal parts of the service entrance, such as the metal box of the service switch, as well as the service entrance conduit or the armor[1] of service entrance cable. If the branch-circuit wiring is metallic, that is, any type of conduit or armored cable, this metal raceway is automatically grounded because it is anchored to the service switch. The equipment ground also includes motor frames, switchboard frames, and similar equipment, which, however, need not be considered in residential wiring because, if metal raceway is used for branch circuits, such equipment is automatically grounded. If a nonmetal system such as knob and tube or nonmetallic sheathed cable is used, such miscellaneous equipment need not be grounded in residential wiring.

For residential purposes system and equipment grounds are combined and handled by a single grounding wire.

Method of Grounding.—The usual ground connection is to a water pipe of a city water system. Use the cold-water piping, not the hot, because the former runs more directly

---

[1] According to Code definition, only the type of service entrance cable shown in Fig. 12-6 is armored. The armor is grounded through the connector, the outer fabric cover being removed before the connector is fastened to the cable. The type shown in Fig. 12-3 has a flat steel protective tape, which is not armor in the sense of the Code definition, and grounding of the tape is not required, since it is automatically grounded when the neutral wire is grounded.

to the ground. Make the ground connection as close as practical to the meter, or if at all possible, to the street side of the meter; on the other hand, keep the ground wire as short and direct as possible. Other things being equal, it is probably best to run the ground wire to the nearest cold-water pipe.

In the absence of a continuous underground water pipe, the metal framework of a building may be used, or even the gas piping. The local inspector should be consulted. In the absence of all such objects, use an artificial ground, as described later.

Grounding Wire.—The ground wire does not need to be insulated, although there is no objection to using insulated wire. It may never be lighter than No. 8, which serves the purpose when the largest service conductor is not heavier than No. 2. If the largest service conductor is No. 1 or 0, use No. 6. For heavier service conductors, see Chap. 26. There is no objection to using a grounding wire larger than the minimum required by the Code. Note however that when an "artificial ground" (as described later) is used the grounding wire never need be larger than No. 6 (Sec. 2594).

If No. 4 wire is used, it requires no further protection such as conduit; it may be run open or concealed; it may run directly to ground without following the exact contour of the building. It may be stapled to the building, but this is not required. Common sense, of course, dictates that it be guarded against mechanical injury if in a location where it might be disturbed.

If No. 6 wire is used, it requires no further protection such as conduit, provided that it closely follows the surface of the building and is rigidly stapled to it, assuming further that it is free from exposure to mechanical injury. If these conditions are not met, as is quite usual, then it must be given mechanical protection in the same way as No. 8, which the next paragraph covers.

If No. 8 wire is used (or No. 6 wire neither following the surface of the building, nor stapled to it), it must be run inside of conduit, or it may be the armored type of wire shown in

Fig. 17-17, consisting of bare wire plus armor. If it is conduit, it must be attached to the service switch by locknut and bushing; if it is armor, with a connector of the type used on armored cable. At the water pipe end, either conduit or armor is fastened to the same clamp by which the ground wire is attached to the pipe.

National Elec. Products Corp.

FIG. 17-17.—Armored ground wire. The conductor is not insulated.

M. B. Austin Co.   *M. B. Austin Co.*   *M. B. Austin Co.*

FIG. 17-18.—Ground clamp for bare wire without protective armor.   FIG. 17-19.—Ground clamp for armored ground wire.   FIG. 17-20.—Ground clamp for use with ground wire run through conduit.

Ground Clamps.—There is an almost endless variety of ground clamps on the market, all serving the same purpose. Figure 17-18 shows a common clamp fitting ½-, ¾-, or 1-in. water pipe. For the smaller sizes reverse the lower jaw. Larger sizes are available for larger size pipe. Use it with bare ground wire without further protection.

The type in Fig. 17-19 is very similar except that there is an extra clamp to which the armor of armored ground wire is clamped. The type in Fig. 17-20 is also similar except that it has a still larger fitting in which conduit is clamped if used as protection for the ground wire.

The type of ground clamp should be carefully selected. The ordinary metal-strap type is prohibited by Sec. 2615. If the pipe to which the ground connection is made is iron pipe, the ground clamp should be made of iron. If the ground connection is made to copper or brass pipe, or a copper or copper-coated rod, the clamp should be made of copper or brass. Unless this point is observed, electrolytic action is likely to set in, resulting in a high-resistance ground which is not much better than no ground at all.

Avoid Solder Connections.—The 1947 Code in Sec. 2614 prohibits joints that depend on solder, so far as grounding wires are concerned. Use only joints dependent upon solderless or "pressure" connectors; do not use solder.

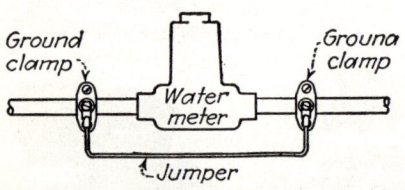

Fig. 17-21.—A jumper should be placed around the water meter.

Water Meters.—It is not unusual for a water meter to be removed from a building, at least temporarily while testing. If the ground connection is made to a water pipe between the meter and some other part of the building, removing the meter then leaves the system ungrounded, which leaves a temporary hazardous condition.

In some cases the joints between the water pipes and the meter are very poor joints, electrically speaking—practically insulated. If the ground of the electrical system is between the water meter and some other part of the building, it results in a "ground" apparently meeting Code requirements, but actually no ground at all. This is very dangerous. Therefore the Code in Sec. 2612a requires that when the ground connection is not made on the street side of the water meter a jumper be installed across the meter, as shown in Fig. 17-21. Two ground clamps are used; the size of the jumper wire is the same as used for the ground proper.

Most home owners have not the slightest conception of the importance of a good ground. Ground connections have even been removed by some misguided or uninformed home owners. This has prompted some wide-awake manufacturers to provide with their ground clamps printed tags intended to be permanently attached to ground clamps when installed, caution-

INSTALLATION OF SERVICE ENTRANCE

ing the occupant of the premises to leave ground connections intact, for their own safety. It is recommended that such tags when provided be attached to ground clamps as they are installed.

Connections within Service Switch.—The neutral of most service switches consists merely of a strap with a number of terminals. This terminal strap is usually not insulated from the steel cabinet of the switch but directly grounded to it; consequently the neutral wires are grounded to the cabinet when they are connected to these terminals. The service conduit is also fastened to the cabinet, as is the conduit or armor on the wires to the branch circuits. Therefore it would seem sufficient to run

M. B. Austin Co.
FIG. 17-22.—A grounding bushing.

one ground wire from this neutral strap to ground, to ground the entire installation effectively. In practice, however, it has been found that the resistance created by the various locknut-and-bushing joints is too high; therefore the Code requires further bonding together.

Grounding Bushings.—At all points where the service or other conduit enters the service switch, instead of an ordinary bushing use a grounding bushing, one type of which is shown in Fig. 17-22. The setscrew shown goes through the bushing and bites into the metal of the service switch, preventing the bushing from turning, thus ensuring that the joint will always be at least as good as when first installed. In addition, a bonding conductor can be clamped into the lug, and from there run to the neutral strap on the switch, or, as is frequently the case, to a grounding terminal which is provided in some switch cabinets, separate and apart from the neutral strap. In that way all parts are completely bonded and effectively grounded.

The use of grounding bushings is not required when service entrance cable is used, unless it is the type shown in Fig. 12-6.

Complete Ground.—A complete ground for the average residential job is shown in Fig. 17-23. In this picture only the grounded or neutral wires are shown, the "hot" wires being omitted for the sake of simplicity. Grounding bushings are used at points A, B, and C. Sometimes the service switch also has at some convenient point D a terminal which is merely a setscrew in the metal of the box. Wires are run from the

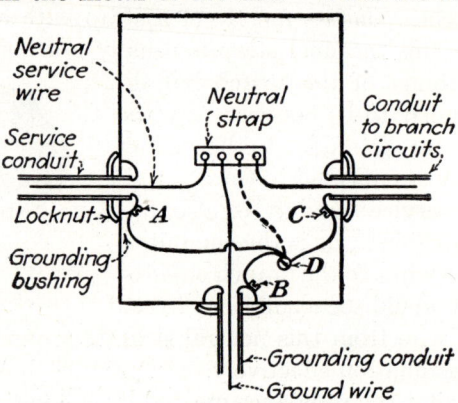

Fig. 17-23.—Typical grounding scheme at entrance switch of residential job. Only the grounded-neutral wires are shown. The detail used varies in different localities.

grounding bushings to this point D and usually also from there to the neutral wire, as shown by the dotted line.

The exact method of grounding varies considerably between various localities, and it is always well to consult the local inspector.

Artificial Grounds.—When a city water system is not available, a substitute or artificial ground is used. The usual form is a driven pipe or rod, which must go at least 8 ft. into the earth. Grounding to the pipe in a dug well is not recommended. Often this leads to exceptionally long ground wires; furthermore, wells sometimes go dry, resulting in no ground at all. On the other hand, if the well is a driven well located close to the point of the logical ground connection, its casing makes an excellent ground.

Pipe may be used, provided it is galvanized and at least $\frac{3}{4}$-in. size. Solid rod must also be galvanized and the same size. Copper rods or approved substitutes need be only $\frac{1}{2}$ in.

in diameter. The most common substitute which the Underwriters have approved is the Copperweld type of rod—a rod of steel with a layer of copper welded to the outside.

Appleton Elec. Co.
FIG. 17-24.—A grounding elbow, generally used with artificial grounds when the entrance wires run through conduit.

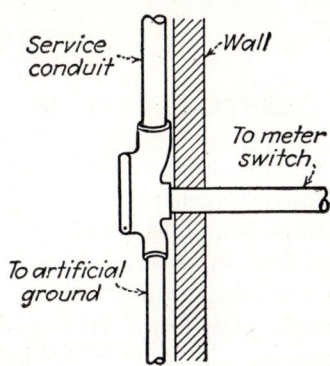

FIG. 17-25.—Installation showing use of the grounding elbow shown in Fig. 17-24.

The Code requires that the ground rod or other artificial ground be entirely independent of and kept at least 6 ft. from any other ground of the type used for radio, telephone, or lightning rods.

When an artificial ground is used, usually the ground rod is out-of-doors, therefore it is necessary to bring the grounding wire out of the building. In many localities the inspector will require a special type of entrance ell similar to that shown in Fig. 17-9 but with an extra opening in the bottom for the ground wire. This is shown in Fig. 17-24, and, in turn, Fig. 17-25 should make its use clear.

M. B. Austin Co.
FIG. 17-26.—A meter ring, used with artificial grounds when service entrance cable is used.

When service entrance cable is used, a meter ring of the type shown in Fig. 17-26 is sometimes used. This is slipped between the service entrance cable connector and the meter socket or the weatherproof meter cabinet. The ground wire is attached to it and from there run to ground.

CHAPTER 18

INSTALLATION OF SPECIFIC OUTLETS

In previous chapters installations of electrical devices were considered in rather general fashion; in this chapter the exact method of installing a variety of outlets using assorted materials will be discussed in detail. Only methods used in *new work* (buildings wired while under construction) will be explained. *Old work* (the wiring of buildings *after* their completion) will be described in a separate chapter.

In wiring buildings with conduit, the conduit is installed, all the outlet and switch boxes are mounted, and all similar details handled while the building is in the early stages. This is termed "roughing-in." The wires are not pulled into the conduit until after the lathing, plastering, papering, and similar work is finished, and obviously the switches, receptacles, fixtures, and other devices cannot be installed until the building is practically completed. However, to avoid repetition later, the pulling of the wires with the installation of the box will be included in this chapter. If cable or knob and tube systems are used, the wires are automatically installed in the roughing-in process.

Each type of outlet will be treated separately. In the pictures the outlet under discussion will be shown in a number of different ways, as follows:

1. As it would appear on a blueprint.
2. As it would appear in diagrammatic or schematic fashion.
3. In pictorial fashion using conduit.
4. In pictorial fashion, using cable. The picture will show armored cable, but nonmetallic sheathed cable may be used instead.
5. In pictorial fashion, using knob and tube wiring.

The same basic details shown in Fig. 18-1 will be used in

INSTALLATION OF SPECIFIC OUTLETS 287

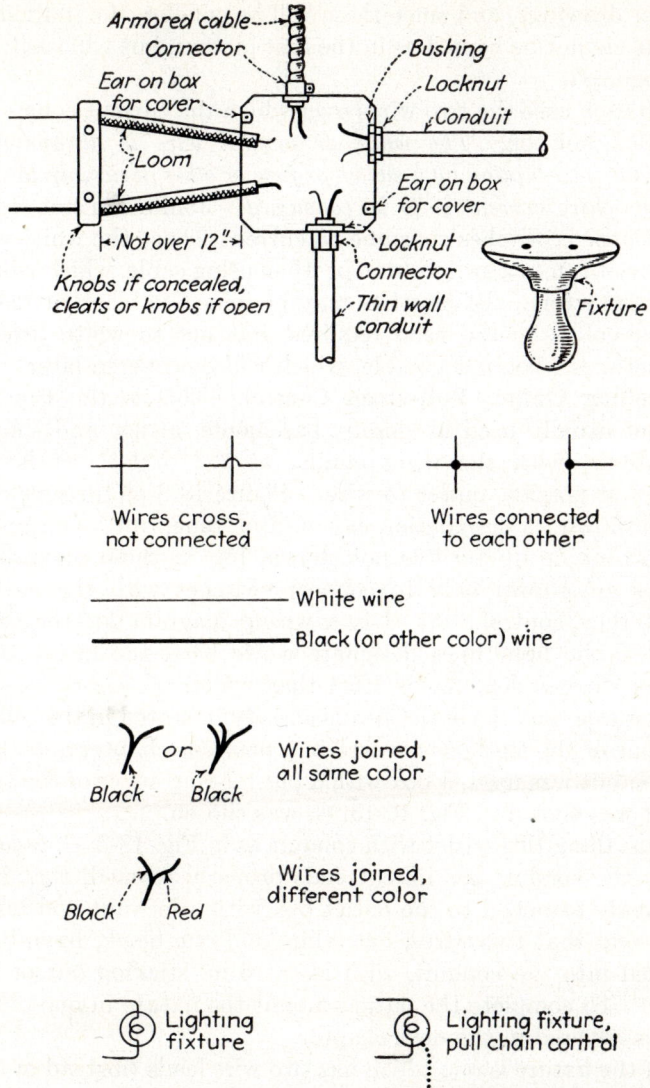

FIG. 18-1.—Study these symbols well so that other diagrams in this chapter will be clear.

other drawings, and since these will be smaller, the individual parts cannot be named as in the first picture, but will easily be recognized.

In each case the two wires over which the current comes are labeled SOURCE. *The white or neutral wire is always run, without interruption by a switch or fuse or other device, up to each point where current is to be consumed.* Joints are not interruptions. Switches consume no current; hence the white wire does not run to a switch (except when using cable, which will be covered later). Black wires may be joined to black or red or other colors as the need requires, but not to white (except sometimes when using cable, which will be covered later).

Ceiling Outlet, Pull-chain Control.—This is the type of outlet usually used in closets, basements, attics, and similar locations, with the wires ending at the outlet. It is the simplest possible outlet to wire. Figure 18-2 pictures it. At *A* is shown its designation as found on blueprint layouts; the wire running up to it is not shown, for, in these blueprints, wires are shown only to connect switches with the outlets that they control. At *B* is a wiring diagram for the same outlet; the light lines designate white wire, the heavy lines black wire, or some color other than white.

Assume that the outlet box is already mounted in the ceiling by one of the methods covered in a previous chapter and that, if conduit was used, a box with a plaster-ring cover of the type that was shown in Fig. 10-13, *C*, was chosen.

Installing this outlet with conduit as in Fig. 18-2, *C*, assume that the conduit has its cut ends properly reamed, that it is properly attached to the outlet box with a locknut and bushing, and that two wires, one white and one black, have been pulled into the conduit, with about 6 in. sticking out of the box. To complete the outlet, mount the fixture in one of the ways covered in the next chapter.

If the fixture is one which has two wire leads (instead of two terminals to which the wires from the outlet box can be attached), the wiring is still the same except that a couple of splices must be made in the box, as shown in Fig. 18-2, *D*.

INSTALLATION OF SPECIFIC OUTLETS 289

If thin-wall conduit (EMT) is used instead of rigid conduit, the same procedure as with rigid conduit prevails except that the threadless fittings such as were shown in Figs. 11-10 and 11-11 are used instead of the locknuts and bushings used with rigid conduit.

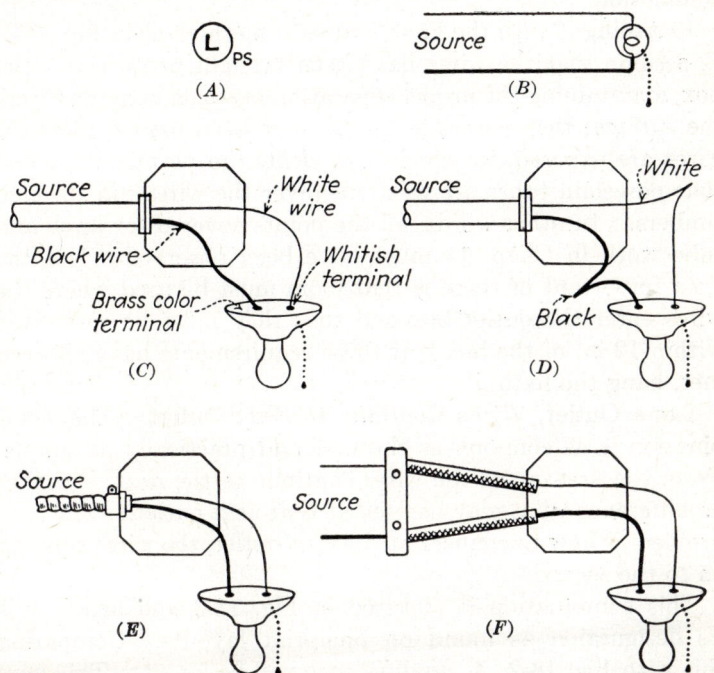

Fig. 18-2.—A simple hookup of a pull-chain outlet, with wires ending at that outlet.

Installing this same outlet with armored cable, as shown in Fig. 18-2, E, assume that the cable has been properly cut, a fiber bushing inserted between armor and wires, a connector solidly attached to the cable, and the connector in turn rigidly secured to the box, as was explained in a previous chapter. The cable must be anchored at intervals not exceeding $4\frac{1}{2}$ ft., and also within 12 in. of the outlet box. There is then nothing further to do except to mount the fixture.

If nonmetallic sheathed cable is used instead of armored cable, the only difference is that a slightly different style of connector is chosen.

If flexible conduit is used, follow the procedure for armored cable, except that the wires are pulled into the job after completion.

Installing it with the knob and tube method, as in Fig. 18-2, F, assume that the wires have been brought up to the outlet box, maintaining the proper separation between wires and from the surface; that porcelain knobs have been used (unless the wires are exposed, in which case cleats are permissible); and that porcelain tubes are used wherever the wires run through timbers. In other words, all the points covered for knob and tube work in Chap. 11 must have been observed. Not the least important of these is that loom must be used where the wires enter the outlet box and that they must be supported within 12 in. of the box. If these requirements have all been met, hang the fixture.

Same Outlet, Wires Continue to Next Outlet.—This combination is as common as the first and practically as simple. From the first outlet the wires continue to the next; it makes no difference what may be used at that next outlet. The only problem is how to connect at the first outlet, the wires running on to the second.

This combination is pictured in Fig. 18-3 and again A is its designation as found on blueprint layouts. Comparing this with Fig. 18-2, A, no difference will be found. This may be confusing, but in blueprint layouts the wires between different outlets are not indicated except those wires between switches and the outlets they control. It is up to the one making the installation to use his own good judgment as to the exact fashion of hooking together different outlets. At B is shown the wiring diagram for the combination.

At C is shown the outlet using conduit. Compare it carefully with Fig. 18-2, D. The new outlet, Fig. 18-3, C, is the same as the former except for the addition of two new wires running on to the second outlet at the right, and these two wires have been shown in dotted lines to distinguish them easily from the former wires. Simply join all the black wires together, also all the whites; solder, tape, and the job is finished.

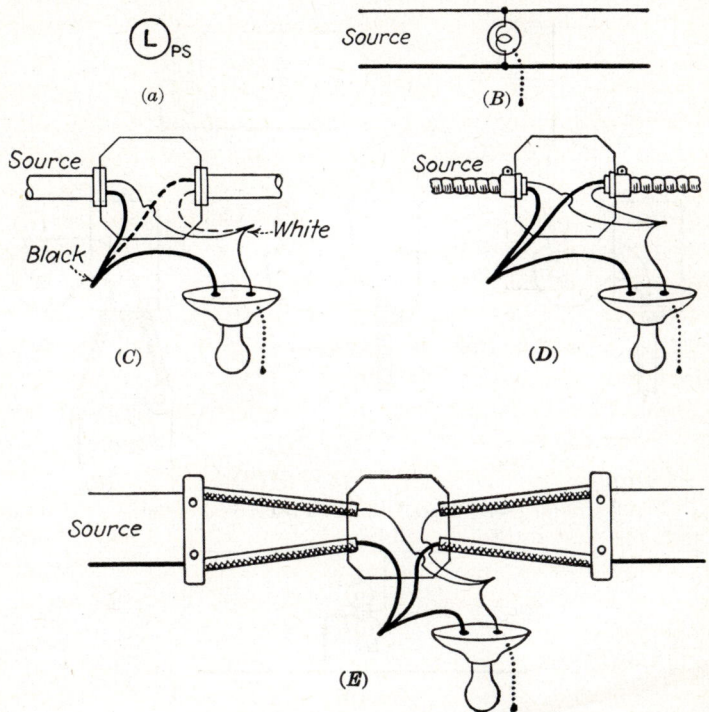

FIG. 18-3.—The hookup shown in Fig. 18-2, but with the wires running on to another outlet.

In Fig. 18-3, D and E, is shown the same outlet but with cable and knob and tube. Detailed explanation should not be necessary.

Receptacle Outlet.—In Fig. 18-4 at A is shown the designation for this outlet as found on blueprint layouts; at B is a wiring diagram. To wire this outlet, merely attach the wires to the receptacle.

At D and E is shown the same outlet wired with cable and knob and tube; these are so simple that no further clarification is needed.

Receptacle Outlet, Wires Continue to Next Outlet.—In Fig. 18-5, *A*, is shown the wiring diagram of the circuit in

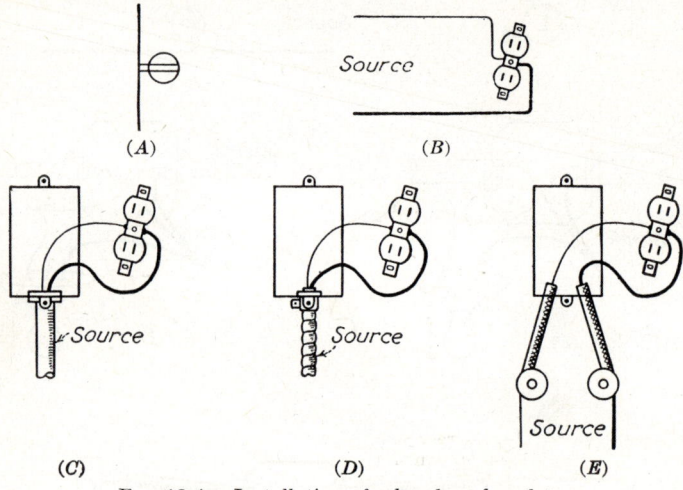

Fig. 18-4.—Installation of a baseboard outlet.

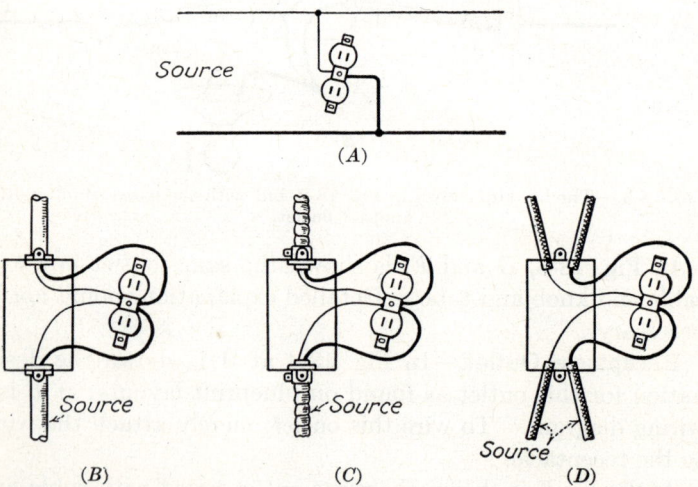

Fig. 18-5.—Baseboard outlet, with wires running on to another outlet.

question. At *B, C, D* is shown the actual installation using conduit, cable, and knob and tube; again little explanation should be necessary. Simply run the incoming white wire to one of the terminals on the receptacle, and from that terminal continue with another white wire to the next outlet. Do the same with the black wire.

Because it is frequently necessary to do this, most receptacles are provided with double terminal screws, so that two different wires can be attached to the same terminal, as

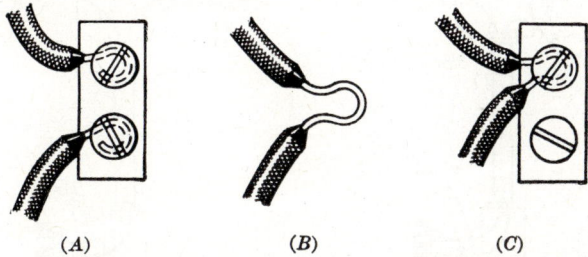

(A)　　　　　　　*(B)*　　　　　　　*(C)*

Fig. 18-6.—Most duplex receptacles have double terminal screws, for convenience in continuing wires on to next outlet.

shown in *A* of Fig. 18-6. This is much simpler than connecting two different wires under the same terminal screw, which the Code prohibits in Sec. 1117. If conduit is used, it may be far more convenient to pull a continuous wire from the SOURCE to box 1 to box 2 to box 3, than to pull one length from the SOURCE to 1, a second length from 1 to 2, and another from 2 to 3. Of course, in that event a loop of wire is left sticking out at each box, as shown at Fig. 18-6, *B*. The insulation is then removed, as shown in *B* of the same picture, and the conductor clamped under one of the two terminal screws, as shown at *C*. This method is the preferable one. Remove just enough insulation from the wire so that the bare uninsulated conductor will not be exposed for any distance from the terminal screw after installation.

Outlet Controlled by Wall Switch.—Naturally this is a very common outlet and fortunately very simple to wire. Figure 18-7, *A*, shows the blueprint symbol, and *B* shows the wiring

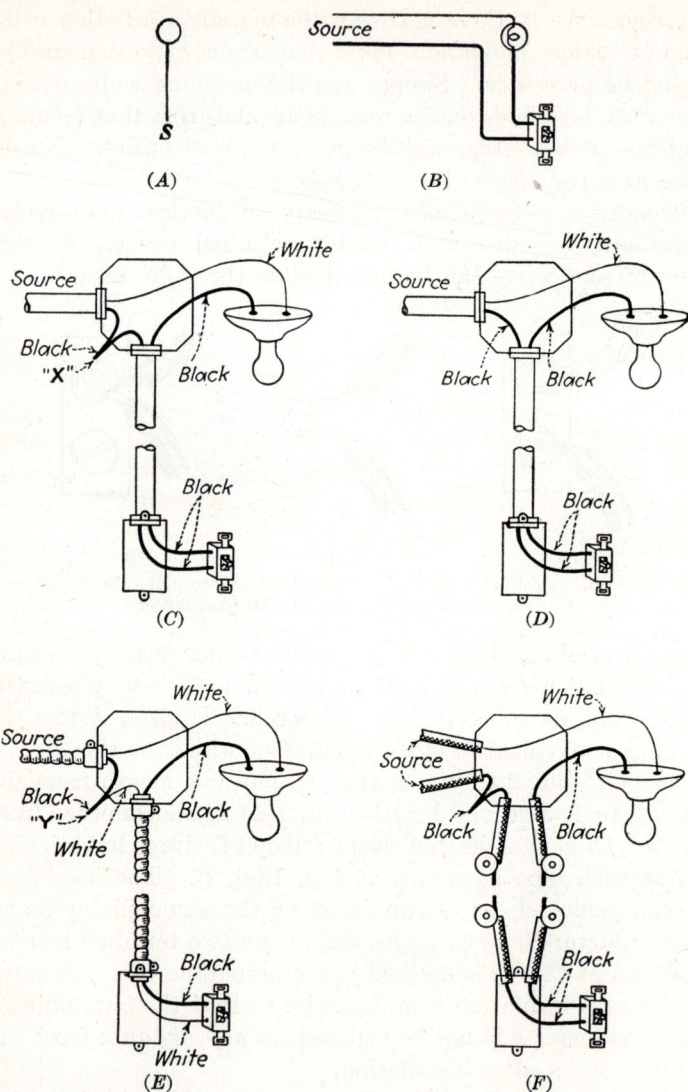

Fig. 18-7.—Fixture controlled by wall switch (see also Fig. 18-10).

diagram. At C is shown the outlet wired with conduit. The white wire is run directly to the fixture. Two blacks are run from the outlet box to the switch box, where they connect to the switch; the upper ends are connected, one to the black incoming wire from SOURCE, the other to the fixture, and the job is finished. At D is shown the optional method whereby one continuous black wire is brought all the way through to the switch box, instead of having a joint at point X in C.

When wiring this outlet with cable, either armored or non-metallic, as at E, a difficulty is encountered. According to everything learned up to this point, not only the wire from the outlet box to the switch, but also the wire running from the switch back to the fixture, should be black, since neither one is a grounded wire. On the other hand, the cable containing these two wires has one black and one white wire. Should manufacturers, distributors, and contractors then be forced to stock a special cable containing two black wires, just for this purpose? That would be impractical.

The Code in Sec. 2006b permits an exception to the general rule that the ungrounded conductor, and only the ungrounded conductor, must be white. This section permits for a switch loop (as the wiring between an outlet and the switch which controls it is called) the use of 2-wire cable containing one black, one white wire, even if its use does not fulfill the general rule. Under this exception the cable may be used provided that the black wire is made to run directly to the fixture. This leaves only one place to connect the white wire of the switch loop, and that is to the black wire in the outlet box. This is the only case where it is permissible to connect a black wire to a white wire, and it pertains only if cable is used. .

Study this rule well: when using cable for a switch loop, the wiring up to the outlet box upon which the fixture is mounted is standard, including connection of the white wire from SOURCE to the fixture. The black wire of the switch loop connects to the fixture. The fixture will then have two wires connected to it: one black and one white. The white wire of the cable of the switch loop is then connected to the black wire in the outlet box, contrary to the general rules, but permitted in this one case by Code Sec. 2006a.

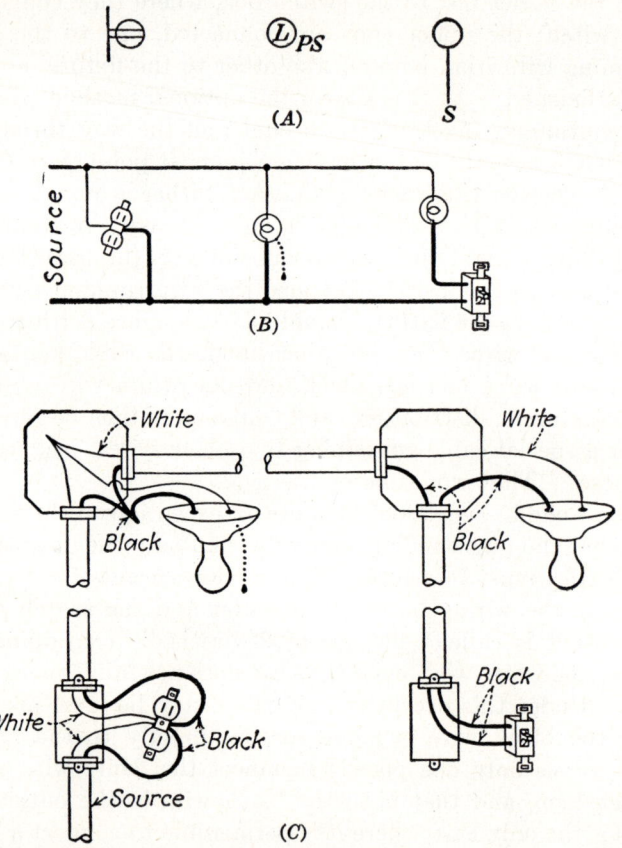

Fig. 18-8.—Combining the outlets of Figs. 18-2, 18-4, and 18-7 into one three-outlet combination.

The wiring using the knob and tube method, as shown in Fig. 18-7, *F*, is most simple, for it is exactly like the conduit method so far as connections and wire colors are concerned.

Combining Three Outlets.—Three different outlets having been wired, they can be combined into one combination of three outlets, as shown in Fig. 18-8. As usual, *A* shows the blue-

INSTALLATION OF SPECIFIC OUTLETS 297

print symbols, *B* the wiring diagram, and *C* the three outlets as wired with conduit. All the points have been gone over in detail, and if they have been carefully studied, this combination should present no problem. If any point is not clear, go back to the idea of messengers chasing each other along the

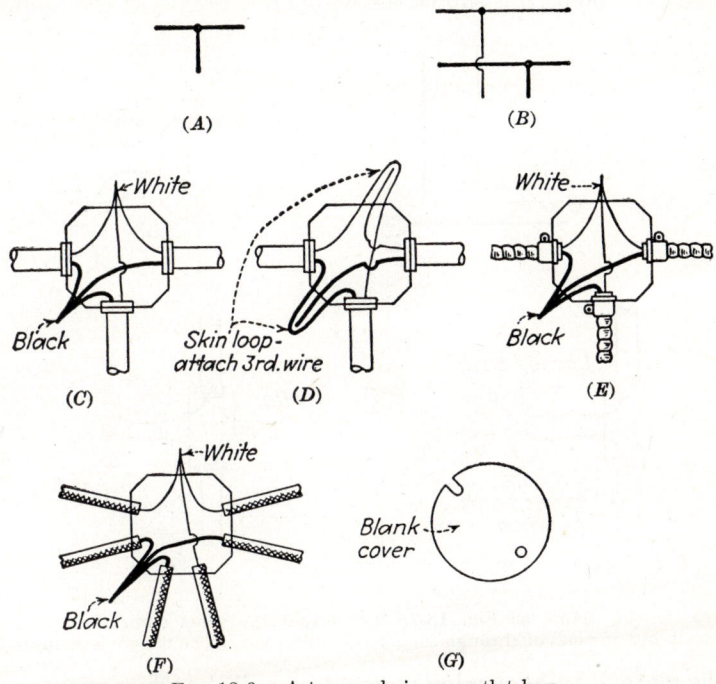

Fig. 18-9.—A tap made in an outlet box.

different wires, in on the white wire from SOURCE, along that wire up to every point where current is to be consumed, and from each such point back over the black wires through switches, if used, until they emerge at the black SOURCE wire.

Taps.—At times an outlet box is used merely to house a tap where one wire branches off from another. Sometimes, especially in conduit work, it is difficult to pull wires into a long length of conduit, so a "junction box" is installed which will serve as an intermediate pulling point. Whenever a box is used only for connections, it is always covered with a blank cover. The Code requires all junction or pull boxes to be placed in locations permanently accessible without removing any part of the building (Sec. 3717).

Figure 18-9, *A*, shows how taps are indicated in blueprint layouts, and at *B* is shown the wiring diagram. At *C* is shown

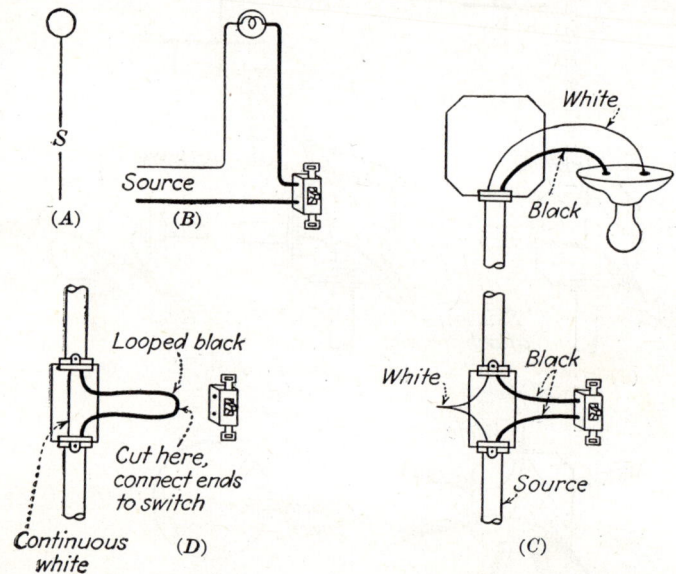

Fig. 18-10.—Same as Fig. 18-7, except that the wires enter through the switch box instead of through the outlet box on which the fixture is mounted.

the method using conduit; merely join all the white wires and then all the blacks. At *D* is shown an optional method, when, instead of three ends of wire of each color, one loop of each color is used, formed by pulling a continuous wire through the box, the ends of the loop being skinned and joined to the remaining ends of the wires to the next outlet. *E* and *F* show the same outlet using cable and knob and tube.

Outlet with Switch, Feed through Switch.—Switches are connected to the outlet which they control in different ways. The source wires do not always run through the ceiling to the outlet box on which the fixture is installed and from there on

INSTALLATION OF SPECIFIC OUTLETS 299

to the switch, as in Fig. 18-7, already discussed. Sometimes the SOURCE wires come from below, run through the switch box, and then on to the ceiling outlet where they end, as in Fig. 18-10. At A is shown the usual blueprint symbol, and B shows the wiring diagram. At C is shown the outlet using the con-

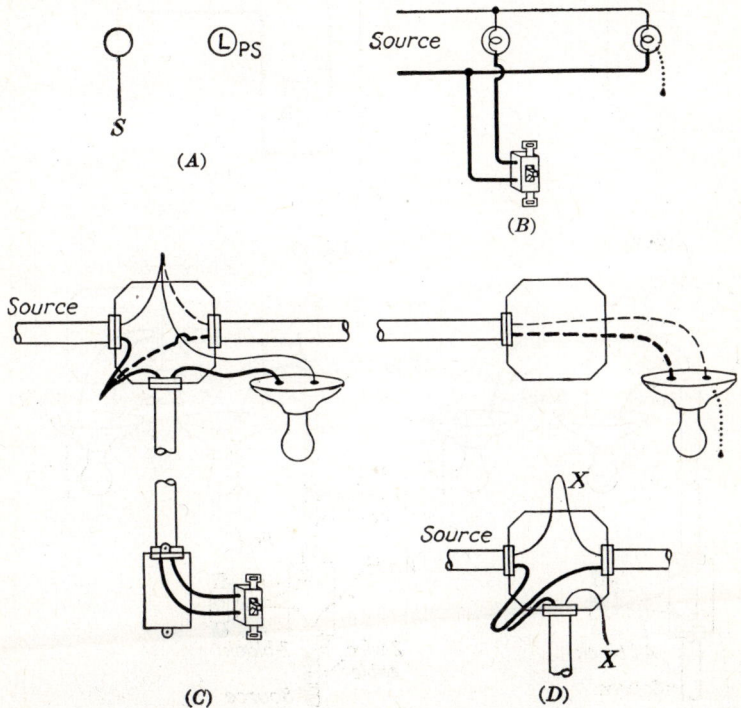

FIG. 18-11.—The switch controls the first fixture; wires run on to a second fixture which is controlled by a pull chain.

duit system, and little explanation is needed. At D is shown an optional method of handling the wires at the switch box, by pulling the white wire straight through. The black wire is also pulled straight through but with a loop which is later cut, the two ends being connected to the switch.

The diagram for this outlet when wired with cable is not shown because there is no new problem. When the cable feeds through the switch box, there is no difficulty with the

300   RESIDENTIAL AND FARM WIRING

colors of the wires in the cable as in a previous example. The wires can be run through to completion of the outlet without the need of joining black to white. Likewise when

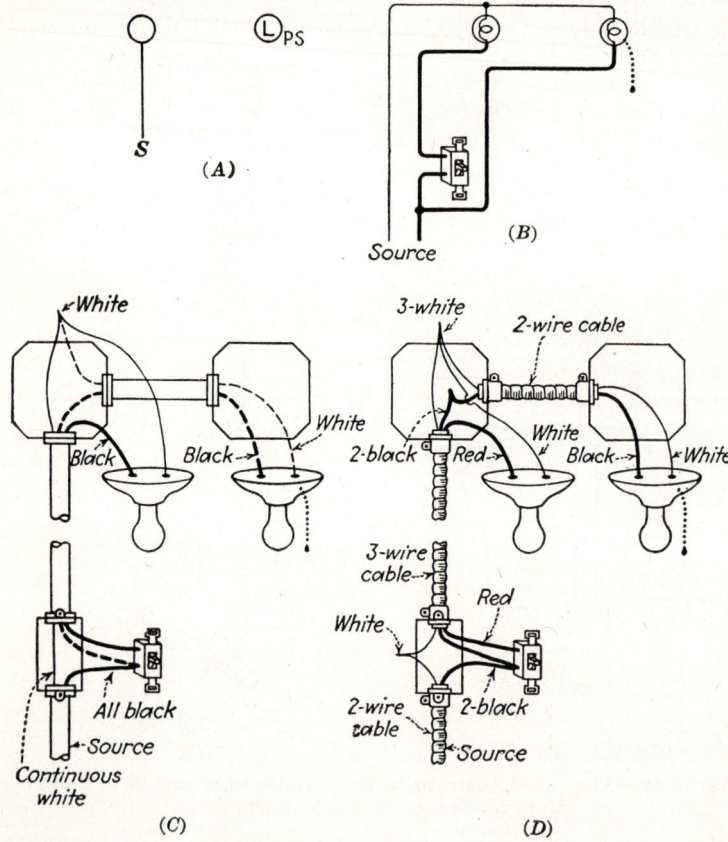

Fig. 18-12.—This is the same as Fig. 18-11 except that the wires from SOURCE enter through the switch box.

wired with knob and tube system, no problem comes up that has not been met before.

Outlet with Switch, with Another Outlet.—This is simply a combination of two outlets that have already been covered separately. The wiring of an outlet with wall-switch control was covered in connection with Fig. 18-7. The wiring of an outlet with pull-chain control was covered in connection with Fig. 18-2. The two have been combined in Fig. 18-11, the left-hand portion of which is identical with Fig. 18-7; to it have been added in dotted lines the wires of Fig. 18-2, making the new combination as shown. At D is shown an optional method of handling the wires through the outlet box, the wires from the fixture being connected at the points marked X. No new problems are involved either in the cable method or in the knob and tube method; for that reason they are not shown.

If the wires from SOURCE instead of coming in through the ceiling outlet come in from below through the switch box, the problem is different in that three wires instead of two must run from the switch box to the first outlet box, as shown in Fig. 18-12, B. A good way to analyze this combination is to consider first the right-hand outlet with the pull chain. Both a white and a black wire *must* run to this from SOURCE, uninterrupted by any switch, so that the light can always be controlled by the pull chain. Then run the third wire from the switch to the left-hand outlet to control that.

Analysis of Fig. 18-12, C, shows that it consists of a combination of Figs. 18-10, C (wires in solid lines), and 18-2 (wires in dotted lines).

If instead of conduit, cable is used, as in Fig. 18-12, D, the problem is equally simple. If the wires are fed through the switch box, there is no problem in connection with the colors of the wires. Merely connect white to white in the switch box, and then continue the white to each of the two fixtures. The remaining colors are as shown in the picture.

Switch Controlling Two Outlets.—When a switch is to control two outlets simultaneously, the connections are most simple. Merely wire the switch to control one fixture, then continue the white wire from the first fixture to the second, and do the same with the black.

As in the other pictures, in Fig. 18-13, A shows the blueprint symbols, B the wiring diagram, and C the combination using conduit. Compare this with Fig. 18-7, C; there is no difference except that these wires have been continued as shown in the dotted lines. To avoid all the joints shown in the outlet box for the first fixture, several of the wires may be pulled through as continuous wires, making a neater job.

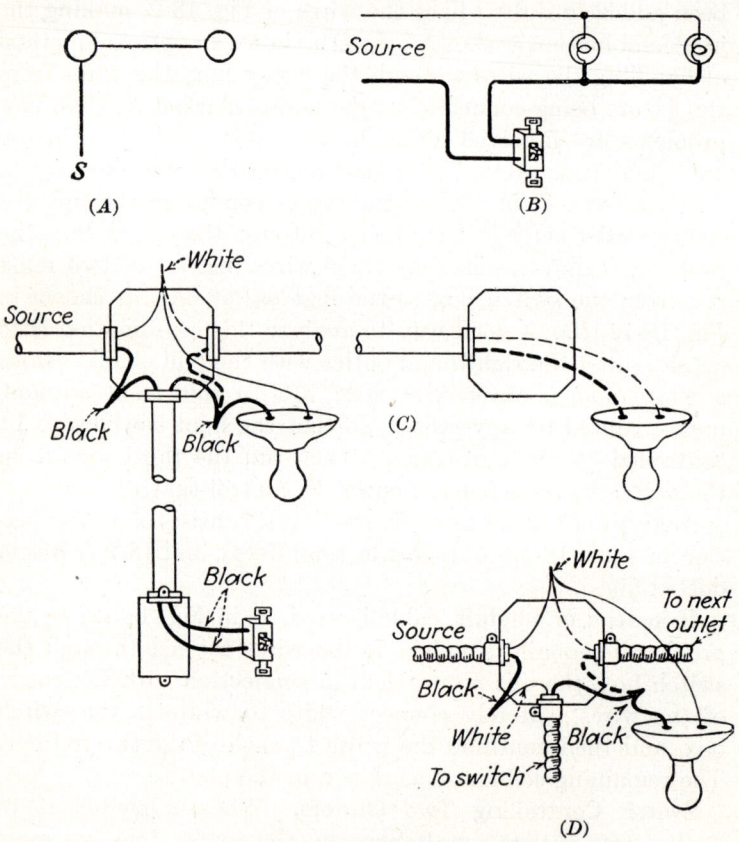

Fig. 18-13.—A switch controlling two separate fixtures.

If using cable, there is again the problem of having to use in the switch loop a cable that has one black and one white wire, instead of the two blacks that should be used. Handle it as in Fig. 18-7, *D*. The white wire from SOURCE goes to each of the two fixtures. The black wire in the switch loop also goes to the first fixture, then on to the second. That leaves only two unconnected wires, the black wire from SOURCE and the white wire in the switch loop; connect them together as before, as permitted in the Code's exception.

Three-way Switches.—When a pair of 3-way switches controls an outlet, there are many possible combinations or sequences in which the SOURCE, the two switches, and the outlet may be arranged; a great deal depends on where the SOURCE wires come in. The most common are

> SOURCE—Switch—Switch—Outlet.
> SOURCE—Outlet—Switch—Switch.
> SOURCE—Switch—Outlet—Switch.

A fourth is the sequence where the SOURCE comes into the outlet box, from which point two runs are made, one to each switch.

These sequences are shown in Fig. 18-14, parts $A1$, $A2$, $A3$, and $A4$; the wiring diagrams are shown in $B1$, $B2$, $B3$, and $B4$. Comparing $B1$, $B2$, $B3$, and $B4$, you will see little difference except the exact location of the light which the switches control.

Reviewing the subject of 3-way switches, one of the three terminals on such a switch is a "common" terminal, corresponding to the middle terminal of an ordinary porcelain-base single-pole double-throw switch shown in Fig. 4-21; this terminal is usually identified by being of a different color from the other two. The exact location of this common terminal with relation to the other two varies with different brands; for the purposes of this chapter, where 3-way switches are shown in pictorial fashion, the terminal which is alone on one side of the switch will always be the common terminal.

Reviewing the subject a bit further, the incoming black wire from SOURCE goes direct to the common or marked terminal of either switch. From the corresponding terminal of the other switch, a black wire runs direct to the proper terminal on the fixture. From the remaining two terminals on one switch, wires are run to the corresponding terminals of the other switch, which are the only two terminals on that switch to which wires have not already been connected. To complete the circuit, connect the incoming white wire from source to the fixture.

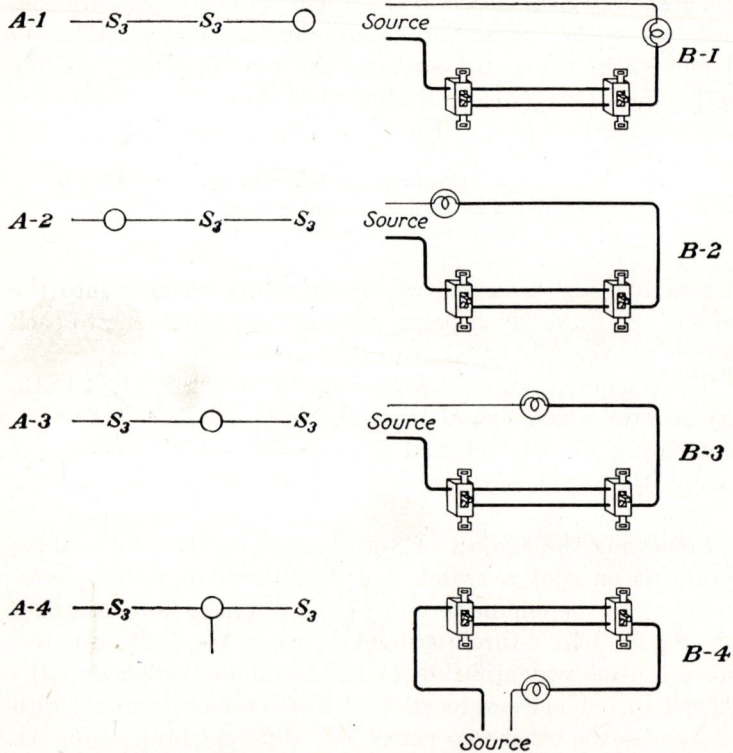

Fig. 18-14, Part 1.—Four different sequences of parts in a circuit consisting of a fixture and a pair of 3-way switches.

With these facts in mind, the wiring of any combination of 3-way switches with conduit becomes extremely simple. Assuming that the boxes and conduit have been properly installed, as shown in Fig. 18-14, $C1$, which covers the sequence of $A1$, the white wire from source is pulled through the switch boxes up to the outlet where the fixture is to be used; the black wire from source is run to the common terminal of the nearest

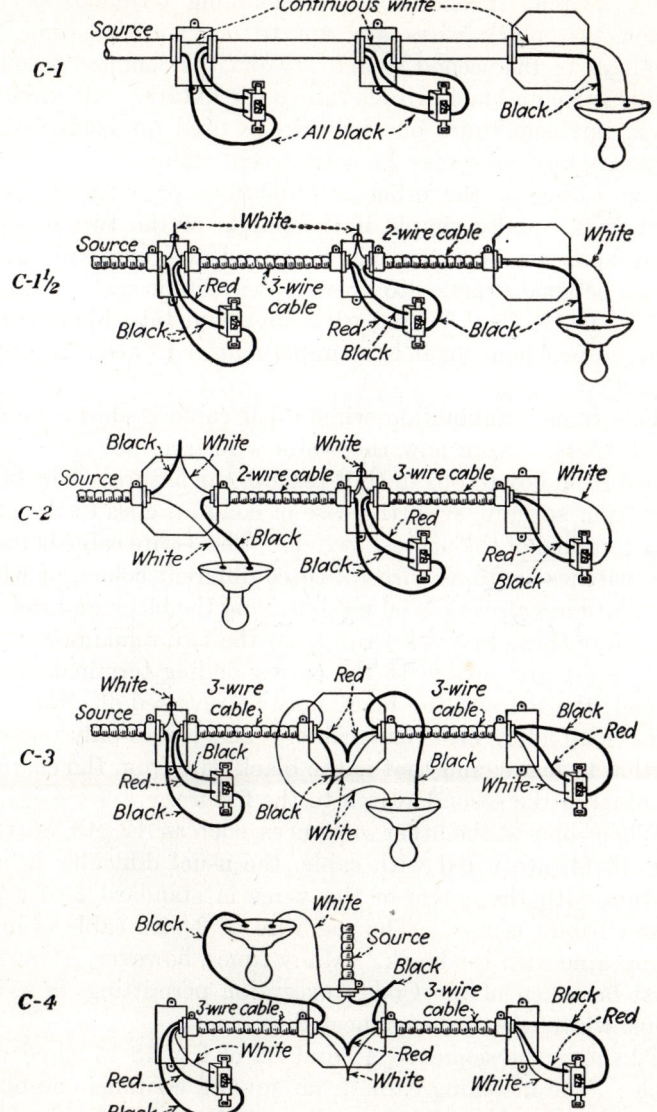

Fig. 18-14, Part 2.—Wiring methods of the combinations shown in Part 1 of this figure.

3-way switch. From the two remaining terminals of this switch two black wires are run to the corresponding two terminals of the second switch. From the common terminal of this switch a black wire is run to the fixture. All wires are black, but sometimes one red wire is used for identification purposes; any color may be used except white.

The wiring of the other combinations or sequences with conduit is equally simple if the points of the two previous paragraphs are borne in mind, and no diagrams are shown. It will be good practice to draw the circuits in fashion similar to Fig. 18-14, $C1$. Wiring with knob and tube likewise presents no problem, for it is a simple matter to keep the colors correct.

This same combination wired with cable is shown in Fig. 18-14, $C1\frac{1}{2}$. Note how the white wire from SOURCE is continued from box to box until it reaches the fixture. The black wire from SOURCE, as in the case of conduit, goes to the common terminal of the nearest switch. The 3-wire cable between the switches contains wires of three different colors, of which the white has already been used, leaving the black and the red. Therefore these two wires run from the two remaining terminals of the first switch to the corresponding terminals of the second; the red and the black may be reversed at either end, being completely interchangeable. This leaves only one connection to make, and that is the black wire from the common terminal of the second switch to the fixture.

When some of the other sequences, such as $A2$, $A3$, or $A4$ in Fig. 18-14, are wired with cable, the usual difficulty in connection with the colors of the wires in standard 2-wire and 3-wire cables is met. The red wire of 3-wire cable is interchangeable with the black. Many times, however, advantage must be taken of the Code's exception permitting, in switch loops, white wire to be connected to black.

$C2$ shows the sequence $A2$ and $B2$ of Fig. 18-14 wired with cable. The incoming cable from SOURCE contains one black, one white wire; the white runs direct to the fixture. The Code requires that the other wire on the fixture may not be white, consequently the black wire of the 2-wire cable that runs to the first 3-way switch is attached to the fixture; the opposite end of it is connected to the "common" terminal of the first 3-way switch. That leaves in the outlet box on which the fixture is mounted only two unconnected wires: the black wire from SOURCE and the white wire of the next run of cable. Connect them together, contrary to the general rule, but permitted by the Code for switch loops. From the first 3-way switch to the second, 3-wire cable is used. Since one of these 3 wires is white, connect it to the white wire of the 2-wire cable and continue it on to the "common" terminal of the second switch. That leaves one black and one red wire between the two switches, and they are connected to the two remaining terminals of each switch, completing the installation.

In wiring the sequence of $A3$ and $B3$ of Fig. 18-14, as pictured in $C3$, similar problems arise. There is a 2-wire cable from SOURCE entering the first switch box; from that point a length of 3-wire cable runs to the outlet box in the center; and from there another length of 3-wire cable runs on to the second switch box. The white wire from SOURCE is continued from the first switch box direct to the fixture, as the Code requires. The black wire from SOURCE runs direct to the common terminal of the first switch. Going on to the fixture, the second wire on the fixture may not be white; therefore make it black and continue it onward to the common terminal of the second switch. That leaves unconnected two terminals on each of the two switches, and our problem is to connect them to each other. There are yet two unused wires in each run of 3-wire cable, a black and a red in the one, and a white and a red in the other. Therefore make one continuous red wire out of the two reds, make a continuous white-black out of the other two, and connect the extreme ends to the two remaining terminals on each of the switches, respectively. This completes the connections.

In the case of the sequence of $A4$ and $B4$ of Fig. 18-14 pictured in $C4$, the problems are similar, and the student should have no difficulty in determining for himself why each wire is of the color indicated. The fundamental rule is that the white wire from SOURCE must go to the fixture, and the second wire on the fixture may not be white.

Pilot Lights.—In Fig. 18-15 is shown a frequently used combination toggle switch and pilot light, together with its internal

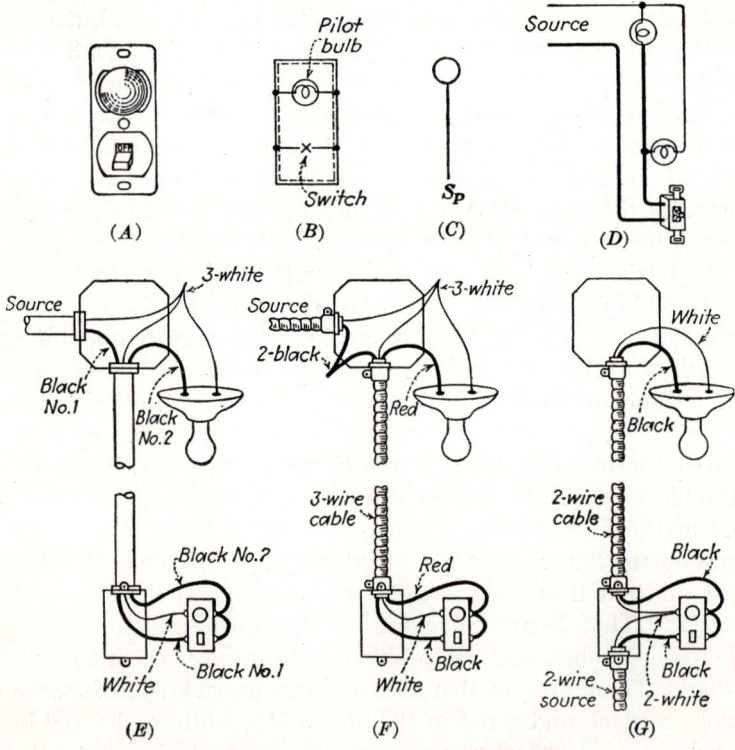

Fig. 18-15.—A switch with a pilot light.

wiring diagram. This is nothing more or less than a separate switch and a separate pilot light in a single housing. The arrangement of the terminals on another brand may be totally different from that shown in the picture. A pilot light is used at a switch which controls a light that is not visible from the switch, for example, at a switch in the house controlling the light in a garage; it is used simply as a reminder that another light is on.

In the same figure at C is shown the blueprint symbol for this combination and at D the usual wiring diagram. Compare this with Fig. 18-13, B; it is merely a case of one switch controlling two different lights, one of which happens to be located at the same point as the switch.

Using the conduit system, the connections are shown at E. The incoming white wire from SOURCE runs directly to the first fixture and is extended from there to the second fixture, which in this case happens to be the bulb in the combination device. The incoming black wire from SOURCE runs directly to the switch. From the other side of the switch, a black wire runs to the first bulb and from there on to the second bulb, finishing the job. Note in the diagram that the two black wires have been labeled "No. 1" and "No. 2"; the two are not interchangeable at the switch end. This is a good example of a case where it is desirable to make the third wire red for identification purposes, in which case the incoming black wire from SOURCE would run directly to the switch terminal, and red would be substituted for the black No. 2.

Wiring the combination with armored cable, as shown in Fig. 18-15, F, presents no problem. If the wires from SOURCE come in through the switch box, the problem is still simpler, as G shows.

Switched Receptacle Outlets.—There is a growing trend toward controlling receptacle outlets with switches, so that all floor and similar lamps can be controlled at one time. No great problem is involved; simply consider the receptacles as so many fixtures, and connect the devices accordingly. Go through the process of connecting three receptacle outlets with a pair of 3-way switches. There can be a great many different sequences of outlets and switches; that shown in Fig. 18-16 at A and B is perhaps as common as any. In using conduit, the problem is simple indeed. Run the white wire from SOURCE to each of the three receptacles; connect the remaining terminal of each of the three receptacles together with black wire, and

310 RESIDENTIAL AND FARM WIRING

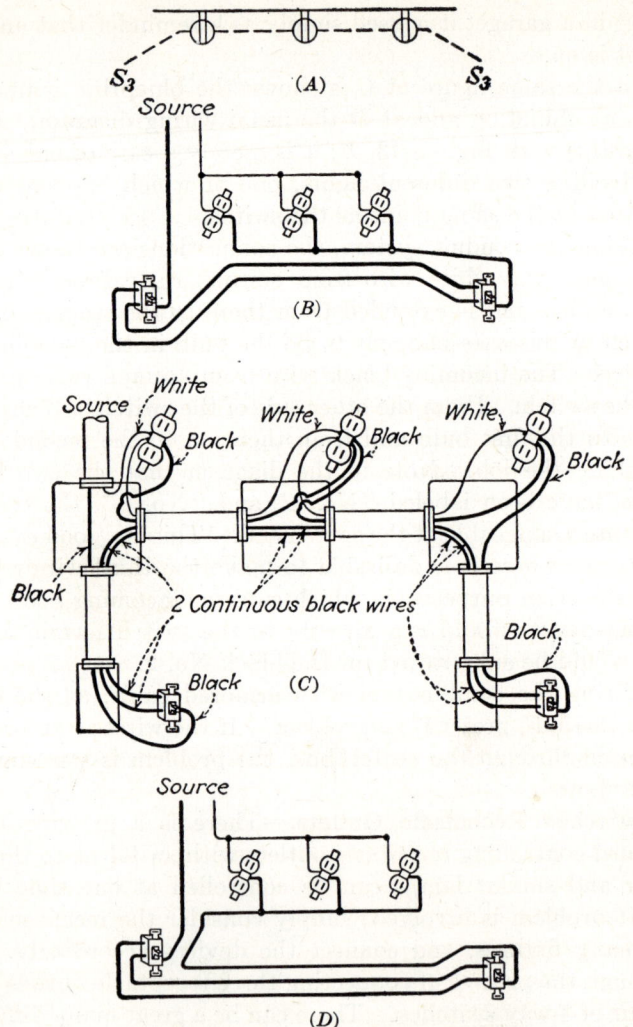

Fig. 18-16.—Switched baseboard outlets.

continue to the common terminal of one of the 3-way switches. From there run two wires over to the other 3-way switch. To the common terminal of this second switch, connect the black wire from SOURCE, and the job is finished. It is pictured in Fig. 18-16, *C*. All the necessary wires in the boxes housing the receptacles will badly crowd the ordinary switch boxes, so the preferable method is to use 4 in. square boxes with raised covers designed to take a duplex receptacle (see Fig. 10-13, *A*).

To wire this same combination using cable is practically impossible with the particular sequence shown, because it requires four wires at some points, and 4-wire cable is not stocked by dealers. Therefore when using cable, it is best simply to modify the sequence to that shown in Fig. 18-16, *D*, which requires nothing more than 3-wire cable.

Two-circuit Duplex Receptacles.—When a receptacle outlet is controlled by a switch, there is the objection that it is impossible to run vacuum cleaners and similar devices without having the switch on, nor can electric clocks be used. Therefore it is customary to use duplex receptacles so designed that one half of each can be permanently live for clocks or appliances and the other half switched for floor lamps and similar devices. A receptacle of this type was shown in Fig. 13-1. It differs little from the ordinary receptacle in outward appearance, but careful examination will disclose that the contacts in the two halves have separate terminals. Figure 18-17 shows the blueprint symbol in *A*. Note that there is no standardized symbol for such an outlet but that it is classed as a special outlet with a small subscript letter alongside it. The specifications will describe the outlet in detail.

The wiring of this combination presents no new problem. The white wire from SOURCE runs to one terminal of each half of the receptacle; frequently both halves are internally joined so that there is but a single terminal which would be alone on one side of the receptacle. The black wire from SOURCE runs to the terminal of one half of the receptacle, and from there is continued to the switch. From the switch the black wire runs back to the terminal of the other half of the receptacle. All this is shown in *B* of Fig. 18-7.

If cable is used, again the difficulty is met that one of the wires in the cable is white where both should be black; take advantage of the Code's special dispensation, and attach the white wire in the cable of the switch loop to the incoming black wire from source, as shown in *C* of Fig. 18-7.

If 3-way switches are used, the problem of getting the colors correct is more difficult but may be solved exactly as in the case of the outlets shown in Fig. 18-4.

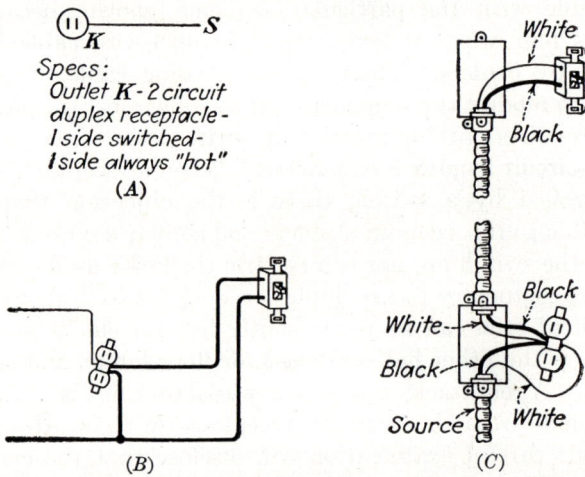

Fig. 18-17.—Wiring 2-circuit duplex receptacles so that one half of each outlet is permanently connected, the other half controlled by a wall switch.

Combining Outlets.—Just as in the early part of this chapter the outlets of Figs. 18-2, 18-4, and 18-7 were combined into one three-outlet combination of Fig. 18-8, so outlets may be combined into any desired combination with any desired total number of outlets, which then forms a circuit running back to the fuse cabinet. To add an outlet at any point, connect the white wire of that outlet to the white wire of the previous wiring, and the black wire of the new outlet to any previous wiring where the black wire can be traced back to the original source without being interrupted by a switch. Simply attach the new outlet at any point on the previous wiring where a bulb connected to the two points in question would be permanently lighted. Review Chap. 4 in connection with Fig. 4-18 if this point is not entirely clear.

INSTALLATION OF SPECIFIC OUTLETS 313

Testing.—When the roughing-in work has been finished, and before the work of lathing and plastering has been completed, the installation must be tested. Then in case of error or mishap, the wiring is still accessible for correction. With conduit wiring, since the wires are not pulled in until after the completion of the building, the test is made at that time.

Usually the test device consists of a doorbell or buzzer in connection with two dry cells connected in series, as shown in Fig. 18-18. Tape the bell to the cells; also tape the test leads to the cells so that, if the entire test unit is lifted by the test

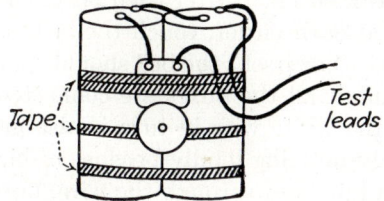

FIG. 18-18.—Test outfit consisting of two dry cells and a doorbell.

leads, there will be no strain on the bell or on the dry-cell terminals.

Before proceeding to test, go around to each outlet, remove insulation from the wires, and twist together all those which will ultimately be permanently connected to each other. Leave those to which a fixture or receptacle is to be attached, sticking freely out of the outlet. At all points where a switch is to be installed, temporarily twist together all the wires that will later be attached to any one switch. Be sure that no exposed bare wire is allowed to touch an outlet box or conduit or the armor of cable.

Testing Conduit Installation.—Insert fuses in their holders in the fuse cabinet where the branch-circuit wires are attached; touch one test lead of the test bell to the white or grounded wire, and the other to each of the black wires for the respective circuits in turn. The bell should not ring; if it does ring it indicates either a short circuit from the white to the black wire somewhere in the circuit, or a ground from the black wire to the conduit, possibly at an outlet box where the black skinned wire is allowed to touch the metal of the box or conduit. If this test checks, remove the bell from the dry cells and attach the two leads from the dry cells to the black and white wires of one circuit. Then take the bell to each outlet where a fixture or receptacle is to be installed. Touch it across the black and white wires; in each case it should ring, just as the bulbs in your fixture or floor lamp will later light when attached to the same wires. Of course, this assumes that previously all the wires which go to any one switch have been temporarily twisted together, thus duplicating the condition of all switches turned on. After each check across the black and white wire at each outlet, touch the bell across the black wire and the outlet box itself; the bell should again ring because through the conduit all the boxes are connected together and grounded, and the white wire in turn is also grounded. The bell will probably not ring loudly because of higher resistance through the conduit than through the wire, but it should ring nevertheless. In making this test, if the conduit and boxes have black-enamel finish, it will be necessary to scrape off some of the enamel before touching the bell to the box, for the enamel is an insulation which might prevent the bell from ringing. If the bell rings feebly, a poor job has been done somewhere; probably the locknut on one or more boxes has not been run down tightly enough. Grounding is a safety precaution and must be properly done. If the bell rings at each point, the wiring is all right.

Testing Armored-cable Installation.—The test is exactly the same as with conduit.

Testing Nonmetallic Sheathed Cable and Knob and Tube Installations.—Since the outlet boxes are not connected to each other, the bell cannot ring when touched to the black wire and the box. However, the remainder of the test is the same as with other systems.

If all tests check, proceed to finish up the installation as covered in the next chapter.

CHAPTER 19

FINISHING: INSTALLATION OF SWITCHES AND OTHER DEVICES

In the previous chapter the roughing-in of a considerable assortment of outlets was considered. Assume that the house has been finished and is ready for the installation of the switches and receptacles, the wall plates, the fixtures, and so on.

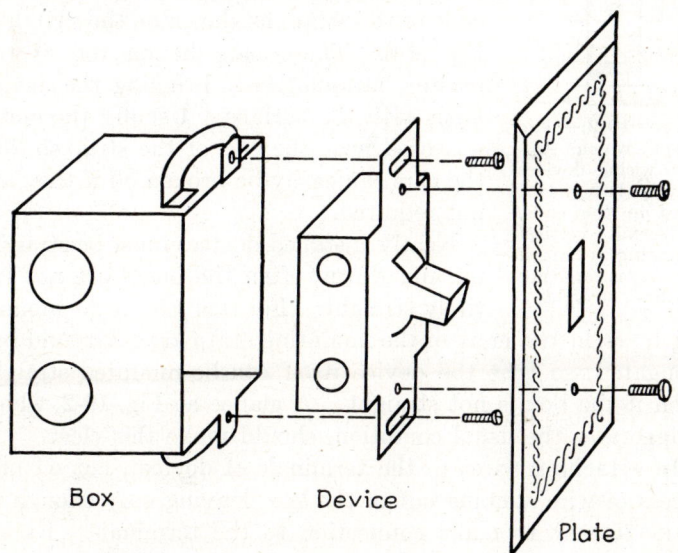

FIG. 19-1.—The device is mounted on the switch box but the wall plate is mounted on the device.

Installing Switches, Receptacles, etc.—Every device of this kind is provided with a metal strap which has holes in the ends, so spaced as to fit over the holes in the ears of a switch box, on which it is mounted by means of machine screws that come with the device. The wall plate in turn is anchored to the device, not the box (see Fig. 19-1).

For a neat installation, the strap of the device must be flush with the front of the plaster. Since the plastering is done after the switch boxes are installed, the front edges of the boxes are not always flush with the plaster; usually they are,

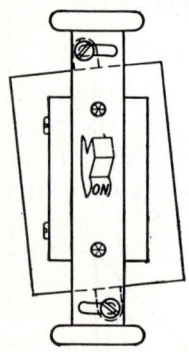

FIG. 19-2.—The straps which support wiring devices have elongated holes in the ends, to permit vertical mounting even if the boxes are not mounted straight.

and should be, a trifle below the surface of the plaster. Other means must therefore be used to mount the devices flush with the plaster. A simple method is to insert small washers between the box and the strap of the device; most devices include a number of washers for that purpose. Some devices come equipped with "plaster ears" on the ends of the strap, as shown on the switch in Fig. 4-6. These ears lie on top of the plaster, automatically bringing the device flush with the surface. Usually the metal is scored near the end of the strap so that the ears can easily be broken off if they are not required.

Neatly installed devices must be straight up and down; often the boxes are not entirely straight. For this reason the mounting holes in the ends of the mounting strap are not round but elongated, so that the device itself can be mounted straight even if the box is not straight. A glance at Fig. 19-2, which exaggerates the usual condition, should make this clear.

In attaching wires to the terminals of devices, cut off any excess of wire sticking out of the box, leaving only enough to make it easy to make connection to the terminals. Excess wire crowds the box and sometimes makes it difficult to insert the device with any amount of clearance. Use care in attaching the wires to the terminals, skinning off only enough insulation to make the connection. The insulation of the wire should extend up to the terminal. *There must be no bare wire exposed between the terminal and the end of the insulation.*

Soldering.—At this point all the wires that need to be permanently joined must be soldered. The method used has already been covered in a previous chapter. For soldering wires at the ceiling, a solder pot of the type shown in Fig. 19-3 will be very useful. The solder in the pot is melted by means of the usual blowtorch.

Attaching Wall Plates.—After the device has been installed in a switch box, a wall plate must in turn be attached by means of the screws that come with the plate. If the device has been properly mounted, the plate will fit snugly against both the device and the wall. If the device has been mounted slightly below the surface of the plaster, do not pull up too tightly on the screws holding the plate, for this will distort or damage the plates; it is not unusual to crack the bridge in the center of a bakelite duplex receptacle plate by pulling up too tightly. If the switches, receptacles,

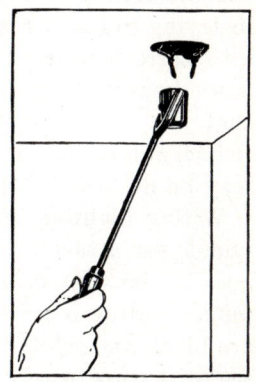

Paul W. Koch & Co.

Fig. 19-3.—A solder dipper is handy in soldering wires projecting out of ceiling outlets.

or other devices have plaster ears, the problem is automatically solved. If they do not have such ears, it is best to use spacing washers between the outlet box and the strap of the device, in order to bring the device flush with the plate.

If the box is of the 2- or 3-gang type with a number of separate devices, the mounting of the plate will not be entirely simple, because of the elongated holes in the mounting holes of the individual devices, as mentioned in an earlier paragraph. These elongated holes are a tremendous advantage in mounting devices in a single-gang box; they are a nuisance in multi-gang boxes, because they permit mounting several devices so that they are not entirely parallel with each other, as compared with the absolutely parallel openings in a 2- or 3-gang plate. The only thing that can be said about mounting devices in multi-gang boxes is that extreme care must be used to see to it that all the devices are absolutely straight up and down, that is, that they are absolutely parallel to each other; then the holes for screws in multi-gang plates will automatically match up with the tapped holes in the straps of the individual devices mounted in the multi-gang boxes. Unless this precaution is observed, a great deal of time will be wasted in trying to insert screws through openings for them in plates, into corresponding holes in devices under the plate, which holes however will be found to be displaced far enough so that the mounting screws will enter with great difficulty (which tends to crack the plates) or not enter at all—there may be no visible holes for them to enter.

Wiring Lighting Fixtures.—The fixture may have two terminals for attaching the wires, in which case the white wire goes to the whitish terminal, the black wire to the other terminal. More often the fixture has two wire leads. If these are black and white, there is no problem. Usually they consist of fixture wire, as described in Chap. 6: one of them a solid color, the other of the same color but identified with a colored tracer in the outer fabric. The identified wire with the tracer is the neutral and corresponds to the white wire in the outlet box. In case identification is not positive, trace the wires down into the fixture; the one that connects to the outer screw shells of the individual sockets is the neutral.

Hanging the Fixture.—There are many ways of mounting lighting fixtures, all dependent on the style and weight of the fixture, the particular box involved, and the method of mounting the box in the ceiling or wall.

Simple fixtures sometimes mount directly on top of outlet boxes by means of bolts which fit into the ears on the boxes. This method is shown in Fig. 19-4 and requires no further description. At times the fixture is too large to permit direct mounting in this fashion, in which case a strap is used, as shown in Fig. 19-5. The strap is first attached to the outlet box, the fixture attached to the strap. A detailed explanation should not be necessary.

As often as not, a fixture stud, such as is shown in Fig. 19-6, is used in mounting the fixture. The stud is attached to the bottom of the switch or outlet box by means of bolts, through holes provided for the purpose. Some boxes have the stud as an integral part of the box. If a hanger of the types that

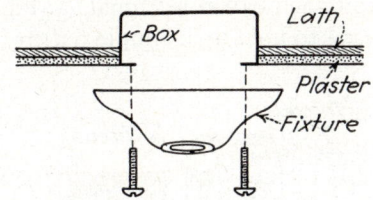

FIG. 19-4.—Simple fixtures are mounted directly on the box.

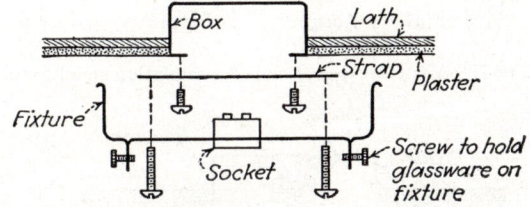

FIG. 19-5.—Often larger fixtures are mounted on a strap, the strap then being mounted on the box.

All-Steel Equip. Co.

FIG. 19-6.—Fixture studs are mounted on the bottom of boxes, to support fixtures.

were shown in Fig. 10-10 is used, the stud that is part of the hanger goes through the center knockout in the box, serves to anchor the box to the hanger, and at the same time permits the stud to be used for supporting the fixture. The outside of the stud is tapped to fit $\frac{3}{8}$-in. trade-size pipe; sometimes there is an inner female thread fitting $\frac{1}{8}$-in. trade-size pipe.

Figure 19-7 shows the fittings usually used, called the "lockup unit." It consists of a reducer fitting over the fixture stud, a length of $\frac{1}{8}$-in. running-thread pipe, and a nut to hold the assembly together, the nut usually being of an ornamental nature and then called a "finial." Figure 19-8 shows the same parts used to hold up a simple fixture. It is a simple

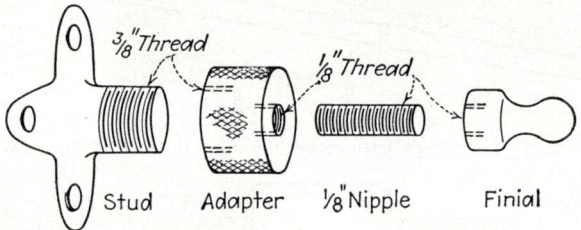

Fig. 19-7.—A typical lockup unit for mounting small fixtures.

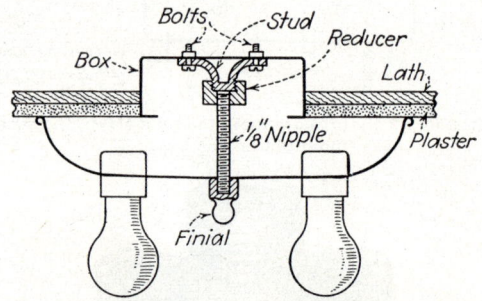

Fig. 19-8.—This shows the parts of Fig. 19-7 being used to hold up a fixture.

matter to drop down the fixture while making connections, then to mount it on the ceiling.

Assuming that the fixture is a larger unit, such as the conventional five-light drop or a similar type, the mounting is similar, and Fig. 19-9 should make it clear. The top of the fixture usually consists of a hollow stem with an opening on the side through which the two wires from the fixture emerge. The top of the stem is threaded to fit on the fixture stud, and the mounting is as shown in the picture. The canopy is dropped down while the connections are being made and slipped back flush with the ceiling when that detail is completed.

Sometimes the wires from the fixture come out of the end of the stem instead of through an opening in the side. In that case a "hickey," shown in Fig. 19-10, is used between the end

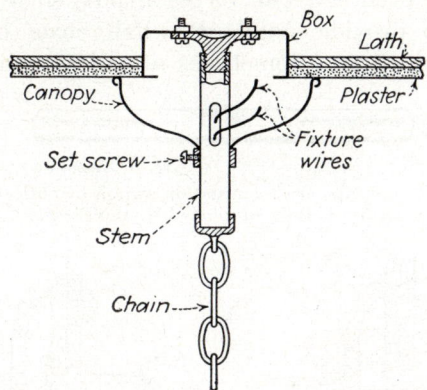

Fig. 19-9.—The usual method of mounting larger fixtures.

Kwikon Co.
Fig. 19-10.—A hickey, used between fixture stud and the end of the stem on the fixture.

Kwikon Co.
Fig. 19-11.—In deep boxes it may be necessary to use an extension piece over the fixture stud.

of the stem and the fixture stud. Sometimes the stud is too short or the box too deep, in which case an extension piece, as shown in Fig. 19-11, is used. Fixtures weighing more than 50 lb. must be supported independently of the outlet box (Sec. 4132).

Mounting Wall Brackets.—The method of mounting depends to a large degree on the type of box used. Many brackets today are of rather dainty design, too narrow to cover up a 4-in. or even a 3¼-in. octagon box, so it has become customary to provide standard switch boxes on which to mount wall brackets. Sometimes a stud is mounted on the

M. B. Austin Co.

Fig. 19-12.—Fixture straps are mounted on switch or outlet boxes, and the fixture is then supported by the strap.

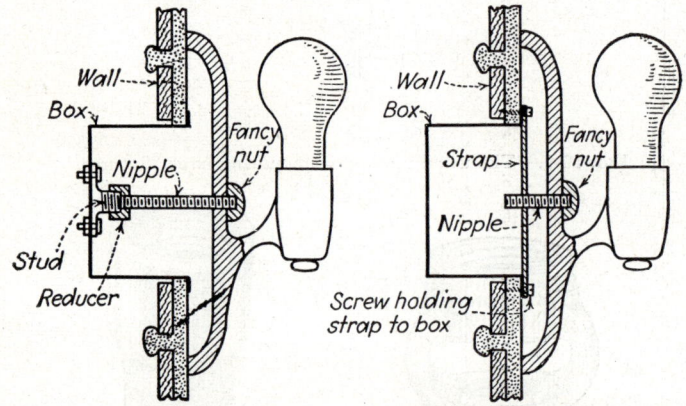

Fig. 19-13.—Wall bracket mounted on switch box by means of fixture stud in bottom of box.

Fig. 19-14.—Wall bracket mounted on switch box by means of fixture strap mounted on box.

bottom of the box; in that case the mounting is completed with the lockup device that was shown in Fig. 19-7, the completed installation having the appearance shown in Fig. 19-13. More usually a fixture strap, such as shown in Fig. 19-12, is first mounted on the switch box, the fixture in turn being mounted on the strap, all as shown in Fig. 19-14.

Even more convenient is a special type of switch box that incorporates a movable bridge, as shown in Fig. 19-15. Very similar is the cover fitting on top of a 4 in. square box, with a similar movable bridge, as shown in Fig. 19-16. Either of these devices is most handy when mounting brackets in pairs because they can then be adjusted to precisely the same height above the floor.

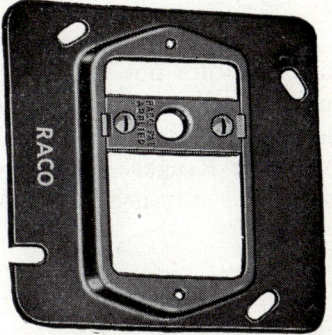

All-Steel Equip. Co.
FIG. 19-15.—Switch boxes with movable bridges are most convenient in adjusting a pair of brackets to exactly the same height.

All-Steel Equip. Co.
FIG. 19-16.—When square boxes are used instead of switch boxes, this cover serves the same purpose as the box at the left.

Adjusting Height of Fixtures.—A fixture with chain is adjustable as to the height above the floor and to compensate for ceilings of different heights. The height is simply controlled by removing as many chain links as required. The actual height will be governed by personal preference and location. If the fixture hangs above a dining-room table, hang it at least 24 in. and preferably 30 to 36 in. above the table. Again this will be dependent upon the type of fixture, the ceiling height, and similar factors.

CHAPTER 20

MISCELLANEOUS WIRING

In the wiring of average homes there are a number of problems that are not readily grouped with those discussed in any of the previous chapters. Accordingly they have been gathered here into a separate chapter.

Electric Ranges.—The problem of wiring for ranges, from the service entrance up to the fuse cabinet or circuit breaker,

Bryant Elec. Co.

Fig. 20-1.—Heavy-duty receptacles in flush and surface types, in homes used almost exclusively for ranges, which are connected to them by means of the pigtail shown.

has already been covered. From this point onward the wiring is most simple. Practically all ranges are 115/230-volt devices. When they are turned on at maximum heat, they operate on 230 volts; when on low heat they operate on 115 volts. Therefore it is necessary to run three wires to the range.

The Code provides that there must be a disconnecting means for every permanently installed appliance rated above 1,650 watts. This may be a cord and plug arrangement, and this is usually used for ranges. Figure 20-1 shows several heavy-duty 3-wire 50-amp. receptacles, as well as a 3-wire plug with attached pigtail leads. The receptacle is installed at the point where the range is to be located. From the receptacle three wires are run back to the fuse cabinet or circuit breaker.

The wires may be any type used for house wiring, such as rubber-covered wires in conduit, knob and tube, or armored or nonmetallic sheathed cable. Service entrance cable may also be used (Code, Sec. 3382), in which case the bare conductor must be used as the continuation of the incoming neutral wire. Service entrance cable may be used in interior wiring only in connecting electric ranges, never for other purposes.

As to size of wire for serving an electric range, No. 6 with a No. 8 neutral is commonly used; No. 8 with No. 10 is often acceptable (see page 201).

The 1947 Code in Sec. 2560 provides that the frame of an electric range must be grounded. This may be done by running a wire from the frame to ground, or by grounding the frame to the neutral wire serving the range. No other appliance or device may be grounded in this latter fashion.

Water Heaters.—Water heaters are almost invariably designed to operate on 230 volts and are never combination 115/230-volt devices like ranges. Therefore only two wires are required, which may be any style, as used for ordinary wiring. The white neutral wire is not run to the water heater; consequently, if cable is used which has one white and one black wire, it is necessary to paint the ends of the white wire black (Code, Sec. 2006a).

A disconnecting means is required, and this is usually a switch of the type shown in Fig. 20-2. However, any switch rated at more than the maximum amperage consumed by the heater may be used. It must be a double-pole two-fuse switch. If leads are run from the switch back to fuses in the fuse cabinet or to a circuit breaker, the switch need not be fused. If, however, they run to a separate meter, then the switch must be classified by the Underwriters as a service switch and must be rated at least 30 amp.; it must be fused (for the size fuse to use, see Chap. 12).

Low-voltage Wiring.—In this term is included wiring for doorbells and other signals, thermostats, and similar devices operating at low voltages. Usually this means 30 volts or less.

The power for operating such circuits is usually derived from small transformers. Under no circumstances may low-voltage

FIG. 20-2.—Electric water heaters require a disconnecting switch on the order of that shown here.

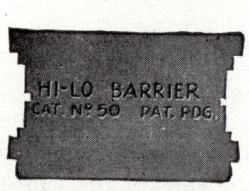 

All-Steel Equip Co.

FIG. 20-3.—If low-voltage wires enter the same box with regular wiring, the two must be separated by a steel barrier. A common use for such barriers is in connection with radio aerial installations.

wires be run in the same conduit or armor or cable with other wires carrying full voltage. They must come no closer than 2 in. to other wires unless such wires are in conduit. Where the wires come closer than 2 in., use loom or porcelain tubes over the low-voltage wires. They may never enter an outlet or switch box carrying full-voltage wires unless a metal barrier of the same thickness as the walls of the box separates the two types of wiring. In Fig. 20-3 is shown a steel barrier to fit 4 in. square boxes. Note how it is scored at the top so that part can be broken off, thus making one barrier fit covers of various depths. Their use is shown in the same picture. Similar barriers are available to fit other styles of boxes.

Transformers.—If only the usual doorbells and buzzers are to be operated, ordinary doorbell transformers of the type shown in Fig. 20-4 are used. The type shown at A is the surface type used in connection with knob and tube work; that at B is mounted on a combination cover which fits any type of outlet box. When mounted on top of the outlet box, the 115-volt wires are concealed inside the box, and only the low-voltage terminals are exposed. Such transformers have a maximum capacity of about 5 watts and usually deliver somewhere between 6 and 10 volts. They are suitable only for operating a single device at a time.

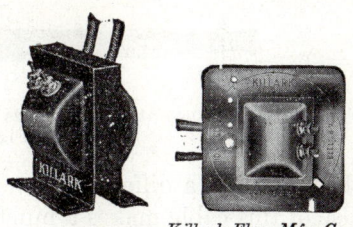

Killark Elec. Mfg. Co.

Fig. 20-4.—Typical transformers for operating doorbells and similar equipment.

Larger transformers are available which give a combination of voltages such as 6, 12, and 18, while again others are available in larger wattage capacity.

Transformers of this type are so designed that, even in case the secondary is short-circuited, the current flowing will be limited to the rating of the transformer. Such transformers are usually rated not over 100 volt-amp., and the type used for residential wiring is seldom over 25 volt-amp. Because of this limited current there is no danger of fire, and because of the low voltage there is no danger of shock. Therefore the Code has no limitations on the type wire used or the installation of it, except those points brought out in the previous paragraph.

The wires used for low-voltage work require and have little insulation. Ordinary bell wire or "annunciator wire," as it is formally called, consists merely of the bare copper with two layers of cotton, wrapped in opposite directions, then paraffined (see Fig. 20-5). Two or more of these wires are often twisted together, with an over-all braid, forming what is known as "thermostat" cable; it is shown in Fig. 20-6. Each wire in

U. S. Rubber Co.

Fig. 20-5.—Wire for low-voltage signal systems such as doorbells requires little insulation.

U. S. Rubber Co.

Fig. 20-6.—Thermostat cable consists of a number of wires of the type shown in Fig. 20-5.

the cable has a different color braid for ease in identification. Use of this cable makes a much neater installation than use of two or more separate wires; there is also less danger of damage to the wires, which would be more a nuisance than a hazard. The usual size of the wire is No. 18, although No. 19 is also used, and the heavier sizes are avail-

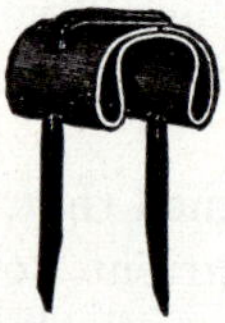

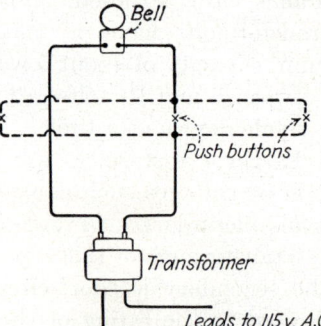

S. H. Couch Co.

Fig. 20-7. Bell wire and thermostat cable are mounted by means of insulated staples.

Fig. 20-8.—The basic diagram for a doorbell is most simple.

able. The size must be chosen to match the length of the run, the load, and the voltage available. For ordinary residential use, No. 18 is universally used.

In use this wire is merely run over the surface or fished through walls without further protection. It is stapled to the surface over which it runs with insulated staples of the type shown in Fig. 20-7.

MISCELLANEOUS WIRING

Low-voltage Circuits.—It is a very simple matter to draw circuits for low-voltage work. Simply consider the transformer as the SOURCE for the circuit, and consider the push buttons as switches, which they are. The basic circuit is shown in Fig. 20-8. Disregard for the moment the dotted lines, and the circuit becomes most simple. If the bell is to be controlled from a number of different push buttons, merely add additional buttons as shown in the dotted lines.

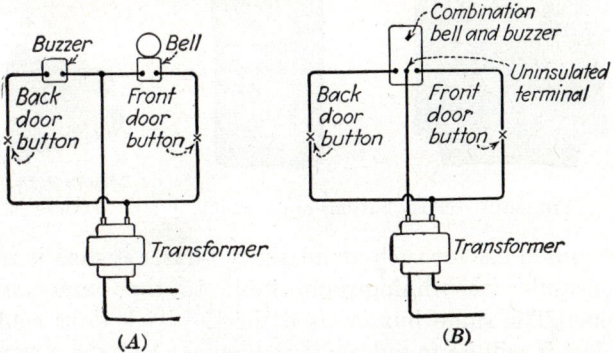

FIG. 20-9.—At left is the diagram for a separate bell and buzzer operating off the same transformer, and at right the diagram for a combination bell and buzzer.

Figure 20-9 shows at *A* a similar circuit but with both a bell and a buzzer, the former for the front door and the latter for the back door. At *B* is shown the same circuit using the familiar combination bell and buzzer. This device has three terminals. One of the three is usually a terminal screw that is fastened directly to the frame of the device, not insulated from it in any way. This is the terminal that runs direct to the transformer; sometimes it is the middle terminal, as shown in the drawing, sometimes it is one of the other terminals. The two remaining terminals go directly to the two push buttons.

Additional buzzer circuits may be operated from the same transformer, as required. Mount the buzzer where desired; run a wire from one terminal direct to the transformer or, for that matter, to any other handy near-by wire that runs direct to the transformer; from the other terminal of the buzzer run a wire to the push button, and from the push button back to the other side of the transformer or, if handy, to a near-by wire that runs directly to the other side of the transformer.

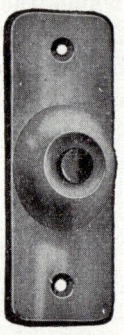

Edwards & Co.

Fig. 20-10.—Push buttons are available in many styles.

A common use for such an auxiliary buzzer system is from a button under the dining-room table to the buzzer in the kitchen. The same buzzer used for the back door could be used, but it will be found more convenient to have a separate buzzer which will have a different tone, so that it can be distinguished from the back-door buzzer.

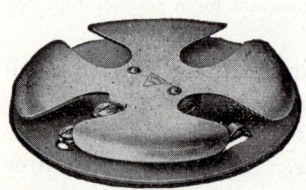

Edwards & Co.

Fig. 20-11.—A floor-tread type of button. It is used under the rug and operated by the foot.

Types of Push Buttons.—Several types of buttons, both surface and flush mounting, are shown in Fig. 20-10; there is a great variety of sizes, shapes, and finishes to suit the user. For apartments the buttons are usually built into the combination mailbox, directory, and entrance telephone or speaking tube. A floor-tread button of the type shown in Fig. 20-11 is used under the rug at the dining-room table to operate the kitchen buzzer; being about 4 in. in diameter, it will operate regardless of the point where the pressure is applied.

Types of Bells.—The ordinary bells and buzzers are none too attractive in appearance, for which reason a type has been

MISCELLANEOUS WIRING   331

developed which fits inside ordinary switch and outlet boxes, being then covered with louvered covers far neater than exposed bells. An assortment of the devices is shown in Fig. 20-12, while Fig. 20-13 shows an installation. Note the barrier sepa-

Edwards & Co.

Fig. 20-12.—Flush, concealed bells, and similar devices are far neater than the ordinary type.

rating the 115-volt wires up to the transformer from the low-voltage wiring to the devices.

Becoming rapidly popular are the chime-type signals which produce a very pleasing note or combination of notes. These are available in a great variety of sizes and shapes, and two

All-Steel Equip. Co.

Fig. 20-13.—An installation of the devices shown in Fig. 20-12. Note the steel barrier separating low-voltage from the regular wiring in the 4-gang box.

of them are shown in Fig. 20-14. Most of the better chimes made today operate off ordinary doorbell transformers. Only the most elaborate ones require a larger transformer delivering about 20 volts; usually if such a transformer is required, it is included with the merchandise.

Telephones.—In ordinary residential work, too frequently no attention is paid to telephones, leaving the problem of installation strictly up to the telephone company. It does a good job, but still in many cases an exposed run of wire remains in view. Therefore in more pretentious homes it is customary to install a length of conduit terminating in a switch box at the location or locations where the instruments are to be installed.

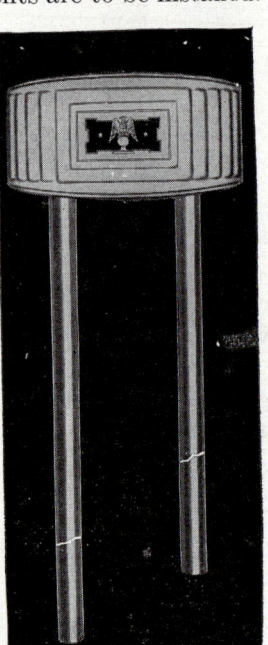

NuTone Chimes, Inc. *Edwards & Co.*

Fig. 20-14.—Chimes give soft, melodious notes and are pleasing in appearance.

Usually the switch box is covered with a special wall plate with a single opening.

Radio Wiring.—Ground wires and leadins from radio aerials are, in most homes, distinct eyesores. This problem should be solved while the house is under construction. Special radio outlets are available, usually in the form of combined radio and power outlets, such as that shown in Fig. 20-15. The upper end consists of a 2-way outlet for aerial and ground, with a special plug so constructed that it cannot possibly be inserted into any other receptacle. It is also available with a

3-way outlet for the modern type of aerial which has two leadins. The bottom half of the outlet is an ordinary electrical outlet. The two halves are separated by a barrier as required by the Code.

In use the radio leadin and the ground wire are brought up to the outlet through the wall. Certainly this is more attractive than having them come through, for example, a living-room window.

It is well to install such outlets at a number of points where a radio might be used, not overlooking the bedrooms and the children's room.

Arrow-Hart & Hegeman Co.

Fig. 20-15.—The upper outlet of this receptacle is for radio aerial and ground. The lower is for regular 115-volt use. A steel barrier separates the two.

Door Switches.—A most handy switch for closets is the built-in door switch. One of these was shown in Fig. 13-3. Opening the door turns on the light; closing the door turns it off. All switches of this type are still decidedly expensive; when they become available at a reasonable price they will achieve the popularity they deserve.

Interchangeable Devices.—Several switch boxes can be joined together to make one 2-gang or 3-gang or even larger box, permitting two or three or more switches, receptacles, and similar devices to be used side by side. However, the more devices used side by side, the larger the wall plate becomes, until it arrives at the stage where it becomes unsightly. Sometimes there is not sufficient room for a 3-gang plate at a particular point on a wall where three switches are to be used. Even if there is room, the holes in the mounting straps of the switches are, as already explained, oval, making it none too easy to mount three switches in a 3-gang box so that a 3-gang wall plate will later fit easily and neatly. Therefore it is not surprising that there were developed devices very small in physical size so that two or three can be used in a single-gang switch box.

One type consists of two devices on a single strap, in various combinations such as outlet and 1-pole switch, outlet and 3-way switch, two switches, switch and pilot light, and similar combinations. Several of these are shown in Fig. 20-16. This type of combination device has the advantage that ordinary

Circle F Mfg. Co.

Fig. 20-16.—Combination units of this kind are often a great convenience, especially where space is limited.

duplex-receptacle wall plates fit, not necessitating the purchase of special plates.

A similar line is produced with three devices on a single strap. The combination might be three single-pole switches, or two single-pole and a 3-way, or an outlet and a switch and pilot light.

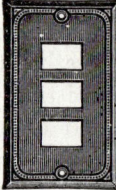

Arrow-Hart & Hegeman Co.

Fig. 20-17.—In this type three devices on a single strap can be installed in a single-gang box. A great many combinations are available.

Hundreds of combinations are possible, and the more popular ones are stocked by the manufacturer. Special wall plates are required and an assortment of both the plates and the devices is shown in Fig. 20-17.

A line of devices is also available in which the individual units are separate and made up into any desired combination by the user or contractor. Basically there are a dozen or so of assorted devices, each available separately; an assortment of them is shown in Fig. 20-18. They are mounted in the field on the skeleton strap shown in A of Fig. 20-19, to which they are simply and quickly anchored as shown in B. In turn, the wall plate of C is mounted on the strap, making the finished product shown in D of Fig. 20-19.

If three or six devices are used, it usually leads to a rather crowded condition of the switch box because of the great

Pass & Seymour.

FIG. 20-18.—Separate devices of this style are assembled on the job into any desired combination.

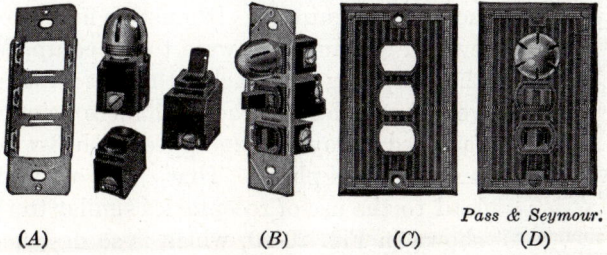

Pass & Seymour.

(A)　　　　(B)　　　　(C)　　　　(D)

FIG. 20-19.—The devices of Fig. 20-18 are assembled on a skeleton strap as shown in steps above.

number of wires involved. It is very desirable therefore to use a 4 in. square box with a raised cover. If the cover which was shown in A of Fig. 10-13 is used, three devices will be accommodated; if the double type is used as shown at B, a total of six devices will be accommodated.

Laundry Receptacle.—Section 2124b of the 1947 Code requires for the first time that the receptacle of the laundry "shall be of the 3-pole type designed for grounding." This type of receptacle will accept a 3-prong plug. In use, two of the prongs on the plug are connected to the two usual wires running to the appliance, for example, the motor of the washing machine. The third prong of the plug is connected to a third wire in the cord, which at the motor end is connected to the frame of the motor. In the receptacle the third opening contains clips connected to ground. When the 3-prong plug is inserted into the 3-prong receptacle, the motor frame is automatically grounded. This makes a much safer installation than is otherwise possible; for in case of a defective motor or other appliance, the operator is definitely protected against shock. This requirement will undoubtedly save many lives by its safety provision.

General Electric Co.

Fig. 20-20.—This receptacle will accommodate either ordinary 2-prong plugs, or special 3-prong plugs which permit grounding of the appliance involved.

On the other hand, note that the Code does not make grounding of the third terminal compulsory. It is the hope that most installations will actually have the third terminal grounded, as a safety measure, and some future Code will no doubt require it. It must be noted too that even if all laundries were today equipped with these 3-prong receptacles, the fact remains that very few indeed of the appliances being manufactured today are equipped with 3-wire cord and 3-prong plugs. That will undoubtedly lead to the use of receptacles similar to the one shown in Fig. 20-20, which is so designed that either the ordinary 2-prong or special 3-prong plugs may be used in connection with it. It is usable with present-day appliances equipped with 2-prong plugs and future appliances equipped with 3-prong plugs.

Plug-in Strip.—No matter how many receptacle outlets are provided in a home, there never seem to be enough. Therefore it will be well to consider, at least for better class homes, the material known as "plug-in strip." This is pictured in Fig. 20-21 and consists simply of a steel channel with a bakelite cover providing outlets at regular intervals. The spacing varies, but for homes 18 in. is popular. The strip is installed in continuous lengths around the room—sometimes on top of the baseboard, giving the effect of being part of it; sometimes imbedded in the plaster so as to be flush with it. Connections are made to the back of the channel with conduit or cable, as to an outlet box.

FIG. 20-21.—Plug-in strip provides outlets at very frequent intervals, making a most flexible and adequate installation.

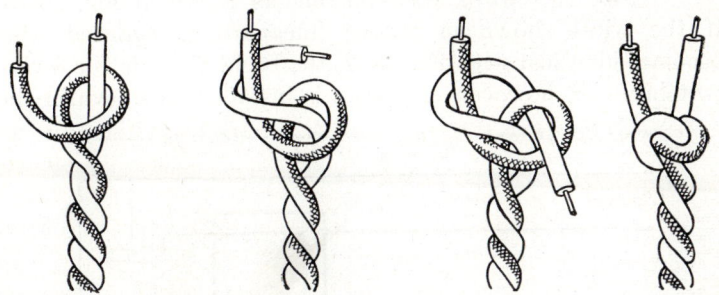

FIG. 20-22.—In assembling drop cords, provide an Underwriters' knot at each end of the cord.

Drop Cords.—In making up a drop cord, assemble the parts so that their weight is supported, not by the copper conductor of the lamp cord used, but rather by the entire structure of the lamp cord, including the insulation and the braid. The simplest way of doing this is to properly install an Underwriters' knot at top and bottom. This knot is simply made, as Fig. 20-22 shows. The drop will be supported from the ceiling by a blank cover with a bushed hole in the center, mounted on any type of outlet box. With open knob and tube, wiring rosettes, such as were shown in Fig. 11-41, are used.

Garages.—Garage lighting may consist of a single light, or it may incorporate a number of lights with an outlet for a trouble light of the type shown in Fig. 20-23, or for a battery charger or similar device. At least one of the lights should be controlled by 3-way switches at both house and garage.

If the light is to be controlled only at the garage, only two wires are required from the house to the garage. An outlet may also be installed, as shown by dotted lines in Fig. 20-24.

If the light is to be controlled by 3-way switches in house and garage, then three wires must be run, as shown in Fig. 20-25. If the wires shown in dotted lines are disregarded, this becomes identical with Fig. 4-22, the basic diagram for 3-way switches. If, however, an outlet is installed as shown in the

Monowatt Elec. Corp.
Fig. 20-23.—A trouble light of this kind is almost a necessity in any garage; provide an outlet for it.

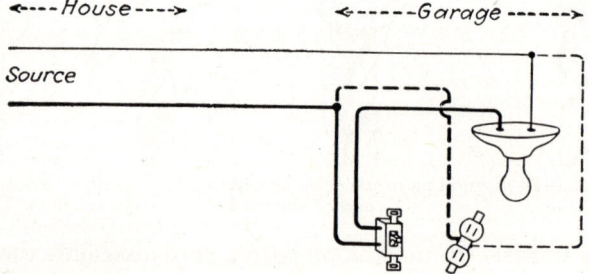

Fig. 20-24.—Simple garage circuit. The light is controlled only by the switch in the garage.

previous diagram, the outlet will be disconnected with the light when it is turned off at either end. This is undesirable because, for example, the outlet may be used for a charger which is to charge the battery in the car overnight, and the

MISCELLANEOUS WIRING

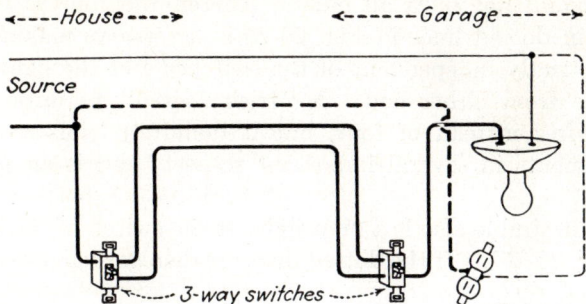

Fig. 20-25.—The garage light is now controlled from either house or garage. The outlet is always on. This requires four wires between house and garage.

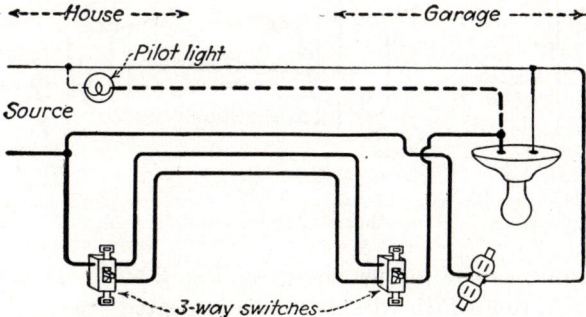

Fig. 20-26.—The same circuit shown in Fig. 20-25, with the addition of a pilot light in the house to indicate whether the garage light is on or not. This requires five wires.

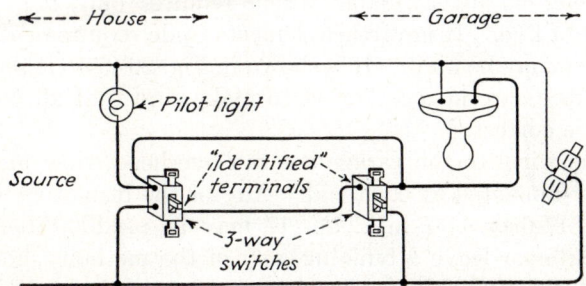

Fig. 20-27.—This circuit using only four wires serves the same purpose as the circuit of Fig. 20-26 using five wires.

light should not burn all night. Therefore a fourth wire as shown in dotted lines in Fig. 20-25 is necessary, making the outlet strictly independent of the switches and the light controllable from either end. A "trick" circuit permits using three wires instead of four, but it definitely violates Code requirements in several important respects and is an unsafe circuit.

Very desirable also is a pilot light at the switch in the house (see Fig. 20-26). If the dotted lines are disregarded, the result

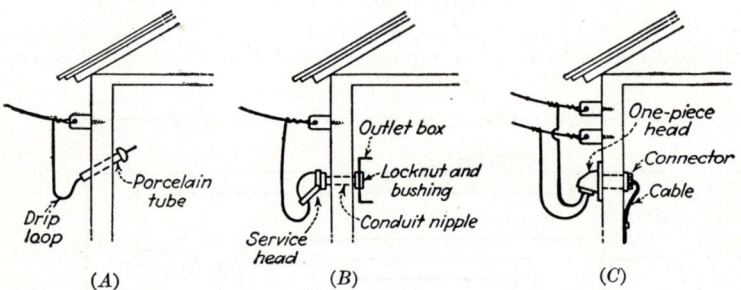

Fig. 20-28.—Several ways of having wires enter the garage. The same methods are used for other wiring, for example, farm buildings.

is the same as the former circuit of Fig. 20-25. To add the pilot light, run a fifth wire as shown in dotted lines.

Whereas the circuit shown in Fig. 20-26 is the usual one when 3-way switches are used, plus a pilot light at the house end, plus a permanently live receptacle at the far end, there is another circuit available which requires only four wires instead of five. It nevertheless meets Code requirements and therefore may be used. It is shown in Fig. 20-27. It requires a bit more care in installation to make sure that all connections are correct.

If the wires to the garage are run overhead, they must be securely anchored at each end. Any of the insulators shown in Fig. 17-6 or 17-7 in Chap. 17 may be used. Where the wires enter or leave a building, any of the methods shown in Fig. 20-28 is suitable. A most convenient fitting to be used at that point is shown in Fig. 20-29 and shown installed in *C* of Fig. 20-28. In any event always provide a drip loop in the wire so that rain will not follow the wire into the building.

Underground Wires.—If wires are to be run underground, several problems beyond those discussed in earlier chapters arise. For alternating-current systems, the Code in Sec. 3018 requires that if a *metallic* raceway is used all the wires of a circuit must be in a single raceway. This includes armored cable, lead-sheathed cables, metallic parkway cables, and other similar metal-clad constructions. Such cables with more than three conductors are practically unobtainable when needed. Therefore when more than three conductors are needed, such cables cannot be used. If, however, cables involving no metal in their armor or sheath are used, two 2-wire cables may be used in place of one 4-wire; one 2-wire and one 3-wire cable may be used in place of one 5-wire.

Killark Elec. Mfg. Co.
FIG. 20-29.—This wall type entrance fitting is most convenient for bringing wires into outbuildings.

The simplest method is to use as many single-conductor lengths of Style USE entrance cable (Fig. 6-9) as required, buried directly in the ground. The construction and use of this and other underground installation methods have already been covered in Chap. 6.

Outdoor Wiring.—In most installations the outdoor wiring is limited to garage wiring, already described, and perhaps an outdoor outlet for Christmas-tree lights and similar purposes. A convenient unit for this purpose, shown in Fig. 20-30, fits flush on the wall and has a flapper-type cover which covers the outlet when not in use. Another, shown in Fig. 20-31, is mounted on an outlet box; there is a screw cover to cover up the outlet when not in use. Outdoor wiring for farms will be covered in a separate chapter.

Festoon Lighting.—At times it will be necessary to install temporary decorative or other outdoor lights fed by overhead runs. This type of lighting is termed "festoon lighting" by the Code. The minimum size wire that may be used is No. 14, except that, in Christmas-tree outfits approved by the Underwriters as complete assemblies, No. 18 may be used. The

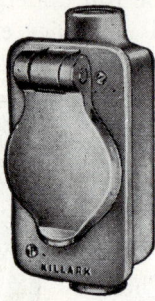

Killark Elec. Mfg. Co.

Fig. 20-30.—Outdoor outlet. The cover closes automatically when the outlet is not in use.

Arrow-Hart & Hegeman Co.

Fig. 20-31.—Another type of outdoor outlet. The cover is screwed on when outlet is not in use.

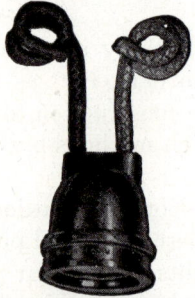

Monowatt Elec. Corp.

Fig. 20-32.—Typical weatherproof socket for outdoor use. Note the groove for a shade holder.

Pass & Seymour.

Fig. 20-33.—Insulating block for supporting streamers on "messenger wires"; required on runs of over 40 ft.

wires must be supported on insulators at each end, and the sockets must be of a type approved for outdoor use, usually of the type shown in Fig. 20-32.

If the span is over 40 ft., the electrical wires alone may not be depended upon for mechanical strength, but they must be supported by a messenger cable, which is usually a steel wire of some kind. The electrical wires are supported from the messenger cable at intervals by means of suspension cleats, one type of which is shown in Fig. 20-33. The individual socket leads must be soldered to the wires, and the points of

Pass & Seymour.

Fig. 20-34.—In this weatherproof socket, stranded wires are laid in the grooves of the socket and the cover is screwed on. The sharp points puncture the insulation and make contact with the conductor.

attachment must be staggered, so that the soldered joint in one wire will not come directly opposite that in the other wire. The wires must clear the ground by a minimum of 10 ft. in residential neighborhoods and by 12 ft. in all other localities.

A pin-point type of socket, as shown in Fig. 20-34, is very handy for streamers in that no soldering is necessary. The wires are merely laid into the grooves in the device and the cover is screwed on. This causes the pin points to puncture the insulation and make contact with the conductor of the wire, making the assembly shown. Only stranded wire may be used for the purpose.

CHAPTER 21

OLD WORK

In old work, or the wiring of buildings completed before the wiring is started, there are few *electrical* problems that have not already been covered. Most difficulties can be resolved into problems of carpentry, in other words, how to get wires and cables from one point to another with the least effort and minimum tearing up of the structure of the building.

In new work it is a simple matter to run wires and cables from one point to another in the shortest way possible; in old work considerably more material is used because often it is necessary to lead the cable the long way around through channels that are available, rather than to tear up walls, ceilings, or floors in order to run it the shortest distance.

No book can give all the answers as to how to proceed in old work; here the common problems will be covered, but considerable ingenuity must be exercised in solving actual problems in the field. A study of buildings while they are under construction will help in understanding what is behind the plaster in a finished building.

Conduit Method.—It is impossible to use conduit in old work without practically wrecking the building. It would be used only where a major rebuilding operation is in process, and installation then is as in new work.

Knob and Tube.—Since the Code requires that all wires fished through walls must be enclosed in separate continuous lengths of loom, this method will not be found very practical because the cost of two lengths of rubber-covered wire and two lengths of loom is at least as much as and usually considerably more than the cost of an equivalent length of armored or nonmetallic cable. The cable is easier to handle and more quickly installed. For these reasons the knob and tube system is little used in old work.

Cable Wiring.—The usual method of wiring in old work is with armored or nonmetallic cable. This material is easily fished through the walls and other spaces. It is sufficiently flexible so that it will go around corners without much difficulty.

Cutting Openings.—To cut good openings for outlet and switch boxes in walls requires a certain amount of skill and a generous measure of common sense. The openings must not be oversize and must be neatly made. Start by marking the approximate location of the box, and, if possible, allow a little leeway so that the opening can be moved a trifle in any direction from the original mark. First make sure there is not a stud or a joist in the way; usually thumping on the wall or ceiling will disclose the presence of timbers. Then dig through the plaster at the approximate location and probe until the space between two laths is found; then go through completely. It would be well to reach through this opening and, with a stiff wire or similar instrument, probe to right and left to confirm that there is no stud or similar obstruction. Assuming that everything is clear, mark the size of the final opening and proceed with the actual cutting, which is done with a hacksaw blade, with the teeth pointing backward, the opposite of the usual fashion. The cutting is done as the blade is pulled, not when pushing the blade away as in usual sawing. If an attempt is made to saw in the usual way so that the work is done while pushing the blade into the wall, there is great danger that the lath will be pulled away from the plaster on either side of the opening, with the result that there may then be a considerable area of plaster unsupported by lath inside. While sawing, hold the hand against the plaster so that it is rigid; otherwise there is a tendency for the plaster to be pulled off the wall.

Temporary Openings.—The openings covered in the preceding paragraph are openings into which a box will later be fitted. In old work it is often necessary to cut temporary openings in odd places to make it possible to pull cable, for example, from the ceiling around the corner into a wall. The cable does not go through the opening; the opening is merely used to get at the cable during the pulling process to help it along, or to get around obstructions in the wall. Such openings must of course be repaired when the job is finished.

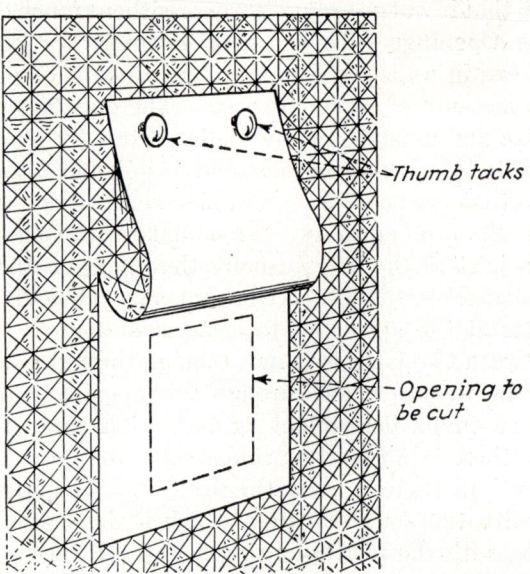

Fig. 21-1.—Sections of wallpaper are easily removed temporarily. Using the top of the cut section as a hinge makes it easy to restore the wallpaper to its original condition, after the installation.

If the room is papered, the paper must be carefully removed in one place and then reinstalled so that the paper will look like the original installation. This is easily done. With a razor blade cut the two sides and the bottom of a square, but not the top. Apply moisture with a rag or sponge, soak the cut portion, and after the paste has softened, lift the cut portion, using the uncut top as a hinge. Fold it upward, and fasten to the wall with a thumbtack. These steps are shown in Fig. 21-1.

When the opening in the plaster is no longer needed, it is easily patched, using plaster of Paris or a ready-mixed plaster, which need only be mixed with water, and set. The same mixture is used to fill the openings around switch and outlet boxes, for the Code does not permit open spaces; the plaster must come up to the box. The section of wallpaper is replaced

 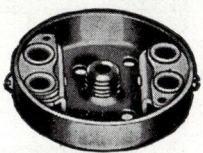

All-Steel Equip. Co.

FIG. 21-2.—In old work, shallow boxes are permitted where the use of standard boxes 1½ in. deep would result in injury to the structure of the building.

by applying fresh paste and letting down the hinged section which was loosened and pinned up while the opening was being made.

Mounting Outlet Boxes.—For new work the Code requires outlet boxes with a minimum depth of 1½ in.; for old work

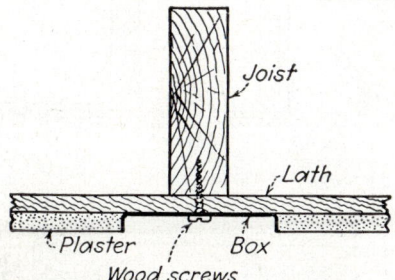

FIG. 21-3.—In mounting boxes directly on the ceiling, attach them to a substantial timber where possible.

this requirement is waived when use of deeper boxes leads to injury of the building. Boxes ½ in. deep are therefore commonly used. Two of these are shown in Fig. 21-2. If the outlet box is located so that it can be attached to a joist or similar substantial timber, install as shown in Fig. 21-3. In similar fashion a box may be mounted directly on lath even if it is not backed up by a joist, as shown in Fig. 21-4. However, this method is to be discouraged because, if a fixture of any substantial weight is attached to the box, damage to the ceiling may follow.

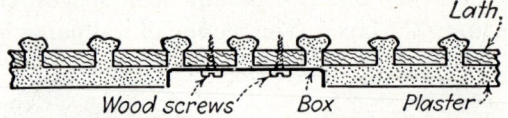

Fig. 21-4.—If necessary to mount boxes directly on lath, attach them to two laths, not to only one. This distributes the weight of the fixture on two instead of one lath.

Appleton Elec. Co.

Fig. 21-5.—An old-work hanger is very handy in mounting a box on the ceiling.

By far the simplest method is to use one of the old-work hangers shown in Fig. 21-5. The method of its use is shown in steps in Fig. 21-5A. First a hole is made in the ceiling at the

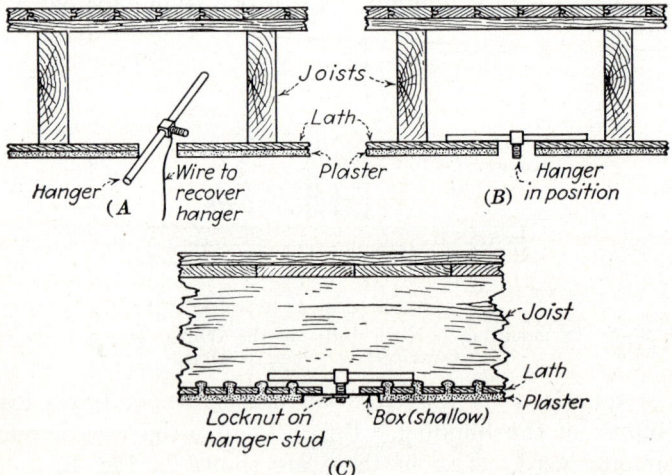

Fig. 21-5A.—Installing an old-work hanger. When the job is finished, the hanger should lie at right angles to the lath.

proper place. Then the hanger is slipped into the hole; note that the hanger has a length of wire attached to the stud so that it is not easily lost inside the ceiling or wall. It is then pulled back by this wire, and the stud only is allowed to project from the opening in the ceiling. Turn the bar crosswise so that it lies at right angles to the lath; this will later distribute the weight of the fixture over a number of laths instead of throwing it all on one or two as is the case when the box is mounted directly on lath. Remove the locknut from the stud, slip

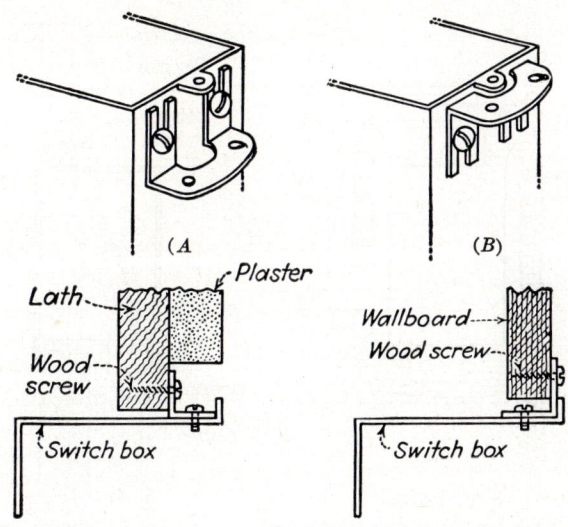

Fig. 21-6.—The mounting ears on switch boxes are reversible. In the position at *A* they are used in mounting boxes on lath under the plaster. Reverse them as shown at *B* for mounting on wallboard or similar material.

the stud through the center knockout of the box, tighten the locknut on the stud inside the box, and the job is finished.

Regardless of the method of mounting, the cable must be attached before the box is mounted in place. This, in the case of ceiling outlets and in similar cases where the cable comes in through the bottom, is no problem. Be sure that the cable connector is rigidly anchored to the cable and that the locknut on the connector is securely driven home before the box is finally mounted.

Often the flooring above the ceiling in which the box is to be installed can be lifted temporarily (as will be explained later). This makes possible a simple installation using a straight bar hanger, used as was shown in Fig. 10-12. Cut an opening in the ceiling for the box, install the box on the hanger, the ends of which have been bent upward, and nail the hanger with the box into place.

Mounting Switch Boxes.—The mounting ears on the ends of switch boxes are adjustable to compensate for various thick-

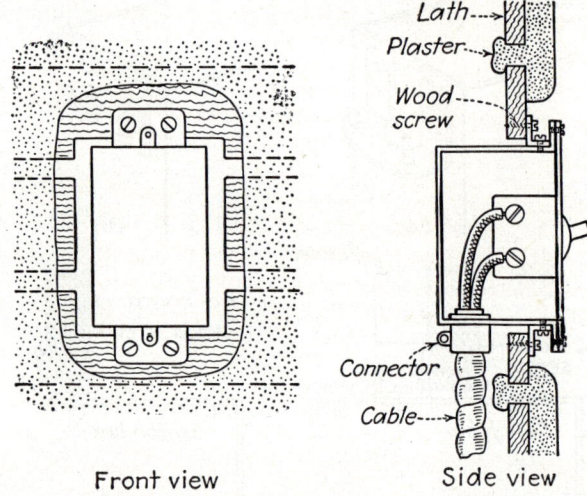

Front view   Side view

Fig. 21-7.—In cutting the opening for a switch box, do not cut away two complete laths. Cut away one and a portion of each of two others.

nesses of plaster. They are also completely reversible, as Fig. 21-6 shows. In the position in which they come on boxes and as shown at A, they are used for mounting such boxes on plastered walls. The ears are fastened to the lath and are of such proportions as to bring the front edge of the box flush with the plaster surface.

In cutting the opening for the switch box, take into consideration the dimensions of the box compared with the width of lath. The ordinary switch box is 3 in. long, while two laths plus three spaces between laths measure more than 3 in. If two full laths are cut away, it will be difficult to anchor the switch box by its ears on the next two laths, for the mounting holes on the ears will then come very close to the edges of the laths, which will split when the screws are driven in. Cut one lath completely and remove part of the width of each of the two adjoining laths; this should be clear from Fig. 21-7.

 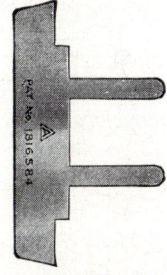

Appleton Elec. Co.

Fig. 21-8.—A hanger for mounting a switch box on wallboard.

If the box is to be mounted on wallboard, or similar material over which there is no plaster, then the mounting ears are reversed, as was shown in *B* of Fig. 21-6, thus bringing the front edge flush with the surface. There are also available special hangers for supporting switch boxes on wallboard and similar materials; the pictures of Fig. 21-8 should make their use clear.

If the cable runs into the bottom of the box, there is no problem involved in cutting the right size of opening. If, however, the cable runs into knockouts in the end of the box, as shown in Fig. 21-7, it is not so simple. If the cable is rigidly attached to the box with a connector before the box is mounted, then it will no longer be possible to get the box into the opening—the cable is in the way. If the opening is made big enough so that a box that has been preassembled with cable and connector will slip through easily, there will be a very sloppy fit that no self-respecting workman will tolerate. To do a good job, follow the procedure outlined in Fig. 21-9. Cut the opening only big enough for the box, plus about ⅛ in., or the thickness of the wire inside of the cable. Leave a generous length of wire sticking out of the cable. Attach the connector to the cable, remove the locknut from the connector. When ready to install the box, let the wires stick out of the opening in the wall, with the connectors inside the

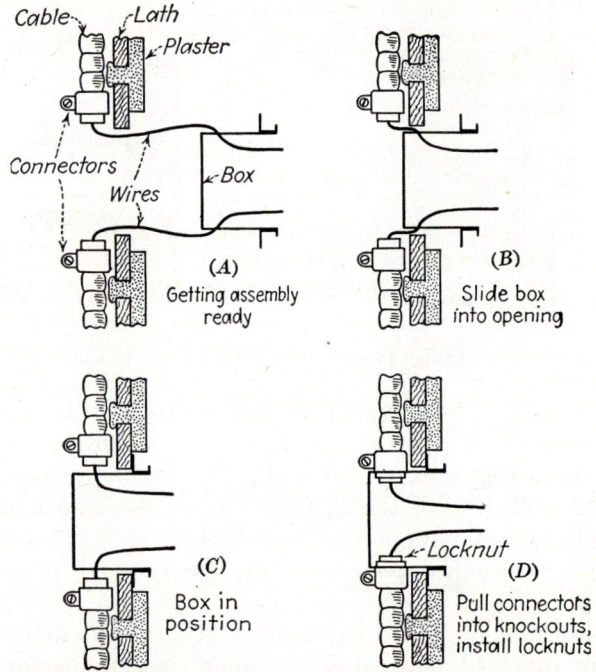

FIG. 21-9.—Installing switch box in opening. The cable is attached by means of locknuts after the box is slid into the opening.

wall. Push the wires through the knockout into the box, and grasp them inside the box. Push the box into the wall; there will be room at the ends of the opening for the wires to slide through into the wall. When the box is in its opening, pull on the wires, pulling the connector into the knockout; then slip the locknut over the connector and tighten.

Cable behind Baseboard.—Assume that there is a wall bracket in the middle of a wall, already wired and controlled by a switch on the fixture, but that now it is to be controlled by a wall switch several feet to the left, but on the same wall. This is a relatively simple job (see Fig. 21-10). First cut the opening for the switch box at *D*. Then remove the baseboard running along the wall at the floor, and cut two holes *B* and *C* behind the baseboard. Then from *B* to *C*, cut a groove or trough in the plaster between two laths; if the plaster is not very thick, it may be necessary to slice away part of the laths.

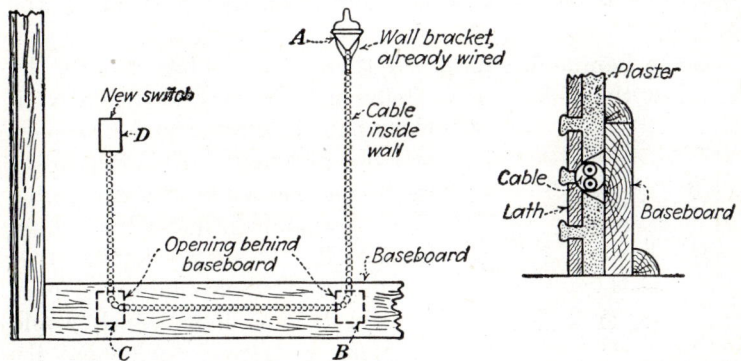

Fig. 21-10.—Often the cable is concealed in a groove in the plaster behind the baseboard.

In any event, the trough must be big enough to receive the cable, as shown in the cross-sectional view of the same picture.

When this has been done, prepare a piece of cable long enough to extend from *A* to *B* to *C* to *D*, with a connector at each end; remove the locknuts. Remove the fixture at point *A*; remove a knockout from the bottom of the outlet box on which the fixture is installed. Then push a fish wire with a hook bent on the end, through the knockout in box *A*, down toward *B*. Reach into opening *B* with another piece of fish wire again with a hook on the end. It will not be difficult to hook the two pieces together so that by pulling at *B* the first piece is pulled in a continuous length from *A* to *B*. Attach the cable to the fish wire, and pull it into the wall through opening *B* until the end appears at *A*. Pull it into place so that the connector slides into the knockout in *A*, tighten the locknut, and the job is finished at *A* except for connecting the wires. Next drop the fish wire in opening *D* until it appears at *C*, and fish the cable up inside the wall until it emerges at *D*, in the meantime laying the cable securely into the trough from *B* to *C* to take up slack. Anchor it at *D* so that it cannot be lost inside the wall; replace the baseboard. Use extreme care that nails are not driven through the cable. All that remains to be done is properly to attach the cable to the box at *D*, mount the box, and install the switch.

Cable behind Molding.—If there is a molding around the room at the ceiling, as is frequently the case particularly in older houses, a considerable amount of labor and material is often saved by laying the cable in a trough behind this molding, instead of behind baseboard. This is particularly true if cable must run around two sides of a room having doors which would interfere if it were run behind the baseboard, or a window which would prevent its being run straight down inside the wall to the baseboard (see Fig. 21-11).

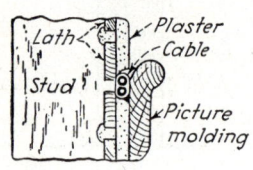

Fig. 21-11.—In older houses, cable can sometimes be run in a trough cut behind a picture molding.

Cable through Attic.—In single-story houses, or when working on the second floor of two-story houses, it is generally entirely practical to run cable through the attic. It is a simple matter to lift a few boards of the usual rough attic flooring and lead the cable around, to avoid all openings in the walls of the living quarters except the opening for boxes. No baseboards need then be lifted. It may require a few feet more of cable, but the saving in labor more than offsets this. Always explore this possibility before proceeding with a more difficult method. For example, in Fig. 21-10 the cable is run from outlet *A* to attic, under the attic floor over to a point directly above outlet *D*, and there dropped down to *D*.

Cable through Basement.—In wiring the outlet of Fig. 21-10 it will frequently be found possible to run the cable through the basement, going straight down below point B into the basement, then over toward the left, then upward again at point C. More usually there will be obstructions in the walls not making this possible in such simple fashion.

If the point where the cable is to run down into the basement is on an outer wall, the construction is apt to be something on the order of that shown in Fig. 21-12. In that case bore a hole with a long-shank electrician's bit, of the type shown in Fig. 21-13, either upward as indicated by arrow A or downward from a point behind the baseboard, as indicated by arrow B, after removing the baseboard. If the cable is to enter the basement from an interior wall, it is usually possible simply to bore directly upward from the basement, as shown in Fig. 21-14.

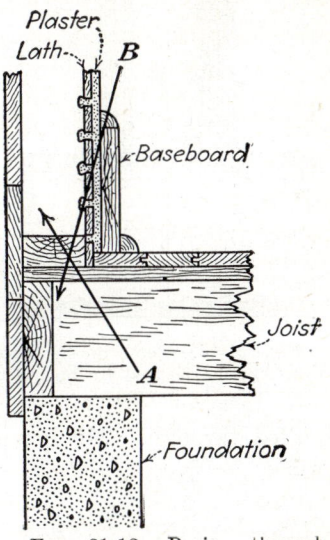

FIG. 21-12.—Boring through obstructions. The actual construction found will vary a great deal. Most problems in old-work wiring are problems of carpentry.

Cable around Corner Where Wall Meets Ceiling.—Figure 21-15 shows this problem: how to lead cable from outlet A in the ceiling to outlet B on the wall around the corner at C. At first glance this may seem difficult, but it is relatively

Greenlee Tool Co.

FIG. 21-13.—Electrician's bit and extension.

simple. In houses that are not very well built, there may be a clear space at the corner C. In that case push a length of fish wire with a hook on the end into the ceiling at A until the hook is somewhere around C. Then push another length of fish wire upward from B until the hook touches the floor above. With one man at A and another at B, it becomes simply a problem of fishing, jiggling, pulling, and twisting the two lengths of fish wire until the hook on one catches the other. Then pull at B until there is a continuous length of fish wire from A to B, attach the cable to the fish wire at A, and pull it into position. It will not come too easily around the corner at C, but, with help at A, it can be pulled through. Much patience is the greatest asset in this work.

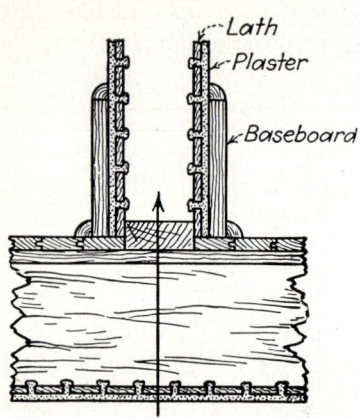

FIG. 21-14.—Sometimes obstructions can be cleared by boring upward from the basement.

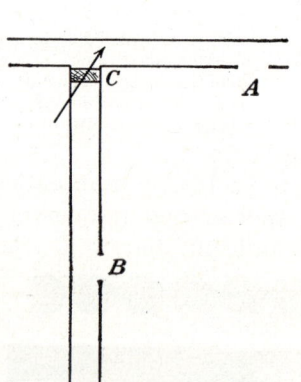

FIG. 21-15.—To get cable from A to B an opening must often be made through obstructions at C.

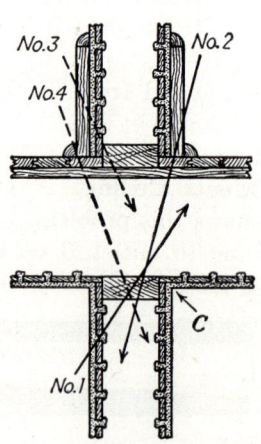

FIG. 21-16.—An enlarged view of point C in the picture at the left.

If the house is well built, there will be an obstruction at point C. Any one of a dozen different types of construction may be used; that shown in Fig. 21-16, which is simply an enlarged view of point C, is typical. The usual procedure is to make a temporary opening in the wall at point C, but on the opposite side of the wall, away from opening B. Bore upward with a long-shank electrician's bit, as shown by the arrow No. 1. Push a length of fish wire into this hole until the end emerges at A. If the opening at C is large enough, push the other end of the wire downward to B, and pull the

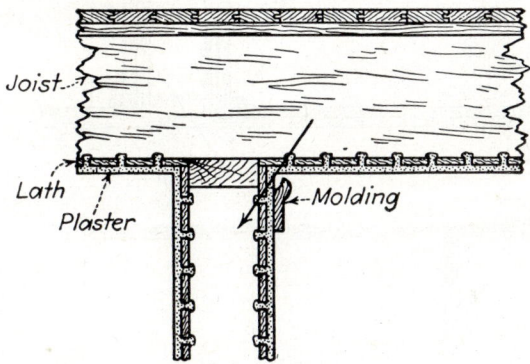

FIG. 21-17.—Sometimes temporary openings can best be made behind a molding.

loop that is formed at C into the wall by pulling at either A or B; there will then be a continuous fish wire from A to B with which to pull in the cable. More usually the hole at C will be small; hence use two lengths of fish wire. Push one through from C to A, leaving a small hook at C just outside the opening. Push another length from C to B, again leaving the hook just outside the opening at C. Hook the two hooks together, pull at B, and it is a simple matter then to pull the longer wire from A through C to B and, with this, to pull in the cable.

If there happens to be another wall directly above point C, it may be better to bore down from above at a point behind the baseboard, as indicated by arrow 2. In that case fish wire is pushed down from above through the bored hole to B; another length from A toward C; when the hooks at the ends engage, pull down at B until a continuous piece of fish wire extends from A through C to B.

If there is a molding around the room at the ceiling, it is usually better to remove the molding and to chisel a hole in the corner, probably chiseling away a portion of the obstruction, to provide a channel for the cable, as indicated by the

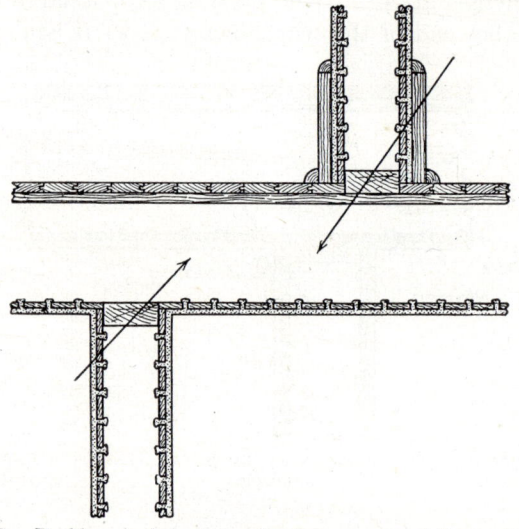

FIG. 21-18.—Problem in bringing cable from a second floor partition into a first floor partition.

arrow in Fig. 21-17. When the molding is replaced, the cable, if it projects a bit, is concealed.

Cable from Second Floor to First.—If the first floor partition is directly below the second floor partition, it is usually simple to bring the cable through by boring, as indicated by arrows 2 and 3 (or 3 and 4) in Fig. 21-16. Use good judgment so that the holes will lie so far as possible in approximately the same plane, thus simplifying the fishing problem. An opening behind the baseboard is usually necessary.

If the first floor partition is not directly below the second floor partition, handling as indicated in Fig. 21-18 will usually solve the problem. Bore holes as indicated by the two arrows.

OLD WORK   359

Lifting Floor Boards.—In many cases the outlet and switch boxes may be so located with regard to wall and ceiling obstructions that it is necessary to lift hardwood floor boards in the floor above. This should be avoided if possible, but where necessary use extreme care in lifting the boards so that when replaced there will be no visible damage to the floor. Attic

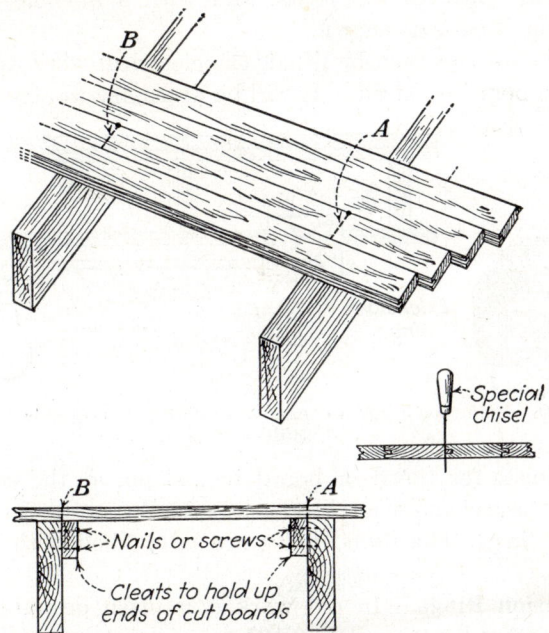

Fig. 21-19.—Steps in lifting and replacing floor boards.

flooring is simply lifted, but the usual hardwood floor with the tongue-and-groove construction presents more of a problem.

It is necessary to first chisel off the tongue on one of the boards. The thinner the chisel used for the purpose, the less the damage that will be done to the flooring. A putty knife with the blade cut off short and sharpened to a chisel edge makes an excellent chisel for the purpose, and a thinner one is not obtainable. Drive it down between two boards, and cut off the tongue (see Fig. 21-19). This should be done to the entire length between three joists, although the picture shows only two joists. Having the cut section extend over a longer space gives the advantage of a better footing when the board is reinstalled. In cutting off this tongue, the exact location of the floor joists can be determined and in this way points A and B in the picture located. Bore a small hole at these two points next to the joists, and with a keyhole saw cut across the boards as shown.

The board can then be lifted, the electrical work done, and later the board replaced. It will be necessary to attach cleats

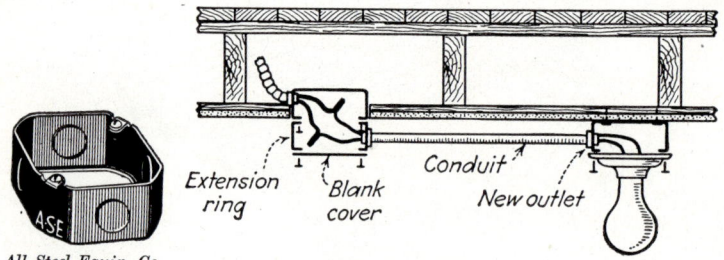

All-Steel Equip. Co.

Fig. 21-20.—Extension rings are handy in adding new outlets to existing outlets.

to the joists for the floor board to rest on, at the cut ends. Anchor these cleats securely so as to give the cut board a really solid footing. The bored holes are later filled with wooden plugs.

Extension Rings.—In old work it is often desirable to be able to extend a circuit beyond an existing outlet. If the wiring is entirely flush, it might entail considerable carpentry if the new outlet were also to be made flush, and at least in certain types of work (such as basements) it will be entirely acceptable to have the new outlet of the surface type. In that case an extension ring of the type shown in Fig. 21-20 is used. Extension rings are, to all intents and purposes, outlet boxes without bottoms, and they are available to fit all kinds of outlet boxes.

Their use should be made clear by the same picture. Simply mount the extension ring on top of the existing outlet box and from there proceed as in any exposed wiring. The extension ring is covered with a blank cover, or with the fixture or other device that may have been installed on the original outlet box.

Use Common Sense and Patience.—No book can outline all the problems in carpentry that will be encountered in old work. The method of construction of houses varies with the age of the house, the general sturdiness of the building, the skill and integrity of the builder, and many other factors. Plenty of patience, coupled with a generous measure of "horse sense," is the greatest asset in old-work wiring.

CHAPTER 22

FARM WIRING

In the average city home, the various electrical devices and appliances are purchased primarily for the convenience and utility which their use provides. On the farm the same devices are also used, but in addition many others are found which are used in the *business* of farming—devices which are bought, not so much for their mere convenience, but rather as an investment on which the farmer expects dividends. Into this classification fall such things as milk coolers, milking machines, cream separators, hammer mills for chopping fodder, silo fillers, corn shellers, water heaters to provide scalding hot water for the dairy, water heaters which during the winter keep water for chickens at a temperature which experience has shown will promote egg production, and dozens of others.

The wiring of farms involves all the problems so far discussed as well as a considerable number of new ones. The maximum wattage in use at one time is apt to be considerably larger than in city homes because of the liberal use of motor-driven devices. There is a great deal of outdoor wiring, either overhead or underground, between the various buildings. Substantial distances are involved, which means that wire sizes must be carefully watched, both to avoid voltage drop and for mechanical strength. Relatively poor grounding conditions are usual. These and other factors will be separately considered in this chapter.

Service Entrance.—If the installation is a very small one, the service entrance will be the same as in ordinary residential wiring. The barn and other buildings will be served by one or two circuits fed from the fuse cabinet or circuit breaker in the house. (Service entrance cable may be used from the fuse cabinet or circuit breaker inside the house, to a point outside the house, where the overhead wires run on to the other building.) This will not permit many motor-driven devices to be used. Generally speaking this scheme should be used

General Elec. Co.

Fig. 22-1.—Really adequate wiring is necessary if large motors are expected to do their work properly.

only if nothing but lights and very small motors are contemplated at the other buildings. Remember, however, that plans change. Sooner or later loads at other buildings will be much greater than originally planned, and expensive rewiring will then be required.

On most farms the maximum amount of power used at one time will be at some point other than the house. If the service entrance wires are run to the house, and wires of sufficient size are run from there to the other locations, more material, including heavier wires, would then be required. Certainly the installation will not be as neat as it might be—too many wires leading back and forth. The present trend is to end the power company's wires at a pole located at some convenient point in the yard. The meter is located on the pole; one set of service wires runs from the pole to the house (terminating in service switch, main fuses, branch-circuit fuses, etc.), and another set of service wires runs from the pole to the barn (also terminating in service switch, main fuses, branch-circuit fuses, etc., as in the house). In other words there are two independent service entrances, one at the house and one at the barn, both fed through a single meter.

The meter on the pole may be one of the outdoor type, which was shown in Fig. 17-1, or the indoor type enclosed in a weather-proof cabinet, as was shown in Fig. 17-2. Practice varies from locality to locality with regard to switching, fusing, and grounding at the pole. In most cases the service wires run through the meter, being neither switched nor fused, but sometimes grounded. The trend also is to ground the equipment at the meter. Consult the local inspector, the power company, or the R.E.A.[1] project superintendent.

A typical installation of this kind is shown in Fig. 22-2. At *A* is shown a top view, for clarity's sake showing only one wire; at *B* is shown a side view. Usually the neutral wire is the topmost of the three; note that it is continuous although a tap is taken off to run down to the meter. The service head should have five openings in the insulating block, for there are five wires in the conduit: one neutral, two "hot" service wires down to the meter, and two "hot" wires from the meter up to the wires leading to the house and barn. The wiring diagram at *C* should make this clear.

An installation problem exists in connecting the wires at the top of the pole. They will be heavy *solid* wires (weatherproof wires are seldom stranded), and soldering would be difficult, even in an ideal location; the wires being located at the top

[1] Rural Electrification Administration.

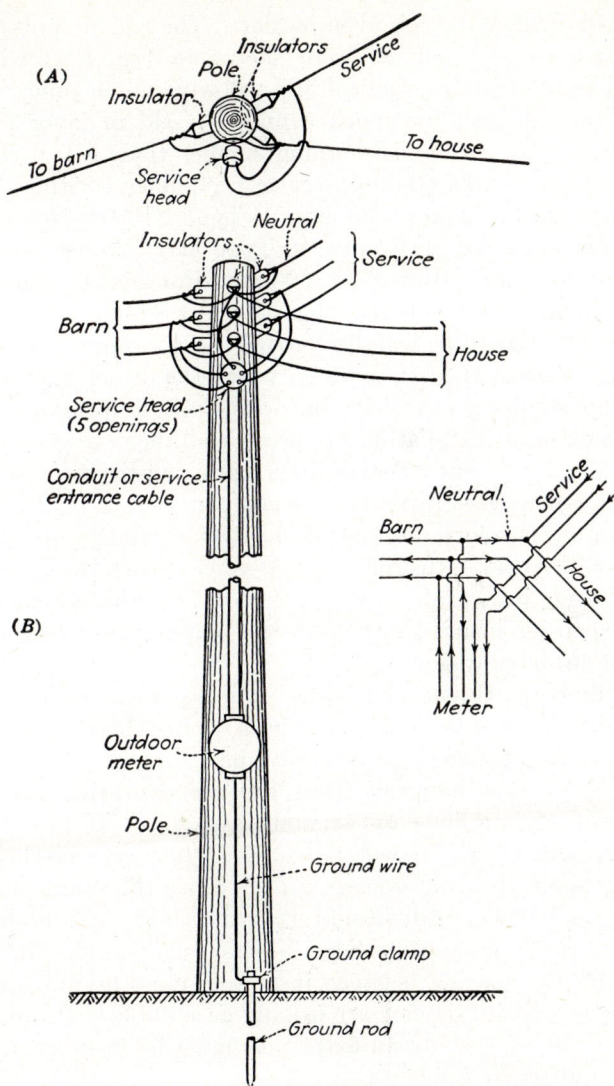

Fig. 22-2.—Typical installation at meter pole.

of a pole makes the job even harder. The use of split-shank type connectors such as were shown in Fig. 8-22 will be found to be entirely practical and will save much time.

As to wire size, too much cannot be said in favor of the heavier sizes. Certainly nothing smaller than No. 6 should be used, permitting 60-amp. service. Number 4 with a carrying capacity of 70 amp. (85 amp. if Type RH), or No. 2 with 95 amp. capacity (115 amp. if Type RH), would be more appropriate, for although a 60-amp. installation was considered generous 5 or 6 years ago, it will certainly not be long before the 100-amp. installation will be considered standard for most farms, at least those on which the owner appreciates the importance of electricity in the *business* of farming.

The 60-amp. installation will provide all the needed capacity for a farm*house*, but it leaves little extra capacity for the farm proper, where electric power is needed for the farming *business*, for motors of every description, heaters for dairy, and many similar purposes. Installing a 100-amp. service in the beginning, even if its full capacity is not immediately utilized, is inexpensive insurance that electric power will be utilized to maximum advantage.

Entrance at House and Barn.—The entrance at the house (and usually also the one at the barn) is installed in the same way as the standard service entrance already discussed in Chap. 17. Weatherproof wires are run overhead from the pole to both buildings and securely anchored. In most cases a minimum of No. 6 will be required both for mechanical strength and to avoid voltage drop. Since the spans may be as long as 150 ft., sturdy insulators are necessary and secondary racks of the type shown in Fig. 17-7 are usually used. In some localities the spacing between insulators must be 8 in.; those with $4\frac{1}{2}$- or 6-in. spacing are usually acceptable. If the span is over 150 ft., usually an extra pole must be installed for an extra support.

From the point where the wires are attached to the house or barn, conduit, or more usually service entrance cable, is run to the service switch and fuse cabinet, as covered in Chap. 17.

FARM WIRING

Use Nonmetal System.—The Code in Art. 300 definitely recommends a nonmetal system, in other words nonmetallic sheathed cable (or knob and tube), for locations where a good permanent ground is not found. Certainly farms fall into that classification; hence conduit and armored cable are seldom used for farm work. The reasons for this are not hard to understand. In barns considerable moisture is always present, and in addition there are other corrosive vapors such as, for

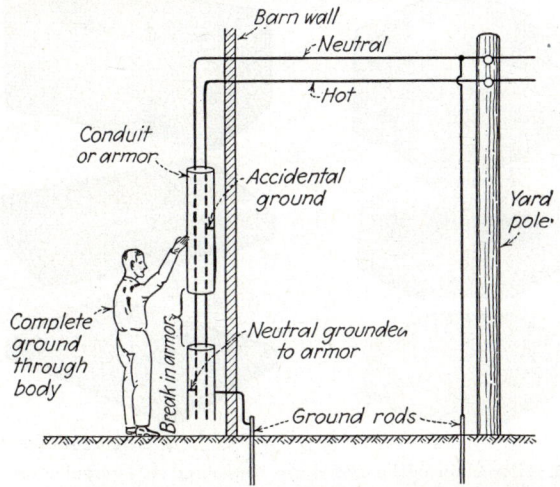

FIG. 22-3.—If there were no break in the armor, the accidental ground shown would blow a fuse. Since the armor has a break, a hazardous condition exists.

example, ammonia from the urine of animals. This quickly attacks the conduit or metal armor, so that the life of the metal is relatively short. As the metal raceway rusts out, it may open the continuous ground that otherwise exists from outlet to outlet in the usual metallic system. If an accidental ground occurs in such a system at a point beyond the break, and a person or an animal touches a part of the metal raceway above the break, the circuit is completed through the body with at least an unpleasant, if not a dangerous, shock. Figure 22-3 should make this clear; the ground through the body is equivalent to touching both wires and may be equally dangerous. Many dairy animals have been killed every year through just such occurences—metallic systems apparently but not actually grounded. For these reasons the nonmetal systems are recommended for such locations.

The objection can be raised that, even if nonmetallic cable is used, dangerous conditions can and will still arise when an accidental ground happens to occur inside one of the usual

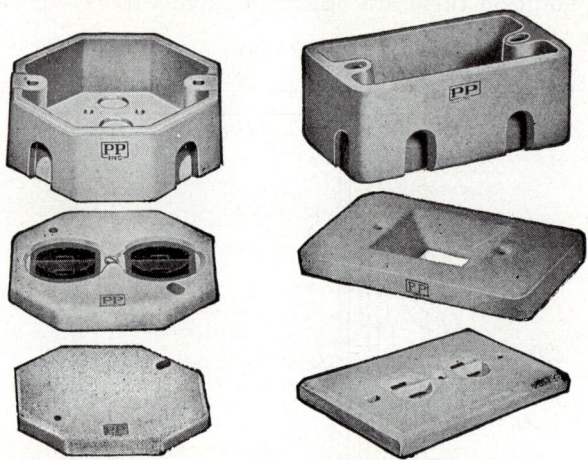

Porcelain Products, Inc.

FIG. 22-4.—Porcelain outlet boxes are becoming very popular for farm use. They make a wiring system completely nonmetallic.

metal outlet boxes; anyone touching the outlet box is then still subject to the same shocks encountered with a metal system with the metal raceway eaten through as outlined in the previous paragraph. To this objection there is no good answer, with the result that nonmetallic outlet and switch boxes and covers have been developed to make the entire system nonmetallic. Such boxes are usually made of porcelain or bakelite, and Fig. 22-4 shows an assortment of them. They are used like other boxes except that connectors are not required, but the cable must be anchored within 8 in. of every box. This is required by Sec. 3710c of the Code.

Such boxes, although commonly used in barns and all other

farm buildings, are not usually required in farmhouses. The local inspector is the one to pass on this point.

There are also available special units, consisting of the outlet box, the cover, and the device such as switch or receptacle,

Monowatt Elec. Corp.

FIG. 22-5.—These handy devices replace outlet box, cover, and wiring device.

all in one unit. A representative assortment of such devices is shown in Fig. 22-5. Their popularity is increasing, not only for wiring barns and similar buildings, but also for basements, attics, cottages—in fact any location where the cable is not to be concealed within the walls of the building. The bakelite devices shown have the additional advantage of all using the same base. The bases may be installed in advance where needed, the devices contained in the covers being added later as the wiring is completed.

Buildings Fed through Another Building.—On farms it usually happens that one or more buildings are served by wires running from another building nearer the meter. In the 1940 Code it was required that all the wiring in the building could be disconnected by a *single* switch. The 1947

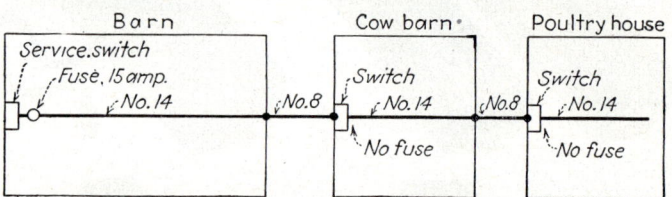

Fig. 22-6.—Whether disconnect switches in outbuildings need be fused or not depends on the size of the fuse at the starting point.

Code in Sec. 2351d merely requires that all the wiring in the building must be capable of being disconnected by one *or more* switches located in or on the building. Therefore if all the wiring in a building can be disconnected by one or more switches, even if they are the ordinary toggle switches used to control lighting outlets, the Code requirements are fulfilled. If however a receptacle outlet remains alive, the Code requirement is not met.

It will be found to be a wise practice to provide a single switch of the general type shown in Fig. 20-2 to disconnect the entire building, even if this is not required. If the wiring is at 115 volts only, with one wire grounded, use a 2-wire 2-pole 1-blade switch. If it is at 230 volts without a grounded neutral, use a 2-wire 2-pole 2-blade switch. If it is the usual 115/230-volt installation with a grounded neutral, use a 3-wire 3-pole 2-blade switch.

Whether this disconnect switch needs to be fused or not depends entirely on the size wires used and the size fuses ahead of the starting point (see Fig. 22-6, which shows several buildings served through the main barn). The wires are No. 14 inside the buildings, but, for mechanical strength, No. 8 is used between the buildings. Since the fuse in the barn is the 15-amp. size, it protects the *smallest* wire in the entire circuit; therefore the switches in cow barn and poultry house need not be fused.

In Fig. 22-7, No. 8 wires run through the barn, between the barn and cow barn, and through the cow barn, serving a motor

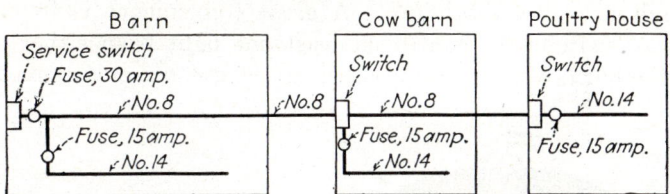

FIG. 22-7.—In this case, fuses are required because the 30-amp. fuse in the barn does not protect the No. 14 wires.

there which requires up to 30 amp. for starting. Therefore a 30-amp. fuse is used in the barn, and since the No. 8 wire continues straight through to the poultry house, this wire must be fused at not over 15 amp. at the point where the change is made to No. 14 wire in the poultry house. Likewise at the point where No. 14 wire is attached to the No. 8 in the cow barn, a fuse block must be used with 15-amp. fuses to protect No. 14 wire.

In some localities the inspector insists on a separate ground at each building, regardless of whether it is served by a separate service from the pole, or through another building. The 1947 Code in Sec. 2524 requires such a separate ground at all buildings housing livestock, as also at any building having two or more branch circuits. The entrance at each such building is considered a service; see page 279 for requirements concerning grounding at services.

Farmhouses.—The wiring in farmhouses is no different from that in city homes, and the procedure is therefore the same as already covered in other chapters. Usually any wiring system may be used in the house, even if the inspector insists on non-metallic sheathed cable for barns and other similar buildings.

Barn Wiring.—The physical make-up of the circuits, that is, the combinations of cable and boxes and switches and receptacles, is not different from that already discussed and therefore needs no further amplification. The chief points to observe are points of practicability and common sense. Locate switches and receptacle outlets so that they cannot be bumped by animals in passing. Locate switches at convenient height so that they can be operated by the elbow; farmers' hands are often both full. A great convenience is to have 3-way switches to control at least one light from either end of the barn. Never use brass-shell sockets; use only porcelain

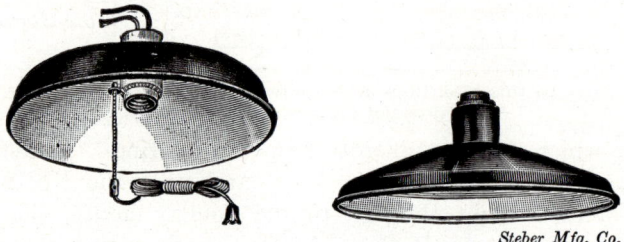

Steber Mfg. Co.

Fig. 22-8.—A 60-watt bulb with a reflector is often as effective as a 100-watt without a reflector. Reflectors become an investment rather than an expense.

or bakelite, for the same reasons that nonmetallic boxes are used.

Plenty of light outlets should be provided; a minimum is considered one light for every two stalls. It is best to locate the outlets for bulbs between joists, so that the bulb does not project too far down into the aisle between stalls, where it might easily be damaged. Since most barn ceilings are dark and dusty, they reflect practically no light. About half the light from an exposed bulb falls on the ceiling and is lost. Provide a reflector for every socket; the area underneath will be lighted almost twice as well as without a reflector. Several types of suitable reflectors are available at prices from 50 cts. upward; two are shown in Fig. 22-8. Their use is a good investment.

Provide a light to illuminate the steps to the haymow. In haymows inspectors frequently require vapor-proof receptacles of the type shown in Fig. 22-9. A vapor-proof receptacle is simply a socket with a tight-fitting glass globe that encloses the bulb. The dust that arises in haymows is inflammable or even explosive, and if an unprotected bulb is accidentally broken, although the lamp burns out instantly, during that instant there is a flash while the filament melts. This flash may set off an explosion; hence the requirement for the vapor-proof receptacles.

Cable should always be installed in a location where it cannot possibly be damaged accidentally. In haymows, cover it with strips of board at all points where it might be damaged by pitchforks. Where it passes through a floor, the Code requires that it be protected by conduit or pipe for at least 6 in.; many inspectors require this protection for about 6 ft. especially where there is danger of hayforks damaging the cable.

Russell & Stoll Co.

Fig. 22-9.—A typical vapor-proof receptacle. They are often used in haymows.

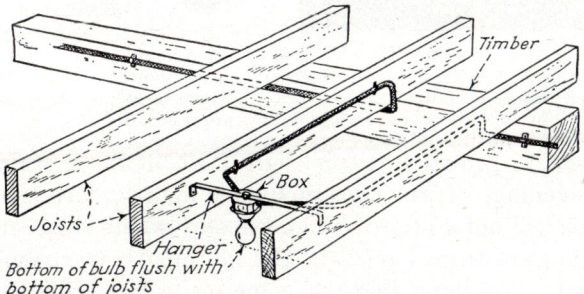

Fig. 22-10.—Keep exposed cables away from the center of aisles. The bottom of the bulb should be very little below the bottom of the joists. Reflectors should be used, extending very little below the bottoms of joists.

Cable in barns and other farm buildings should not be run along or across the bottoms of joists or similar timbers, because this exposes the cable to mechanical injury. The cable will receive good protection if it is run along the side of a joist or beam. More cable will be required to run the cable from the side of an aisle out to the middle for an outlet, then back to the side of the aisle, but consider the extra cost as insurance against damage. Figure 22-10 will show the details of recommended practice.

Poultry Houses.—The only point that should be specially noted is that special wiring is frequently required for lighting designed to promote egg production. It is well known that hens produce more eggs during winter months if light is provided during part of the time that would otherwise be dark.

Sangamo Elec. Co.

FIG. 22-11.—This poultry-house switch properly controls lights, dim and bright, for forcing egg production.

Russell & Stoll Co.

FIG. 22-12.—This weatherproof heavy-duty outlet and plug should be employed where large portable motors are used outdoors.

It is best to provide artificial light both in the morning and in the evening. If the transition from light to dark is abrupt, the hens will not go to roost but will stay where they are when the lights are turned off. In the morning better results are obtained if the light does not come on to full brilliancy suddenly. If a special time switch of the type shown in Fig. 22-11 is used, in the morning it turns on first the dim lights, then bright lights, then when full daylight arrives turns all off. In the evening the procedure is reversed; as darkness sets in, the lights are turned on full. At the time set, the bright lights go out, and the dim lights go on; during this interval the hens go to roost. Shortly thereafter all lights are automatically turned off. The wiring for such clocks is simple, and diagrams are furnished with such clocks.

Be sure that the light falls upon the roosts, for if the roosts remain in darkness when the lights come on, the hens will probably not leave their roosts. Neither will they be able to find the roosts in the evening if they are in darkness while the lights illuminate the rest of the pens. One 40- or 60-watt bulb for every 200 sq. ft. of floor area is usually considered sufficient.

Manually controlled circuits can easily be provided so that one switch controls bright lights, another dim lights.

Steber Mfg. Co.

Fig. 22-13.—Gooseneck fixtures of this type should be liberally used in lighting the farmyard.

Other Buildings.—No particular problems are involved in other buildings. Use only nonmetallic sockets; provide switch control instead of pull chains. Every building should have a receptacle outlet, if for no other reason than to be able to use a trouble light of the type that was shown in Fig. 20-23.

Motors.—Stationary motors should be wired as covered in Chaps. 15 and 28. For portable motors of considerable size it will be necessary to provide heavy-duty outlets; the types used for range wiring, shown in Fig. 20-1, are suitable. If such an outlet must be outdoors, it must be of the weatherproof type, and one style is shown in Fig. 22-12.

Yard Lights.—Every farm will have at least one yard light of the general type shown in Fig. 22-13, usually located at the meter pole. In most cases the light is controlled by two 3-way switches, located at house and barn. A 4-way switch in a weatherproof housing is often located at the pole.

The wiring of a yard light is often haphazard. It is not uncommon to see it wired by tapping one of the two wires from the light, directly to the neutral wire at the pole, running the other to a switch at any convenient location and then on to the nearest "hot" wire. The scheme works but is contrary to Code, for the neutral wire at the pole is a feeder and not a branch circuit; it is not permissible to tap a feeder except to form a branch circuit.

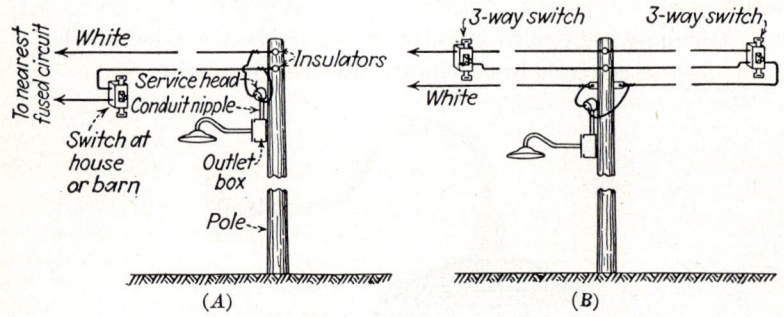

FIG. 22-14.—Good construction in installing yard light.

Today most inspectors will insist on a carefully planned installation. To operate a yard light from one switch, it is necessary to run two wires to it from the nearest fused circuit, and to operate it from two points, it is necessary to run three wires. Figure 22-14 shows a method that makes a weatherproof and mechanically sturdy job out of the installation; it also shows the wiring diagram.

Wires Entering Buildings.—Use any of the methods shown in Chap. 20 in connection with garage wiring.

CHAPTER 23

ISOLATED LIGHTING PLANTS

An isolated plant may be defined as any installation by which the owner manufactures his own electric power. Such installations may be found mostly on farms, in summer camps and resorts, and in similar locations where electric power is not available from power lines, as well as for construction projects and similar undertakings.

Types of Plants.—Such engine-driven generating plants can be classified into two broad groups: those which use no batteries (except automobile type batteries to start the engine), and those which charge batteries from which the power is then supplied to the load when needed.

Battery-less plants are available in a wide range of capacity from about 350 watts output, up to 50 kw. or more output. They may deliver either direct current or alternating current. Those delivering 115-volt (or 115/230 volt) 60-cycle alternating current are by far the more popular. Furnishing current identical with that supplied by power lines in general, including farm "high lines," they are ideal in that they permit ordinary low-cost radios, motors, appliances, and so on to be used, rather than more costly, hard-to-get direct-current devices. When installed where power is expected to be available at a future date, they permit the change to commercial service to be made without changing a single motor or other device.

Occasionally such units are installed requiring manual cranking when power is wanted; most of the time the units are provided with automobile type batteries which crank the engine of the unit, just as in a car. Special controls are also available which make the unit start when a load is turned on and stop when the last light or appliance is turned off.

Such engine-generators are now being commonly used in stand-by service, with controls so arranged that when a commercial power line fails the engine-generator automatically starts and continues to run until commercial service is restored. Such installations are well worth while in any business where a few hours without power would be costly—for example, chicken hatcheries in which, if the incubators are allowed to cool off, thousands of eggs are ruined; radio stations that cannot broadcast without power; greenhouses where lack of power may mean no heat in an oil-burning furnace, and many similar applications.

Generating plants used in connection with storage batteries as part of the load circuit can be only of the direct-current type. The plant charges the battery; the load is taken from the battery. When heavy loads exist, the combined capacity of the generator plus that of the battery can be drawn upon to handle the load. Power is available in limited amounts whether the generator is running or not.

Six-volt Plants.—The capacity of the generator on such plants usually is 150 to 200 watts. The maximum charging rate is about 25 amp. against a battery that is low, dropping off to about 15 amp. or less as the battery becomes charged.

A fully charged battery of the type usually used should not be discharged at a rate exceeding 15 amp. if reasonable life is expected; therefore the maximum wattage that should be used without the generator running is about 6×15, or 90 watts. Adding to this another 150 watts from the generator gives a practical maximum of 240 watts while the generator is running and the battery discharging at its safe limit.

From this the limit of usefulness of a 6-volt plant will be evident. In wiring for the few lights that this plant will operate, remember that while a voltage drop of 1 volt on a 115-volt circuit is less than 1 per cent, on a 6-volt circuit a drop of 1 volt is 16 per cent and will cause bulbs to burn exceedingly dimly. Moreover, a 60-watt bulb on a 115-volt circuit consumes about ½ amp.; the same bulb on a 6-volt circuit consumes 10 amp. Amperage causes voltage drop, so it is essential that relatively large wires be used, and that they be kept very short. Any distance over 50 ft. from the battery is too far if more than 50 watts is involved. The table below gives the limit of the 1-way distance, in feet, that each size wire will carry the wattages shown and still permit reasonably efficient lighting.

Watts at 6 volts	No. 14	No. 12	No. 10	No. 8	No. 6
25	25	40	60	100	150
50	12	20	30	50	75
75	8	13	20	33	45
100	..	10	15	25	40
125	..	8	12	20	30
150	..	..	10	15	25

Reverting once more to the subject of voltage drop, it is not unusual to find in such a 6-volt installation, when a number of 50-watt bulbs are in use, that they burn very dimly on account of the voltage drop. Substituting 25-watt bulbs for the 50-watt cuts both the amperage and the voltage drop in half, so that the 25-watt bulbs burning at normal brilliancy will produce practically as much light as the 50-watt size did.

Switches are usually dispensed with because they would probably introduce a few extra feet of wire with additional voltage drop. Pull-chain control is considered adequate.

Twelve-volt Plants.—Since the voltage is doubled, the amperage for any given wattage is only half that of a 6-volt plant. The voltage drop is only half as great in volts, and only one-quarter as great in percentage. Therefore on 12 volts, the 6-volt table above will carry the different wattages 4 times farther than on a 6-volt plant, with equal efficiency and percentage of voltage drop. For this reason the 12-volt plant is considerably more efficient and useful than the 6-volt plant.

Since the battery voltage is doubled, the wattage available

while the generator is not running is 12 × 15, or about 180 watts, double that of the 6-volt battery.

Thirty-two-volt Plants.—Plants of this voltage have been in use for many years and are entirely practical within their limits. In wattage the generators of such plants usually range from 250 to 1,500 watts. Larger plants are made, but since a 1,500-watt plant charges the battery at about 40 amp. and since 40 amp. is approximately the highest charging rate that most batteries available at a reasonable price will stand without damage, the 1,500-watt is usually considered the practical limit. However, in combination with proportionately larger batteries now becoming available, 32-volt units in capacities as high as 3,500 watts are becoming more popular.

Such plants are entirely suitable for average lighting; radio; small appliances such as fans, sewing machines, and vacuum cleaners; as well as small motors not exceeding $\frac{1}{2}$ hp. Amperages that considerably reduce the life of the battery are consumed when 32-volt motors larger than $\frac{1}{2}$ hp. are used; also wire sizes that border on the impractical are required.

The average battery in use should not be charged or discharged at a rate exceeding 25 amp., and the maximum practical wattage while the generator is not running is therefore 32 × 25, or 800 watts. Larger and more expensive batteries can safely deliver twice this wattage. In any event the capacity of the generator can be added to that of the battery, for periods when considerable power is required.

The table on the next page shows the 1-way distance that various sizes of wire will carry various wattage loads at 32 volts, with reasonable voltage drop.

The wiring for 32 volts is the same as for regular 115-volt work, except that heavier wire sizes must be used. The Code in Sec. 7203 requires No. 12 as a minimum. This has a carrying capacity of 20 amp., which at 32 volts is equivalent to 640 watts. The ordinary No. 14 115-volt circuit has a capacity of 1,725 watts. This should make it evident that for 32-volt use almost 3 times as many circuits will be required as for 115-volt use. If this is not done, fuses will blow very regularly.

The Code in Sec. 7204 requires that not more than eight sockets or receptacles be connected to one circuit, nor a total load exceeding 320 watts. Motors or appliances rated over 320 watts must have a special circuit; it is entirely in order to feed one outlet in the kitchen with a special circuit direct from the fuse cabinet.

Watts at 32 volts	No. 12	No. 10	No. 8	No. 6	No. 4	No. 2	No. 0
100	80	125	200	320	500	800	1,280
200	40	65	100	160	250	400	640
300	25	40	70	100	160	280	400
400	20	32	50	80	125	200	320
500	15	25	40	60	100	160	240
600	..	20	35	50	80	140	200
700	..	18	30	45	75	120	180
800	..	16	25	40	65	100	160
900	..	..	22	35	60	90	140
1,000	..	..	20	30	50	80	120

Grounding is not required unless the wires run overhead between buildings, in which case one of the wires should be grounded.

115-volt Plants.—The wiring for 115-volt plants should be done in the same way as for other 115-volt installations.

Theory of Batteries.—Despite its name a storage battery does not store electricity. At any given moment during a discharge cycle a storage battery operates like a dry cell. In a dry cell the component parts are used up during discharge, and when they are consumed, the cell is dead. In a storage battery the materials in the plates are also used up during discharge, but if an electric current is then forced through the battery in a direction opposite to that in which it flowed during discharge, it will restore the plates to their original condition, and the battery is charged. It is then ready for another cycle. The storage battery is strictly an electrochemical device wherein, during discharge, chemical action creates an electric current; during charge, an electric current causes a chemical action which restores the plates to their original condition.

Ampere-hours.—The capacity of a battery is measured in ampere-hours, abbreviated amp.-hr. The number of amperes multiplied by the number of hours this current flows gives the ampere-hours. One ampere flowing for one hour is one ampere-hour; 5 amperes flowing for 2 hours is 10 ampere-hours; etc.

A very commonly used 32-volt battery has a capacity of 120 amp.-hr. on an 8-hr. basis. This means that, if the battery is fully charged, it can be discharged for 8 hr. at 15 amp. before it is exhausted ($8 \times 15 = 120$). It would seem logical that, if it is discharged at 30 amp. instead of 15, it should take 4 hr. instead of 8 completely to discharge the battery; actually it will take only about $3\frac{1}{2}$ hr. Likewise, if it is discharged at $7\frac{1}{2}$ amp. instead of 15, instead of taking twice 8 or 16 hr. to discharge, it will actually take more nearly 18 hr. The ampere-hour capacity of a battery is not constant; the higher the rate of discharge, the lower the capacity. Batteries are usually rated on two bases: the 8-hr. continuous basis already mentioned, and the 72-hr. intermittent basis. On the latter basis, which presupposes intervals of discharge and rest so spaced that the entire charge of the battery is consumed in 72 hr., the capacity is usually about 33 per cent greater than on the 8-hr. basis. The same battery that has a capacity of 120 amp.-hr. on the 8-hr. continuous basis has a capacity of about 160 amp.-hr. on the 72-hr. intermittent basis.

Efficiency of Storage Batteries.—A battery is not 100 per cent efficient but, when new, has an efficiency of 65 to 70 per cent. In other words, if it takes 10 hr. of charging at a 10-amp. rate to bring a battery up from a discharged to a charged condition; and if it is then discharged at the same 10-amp. rate, it will be fully discharged at the end of approximately $6\frac{1}{2}$ to 7 hr.

Watt-hour Capacity.—Multiplying the ampere-hour capacity of a battery by its voltage gives its watt-hour capacity. Thus the battery mentioned in the previous paragraph, if it is of the 32-volt type, has 160 × 32 or 5,120 watt-hr. capacity on a 72-hr. intermittent basis. It will therefore light a 100-watt bulb for about 51 hr. It is a simple matter to determine how long one charge of a battery should last. For example, on a small installation the calculation would be approximately as follows:

	Watts	Hours per week	Watt-hours
1 bulb	25	10	250
1 bulb	50	12	600
1 bulb	100	2	200
1 bulb	25	20	500
Radio	65	14	910
¼ hp. motor	250	2	500
Vacuum cleaner	200	2	400
Total for week	...	..	3,360
Average per day	...	..	480

Since the battery has a capacity of 5,120 watt-hr. and since 480 watt-hr. are used per day, a fully charged battery should last 5,120/480, or approximately 10 days before requiring recharging.

Life of Batteries.—Heavy-duty batteries designed for 32-volt use have a normal life of 250 to 350 cycles of charge and discharge. Knowing how many days a normal charge lasts, it is not difficult to calculate the probable life under any given circumstances. For example, in the battery of the above example, 300 cycles of 10 days is equivalent to 3,000 days, or about 8 years. Normal life presupposes good care.

Care of Batteries.—Instructions are usually furnished by the manufacturer with batteries, but a brief résumé of what constitutes good care should not be amiss here. Many owners feel that, if they keep the water level in the cells at the proper level, they have done all that is required. This is not by any means sufficient. For maximum life the battery should be fully charged, then used until it is practically discharged; the process should be repeated through regular cycles of charge and discharge. Keeping a battery always fully charged, charging it immediately when it is slightly discharged, often cuts the life of the battery in half. Never fully charging the battery, but leaving it always in a partially discharged condition, ruins it even more quickly. It is absolutely necessary to cycle the battery if normal life is to be expected.

About once a month the battery should be overcharged, that is, the charging continued for several hours even if hydrometer readings indicate that it is fully charged.

A battery should never stand idle in a discharged condition. Even if it is fully charged, it should not stand idle for more than 60 days at a time; every 60 days it should be discharged slowly, and recharged promptly.

CHAPTER 24

WIRING APARTMENT HOUSES

If an apartment is considered merely as that space within a building which is occupied by one family, no new wiring problems of any consequence are encountered. If the apartment house is considered in its entirety as a multi-family dwelling, a number of new problems arise.

Planning an Individual Apartment.—To determine the minimum number of circuits required by Code for any single apartment, proceed as outlined for a single-family dwelling in Chap. 12. For lighting, allow 2 watts per square foot. For example, a small apartment of 700 sq. ft. will require 700×2, or 1,400 watts, which means one circuit. To this must be added a separate No. 12 circuit for appliances, just as in the case of the single-family house, thus making two circuits the minimum. This may not be sufficient for practical living, and an extra circuit would reflect sensible planning. Naturally, too, an additional circuit must be provided for each appliance consuming more than 1,650 watts, for example, an electric range.

Service Entrance Problems.—In practically all cases there is but a single service drop for the entire building. In most cases each tenant pays for the power he consumes, so there is a separate meter for each tenant, plus usually another meter to carry hall lights, oil-burner motors, and similar loads. The service drop therefore must feed a number of separate meters and disconnecting means. If there is a common space available, accessible to all tenants, such equipment should be grouped there. The Code in Sec. 2351b requires that each tenant must have access to his disconnecting means.

If there are *not over* six meters and disconnecting means,

it is not necessary to provide a main disconnecting means and overcurrent protection ahead of them. Instead each meter is, through its overcurrent device and disconnecting means, connected directly to the service entrance wires, as outlined in Fig. 24-1.

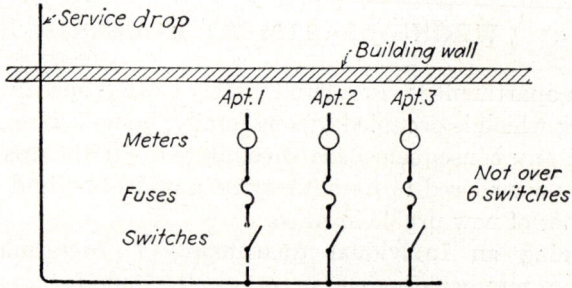

FIG. 24-1.—No separate switch or overcurrent device is required in multiple-occupancy installations if not over six separate entrance switches are used.

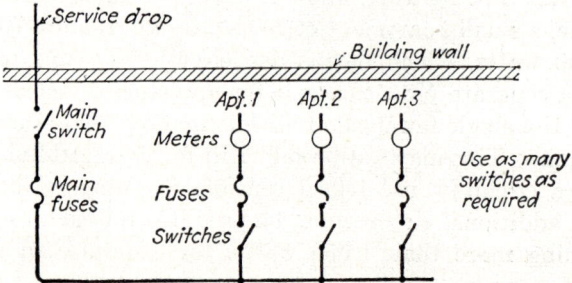

FIG. 24-2.—If more than six separate switches are used, a separate entrance switch and overcurrent protection are required.

If there are *more than* six meters and disconnecting means, it is necessary to use a disconnecting means and overcurrent protection ahead of such equipment, as shown in Fig. 24-2.

The switches and overcurrent devices for the individual tenants are selected as if each tenant were in a separate building. Usually for the sake of neatness and ease in installation they are of the ganging type, as shown in Fig. 24-3.

An alternative scheme frequently used in connection with outdoor meters is to lead the main service entrance wires to

WIRING APARTMENT HOUSES 387

a number of meters on the outside of the building. From each meter, service entrance wires run to a service switch and overcurrent protection inside the building, all as pictured in Fig. 24-4. If there is a readily accessible common space available, *not over six* sets of entrance equipment may be used; if there is

Colt's Patent Fire Arms Mfg. Co.

Fig. 24-3.—Ganging-type switches save space and make an exceptionally neat installation.

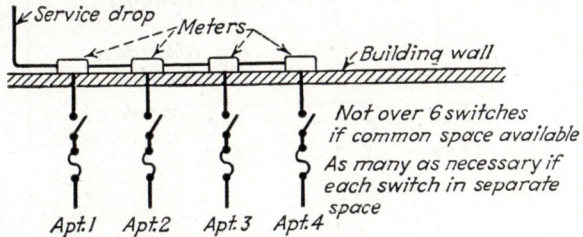

Fig. 24-4.— This construction may be used with not more than six separate entrances if a common space for all the switches is available. There is no limit if each switch is in a separate space.

no such common space available but each meter is in a separate space, then as many sets as required may be used.

Branch-circuit Overcurrent Protection.—In a small apartment building all the overcurrent devices for the entire building will probably be located at the service entrance. The group for each individual apartment will probably be incorporated with the disconnecting means for that apartment. Each separate circuit runs from such an overcurrent device to the apartment, as it would in a single-family house, and as shown in Fig. 24-5. In a large apartment this would involve extremely long runs, would require a great deal of material, and would prove most inconvenient to tenants. Accordingly, a feeder is usually run from the service entrance equipment in the basement to each apartment, the branch-circuit overcurrent protection such as fuses then being located at the apartment, as shown in Fig. 24-6. A little study will show that the basic scheme for Figs. 24-5 and 24-6 has already been studied in connection with Figs. 12-1 and 12-2.

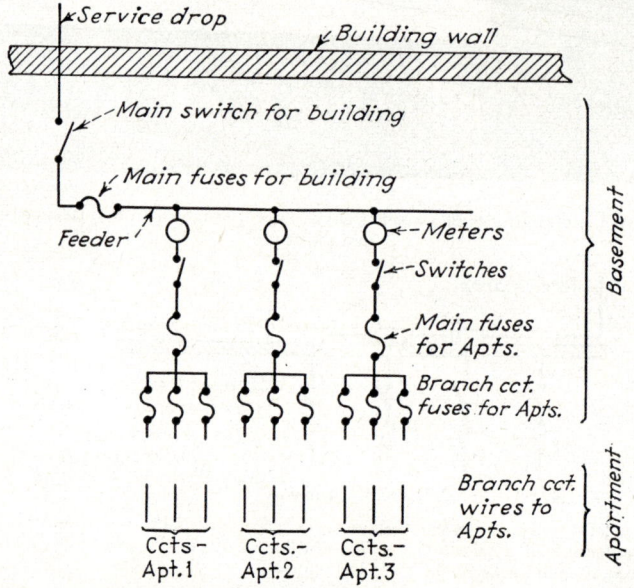

FIG. 24-5.—In small apartment buildings, the branch-circuit fuses are often installed with the main switches, in the basement.

Determining Feeder to Individual Apartment.—The feeder from the disconnecting means to the overcurrent devices at the individual apartment corresponds to the service entrance wires in the case of the single-family house. Its size is determined in general in the same way, as already discussed on pages 192 to 202. However, while in the single-family house a demand factor of 30 per cent is used for that portion of the watts above 2,500 watts, in the case of the feeder to an apartment the demand factor is 100 per cent for the first 3,000

WIRING APARTMENT HOUSES

watts; 35 per cent for the remainder, including all lighting and small appliances, but excluding ranges.

For an apartment of 700 sq. ft. this makes 1,400 watts for lighting, plus 1,500 watts for small appliances, or 2,900 watts altogether. Since the total is less than 3,000 watts, the demand factor is 100 per cent and the full 2,900 watts must be counted. At 115 volts this is equivalent to 2,900/115, or

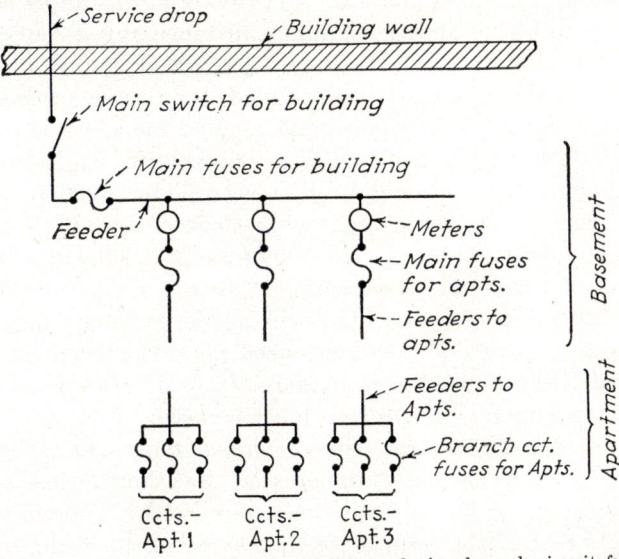

Fig. 24-6.—In larger apartment buildings, placing branch-circuit fuses in the basement would be wasteful of material and inconvenient. Therefore a feeder is run to each apartment, and the branch-circuit fuses are located at the individual apartment.

25.3 amp., which makes No. 10 wire the minimum; Sec. 2201 of the Code also requires No. 10 as a minimum (see page 184). If the apartment were larger, of say 1,600 sq. ft. area, the calculation would be $1,600 \times 2$, or 3,200 watts for lighting, plus 1,500 watts for small appliances, or 5,100 watts altogether. Counting the first 3,000 watts at their full value, plus 35 per cent of the remainder of 2,100 watts or a net 735 watts, makes a total of 3,735 watts. At 115 volts this is equivalent to 32.6 amp., for which No. 8 is the minimum permissible. More likely one would consider the load a 115/230-volt load and run a 3-wire feeder capable of carrying 3,735/230 or 16.3 amp., which would be theoretically No. 12, actually No. 10 in accordance with Sec. 2201.

In this connection do not overlook the requirement of Code Sec. 2202, which specifies that the wire used must be of sufficient size so that the voltage drop will not exceed 1 per cent. See tables on pages 106 and 107; divide all distances shown by two to arrive at the maximum distance any given size of wire will carry a specific load with 1 per cent voltage drop.

Assume that a range is to be added, consuming a maximum of 9,000 watts. The 80 per cent demand factor as permitted for single-family houses is also permissible for an individual apartment, but it would be better to allow 8,000 watts as recommended in connection with Code Table 29, Col. A. Adding 8,000 watts to the previous total of 2,900 watts makes a total of 10,900 watts altogether. Since a range operates at 115/230 volts, obviously a 3-wire feeder must be installed, and the amperage at 115 volts need not be determined. At 230 volts the amperage is 10,900/230, or 47.4 amp. Therefore a minimum of No. 6 wire must be used.

However, the neutral wire serving a range can never be made to carry as many amperes as the "hot" wires sometimes carry, as has already been discussed. Therefore the Code in Sec. 2203g permits for the *neutral* of the feeder a wire smaller than for the "hot" wires. Consider only 70 per cent of the allowance for the range, so far as the neutral is concerned. In the example above, the carrying capacity of the *neutral only* would be calculated as follows: The amperage capacity that must be provided for lighting and small appliances has already been calculated as 12.6 amp. For the neutral of the range the calculation is $(0.70 \times 8,000)/230$, or 5,600/230 or 24.3 amp. The final answer then is $12.6 + 24.3$, or 36.9 amp., making No. 8 adequate unless a larger size is required to avoid excessive voltage drop.

Determining Service Entrance.—The minimum size of the service drop wires for the building as a whole is determined by the maximum probable load *in the entire building* at any given moment. The method of arriving at this probable maximum is very similar to that used for single-family houses: the lighting, the small appliances, and range loads are considered separately.

The greater the number of apartments in a building, the less the likelihood that all tenants will at the same time be consuming current at the maximum rate available to the individual apartment. Therefore the Code permits a demand factor to be applied. This demand factor is applied on the gross computed total watts figured on the basis of 2 watts per square foot of total area for all apartments, plus the minimum for small appliances for each apartment, applied as follows:

First 3,000 watts................................	100 per cent
Next 117,000 watts.............................	35 per cent
All above 120,000 watts.......................	25 per cent

For ranges there is no likelihood whatever that all will ever be used at their maximum capacity at the same moment; the Code in Table 29 (see Appendix) permits a demand factor that varies from 75 per cent in the case of two small ranges consuming less than 3,500 watts each, to as little as 16 per cent in the case of 61 or more ranges each consuming 3,500 watts or more.

However, the 1947 Code contains a simplification in column A of Table 29, which shows a figure in watts that may be used as the maximum demand for any given number of ranges consuming not over 12,000 watts each. This is far simpler than taking each range separately, determining its maximum capacity, multiplying by the number of ranges involved, and multiplying in turn by the proper demand factor for that number of ranges to arrive at the total watts that must be allowed for the total range load.

Planning Three-apartment Installation.—Assume a building containing three apartments of 700 sq. ft. each or 2,100 sq. ft. in total, plus the usual basement. Each apartment will have two circuits, as determined earlier in this chapter. Each circuit will probably run direct to the overcurrent device for that circuit in the basement. The service entrance will probably be in accordance with Fig. 24-1 or 24-4. There is little to calculate except the service entrance.

Service Entrance for Three-apartment Building.—The maximum probable load is very simply calculated in accordance with preceding paragraphs, as shown in the following table:

	Gross computed watts	Demand factor, per cent	Net computed watts
Lighting, 2,100 sq. ft. at 2 watts..........	4,200		
Small appliances, 3 apartments at 1,500 watts.............................	4,500		
Total gross computed watts............	8,700		
First 3,000 watts.......................		100	3,000
Remaining 5,700 watts..................		35	1,995
Total net computed watts............			4,995

The total of 4,995 watts covers only the three apartments proper. It does not make allowance for the basement, and it is well to allow 1,500 watts for basement lighting, the outlets for the tenants' washing machines, and similar devices. This makes a total of 6,495 watts, which at 230 volts is equivalent to 28.2 amp. Theoretically then No. 10 wire which has a capacity of 30 amp. may be used. However the Code in Sec. 2304a requires a minimum of No. 8. It would be entirely logical to use a minimum of No. 6, for it is likely that the small load estimated for the building will in due course of time be greatly increased. The No. 6 will provide a reserve for such future expansion.

If an electric range consuming not over 12,000 watts is added to each of the three apartments, column A of Table 29 shows that 14,000 watts in total must be allowed for that purpose in calculating feeder capacity. Adding this to the 6,495 watts already determined for lighting and small appliance load produces a total of 20,495 watts, which at 230 volts is equivalent to 89.1 amp. The smallest wire permissible would be No. 2 with a carrying capacity of 90 amp. It would be used in connection with a 100-amp. switch and 90-amp. fuses, but it would provide no reserve capacity whatever. It would be sensible to use a larger wire such as No. 1 with 110 amp. capacity, or No. 0 with 125 amp. capacity.

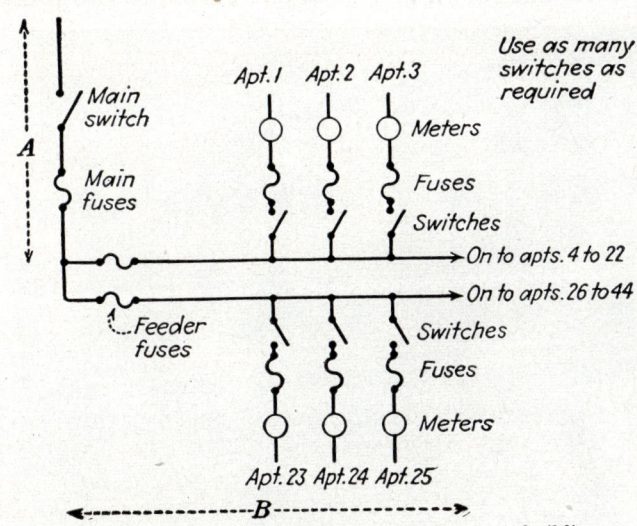

Fig. 24-7.—Feeder diagram for larger apartment building.

Instead of using column A of Table 29, column B or C may be used, depending on the capacity of each range. Assuming that the ranges have a capacity of 8,000 watts each, the total would be 24,000 watts; column C shows the demand factor to be 55 per cent, which applied to 24,000 watts leads to an allowance of 13,200 watts, substantially the same as the 14,000 watts shown in column A. It will usually be found to be quicker and more convenient to use the ready-made answers of column A than to calculate the answers from column B or C.

Planning 44-apartment Installation.—Assume a larger building containing 44 apartments each 700 sq. ft. in area. Since each individual apartment is the same size, it will be wired in the same fashion as in the previous example.

Service Entrance.—As 44 meters are involved, it is probable that they will be arranged in two banks of 22 each. Since more than six services are involved, a main disconnecting means with overcurrent device will be required; the wiring diagram will be that of Fig. 24-7 and the actual installation similar to that shown in Fig. 24-8. There are two problems

Colt's Patent Fire Arms Mfg. Co.
Fig. 24-8.—A typical installation in a large apartment building.

involved: calculation of the main feeder A and the two subfeeders B.

The main feeder A will carry the entire load for the building. Assuming that half of the apartments are equipped with electric ranges consuming a maximum of 8,000 watts, the calculations are as shown in the table at the top of page 395.

At 230 volts, 82,850 watts is equivalent to 360 amp. According to Table 1 of the Code, if ordinary Type R rubber-

WIRING APARTMENT HOUSES

covered wire is used, 700,000 c.m. cable is the minimum permissible. Reference to Chap. 25, however, will show that if Type RH is used, the size may be reduced to 500,000 c.m.

	Gross computed watts	Demand factor, per cent	Net computed watts
Lighting, 30,800 sq. ft. at 2 watts.......	61,600		
Small appliances, 44 apartments at 1,500 watts............................	66,000		
Total gross computed watts..........	127,600		
First 3,000 watts....................	....	100	3,000
Next 117,000 watts..................	....	35	40,950
7,600 watts above 120,000...........	....	25	1,900
22 ranges at 8,000 watts.............	176,000	...	37,000*
Total net computed watts...........	....	...	82,850

* Column A, Table 29 of Code.

The neutral of the three service entrance wires may be smaller than the two hot wires; the method of calculating this will be covered in the next chapter.

Each of the feeders B carries 22 apartments, 11 of which have ranges. The size of these feeders is calculated in the same way, as follows:

	Gross computed watts	Demand factor, per cent	Net computed watts
Lighting, 15,400 sq. ft. at 2 watts.......	30,800		
Small appliances, 22 apartments at 1,500 watts............................	33,000		
Total gross computed watts..........	63,800		
First 3,000 watts....................	......	100	3,000
Remaining 60,800 watts.............	......	35	21,280
11 ranges at 8,000 watts.............	88,000	...	26,000*
Total net computed watts...........	......	...	50,280

* Column A, Table 29 of Code.

At 230 volts, 50,280 watts is equivalent to 219 amp. This current can be carried, according to Table 1 of the Code, by 300,000 c.m. cable, Type R, or by No. 0000 Type RH rubber-covered wire. Bear in mind that the wire sizes so computed are the minimum permissible to meet Code requirements. Larger sizes may be required to keep within the 1 per cent voltage drop specified by Code as maximum, or to provide full adequacy in the wiring.

If each of the 44 apartments is to be equipped with an electric range, calculations similar to those in the examples above will quickly show the proper sizes of feeders. The demand factors permitted by Sec. 2203 and Table 29 must be carefully observed.

Service Entrance Switch.—Since the maximum amperage as determined for the main feeder was found to be 360 amp., the service switch must have at least 360 amp. capacity. The next standard size above that figure is the 400 amp., and that size may be used. It will however allow only a small amperage for new future loads; additional ranges, for example, may be installed. It would be wise to use the next larger size rated at 600 amp. to provide for probable future increases in load. The rating of the fuse in the switch is determined by the carrying capacity of the feeder selected.

Since the subfeeders B will have a carrying capacity of 225 to 250 amp., they will not be protected by the 400-amp. or larger main fuse. Therefore extra overcurrent devices rated not more than the carrying capacity of the feeder wires must be installed where the feeders connect to the larger switch, in order to protect the smaller wires. All this is shown in Fig. 24-7.

Low-voltage Wiring.—The usual doorbell and buzzer system will be installed in accordance with the principles already outlined in other chapters. In addition it is necessary to take into consideration the problem created by the longer lengths of wire involved in buildings of substantial size.

In the wiring of fairly large apartments it is not uncommon for the doorbell and buzzer system to be installed in accordance with the diagram of Fig. 24-9. Theoretically this diagram is correct, but if ordinary No. 18 wire is used, as in residential work, it will be found that the more distant bells ring rather faintly because of the substantial voltage drop in the long run of the small wire. A drop of 2 volts in a 115-volt

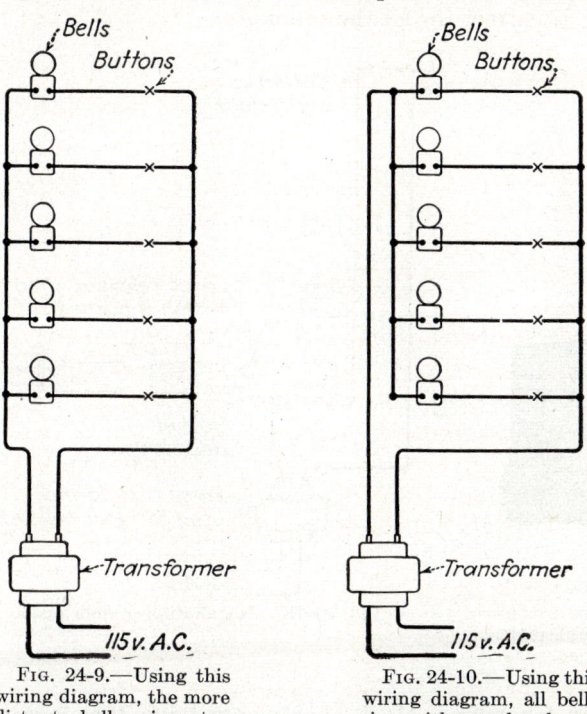

FIG. 24-9.—Using this wiring diagram, the more distant bells ring too faintly, the near-by ones probably too loudly.

FIG. 24-10.—Using this wiring diagram, all bells ring with equal volume. It requires only a little more material than the other.

circuit is not so serious, but when the starting voltage is only about 10 volts or thereabouts, a 2-volt drop is of the order of 20 per cent. If the transformer voltage is stepped up sufficiently so that the more distant bells ring properly, the near-by bells ring too loudly. A larger size of wire helps, but the distant bells still ring less loudly than the ones nearer the transformer.

The solution is to use the circuit of Fig. 24-10. A little more wire is involved, but if this circuit is analyzed, it will be found that the number of feet of wire involved for any one bell is exactly the same as for any other bell. Accordingly all will ring with equal volume; a transformer voltage that is correct for one is correct for all the others.

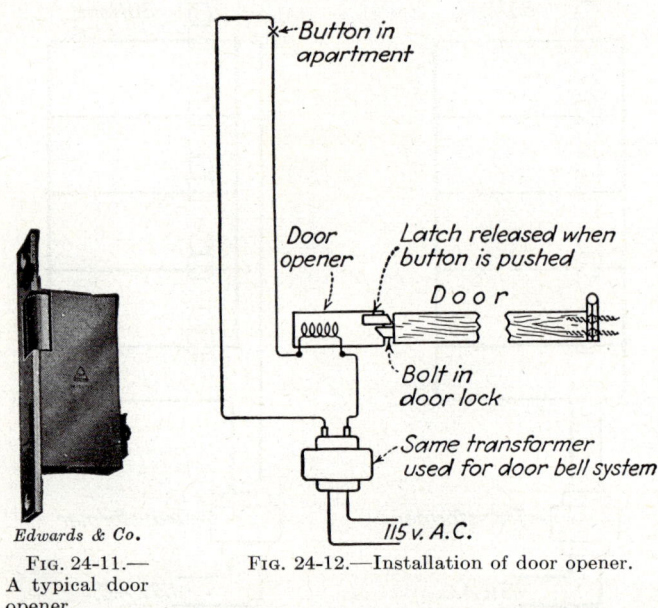

Edwards & Co.
Fig. 24-11.—A typical door opener.

Fig. 24-12.—Installation of door opener.

Door Openers.—Most apartments have the door leading into the inside hall equipped with a door opener so that intruders cannot enter. Pushing a button in any apartment releases a latch which permits the door to be opened. A typical door opener is shown in Fig. 24-11. It consists simply of an electromagnet, similar to that found in a doorbell, which releases a latch when the button is pushed, permitting the door to be swung open. The opener is mortised into the door frame opposite the lock in the door. The diagram is most simple, as Fig. 24-12 shows.

WIRING APARTMENT HOUSES

Miscellaneous.—An aerial system for the tenants' use is often installed, using outlets of the type that were shown in Fig. 20-15. Devices are available which make it possible to have a single aerial on the roof serve efficiently for all the tenants, thus eliminating the hopeless jumble of aerials and leadins which is inevitable when each tenant installs his own aerial system.

All-Steel Equip. Co.
Fig. 24-13.—This laundry-box outlet may be padlocked by the tenant.

In the basements of small apartment buildings it may be found expedient to install separate laundry boxes of the type shown in Fig. 24-13. Use of these boxes, one for each tenant, with a connection to his meter, will permit each to use only the power for which he himself pays. The box can be padlocked by the tenant, making it strictly his own.

CHAPTER 25

1947 CODE REQUIREMENTS WITH RESPECT TO WIRE

It is suggested that the reader at this point review Chap. 6, which outlined many basic principles that will not be repeated in this chapter.

What Determines Carrying Capacity of Wire.—Before entering into a discussion of the 1947 Code and its provisions concerning wire, it will be well to give thought to the reasons why the carrying capacity of any given size of wire varies with the kind of insulation on the wire and the method of installation.

Copper is not harmed by heat; insulation is harmed by heat. If insulation is overheated, it is harmed in various ways, dependent on the degree of overheating and the kind of insulation. Some kinds melt, some harden, some burn. In any event insulation loses its usefulness if overheated, leading to breakdowns and fires.

The carrying capacity in amperes specified in various tables for any particular kind and size of wire is the amperage that it can carry without increasing the temperature of its insulation beyond the danger point. Ordinary rubber insulation will stand the least heat; consequently rubber-insulated wire has the lowest carrying capacity of all the different kinds. Asbestos will stand the most heat; consequently asbestos-insulated wire has the highest carrying capacity. The temperature of the asbestos-insulated wire when carrying its rated amperage will be higher than the temperature of the rubber-insulated wire carrying its rated amperage, but its insulation, being designed for it, will not be harmed by the higher temperature.

The rated carrying capacity of each kind and size of wire is based on the assumption that the wire is installed in a room temperature of 30°C., or 86°F. The table on pages 403 to 405 shows the maximum temperature that the insulation of different types of wire is permitted to reach. That temperature will be reached if the wire is carrying its rated amperage in a room that has a temperature of 30°C., or 86°F.

If the room temperature is higher than the assumed standard, then the insulation of a wire while carrying its full rated amperage will reach a temperature higher than is safe or permissible. Therefore when installed in hot locations, the rated amperages must be reduced. How to apply the proper correction factors will be explained later.

Previous Codes.—In order to appreciate fully the provisions of the 1947 Code with respect to wire, it will be necessary to review the treatment of this subject in earlier Codes. The 1937 and earlier Codes recognized only three kinds of insulation on wires: rubber, varnished-cambric, and "others." The table of carrying capacities consisted of three columns, corresponding to the three kinds of insulation. The carrying capacity was the same, regardless of whether the wires were installed in conduit or mounted in free air; no provisions were made for corrections dependent upon room temperature.

By the time the 1940 Code was established, several new types of wire had become available, such as synthetic insulation (Type SN), latex-insulated (Type RU), and also types with the usual *grades* of insulation but with *less of it* (Types RPT and RHT). The table of carrying capacities grew from three columns to seven, then multiplied by two to provide two tables, one to be used when the wire is installed in conduit or in the form of cable, the other when installed as open wiring (which was entirely sensible because wire mounted in the open radiates its heat and therefore can carry a higher amperage). As compared with the 1937 Code, the 1940 edition greatly reduced the carrying capacity of the larger sizes; in some cases the reduction was over 50 per cent, thus requiring the installation of wires twice as heavy as were required under the 1937 Code. Moreover, smaller sizes of wire were given precise carrying capacities such as 18, 31, 54 amp., with no available fuse sizes to correspond.

All told, the spirit of reform that apparently overcame those who established this part of the 1940 Code apparently carried too far, with the result that the provisions of the 1940 Code with respect to wire were rather flagrantly disregarded as unworkable. The impact of war, with the extreme necessity for conserving copper, further upset the possibility of enforcement. Interim amendments were therefore issued more or less permitting use of the 1937 setup.

The 1947 Code.—During the 7 years that passed between the 1940 and 1947 Codes, insulations in general were very greatly improved in quality, and new styles of insulation were produced. The permissible carrying capacities are now much greater than under the 1940 Code, although in most cases not so high as under the 1937 Code; the smaller sizes are greater than under the 1937 Code. All carrying capacities are rounded off so that all values end in 5 or 0.

The presentation and the entire setup under the 1947 Code have been considerably simplified as compared with the 1940, although they are still more complicated than the 1937, considering the fact that there are more kinds of wire.

Types R, RP, RH Rubber-covered Wires.—The 1940 Code recognized these three grades of insulation on rubber-covered wires. The insulations were considered safe so long as their temperature did not exceed 50, 60, and 75°C., respectively. Three grades of insulation however proved impractical from a manufacturing and stocking standpoint, especially considering the various colors that had to be made available. The 1947 Code takes this into consideration, and accordingly has abolished the Type RP, and thus recognizes only two types: *improved* Type R (equivalent in quality to the abolished Type RP, not harmed unless the temperature of the insulation exceeds 60°C., or 140°F.) and Type RH (same as the Type RH under the 1940 Code, and not harmed unless the temperature of its insulation exceeds 75°C., or 167°F.).

From the foregoing it should be obvious that for a period of time, in changing from the 1940 to the 1947 Code, there will be available two grades of Type R wire: the old or 1940

Conductor Insulations

Trade name	Type letter	Insulation	Thickness of insulation	Outer covering
Rubber-covered fixture wire— solid or stranded	RF-64 RF-32	Code rubber Code rubber	18 .... 1/64 in. 18–16 .... 2/64 in.	Cotton Cotton
Rubber-covered fixture wire— flexible stranding	FF-64 FF-32	Code rubber Code rubber	18 .... 1/64 in. 18–16 .... 2/64 in.	Cotton Cotton
Thermoplastic-covered fixture wire—solid or stranded	TF	Thermoplastic	18–16 .... 2/64 in.	None
Thermoplastic-covered fixture wire—flexible stranding	TFF	Thermoplastic	18–16 .... 2/64 in.	None
Cotton-covered, heat-resistant fixture wire	CF	Impregnated cotton	18–14 .... 2/64 in.	None
Asbestos-covered, heat-resistant fixture wire	AF	Impregnated asbestos	18–14 .... 2/64 in.	None
Code	R	Code rubber	14–12 .... 2/64 in. 10 .... 3/64 in. 8–2 .... 4/64 in. 1–4/0 .... 5/64 in. 213–500 .... 6/64 in. 501–1,000 .... 7/64 in. 1,001–2,000 .... 8/64 in.	Moisture-resistant, flame-retardant fibrous covering
Heat-resistant	RH	Heat-resistant rubber	14–12 .... 2/64 in. 10 .... 3/64 in. 8–2 .... 4/64 in. 1–4/0 .... 5/64 in. 213–500 .... 6/64 in. 501–1,000 .... 7/64 in. 1,001–2,000 .... 8/64 in.	Moisture-resistant, flame-retardant fibrous covering
Moisture-resistant	RW	Moisture-resistant rubber	14–10 .... 3/64 in. 8–2 .... 4/64 in. 1–4/0 .... 5/64 in. 213–500 .... 6/64 in. 501–1,000 .... 7/64 in. 1,001–2,000 .... 8/64 in.	Moisture-resistant, flame-retardant fibrous covering

Conductor Insulations.—(*Continued*)

Trade name	Type letter	Insulation	Thickness of insulation	Outer covering
Latex	RU	90% unmilled grainless rubber	14–10..................18 mils 8–6......................25 mils	Moisture-resistant, flame-retardant fibrous covering
Thermoplastic	T	Flame-retardant thermoplastic compound	14–10....................2/64 in. 8.........................3/64 in. 6–2.......................4/64 in. 1–4/0....................5/64 in. 213–500.................6/64 in. 501–1,000...............7/64 in. 1,001–2,000.............8/64 in.	None
Moisture-resistant thermoplastic	TW	Flame-retardant, moisture-resistant thermoplastic	14–10....................2/64 in. 8.........................3/64 in. 6–2.......................4/64 in. 1–4/0....................5/64 in. 213–500.................6/64 in. 501–1,000...............7/64 in. 1,001–2,000.............8/64 in.	None
Thermoplastic and asbestos	TA	Thermoplastic and asbestos	Th'pl'. Asb. 14–8............20 mils 20 mils 6–2.............30 mils 25 mils 1–4/0...........40 mils 30 mils	Flame-retardant cotton braid
Varnished cambric	V	Varnished cambric	14–8......................3/64 in. 6–2.......................4/64 in. 1–4/0....................5/64 in. 213–500.................6/64 in. 501–1,000...............7/64 in. 1,001–2,000.............8/64 in.	Fibrous covering or lead sheath

Asbestos and varnished cambric	AVA and AVL	Impregnated asbestos and varnished cambric	(Dimensions in mils)
			                       AVA AVL
			                VC asb. asb.
			14–8 (solid only).....30 20 25
			
			                       AVA AVL
			           1st 2nd 2nd
			          asb. VC asb. asb.
			14–8...........10 30 15 25
			6–2............15 30 20 25
			1–4/0..........20 30 30 30
			213–500........25 40 40 40
			501–1,000......30 40 40 40
			1,001–2,000....30 50 50 50
				AVA-asbestos braid
				
				AVL-asbestos braid and lead sheath

CODE REQUIREMENTS WITH RESPECT TO WIRE

Conductor Insulations.—(Continued)

Trade name	Type letter	Insulation	Thickness of insulation	Outer covering

Asbestos and varnished cambric	AVB	Impregnated asbestos and varnished cambric	VC Asb.
			18–8 (solid only).........30 20
			6–2 (solid only)..........40 30
			1–4/0 (solid only).......40 40
			
			                                       2nd
			                           Asb. VC asb.
			14–8................10 30 15
			6–2.................15 30 20
			1–4/0...............20 30 30
			213–500............25 40 40
			501–1,000..........30 40 40
			1,001–2,000........30 50 50
				Flame-retardant cotton braid (switchboard wiring)
				
				Flame-retardant cotton braid

Asbestos	A	Asbestos	14.......................30 mils 12–8....................40 mils	Without asbestos braid
Asbestos	AA	Asbestos	14.......................30 mils 12–8....................30 mils 6–2.....................40 mils 1–4/0...................60 mils	With asbestos braid
Asbestos	AI	Impregnated asbestos	14.......................30 mils 12–8....................40 mils	Without asbestos braid
Asbestos	AIA	Impregnated asbestos	Sol. Str. 14...............30 mils 30 mils 12–8.............30 mils 40 mils 6–2..............40 mils 60 mils 1–4/0............60 mils 75 mils 213–500......................90 mils 501–1,000...................105 mils	With asbestos braid
Paper		Paper		Lead sheath
Slow-burning	SB	3 braids impregnated fire-retardant cotton thread	14–10....................3/64 in. 8–2......................4/64 in. 1–4/0....................5/64 in. 213–500..................6/64 in. 501–1,000................7/64 in. 1,001–2,000..............8/64 in.	Outer cover finished smooth and hard
Slow-burning weatherproof	SBW	2 layers impregnated cotton thread	14–10....................3/64 in. 8–2......................4/64 in. 1–4/0....................5/64 in. 213–500..................6/64 in. 501–1,000................7/64 in. 1,001–2,000..............8/64 in.	Outer fire-retardant coating
Weatherproof	WP	At least three impregnated cotton braids or equivalent		

The fibrous covering over individual rubber-covered conductors of lead-sheathed or multiple-conductor cable is not required to be flame-retardant. For armored cable, see Code Sec. 93341. For nonmetallic-sheathed cable, see Code Sec. 93361.

variety and the improved 1947 variety. To distinguish one kind from another, look at the Underwriters' label on the coil of wire: the improved variety will be overstamped "1947 Code."

Types RPT and RHT Rubber-covered Wire.—The 1940 Code recognized these two types, which were identical with Types RP and RH as to *quality* of insulation, but were provided with a thinner wall of it. These types were recognized only in Nos. 14 to 8 and permitted only for rewiring in existing raceways. The 1947 Code abolishes these two types, but it should be noted that the Types R and RH under the new Code have, in Nos. 14 and 12, a wall of insulation only $\frac{2}{64}$ in. thick, which is the same as the old Types RPT and RHT in those two sizes. The quality of insulation has very greatly improved since 1940, making this change in wall thickness possible.

Type R vs. Type RH Rubber-covered Wire.—In the larger sizes, Type RH has considerably greater carrying capacity, size for size, than the Type R; since it can carry more amperage, a smaller size may be used in Type RH in place of a larger size of Type R. The more expensive Type RH then often becomes less expensive for a particular amperage than the cheaper Type R. This is especially true when the use of smaller size of Type RH also permits a smaller size of conduit to be used. For example, to carry a 200-amp. 3-phase load in conduit, if Type R wire is used, three 250,000-c.m. cables will be required, which in turn means that $2\frac{1}{2}$-in. conduit must be used. If Type RH wire is used, No. 000 is sufficient, requiring only 2-in. conduit. Under the 1940 Code, using Type R insulation, 300,000-c.m. cable in 3-in. conduit would have been required.

Varnished-cambric Insulation.—Although rubber is an excellent insulator, it deteriorates rapidly under conditions of extreme heat. Moreover, the rubber must be fairly thick to withstand high voltages. It has been found that cambric cloth treated with certain insulating varnishes will safely withstand, without deterioration, higher temperatures than rubber; a given thickness will withstand, without breaking down, higher voltages than an equivalent thickness of rubber.

This simply means that a conductor of a given size will safely carry more amperes when insulated with varnished cambric than when insulated with rubber; consequently the thickness of the insulation may be reduced. For a given voltage and amperage, varnished-cambric insulated wire can be of a smaller over-all diameter than rubber-covered wire. Particularly where relatively high amperages are involved, the use of varnished-cambric wire may permit using smaller sizes of conduit; sometimes physical conditions prevent using con-

National Elec. Products Corp.

FIG. 25-1.—Varnished-cambric insulation wire. This type withstands heat better than rubber-covered wire and is smaller in size.

duit of a size that would be required were rubber-covered wires used, although the smaller conduit required for the smaller varnished-cambric wire is usable. At other times an installation may be made using conduit which appears entirely adequate; later it may be found that higher amperages are required. The conduit in use may not permit larger rubber-covered wire to be installed, but, by the use of the varnished-cambric wires of smaller diameter, the same conduit can be used, thus providing the higher amperage required.

For example, to carry 150 amp., No. 000 rubber-covered wire with an over-all diameter of 0.73 in. is required. If the varnished-cambric type is used, only No. 0 with an over-all diameter of 0.58 in. is required.

Wire insulated with varnished cambric only, or with varnished cambric plus an overbraid of cotton or asbestos as shown in Fig. 25-1, may be used only in dry locations. If it has also a sheath of lead, it may be used in wet locations (Code Sec. 3102). If the insulation consists of varnished cambric only (Code Type V), the wire may be used only where its operating temperature when carrying its rated current does not exceed 85°C., or 185°F. If it has also a layer of asbestos and a final braid of cotton (Code Type AVB), the limits are 90°C., or 194°F., and if it has a layer of asbestos plus a final braid of asbestos (Code Type AVA), it may be used up to 110°C., or 230°F.

U. S. Rubber Co.

Fig. 25-2.—Slow-burning wire is used where considerable heat exists.

Slow-burning Wire.—If the temperature exceeds that permitted for varnished cambric but is not over 194°F. (90°C.), a slow-burning wire of the type known as SB is to be used (Code Sec. 3102). It is pictured in Fig. 25-2 and may be used only in permanently dry locations. It is commonly used on switchboards and panelboards where a great number of conductors are in use, close to each other, and generating considerable heat.

U. S. Rubber Co.

Fig. 25-3.—Asbestos insulation wire is used under conditions of extreme heat.

Asbestos-covered Wire.—If the temperature exceeds 194°F. (90°C.), the limit for slow-burning wire, asbestos-covered wire, Type A, must be used. It may be used only in permanently dry locations (Code Sec. 3102). This wire is made in various types, the most common of which appears in Fig. 25-3.

Slow-burning Weatherproof Wire.—This wire, known as Type SBW, is more or less interchangeable with the asbestos wire except that it may be used only in permanently dry locations for open wiring where the wires are supported on insulators and spaced as required for open wiring; the temperature limits are 90°C., or 194°F. (Code Sec. 3102).

Types T and TW Insulation.—The 1940 was the first Code to recognize wires with insulation made of various synthetic plastics, *containing no rubber*. This type of wire was designated Type SN (= synthetic). It was permitted only in sizes not heavier than No. 0000, and its use was confined entirely to rewiring in existing raceways.

Between 1940 and 1947 came the intervening war years. Rubber was unobtainable, for all practical intents and purposes. Under these stimuli, the progress in improving the electrical and mechanical properties of plastic insulations was most extraordinary, telescoping into a few years progress that was probably equivalent to what might have taken place in 20 ordinary years without the spur of war emergency. It is therefore no surprise that the 1947 Code gives much greater recognition to this new type of wire than did the 1940 Code.

The 1947 Code has redesignated this wire as Type T (for "thermoplastic") insulation, which describes its nature scientifically, and to differentiate it from insulations of *synthetic* rubber, now considered the equivalent of natural rubber; see footnote, page 87). Type TW is a modified type that is especially resistant to water.

Under the 1947 Code, Type T or TW may be used for *all* general purposes in Nos. 14 to 0000. For open wiring on insulators it may be used in all sizes from No. 14 to 2,000,000 c.m., the largest recognized size.

This new type of insulation, which has in its make-up no trace of rubber either natural or synthetic (artificial), consists of various plastic compounds differing somewhat from manufacturer to manufacturer. Basically, the compound falls into what chemists call "plasticized polyvinal chlorides." This material for purposes of insulation retains practically all the good and proved characteristics of rubber and, in addition, has better mechanical strength; still more important, it does not deteriorate under exposure to sunlight, acids, oils, and other chemicals which ruin rubber. On the other hand it must be said that thermoplastic insulation will stiffen and become brittle at low temperatures—lower than 0°F. Therefore this kind of wire should not be installed in very low temperatures, for the insulation may crack or even fall off.

Of course if installed in ordinary temperatures, it is still usable at subzero temperatures, if once installed the wires are not subject to movement.

Since this type of insulation is in itself flame-retardant, tough mechanically, and also quite smooth, no outer braid of cotton or similar material is required, as is the case with all other insulations. The net result is a wire which *size for size* is no larger in diameter, and in most cases is a good deal smaller, than other types of approved wire. Smaller wires mean less labor in installation. Watch this type of wire for future popularity and general use.

Type RU Insulation.—This is a completely new type which was recognized for the first time in the 1940 Code. The insulation, instead of being applied to the wire in one thick layer, is applied by running the wire repeatedly through a liquid rubber compound known as latex, with a drying or vulcanizing process between successive applications. The result is a completed wall of insulation which consists of many layers thoroughly welded together, of an exceeding high insulating value, giving a very high value of both mechanical strength and insulating values per unit of thickness. Because of this the total wall of insulation is much thinner than in any other type of wire, which naturally makes the over-all diameter smaller also. A cotton layer over the top, with a flame-retardant finish, completes the assembly.

In the 1940 Code this new type of wire was recognized only in Nos. 14 to 10 and permitted only for rewiring in existing raceways. The 1947 Code recognizes this type in Nos. 14 to 6, and it may be used for all general purposes. It seems likely that this type of wire will gain in popularity as time goes on, because of its extraordinary insulating qualities and other advantages.

Other Types.—Other types are shown in the table on pages 403, 404, and 405, but since these will rarely be used in installations of the scope covered by this book, they will not be covered in detail here.

Using Code Table 1.—At first glance this table may seem very complicated, but for installations within the scope of this book it is quite simple. Remember that the carrying capacities shown for different sizes apply only if the following conditions are *all* met:

1. The wires are used inside a raceway (conduit) or in the form of cable. (If exposed or concealed knob and tube work is used, use the carrying capacities shown in Table 2.)
2. Not more than 3 wires are used in the same conduit or cable. The neutral wire is not counted except in the case of a 3-wire circuit consisting of two phase wires and the neutral of a 4-wire 3-phase system (Note 5, Tables 1 and 2). (If 4 to 6 wires are used, reduce the capacities to 80 per cent, and if 7 to 9 wires are used, to 70 per cent of the values shown.)
3. The room temperature is not over 30°C. (86°F.). [If higher room temperatures are encountered, apply the correction factors shown below the table. For example, if No. 8 Type RH wire with a normal carrying capacity of 45 amp. is to be used in a room temperature of 40°C. (104°F.), the corrected carrying capacity is 45 × 0.88 or 39.6 amp.]

Bare Wire.—When its use was permitted under the 1937 and earlier Codes, bare wire was assigned current-carrying capacity considerably higher, size for size, than that of rubber-covered wire. Under the 1940 and 1947 Codes bare wire (where its use is permitted) may carry no more current than the same size of the particular type of *insulated* wire used with it.

PART 3
ACTUAL WIRING: NONRESIDENTIAL PROJECTS

Part 3 of this book covers the same subject matter as Part 2 but applies to nonresidential structures, such as factories, stores, schools, and similar projects.

Buildings of this type involve greater amounts of power, higher amperages, heavier wires, and other problems not met in residential work. Nevertheless the method of installation is in most respects greatly similar to that employed for residential work, and accordingly only *new* problems will be here explained.

Only the smaller projects are included. The very large projects, such as skyscrapers and steel mills, have been deliberately avoided as being beyond the scope of this book. This is also the case with all wiring at voltages in excess of 600, transformer vaults, and similar subjects which are encountered only in the larger projects.

CHAPTER 26

PLANNING NONRESIDENTIAL INSTALLATIONS

The wiring of nonresidential projects follows the same basic principles covered in Parts 1 and 2 of this book, but a considerable number of new problems arise. Much larger amperages must be handled than is customary in ordinary residential work. Sometimes the voltages are higher. Frequently polyphase power is involved in addition to the usual single phase. Devices and materials are used which are not common in residential work. Some points, which in residential work are left to the discretion of the contractor, are covered specifically by the Code for nonresidential work.

Heavy-duty Lampholders.—A "lampholder," which term is seldom met outside the Code, is simply a socket or other device by means of which current is carried to the bulb. A "heavy-duty" lampholder is the ordinary mogul socket, or any other type if more than 300 watts is involved, for example, the bipost type described in Chap. 14.

Many types of circuits in nonresidential work are restricted, so far as lighting is concerned, to lampholders of the heavy-duty type. When a lighting fixture contains in a single unit both heavy-duty lampholders and smaller sockets for ordinary bulbs, it may still be used on a circuit which is ordinarily restricted to the heavy-duty type.

Branch Circuits.—The general provisions regarding branch circuits outlined in Parts 1 and 2 apply not only to houses, but also to "apartments, guest rooms of hotels and clubs and in other occupancies used for dwelling purposes." For nonresidential occupancies the requirements are totally different.

In nonresidential occupancies each outlet is assumed to carry a specific load, which automatically limits the number of outlets per circuit. If the outlet is to serve a heavy-duty lampholder, an arbitrary minimum load of 5 amp. is assumed for that outlet. Every other outlet[1] is assigned an arbitrary minimum load of 1½ amp. These are minimum specifications, and if, for example, 750-watt bulbs are definitely specified, consuming roughly 7 amp. each, obviously allowance must be made for that amperage instead of the Code minimum of 5 amp.

From this starting point it is a simple matter to determine how many outlets may be served by any particular branch circuit. In this calculation it is necessary to bear in mind the requirement of Sec. 2116 of the Code, which specifies that, if a circuit supplies a continuous load, for example, store lighting, the load shall not exceed 80 per cent of the capacity of the circuit. The presumption is that, if some of the outlets on the circuit are controllable by individual switches, the load is not continuous.

Fifteen-ampere Branch Circuits.—The basic requirements are the same as for residential work. However, since each outlet is limited to 1½ amp., obviously each circuit may have not over 10 outlets. If any of the outlets serves a heavy-duty lampholder, the number of outlets is reduced in proportion.

Twenty-ampere Branch Circuits.—In nonresidential work the 20-amp. circuit is quite generally used for lighting, as also for small power loads. Wired with No. 12 wire, it is provided with 20 amp. overcurrent protection.

If the circuit serves *only* lighting outlets, the sockets may be of the type designed for fluorescent lighting, or may be of the ordinary medium-base type if made of porcelain *and* if they do not have built-in switches such as pull-chain, key, or similar

---

[1] Where multi-outlet assemblies of the type described on pp. 336 and 337 are used, the Code specifies, in Sec. 2116c3, that "each 5 feet or fraction thereof of each separate and continuous length shall be considered as one outlet of not less than 1½ ampere capacity; except in locations where a number of appliances are likely to be used simultaneously when each one foot or fraction thereof shall be considered an outlet of not less than 1½ amperes."

PLANNING NONRESIDENTIAL INSTALLATIONS

type. Under all other conditions heavy-duty sockets must be used.

Receptacles used on the circuit must be of the 20-amp. type with two exceptions: Ordinary 15-amp. receptacles may be used if the circuit serves only small appliances and lighting units with heavy-duty sockets, and also if the receptacles are for "fixed lighting units.[1]"

A 20-amp. circuit has a capacity of 115 × 20, or 2,300 watts. If the common 4-tube 40-watt fluorescent unit is used for lighting, the error may be made of dividing 2,300 by 160 and arriving at an answer of 14 such units per circuit. However, as pointed out in another chapter, the 40-watt rating of a fluorescent lamp is that of the lamp itself; its ballast requires additional power; the lamp does not have 100 per cent power factor. The over-all wattage of a 4-lamp unit is more nearly 200 watts, and considering power factor, each unit consumes about 2 amp. The maximum capacity then is 10 units per circuit, or 8 units if the lighting is continuous. Moreover, since in nonresidential work the runs are often quite long, loading the circuit to its full capacity may easily lead to excessive voltage drop. It is wise to limit carefully the number of units per circuit.

If any outlet serves a heavy-duty socket, the Code requires a minimum of 5 amp. per outlet, which means a maximum of four per 20-amp. circuit, reduced to three if the entire circuit is controlled by a single switch.

Thirty- and Fifty-ampere Branch Circuits.—The details of these circuits have already been covered on page 180. Note

---

[1] The Code definition reads: "Fixed lighting units are those that are intended to remain in fixed positions and are connected to the permanent wiring either directly, or through receptacles provided to facilitate servicing and replacements." This has reference primarily to fluorescent lighting units, which are usually quite large and bulky and frequently require cleaning. Consuming small wattages, plug-and-receptacle connections are adequate to the small current involved. The plug-and-receptacle arrangement permits the entire unit to be disconnected and brought to ground level for cleaning and servicing.

that 15-amp. receptacles for fixed lighting units may not be used, as in the case of the 20-amp. circuit.

Which Circuit to Use.—A great many factors will influence the choice between 15-, 20-, 30-, and 50-amp. circuits. If each fixture is on a separate circuit controlled by a switch on the panelboard, then naturally the lightest wire permissible would be used, considering the amperage involved and not overlooking voltage drop.

If a number of outlets are to be on one circuit and controlled simultaneously by one switch on the panelboard, then the heavier circuits will automatically be required. If a number of outlets are to be placed on one circuit, but individually controlled by pull chains or other local switches, the heavier circuits will probably be found more economical.

Taps.—On 20-amp. and heavier circuits, taps to individual lampholders or fixtures, or, if not over 18 in. long, those to receptacles which supply lampholders, may be smaller than the wire used in the circuit proper. For these purposes No. 14 wire may be used except on the 50-amp. circuit, where No. 12 is the minimum. This is subject to the restriction that the specific load served by the tap in question must not exceed 15 amp. in the case of the No. 14 wire, and 20 amp. in the case of No. 12. If the specific load is greater, larger wire must be used.

Appliances.—The requirements for nonresidential use are the same as for residential use; therefore this subject need not be covered again (see Chap. 12).

Motors.—The wiring of electric motors is a sufficiently complex subject to warrant an entirely separate chapter, which will follow later.

Service Entrance Problems.—Before going into this subject, it will be well to review a few definitions that were originally covered in Chap. 12. Service conductors are the wires that extend from the power company's distribution system up to the service switch. The service drop is that portion of the service conductors which runs overhead; the service drop ends where the wires attach to the building. The service entrance conductors consist of that portion of the service conductors from the point where the service drop ends up to the service switch. If the service is underground, there is no service drop, and the entire underground run of wire from the power company's wires up to the service switch then makes up the service entrance conductors.

A building is defined by the Code as "a structure which stands alone or which is cut off from adjoining structures by unpierced fire walls."

Several Service Drops per Building.—This subject is thoroughly covered by the Code in Sec. 2321, which reads as follows:

2321. Number of Drops. No building shall be supplied from the same transformer, or from the same secondary distribution system, through more than one service drop, except as follows:

a. Fire Pumps. If a separate service is required for fire pumps.

b. Emergency Lighting. If a separate service is required for emergency lighting purposes.

c. Capacity Requirements. If capacity requirements make multiple services desirable.

d. Buildings of Large Area. By special permission, if more than one service drop is necessary due to the area over which a single building extends.

e. Multiple-occupancy Buildings. By special permission, in multiple-occupancy buildings where there is no available space for service equipment accessible to all of the occupants.

The exceptions noted above should require no great amount of explanation. Obviously it is desirable to have a separate source of power available for fire pumps and for emergency lighting. Likewise, where a large building is occupied by a number of tenants, it would be objectionable to have one service entrance controllable by one tenant, with the other tenants not able to get at the service switch at all. In that case a number of service drops may be used, although generally it would perhaps be better to contend with one drop, with several sets of service entrance conductors.

It should be noted that a single-phase distribution system

and a polyphase distribution system are considered separate systems, so that it is entirely in order to serve a building with a single-phase drop for lighting and similar purposes and also a polyphase drop for the power requirements.

Several Sets of Service Entrance Conductors per Building. Generally speaking only one set of service entrance conductors is permitted per building, but there are a number of exceptions. Obviously, where more than one service drop is permitted, as discussed above, each drop will require its own set of service entrance wires.

In a multiple-occupancy building it is usually necessary to provide each tenant with a separate meter with its disconnecting means and overcurrent protection. The several methods that may be used are the same as already covered in connection with apartments in Chap. 24 and as shown in Figs. 24-1, 24-2, and 24-4.

Skeleton of Nonresidential Installation.—In a small installation the cabinet housing the service switch in most cases contains the main overcurrent protection and often also the branch-circuit overcurrent protection. In larger installations the distances involved and the number of branch circuits in use usually make it totally impractical to lead all circuits back to a common starting point. In that case the wires run from the service switch to a switchboard; from the switchboard, feeders are run to panelboards; from the panelboards, individual circuits are run as required.

Figure 26-1 shows at *A* a typical single-story building which might be a factory or office building or store. At *B* is shown a similar layout in a three-story type, while at *C* is shown a somewhat more elaborate installation.

Switchboards and Panelboards.—Switchboards and panelboards are nothing but convenient distribution points where one incoming set of wires is broken up into more and more individual runs of wire. All necessary switches, overcurrent devices, instruments, and similar accessories are located at such points. Look at such a system as you would a big oak tree: the trunk is the service entrance wire, the point where

PLANNING NONRESIDENTIAL INSTALLATIONS 421

the trunk breaks up into half a dozen large branches is the switchboard, and the points where the large branches in turn split up into smaller branches are the panelboards.

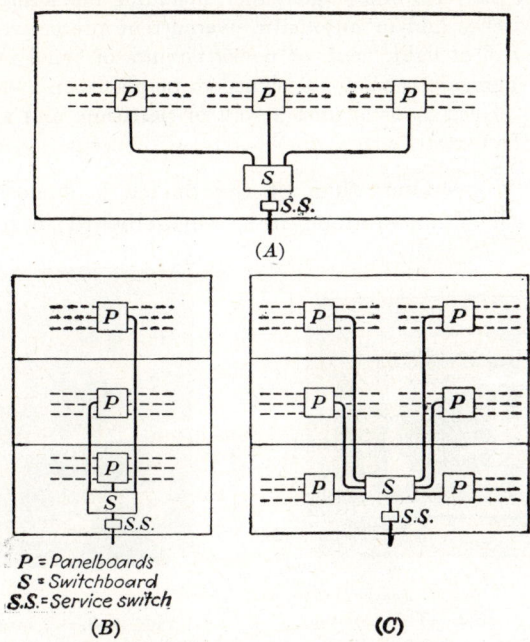

FIG. 26-1.—Typical distribution systems of switchboard and panelboards.

There is nothing in the Code which requires that an installation must have one switchboard plus a number of panelboards. These devices are installed to suit the convenience of the user. Often the service wires run from the service switch to a main panelboard and from there to other panelboards. As a matter of fact, it is difficult to define when a panelboard ceases to be a panelboard and becomes a switchboard. The Code, however, makes some distinctions and defines the two as follows:

Switchboard: A large single panel, frame, or assembly of panels, on which are mounted, on the face or back or both, switches, overcurrent and other protective devices, buses, and usually instruments.

Switchboards are generally accessible from the rear as well as from the front and are not intended to be installed in cabinets.

Panelboard: A single panel, or a group of panel units designed for assembly in the form of a single panel; including buses and with or without switches and/or automatic overcurrent protective devices for the control of light, heat, or power circuits of small individual as well as aggregate capacity; designed to be placed in a cabinet or cutout box placed in or against a wall or partition, and accessible only from the front.

Generally speaking, then, if the device is enclosed in a cabinet with a master door, it is a panelboard; if mounted

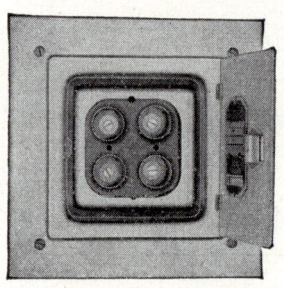

Square D Co.
FIG. 26-2.—This simple fuse cabinet is also a panelboard.

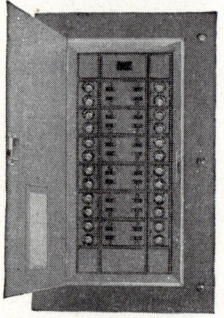

Square D Co.
FIG. 26-3.—A larger fuse cabinet or panelboard. This particular unit contains toggle switches, each switch controlling one circuit.

away from a wall and if accessible from back as well as front, it is a switchboard. There is no precise line of demarcation between the two.

A simple fuse cabinet of the type shown in Fig. 26-2 is a panelboard. A larger panelboard is shown in Fig. 26-3. If the device were not in a cabinet but on a separate stand, it would be a switchboard. In addition to the branch-circuit overcurrent protection there may be a switch for each circuit, so that the entire circuit can be controlled by throwing the proper switch. The fuses may be ordinary plug fuses or the largest type of cartridge fuses, or circuit breakers may be used instead. Not more than 42 overcurrent devices may be installed in a single cabinet.

In addition the panelboard may contain a main switch disconnecting the entire panelboard, and also main overcurrent

Bull Dog Electric Products Co.

Fig. 26-4.—A small switchboard. There is no door over the entire mechanism, so the device is not a panelboard but a switchboard. The small doors shown are the dead fronts of the individual devices.

devices protecting the entire panelboard. The main overcurrent protection is *required* on every panelboard that serves only lighting and appliance circuits if it is fed by wires which, in turn, are protected by overcurrent devices rated above 200 amp.; the overcurrent device in the panelboard must not be greater than the rating of the panelboard in amperes. For example, a 100-amp. panelboard may be fed from wires which, in turn, are fused at 150 amp.; in that case no main overcurrent protection is required at the panelboard. If, however, it is fed by wires fused at 250 amp., then overcurrent devices not over 100 amp., the rating of the panelboard, are required on the panelboard.

Feeders.—All the wires in an electrical system are termed "feeders" except the wires beyond the final overcurrent device, which are known as "branch-circuit" wires. (Exception: when the overcurrent device is used for motor *running* protection, this definition is not correct; this will be covered fully in Chap. 28.) The wires from the service switch up to the switchboard constitute a feeder. The wires from the switchboard to each panelboard are feeders. When a panelboard feeds smaller subpanels, the feeders to such subpanels are sometimes known as "subfeeders."

Feeder Sizes.—Into the feeder classification fall the service entrance wires also, so far as method of calculation of the size is concerned. This calculation is not a difficult procedure and is substantially the same as outlined in Chap. 12 in connection with ordinary residential work, except that the heavier loads as well as the varying Code requirements of watts per square foot must be taken into consideration. Total the watts required for lighting, plus appliances, plus motors; then divide by the voltage to arrive at the amperage, which, in turn, establishes the size wire required.

Feeders—Lighting Load.—The watts per square foot required by the Code for the purpose of such calculations vary considerably with the type of occupancy of the building and are found in Sec. 2203 of the Code (see Appendix). Reference to this table shows that the requirement varies from $\frac{1}{4}$ watt per square foot in storage warehouses to 3 watts per square foot in schools and stores. Demand factors, also shown in Sec. 2203 of the Code (see Appendix), reduce this in many cases. Later chapters will cover the different types of occupancies in detail.

Feeders—Appliance.—Handle as in residential work.

Feeders—Motor.—The Code in Tables 21, 22, 23, and 24, all of which will be found in the Appendix, specifies the full-load current of different types and horsepowers of motors at various voltages. If only a single motor is involved, add 125 per cent of the amperage, which may be found in the proper table for the motor in question, to the amperage determined for lighting and appliances.

If several motors are involved, add to the amperage determined for lighting and appliances 125 per cent of the amperage of the *largest* motor in the installation, and the actual amperage of each of the other motors. If several motors are of the same size, consider one of them the largest and the others as the smaller motors. When a number of motors are involved, but not all of them are operated at one time, good judgment must be used in creating a demand factor. Likewise, if the motors do not operate continuously but rather intermittently or in regular cycles, a reasonable reduction from the full amperage that would otherwise apply is in order. The local inspector should be consulted in case of doubt.

Determining Size of Service Entrance.—Proceed as in residential wiring. Assume that the total calculated lighting and appliance load, after application of the proper demand factors, amounts to 26,800 watts. The amperage will then be 26,800/230, or 117 amp. Assume the load for motors calculated as outlined is 120 amp.; this makes a total of 237 amp. Table 1 (see Appendix) shows that, if Type R rubber-covered wire is used, 300,000-c.m. cable is the minimum size permitted; if Type RH is used, 250,000-c.m. cable is sufficient.

In like fashion the correct size wires for any other amperage may be determined.

Neutral Feeders.—Most of the time the neutral of a feeder does not carry as much current as the ungrounded wires. This is never true in a 2-wire system, but consider what happens in a 3-wire system. Figure 26-5 shows the usual 115/230-volt circuit, except that two separate neutrals have been run instead of one. The voltage between A and B is 115 volts; between

C and D it is also 115 volts. Between A and D the voltage is 230 volts.

Assuming a 10-amp. load on A and B, also a 10-amp. load on C and D, the current flows in each of the four wires in the

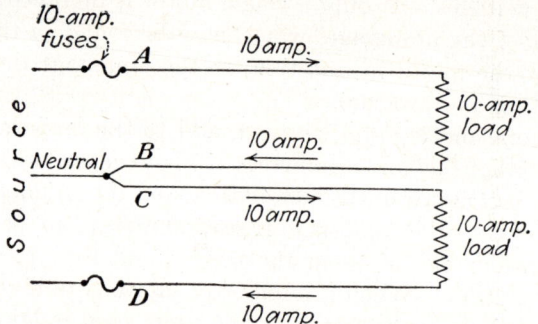

Fig. 26-5.—Two 2-wire circuits operating from a 3-wire feeder.

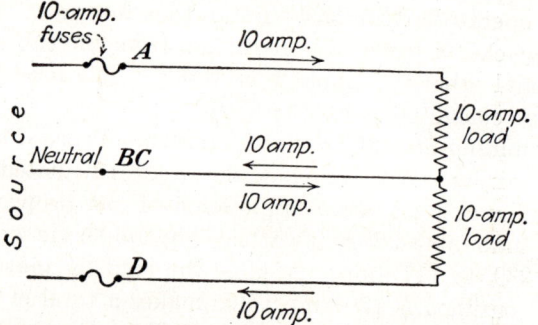

Fig. 26-6.—The two 2-wire circuits of Fig. 26-5 here are wired with a common neutral, which saves material and reduces voltage drop. Here the load on each half is the same.

amounts shown and in the directions shown by the arrows. This should be evident if first A and B are considered separately, then C and D separately.

Since, however, B and C are connected together, why use two separate wires? It is not necessary, and in practice a single wire is used as shown in Fig. 26-6, where there is one wire BC in place of two separate wires B and C.

Consider now the current flowing in BC. In one direction

PLANNING NONRESIDENTIAL INSTALLATIONS 427

10 amp. flows (as in wire B of the previous example), and in the opposite direction 10 amp. flows (as in wire C of the previous example). The two currents in opposite directions cancel out, and the wire BC carries no current at all. The circuit will work just as well if wire BC is missing entirely; this condition, of course, holds true only if the two loads on the two pairs of wires are absolutely identical.

If, however, one of the two fuses blows, then BC will carry 10 amp. So far as the neutral wire BC is concerned, there is

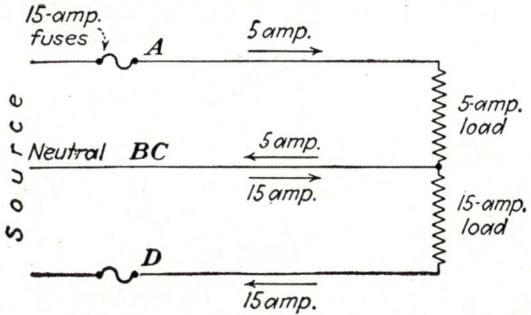

Fig. 26-7.—The same circuit of Fig. 26-6, but with unbalanced loads.

then said to be a maximum unbalance of 10 amp. because no matter which fuse blows, this wire cannot be made to carry over 10 amp. (assuming, of course, that the fuses are not increased above 10 amp.).

Consider now the circuit shown in Fig. 26-7, which is the same circuit except that instead of having two loads each of 10 amp., there is one of 5 amp. and another of 15 amp.; the fuses have also increased to 15 amp. The wire BC carries 5 amp. in one direction, 15 amp. in the opposite direction, or a net actual 10 amp. If the fuse in wire D blows, BC will carry 5 amp., the load on wires A and BC. If the fuse in wire A blows, BC will carry 15 amp., the load on wires BC and D. The maximum unbalance is therefore 15 amp.

Proceed now to Fig. 26-8, which is the same as Fig. 26-7 with the addition of a 20-amp. 230-volt load which is connected only to the wires A and D. The main fuses have been increased to

428   ACTUAL WIRING: NONRESIDENTIAL PROJECTS

35 amp., and two additional fuses of 15-amp. rating are used; hence neither of the two 115-volt loads can be increased above 15 amp. Wire *A* will then carry the same 5-amp. load as before, plus the new 20-amp. load, or 25 amp. altogether. Wire *BC* is not connected to the new load, hence will carry the same current as before, or 10 amp. Wire *D* will carry the same 15-amp. load as before, plus the new 20-amp. load, or

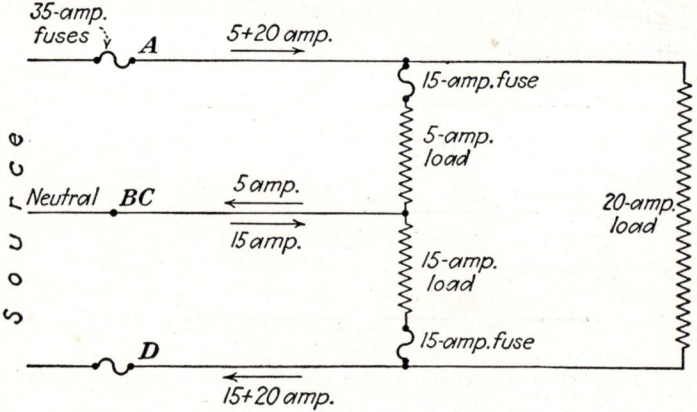

Fig. 26-8.—The circuit of Fig. 26-7, plus a 230-volt load.

35 amp. altogether. If the 35-amp. fuse in wire *D* blows, the new 20-amp. load is disconnected as is the 15-amp. load on *BC* and *D*; the wire will then carry only 5 amp. If the 35-amp. fuse in wire *A* blows, the new 20-amp. load is also disconnected as is the 5-amp. load on *A* and *BC*, and wire *BC* will carry only 15 amp. No matter what is done, the maximum unbalance will be only 15 amp.

Since wires *A* and *D* may be called upon to carry 35 amp. and are protected by 35-amp. fuses, they must have a carrying capacity of 35 amp., and according to Table 1 they will be No. 8 wires if Type R rubber-covered is used. However, so far as wire *BC* is concerned, no matter what is done, it cannot be made to carry over 15 amp., the maximum unbalance. Why then should it be No. 8 like *A* and *D*? There is no reason why it should be; indeed, it need be only big enough to carry 15 amp.; No. 14 is suitable.

Calculating Maximum Unbalance.—The neutral feeder, in accordance with Code Sec. 2203g, must have a carrying capacity equivalent only to the maximum unbalance, which is very simply calculated. From the grand total amperage involved, deduct the total amperage of all 230-volt loads which are not connected to the neutral; the difference is the maximum unbalance. For example:

Total load, 34,500 watts; at 230 volts this is .. 150 amp.
230-volt load, 16,100 watts; at 230 volts this is   70 amp.
Difference................................ 80 amp.

Accordingly, the neutral wire need have only 80 amp. carrying capacity, and Table 1 shows that, if Type R rubber-covered wire is used, it must not be lighter than No. 3. The other two wires naturally must be able to carry the full 150 amp., which in the case of Type R wire means No. 000.

In case the feeder supplies electric ranges, the neutral must have a carrying capacity of not less than 70 per cent of that of the "hot" wires, as determined from column A of Table 29. In other words, ranges must not be considered 230-volt devices (which they are not, because sometimes they operate at 115 volts, sometimes at 230, depending upon the positions of the low-medium-high switches on the ranges) for the purposes of determining maximum unbalance.

In the case of a 5-wire 2-phase system, the Code requires that the maximum unbalance obtained, as outlined above, be multiplied by 140 per cent. Thus, if the calculation shows a maximum unbalance of 80 amp., as above, but the system happens to be 5-wire 2-phase, the neutral wire selected must have a carrying capacity of 140 per cent of 80, or 112 amp.

A demand factor of 70 per cent may be applied to any unbalance in excess of 200 amp. For example, assume a total load of 425 amp., with 100 amp. of load which is not connected to the neutral, making a total unbalance of 325 amp. The

430 ACTUAL WIRING: NONRESIDENTIAL PROJECTS

required carrying capacity for the neutral is then calculated in this way:

200 amp. at 100 per cent demand factor..... 200.0 amp.
125 amp. at 70 per cent demand factor........ 87.5 amp.
Total................................. 287.5 amp.

The neutral wire need then have a carrying capacity of only 287.5 amp., making 500,000-c.m. cable suitable, while the ungrounded wires must be able to carry 425 amp., and accordingly must be 900,000-c.m. cable. These sizes apply if Type R rubber-covered wires are used; with other insulations the sizes vary accordingly.

This 70 per cent demand factor on that portion of the unbalance in excess of 200 amp. applies on 3-wire direct current or single-phase alternating current, also on 4-wire 3-phase and 5-wire 2-phase systems, not on any other systems. However, on a 5-wire 2-phase system, the total unbalance, as mentioned above, must first be multiplied by 140 per cent before the 70 per cent is applied on the excess over 200 amp. If the total unbalance is 240 amp., applying the 140 per cent factor gives 336 amp. 200 amp., plus 70 per cent of 136, or 95 amp., gives 295 amp., which is the required carrying capacity of the neutral.

These calculations apply identically, whether service entrance wires for an entire installation are being figured, or a feeder carrying a portion of a building.

Common Neutrals.—In connection with Figs. 26-6 and 26-7 two separate wires B and C were combined into a single wire BC, because the two were connected to each other and were therefore more or less a single wire anyway. Consider now Fig. 26-9, which shows an incoming 3-wire feeder with its neutral and two main fuses, also six separate 2-wire subfeeders A, B, C, D, E, and F, with six fuses. For each circuit a pair of wires runs back to the feeder, making 12 wires altogether. The six neutral wires are all connected together at the starting point; why run six separate wires? It is not necessary, and the Code, in Sec. 2204, permits one single wire common to a

PLANNING NONRESIDENTIAL INSTALLATIONS 431

number of feeders, in other words a common neutral, under certain conditions. See the next diagram in Fig. 26-10, which shows the same 3-wire feeder with two main fuses and six fuses, as in Fig. 26-9, but instead of six neutral wires, one to

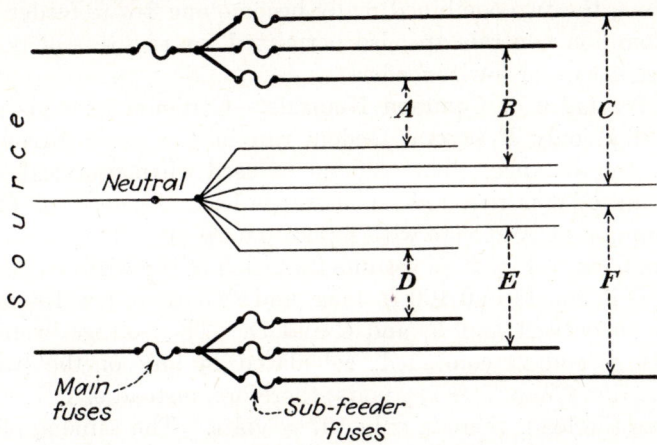

FIG. 26-9.—Six 2-wire subfeeders operating off a 3-wire feeder; note that there are six neutral wires, one for each circuit, but all joined together.

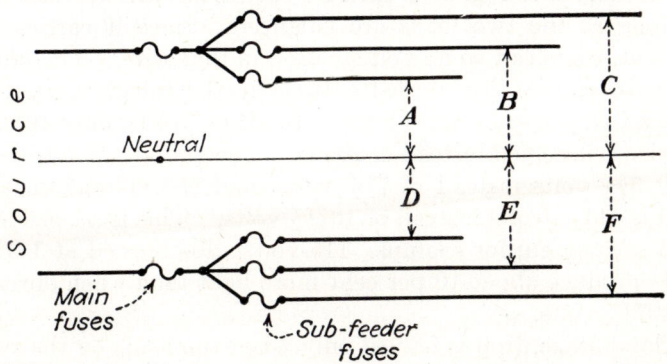

FIG. 26-10.—The six subfeeders of Fig. 26-9 now operate with a single or common neutral. This is permitted by the Code under certain conditions.

each of six circuits, a single neutral wire was used, making only seven wires altogether.

A common neutral is permitted for two or three 3-wire feeders. See Fig. 26-10, which shows the same basic feeders shown in Fig. 26-9, except that the six separate neutrals have now been combined into one. Note also that, while in Fig. 26-9 feeders A and D may be considered two 2-wire feeders and while in Fig. 26-10 they may still be considered two 2-wire feeders, the two combined really become one 3-wire feeder.

Common neutrals are also permitted for two sets of polyphase 4-wire or 5-wire feeders.

Advantages of Common Neutrals.—Common neutrals are practical only if several feeders run in the same direction for some distance. They should be used when practical, for less material is required and there is less voltage drop with a common neutral than with separate neutrals. For example, going back to Fig. 26-5, assume that each of the wires A, B, C, and D is No. 14 and 100 ft. long, and that there is a 15-amp. load on both A and B, and C and D. The voltage drop in wires A and B combined, calculated in any of the ways covered in Chap. 7, is $7\frac{1}{2}$ volts; therefore, instead of 115 volts across the load, there is only $107\frac{1}{2}$ volts. The same applies on the load across C and D. If, however, a common neutral BC is used, as in Fig. 26-6, then BC carries no current whatever so long as the two loads are balanced. Since it carries no current, there can be no voltage drop in that wire. Therefore wire BC can be disregarded entirely in the calculations, and instead only wire A considered. In other words, only 100 ft. of wire is involved instead of 200 ft. The voltage drop is then only $3\frac{3}{4}$ volts instead of $7\frac{1}{2}$ volts, and the voltage on the load is $111\frac{1}{4}$ volts instead of $107\frac{1}{2}$ volts. This is a considerable advantage; for example, 115-volt bulbs burned at $111\frac{1}{4}$ volts produce about 10 per cent more light than when burned at $107\frac{1}{2}$ volts.

The voltage drop is halved only when the loads on the two circuits are exactly balanced. The advantage decreases as one load becomes smaller than the other; when one load is disconnected entirely, the voltage drop is the same as if a separate neutral were used for each circuit.

Calculating Common Neutral.—The Code requires only that the carrying capacity of the common neutral be sufficient for

PLANNING NONRESIDENTIAL INSTALLATIONS 433

the maximum unbalance. How to calculate the size for a single feeder has already been covered. If a common neutral is to be used for several feeders, merely add together the maximum unbalances for all the feeders. If the total is over 200 amp., apply the 70 per cent demand factor on the portion above 200 amp., if the system is one where this is permitted. For example, if three feeders have maximum unbalances of 125, 75, and 190 amp., respectively, or 390 amp. total, calculate the neutral as follows:

If it is a 5-wire 2-phase system, multiply the 390 by the required 140 per cent, giving a total of 546 amp. Then apply the 70 per cent demand factor on the portion above 200 amp., giving 200, plus 70 per cent of 346, or 242, a total of 442 amp. The neutral wire must then have a carrying capacity, per Table 1, of at least 442 amp.

If the system is 3-wire direct current, or single-phase alternating current, or 4-wire 3-phase alternating current, then the neutral must have a carrying capacity of 200, plus 70 per cent of 190, or 133, a total of 333 amp.

For all other systems the neutral must have a carrying capacity of 390 amp.

Consider the sizes of wire involved in the installation shown in Fig. 26-11; assume that it is single-phase alternating current. At the left is a switchboard which contains the main fuses and six other fuses protecting three 3-wire feeders running to panelboards A, B, and C. The three feeders are to run through a single conduit up to point X, so a common neutral may be used up to that point. At X the three feeders separate and run in three different directions to the three panelboards. It is a simple matter to calculate each of the three feeders from point X up to the respective panelboards.

For feeder A, assume a total load of 35 amp., of which 25 amp. is a 230-volt load which is not connected to the neutral. The maximum unbalance for this feeder is therefore 35 minus 25, or 10 amp. The neutral therefore need be only big enough to carry 10 amp., and accordingly No. 14 wire is suitable from X to the panelboard. The ungrounded wires, however, must

434   ACTUAL WIRING: NONRESIDENTIAL PROJECTS

carry 35 amp. and accordingly must be No. 8. Since these wires run directly to the switchboard, the same size is used for the entire length.

For feeder B assume a total load of 25 amp., of which 8 amp. is a 230-volt load unconnected to the neutral. The

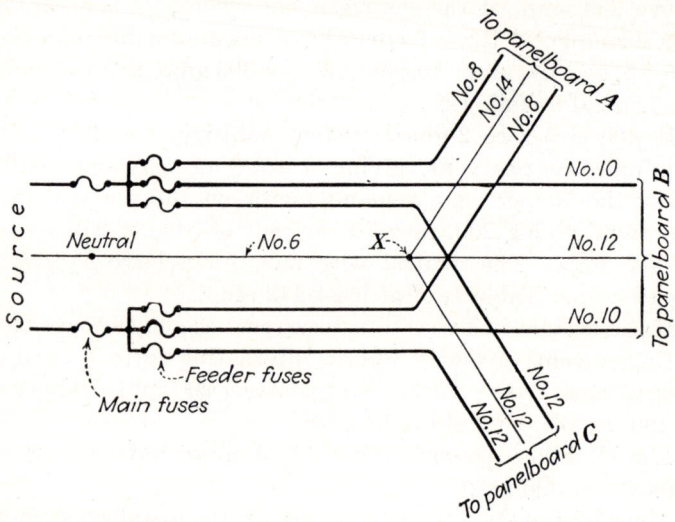

Fig. 26-11.—Three 3-wire feeders with common neutral from switchboard, up to the point where the feeders start running in different directions.

maximum unbalance is 25 minus 8, or 17 amp., and the neutral wire from X to panelboard B must be No. 12. The ungrounded wires must carry 25 amp. and, accordingly, must be No. 10.

For feeder C assume a total load of 20 amp., of which 3 amp. is a 230-volt load unconnected to the neutral. The maximum unbalance is 17 amp., and the neutral from X to panelboard C must be No. 12. The ungrounded wires must carry 20 amp., and No. 12 is suitable. In this case the neutral is the same size as the ungrounded wires.

The maximum unbalances in the three feeders are 10, 17, and 17 amp., respectively, or a total of 44 amp.; consequently the common neutral from the switchboard to point X must have a capacity of 44 amp. If all the load on each of the three panelboards A, B, and C consisted of lighting or other load, with no portion of it unconnected to the neutral, then the maximum unbalance would be 80 amp., requiring No. 2 wire for the neutral.

The wire sizes mentioned above are based on the assumption that Type R rubber-covered wire is used. If other types of insulation are involved, the wire sizes would change therefore in accordance with Table 1. The sizes determined in the calculations are the *minimum* sizes permitted by Code, and good practice will in many instances demand heavier sizes to avoid voltage drop.

Calculating Different Occupancies.—With the above general discussions it should be possible to calculate almost any type of building, taking into consideration the requirements of Sec. 2203 of the Code. However, different types of buildings will be covered in more detail in future chapters.

Grounding.—The Code requirements for grounding may appear at first to be complicated, but for the buildings covered by the scope of this book, they are relatively simple. The theory of grounds and the actual method of grounding of small projects were fully covered in Chap. 17. It will be well for the reader to review the subject there before proceeding with this chapter. There are two different kinds of grounds: system and equipment.

System Grounds.—Direct-current systems are generally grounded at the power station but not at the individual installation. In alternating-current systems, single-phase installations are ordinarily grounded not only at the transformer but also at the individual service. If the service is one of the 2-wire 230-volt type, there would be no ground at the service, although the mid-point of the transformer serving the premises would usually be grounded. Polyphase installations sometimes consist entirely of ungrounded wires; consequently they are not grounded at all. However, a 2-phase 5-wire system usually contains a grounded wire; so does a 3-phase 4-wire 120/208-volt star or Y system. A 3-phase 3-wire delta system sometimes has a fourth grounded wire which runs from the mid-point of one of the three transformer secondaries, and this grounded wire would, of course, be treated exactly like the neutral wire of a single-phase system. If the polyphase system does contain a grounded conductor, it may be grounded at the individual service, but the Code does not require it. It is best always to consult the power company to make certain whether any given polyphase installation does or does not contain a grounded wire.

Equipment Grounds.—The equipment ground is used to ground all cabinets housing service and overcurrent equipment, the conduit or armor of the wiring system, motors, fixtures, and similar equipment. If a metal-clad wiring system, such as conduit or armored cable, is used, the various runs of such a raceway are automatically tied together into a continuous system through connectors or locknuts and bushings at outlet boxes, and the entire system is grounded through the usual ground at the service switch. Devices such as motors, appliances, etc., are considered sufficiently grounded if the metal raceway of the wiring system is securely fastened to the device in the same way as to the outlet boxes.

If the voltage to ground is more than 150 volts, different methods must be used both at such devices and also in making up joints at boxes. This will be covered in the next chapter.

If knob and tube or nonmetallic cable wiring is used, the problem is more complicated. In the case of nonmetallic cable, special cable is available with an additional uninsulated grounding conductor included in the assembly. It is used to tie together all outlet boxes where the local inspector insists, and also to ground specific devices which the Code may require. This latter classification includes all devices in permanently wet locations and all devices operating at voltages above 150 volts to ground. It also includes certain devices regardless of voltage; among the ones likely to be met in installations of the type discussed here are motor controllers, garage equipment, motion-picture projectors, electric signs, transformers (unless mounted on wooden poles and at least 8 ft. above the ground); mercury-vapor lamps if within reach of grounded objects; generator and motor frames in electrically operated organs; lighting fixtures if mounted on metal lath, unless the fixtures are insulated from the lath.

Common Grounds.—A common grounding conductor may be used in practically 100 per cent of the installations within the scope of this book, serving for both system and equipment ground. The size required is simply covered by the Code, in Sec. 2594, and can be determined from the following table:

Size of Largest Service Conductor	Size of Grounding Conductor. Copper, No.
No. 2 or smaller	8
No. 1 or 0	6
No. 00 or 000	4
Over No. 000, to 350,000 c.m	2
Over 350,000 to 600,000 c.m	0
Over 600,000 to 1,100,000 c.m	00
Over 1,100,000 c.m	000

CHAPTER 27

MISCELLANEOUS PROBLEMS IN NONRESIDENTIAL WIRING

In nonresidential installations the conduit system is used in practically all cases. This automatically provides a really good continuous ground. It provides a certain amount of flexibility in that circuits may be changed, wires added, and breakdowns repaired by merely pulling in new wires, with a fair degree of ease and not too much mechanical change in the actual conduit. Where exposed, the conduit is reasonably neat in appearance and certainly affords ample protection for the wires.

Conduit Fittings.—For exposed runs of conduit, it is customary to use, instead of ordinary outlet boxes, cast fittings of the type shown in Fig. 27-1. They are known by various trade names such as Condulets, Unilets, etc. These devices are merely specialized forms of outlet boxes, but, instead of being provided with knockouts which can be removed to form openings, they have one or more ready-made openings. Accordingly, with a few basic body shapes, hundreds of different combinations are available. Each basic type is available for each size of conduit. Each opening is threaded to fit the size of conduit for which it is designed. These fittings are also available with threadless openings but with clamping devices for thin-wall conduit.

A few of the more common types are shown in Fig. 27-1. The Type E with the cover shown is frequently used at the end of a run to a motor or similar device. The LB is commonly used at a point where a run of conduit comes along and then must go at right angles through a wall or ceiling; it is equally useful in going around a beam or similar obstruction.

PROBLEMS IN NONRESIDENTIAL WIRING

Fittings of this kind avoid awkward bends in conduit. The Types LL and LR are handy for 90-deg. turns on a straight run. There are all kinds of combinations, some as complicated, for example, as the Type XA, which obviously is not used very frequently.

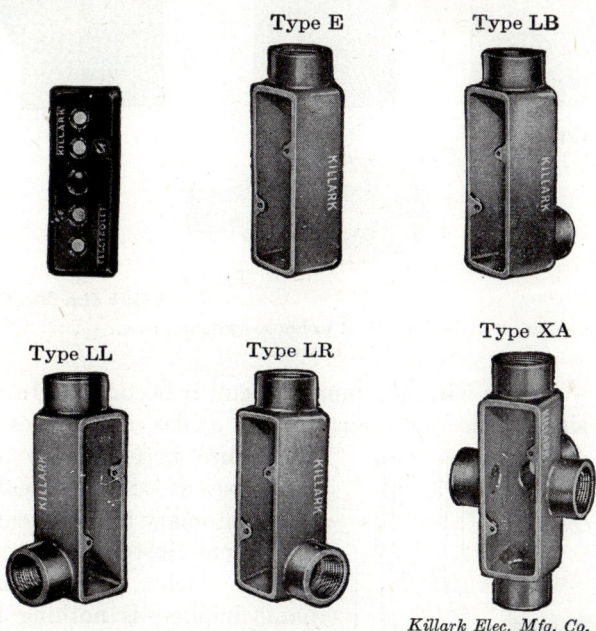

Killark Elec. Mfg. Co.

FIG. 27-1.—For exposed runs of conduit, conduit fittings of the type shown here are commonly used. There are dozens of different shapes or types.

In a different style of body there are available many types similar to the Type FS shown in Fig. 27-2, which is used mostly for the mounting of switches and similar devices. In the same picture is shown a weatherproof cover which will operate a toggle switch mounted in a Type FS fitting—a handy combination for outdoor switches. On exposed runs of conduit, lighting fixtures are mounted on Type P fittings.

Pull Boxes.—Wires of ordinary sizes as used in residential work are sufficiently flexible so that they can be pulled through long lengths of conduit, even if there are offsets and bends.

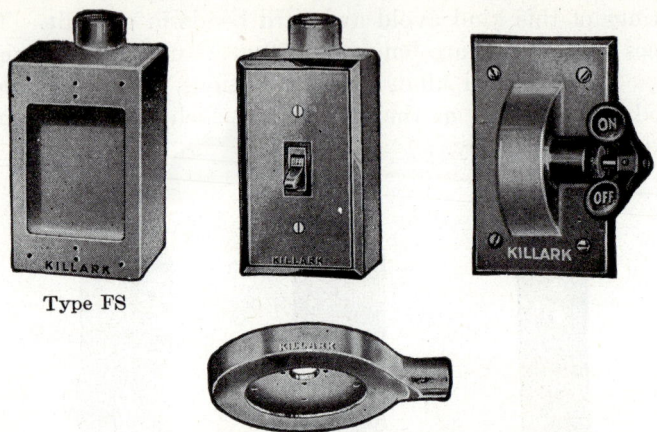

Type FS

Type P

Killark Elec. Mfg. Co.

Fig. 27-2.—Larger fittings are used to house switches, receptacles, and similar devices.

The heavier the wire, the more difficult it becomes. In really heavy sizes, such as the circular-mil cables, it becomes more and more necessary to install pull boxes at strategic locations; it is customary in many cases to use them instead of conduit bends. Such a pull box, as the name implies, is nothing but a steel box located where the wires can be helped along as they are pulled into the conduit. Pull boxes may be used only where they will be permanently accessible. A single pull box is often used for a number of runs of conduit, as shown in Fig. 27-3.

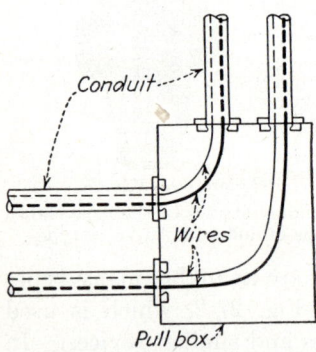

Fig. 27-3.—Pull boxes are used with conduit to make it easier to pull wires through long lengths of conduit, and they also serve other purposes.

Concrete Boxes.—In nonresidential buildings of all types, walls and ceilings frequently are of reinforced-concrete construction. The conduit and the boxes must be imbedded in the concrete if the devices later are to be flush with the surface of the wall. Ordinary outlet boxes may be used, but special concrete boxes are also available. One of these is shown in Fig. 27-4. These boxes have special ears by which they are nailed to the wooden forms for the concrete. Stuff the boxes full of paper before installing; this will prevent concrete from

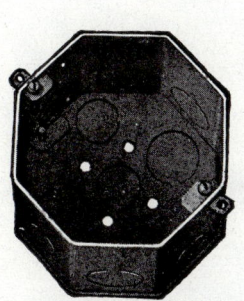

M. B. Austin Co.
Fig. 27-4.—A concrete box designed to be imbedded in the concrete as it is poured.

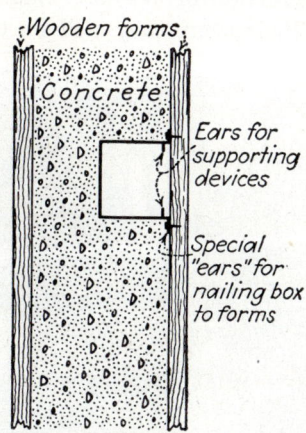

Fig. 27-5.—Concrete boxes are nailed to the wooden forms before the concrete is poured.

seeping in. The conduit and the boxes must be in position before the concrete is poured. When the forms are removed, the conduit and the boxes are solidly imbedded; the interior of the box is clean and ready for use. These boxes come in a variety of depths up to 6 in. Figure 27-5 shows an installed view.

For floor use, special cast boxes are available: these are of the two-piece type so arranged that, even if the box proper is installed crooked in the rough concrete, the top section can be leveled off with respect to the final floor surface. This is accomplished because the two pieces telescope together, as is clearly shown in Fig. 27-6. Receptacles and similar devices cannot in practical fashion be installed flush with the floor, so that it is customary to use nozzles and outlets which raise the final device a few inches above the floor.

Number of Wires in Conduit.—For smaller sizes of wire this was discussed in Chap. 11. For heavier sizes the Code covers the subject fully in Tables 2 to 9 (see Appendix). These tables are clear and need no further explanation here.

Deflection of Wires.—Small wires are so flexible that it is not likely that they will be damaged even by sharp bends.

M. B. Austin Co.

Fig. 27-6.—Adjustable floor box for concrete work. Because the two parts telescope, the exposed portion can always be made flush with the final floor.

In the larger sizes, on the other hand, it is conceivable that, if bent too sharply where they emerge from a run of conduit, the insulation might become damaged to the point where grounds might be caused. The Code therefore requires that ungrounded wires No. 4 and heavier, if they deviate over 30 deg. from the position they would occupy if continued on in the same direction in which they lie in the conduit, must be further protected "by a substantial bushing providing a smoothly rounded insulating surface, unless the conductors are separated from the raceway fitting by substantial insulating material securely fastened in place." This is commonly

PROBLEMS IN NONRESIDENTIAL WIRING 443

accomplished by inserting sheet insulating fiber securely anchored, or by means of special bushings similar to the usual conduit bushings but made of an insulating material.

Moreover, the Code further requires that wires No. 1 and heavier, if running in a vertical position, shall not be deflected at all at the point where they enter or leave a cabinet, unless gutters or empty spaces are provided between the wall of the cabinet and the devices or mechanisms that the cabinet encloses. The width of gutter required varies with the size of the wires in question, as follows:

Feeder size	Minimum width of gutter, inches
No. 1	3
No. 0 to 200,000 c.m	4
211,600 to 500,000 c.m	6
600,000 to 900,000 c.m	8
1,000,000 to 1,400,000 c.m	10
1,500,000 to 2,000,000 c.m	12

This requirement is of greater concern to manufacturers than to contractors, and panelboards and similar equipment

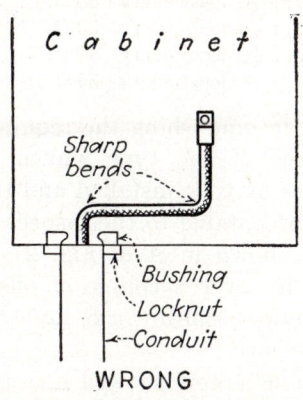

FIG. 27-7.—The bends shown here are too abrupt. The weight of the wire is supported where the wires emerge from the conduit.

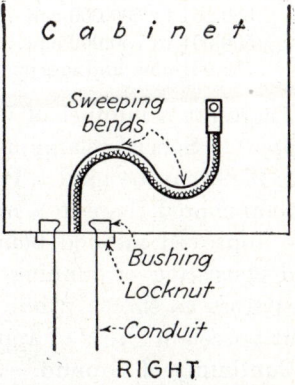

FIG. 27-8.—Let the bends in wires be gentle and sweeping. This avoids grounds where the wires emerge from the conduit.

automatically incorporate the proper gutter widths. Locate cabinets so that the incoming runs of conduit will be so placed as to require a minimum deflection of the wires where they emerge from the conduit, and so that in vertical runs the weight of the wire will not be supported by the bend at the end of the run. Figure 27-7 shows the wrong and Fig. 27-8 the right method. Let the bends in the wires be sweeping and gentle rather than abrupt.

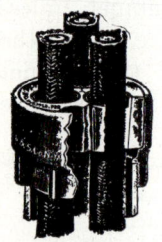

Russel & Stoll Mfg. Co.
FIG. 27-9.—This fitting is very handy in supporting vertical runs of wire.

Supporting Vertical Runs of Wire.—Terminals on panelboards and similar equipment are not designed to support any substantial weight. When there is a vertical run of wire, the weight of the wire itself is considerable, especially in the larger sizes. If such runs of wire are attached directly to terminals, damage may result. The Code therefore requires that in such vertical runs the wire be independently supported at intervals as follows:

No. 18 to No. 0.................	At least every 100 ft.
No. 00 to No. 0000...............	At least every 80 ft.
250,000 to 350,000 c.m............	At least every 60 ft.
350,001 to 500,000 c.m...........	At least every 50 ft.
500,001 to 750,000 c.m...........	At least every 40 ft.
750,001 c.m. and larger...........	At least every 35 ft.

There are a number of ways of accomplishing the required support. Special clamping devices of the type shown in Fig. 27-9 may be used. Pull boxes may be installed and the wire anchored there in a manner acceptable to the inspector, one approved method being that shown in *A* of Fig. 27-10 and consisting of running each wire over a couple of offset insulators as shown, while the method shown at *B* involves split porcelain cleats of appropriate size.

Continuity of Ground.—Previous chapters showed how the various runs of conduit or metallic cable tie together outlet boxes and other equipment into one continuously grounded system. This is accomplished in the case of conduit by means of locknuts and bushings and in the case of cable with the usual connectors. If, however, in any such wiring system one or more of the wires has a voltage above 150 volts to ground, these simple methods are no longer acceptable. Instead the Code gives a choice of several other methods.

If conduit fittings of the type illustrated in Figs. 27-1 and 27-2 are used, that is sufficient for either rigid or thin-wall

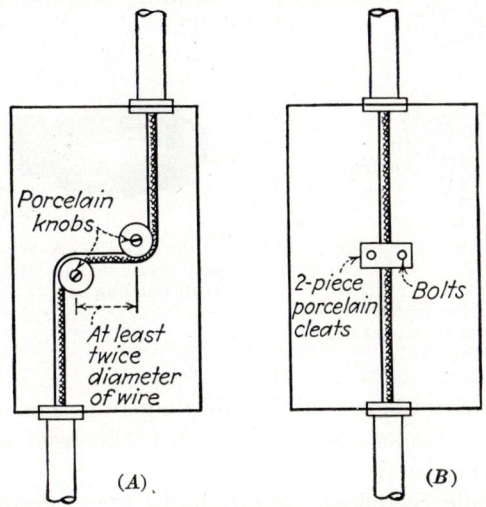

FIG. 27-10.—Two other methods of supporting vertical runs of wire.

conduit. The same fittings may be used for armored cable or flexible conduit, for the connectors that are used with such raceways fit directly into the tapped openings in the fittings.

If ordinary outlet and similar boxes of drawn sheet steel are used, several methods are open for use. The most common so far as rigid conduit is concerned is the double-locknut system shown in cross-section in Fig. 27-11. This involves simply one locknut on the outside of the box and another one inside, plus the usual bushing.

With thin-wall conduit, armored cable, or flexible conduit, the simplest method is to use on the connector involved, inside the box, a grounding bushing of the type that was shown in Fig. 17-22, in place of the usual locknut that is used on such connectors. It is not necessary to use jumper wires from one such bushing to another inside the same box; the screws on the bushings are designed to bite into the box and will stay in place where vibration or other causes may cause the ordinary locknut to come loose. These grounding bushings are also entirely suitable for use with rigid conduit. The grounding locknut of Fig. 27-12 serves the same purpose.

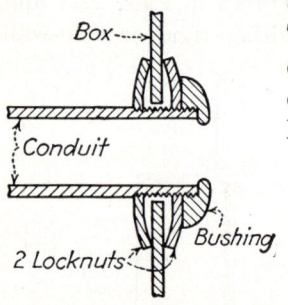

M. B. Austin Co.

Fig. 27-11.—When the voltage *to ground* is over 150, use the double-locknut construction shown here, instead of the ordinary construction that was shown in Fig. 10-7.

Fig. 27-12.—A special type of locknut with bonding screw.

In case the run of conduit in question is the service conduit, any of the schemes shown above may be used except the double-locknut method.

Double-pole Switches.—When bulbs are operated on two ungrounded wires, only double-pole switches which open both wires may be used. This is only part of the general rule that switches must always open all ungrounded wires, although there are a few exceptions to this in connection with motors, which will be covered in a separate chapter.

"T" Rating Switches.—Ordinary light bulbs, particularly in the larger sizes, consume a very heavy amperage for a brief moment when they are first turned on. For example, a bulb that consumes only 2 amp. when burning at full brilliancy may consume nearly 20 amp. for a small fraction of a second when first turned on. This cold inrush is a rather severe test for the switches that control the bulbs, and many switches rated at 10 amp. and giving entirely satisfactory service under average conditions will not stand up when used to control bulbs consuming 10 amp. Therefore switches have been developed which are especially designed to withstand the short but very large amperage inrush found with bulbs. Such switches have what the Underwriters and the Code call a "T" rating (for tungsten, the material from which the filaments of ordinary incandescent bulbs are made). They look like ordinary switches but can be identified by the letter "T" stamped on their mounting straps, after their voltage rating.

If used to control ordinary incandescent (filament) style bulbs, switches *without* the "T" rating may be used only in residential work, and only to control permanently installed fixtures or lighting outlets in a single room. However, "T" rated switches cost so very little extra that their use is recommended throughout, since the slight extra cost is merely insurance against frequent replacement. For all other occupancies, "T" rated switches must be used to control incandescent lamps.

If used for noninductive loads other than incandescent lamps (such as, for example, appliances), the switch need not be the "T" rated type, but must have an amperage rating not less than that of the load controlled. For controlling inductive loads (such as transformers and motors) the switch must have an amperage rating of at least *twice* that of the load controlled.

Ordinary switches are available in 10-, 20-, and 30-amp. ratings. Almost every switch carries a dual rating, the most ordinary being 10 amp. at 125 volts or 5 amp. at 250 volts. Select switches to suit the amperage, the voltage, and the type of load involved.

Surface Metal Raceway.—This style or method of wiring is seldom seen in homes but is widely used in industrial work, especially for making additions to existing installations, or in original installations where numerous future changes are probable. A number of different brands are available, all operating on the general principle of a two-piece metal channel.

448 ACTUAL WIRING: NONRESIDENTIAL PROJECTS

In use one piece is securely fastened to the wall, ceiling, or floor; then the other piece is snapped on the first, in cover fashion.

One type, with a number of the fittings used, is shown in Fig. 27-13, and no great amount of explanation should be

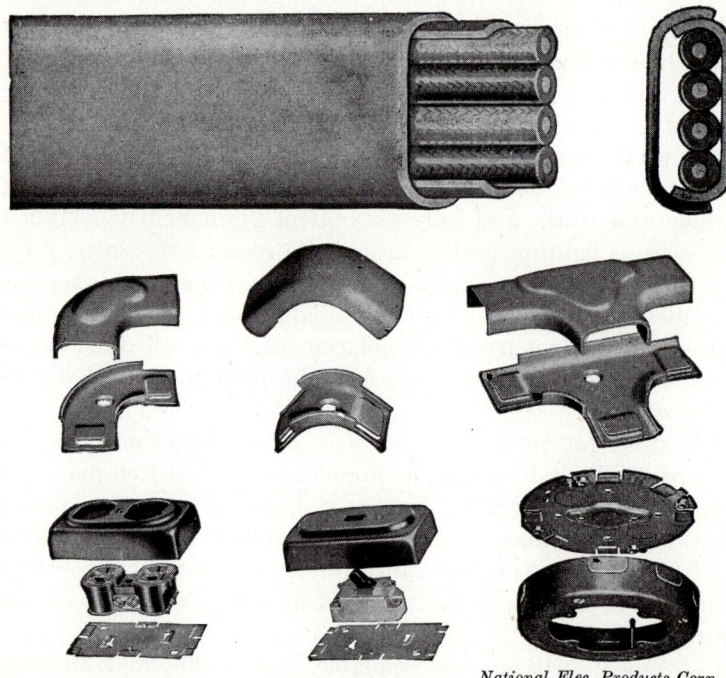

National Elec. Products Corp.

FIG. 27-13.—Surface metal raceway and fittings. This material is most convenient where frequent changes must be made, or where concealed wiring is not practical.

necessary. The material comes in a number of sizes and types; which to use depends on the number and sizes of wires involved, as well as the purpose to be served. It may run through walls if a continuous piece is used. It is used not only for the usual wiring but frequently also for signal and telephone wires and similar purposes. Wires of two separate systems may never be mixed in the same channel.

The Code limits this material to exposed runs in dry locations at voltages not in excess of 150 volts to ground. It may not be used where exposed to severe mechanical injury,

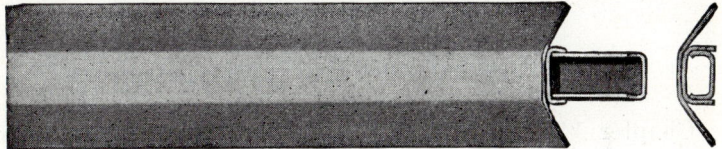

National Elec. Products Corp.

FIG. 27-14.—This type of surface metal raceway is flat and may be used on the floor.

although the type shown in Fig. 27-14 is approved for use on floors, the abuse which it receives from ordinary foot traffic not being considered as causing "severe mechanical injury." Not more than 10 wires may be installed inside a single channel except for signal purposes. No wire heavier than No. 6 may be used.

CHAPTER 28

NONRESIDENTIAL LIGHTING

Chapter 14 outlined the fundamental that one lumen of light falling on one square foot of area always produces illumination of one foot-candle. This formula cannot be directly applied in lighting problems, and many factors must be considered. For example, assume a room 10 ft. square, with a 10-ft. ceiling height, lighted by a bulb producing 2,000 lumens. Since the floor area is 100 sq. ft., some will assume that the illumination on the floor will be 2,000/100, or 20 foot-candles, forgetting that the light falls also on the walls and ceiling, or on a total of 600 sq. ft. If the light is uniformly distributed, the illumination will be $3\frac{1}{3}$ foot-candles.

The problem is to make all the light produced by a light source fall exactly and only on the area to be illuminated. This, in practice, is impossible, and the following paragraphs will outline the factors involved in arriving at a practical, workable formula.

Room Index.—Obviously a very long room requires a greater number of light sources or fixtures than a square room of the same area. Assuming the proper number of fixtures properly mounted at the correct height and with the correct spacing, the shape of the room still is a considerable factor. The relative efficiency or usability of the total light produced in a room is known as the "room index," and it is customary to indicate this index by the letters A to J, A being the best and J the lowest.

It has been found that rooms which are relatively wide, where the width is $3\frac{1}{2}$ to $4\frac{1}{2}$ times the ceiling height, have a good index, probably A, B, C, or D. If the width is average or only twice the ceiling height, the index will probably be D, E, F, or G. If the room is narrow, in other words if the width is about the same as the ceiling height, the index will be low, probably *G*, *H*, *I*, or *J*. The length is also a considerable factor, and generally, for any given ceiling height, the index is improved as the room is lengthened.

The actual index of a room of any given dimensions can be found in the tables furnished by manufacturers of commercial lighting equipment.

Condition of Walls and Ceilings.—A previous chapter emphasized that walls and ceilings should reflect rather than absorb light. When the lighting system involves fixtures of the direct-lighting type, this factor is of relatively little importance. When semi-indirect fixtures are used, it becomes of considerable importance. When totally indirect fixtures are used, this factor is all-important; the ceiling in this case contributes about two-thirds of the total importance; in other words the walls, generally speaking, could be black, reflecting nothing, and the total over-all efficiency would be reduced only about one-third.

Maintenance Factor.—After a lighting fixture has been in use for some time, it will not transmit or reflect so much light as when it was new because dust will accumulate on the fixtures; the walls and ceilings will also darken with use. Bulbs blacken as they approach the end of their life, and the number of lumens of light produced decreases in proportion.

A well-planned installation will be so designed that the desired foot-candles will be produced, not when the installation is new, but under average conditions over a period of time. Therefore it is necessary to compensate for the depreciation, and this is customarily done by applying a maintenance factor which varies from 60 to 80 per cent, depending on the type of fixtures, the type of walls, the occupancy of the building, and the amount of mechanical maintenance provided. A 70 per cent figure will never be far wrong.

Coefficient of Utilization.—For any given installation, combining the room index with the reflecting ability of the walls and the type of fixture used gives what is known as the "coefficient of utilization." Elaborate tables have been prepared which manufacturers of lighting equipment can furnish. The coefficient of utilization varies for direct lighting from 15 to 70 per cent, for semi-indirect from 10 to 60 per cent, for totally indirect from 1 to 40 per cent.

Formula for Determining Total Lumens Required.—From the known factors it is fairly easy to calculate the lumens required for any particular lighting problem. The formula is

$$\text{Lumens} = \frac{\text{foot-candles} \times \text{square feet}}{\text{coefficient of utilization} \times \text{maintenance factor}}.$$

Assume that an office 20 ft. square, floor area 400 sq. ft., is to be lighted to 20 foot-candles. In line with the modern trend, indirect lighting will probably be used. The ceilings and walls will probably be light so that a coefficient of utilization of 0.25 will not be far wrong. A maintenance factor of 0.70 may be assumed. The formula above then becomes

$$\text{Lumens} = \frac{20 \times 400}{0.25 \times 0.70} = \frac{8{,}000}{0.175} = 45{,}700.$$

In an area 20 ft. square four fixtures are usually used. Referring to the table on page 240, a 500-watt bulb produces about 10,000 lumens. Four fixtures together would therefore produce 40,000 lumens, which is close to the 45,700 theoretical lumens which the formula calls for.

On the same basis, it is fairly simple to estimate the total lumens required for any given area, with any type of lighting fixture, for any number of foot-candles desired.

In a very approximate fashion the watts required for different foot-candles of illumination can be estimated, for experience has shown that

1 watt per square foot produces approximately 3 to 5 foot-candles
2 watts per square foot produces approximately 8 to 14 foot-candles
4 watts per square foot produces approximately 20 to 25 foot-candles
6 watts per square foot produces approximately 25 to 30 foot-candles
8 watts per square foot produces approximately 30 to 35 foot-candles

This table can be used only as a starting point, for there are too many factors to influence the final result.

NONRESIDENTIAL LIGHTING

Selection of Fixtures.—Totally indirect fixtures can be used only in locations where the ceilings and walls are of a light color and can be so maintained. The semi-indirect are suitable for the same kind of use. Direct-lighting fixtures will be necessary in factories and similar locations where it is impossible to keep ceilings clean and relatively light. This subject will be covered in some detail in later chapters in different types of occupancies.

Mercury-vapor Lighting.—Although this style of lighting is now being fast superseded by fluorescent lighting, the mercury-vapor type of bulb was once quite common and is still used in many installations. A typical bulb of this type is shown in Fig. 28-1.

It is available in two sizes: 400 and 250 watts. The bulbs are sensitive to changes in temperature, for which reason, in the case of the 400-watt size, the bulb proper is enclosed inside a second, larger bulb. There is no filament; the lamp is essentially an arc lamp.

Being of the arc type, it cannot be connected directly to the power line but requires a control device in the circuit to control the current in the arc within definite limits. The control device in this case is a transformer, because the bulb will start only at a voltage higher than the operating voltage. Since this transformer is required, obviously the bulb cannot be used on direct-current circuits. Figure 28-2 shows the wiring diagram. This bulb operates at a rather low power factor, which can be corrected by using transformers that have a built-in capacitor, as shown in the diagram. The transformer is usually installed close to the bulb. Figure 28-3 shows several suggested methods.

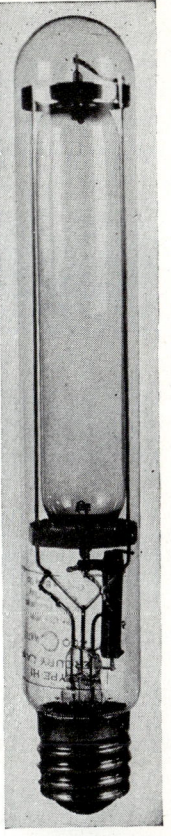

General Elec. Co.

FIG. 28-1.—A 400-watt mercury-vapor bulb. Note that there is a bulb within a bulb—to protect the lamp against changes in temperature which affect its light output.

The chief advantage of the mercury-vapor type of bulbs is that they produce approximately twice as many lumens per watt as the ordinary filament type of bulb. For example, the 400-watt mercury-vapor bulb produces 16,000 lumens; an

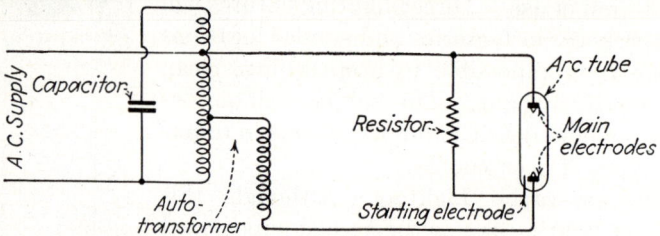

Fig. 28-2.—Wiring diagram for the mercury-vapor type of bulb.

ordinary 750-watt bulb produces 14,500 lumens. The mercury-vapor bulb has a useful life of about 2,000 hr. compared with the approximate 1,000-hr. life of the ordinary type of bulb.

The mercury-vapor bulb has a disadvantage in that the light produced by it is deficient in the colors toward the red

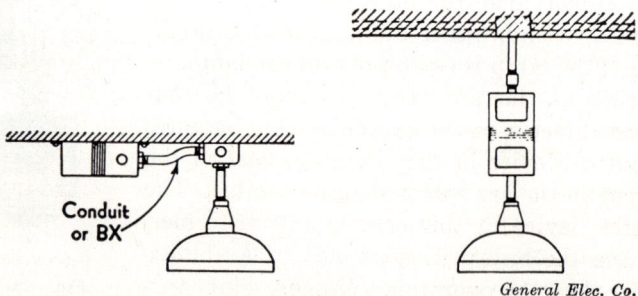

General Elec. Co.

Fig. 28-3.—Typical methods of installing mercury-vapor bulbs with their transformers.

end of the spectrum but strong in the colors toward the blue end of the spectrum. Objects therefore will not appear in their true colors under these mercury-vapor bulbs, and the bulbs can be used only where color discrimination is not essential.

However, this very deficiency or shortcoming can be turned

to good advantage, for the ordinary filament type of bulb produces light that is strong in those colors in which the mercury-vapor type is deficient. Therefore by using a combination of both types the combined light of the two is more like natural sunlight than the light of either one alone. Lighting fixtures are available so that both types of bulbs may be used in the same fixture, and one is shown in Fig. 28-4.

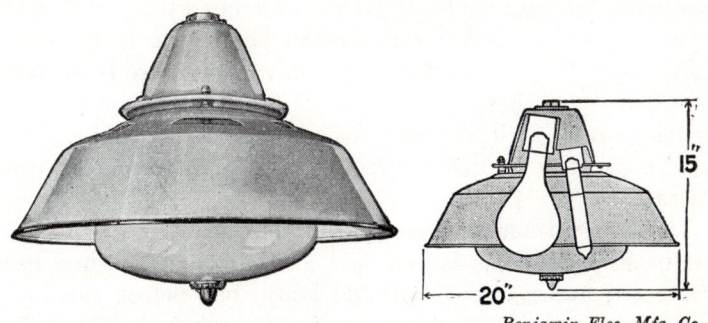

Benjamin Elec. Mfg. Co.

FIG. 28-4.—Typical combination fixture using both mercury-vapor bulb and ordinary filament-type bulbs.

Where color is not too important, using an equal wattage of mercury-vapor bulbs and ordinary filament type bulbs produces a light which is pleasant and entirely acceptable. Where color is of considerable importance, and that includes offices and schools, it is best to select a wattage of each type so that the total lumens produced by the mercury-vapor type of bulb is equivalent to the total lumens produced by the filament type of bulb.

Fluorescent Lighting.—The principle of operation of the fluorescent lamps or tubes has already been covered in Chap. 14. Little more need be said here except to point out that in nonresidential lighting the need for high-power-factor or "power-factor-corrected" fixtures is absolutely essential.

In installing fluorescent fixtures, it is recommended that where possible the installation be by means of a fixed receptacle, into which the fixture is plugged, thus facilitating removal for cleaning and servicing.

Cold-cathode Lighting.—A modification of fluorescent lighting is coming into use; it is known as "cold-cathode" lighting. Once installed, the appearance is very similar to that of the ordinary fluorescent installation. Each lamp or tube, however, is of different construction. The fluorescent lamp has at each end a filament called a cathode, which must be heated before the lamp will light. The cold-cathode lamp has no filaments; the cathode at each end is merely a prod or thimble of metal, which need not be heated before the lamp starts, from which fact it derives its name. Since there is no need for preheating, there is no need for the starter or automatic switch as used with filament-cathode fluorescent lamps. The ballast as such is not used; a special transformer is used instead.

The transformer is so designed that when there is no load on its secondary (as is the case at the moment when it is connected across a cold-cathode lamp, but before the lamp has started) the voltage across the secondary is about 750 volts. This starts the lamp (as pointed out in Chap. 14, a high voltage may also be used to start an ordinary fluorescent lamp even without heating its filaments or cathodes, except that control of the exact voltages is difficult). As soon as current begins to flow through the started cold-cathode lamp, about $\frac{1}{8}$ amp. flows through the secondary of the transformer, which causes voltage drop in the secondary winding, which immediately means a reduced voltage in the neighborhood of 450 volts, at which voltage the cold-cathode lamp continues to operate. Once started, it operates on exactly the same principles as the ordinary fluorescent lamp.

At the present moment there is not entire uniformity or standardization in the equipment offered for cold-cathode lighting. The most common lamp or tube available is one of 25 mm. diameter, 93 in. in over-all length, and designed to consume 120 milliamperes[1] at 450 volts. Some manufacturers however offer tubes of different lengths and consuming different amperages. Ultimately there will no doubt have to be

[1] A milliampere is 0.001 amp.

more standardization to achieve maximum popularity for this type of lighting.

The 93-in. lamp itself consumes about 45 watts, its transformer about 9 watts. As in the case of ordinary fluorescent lighting, the combined wattage must be taken into consideration when thinking in terms of lumens per watt, or footcandles of illumination.

The advantages claimed for cold-cathode lighting include:

1. Instant starting when the switch is turned on.
2. Lower cost because the tubes are said to have a life of 10,000 hr., as compared with much shorter life of ordinary fluorescent.
3. Lower maintenance cost because there are no starters to replace, and because with longer life, replacements are less frequently needed.
4. Slightly higher light output (lumens per watt).

Against these must be considered higher cost per lamp, higher cost per fixture because of longer length, higher cost of transformers because of high voltages, higher installation costs because ordinary building wire does not have sufficient insulation for the voltage involved. Ordinary Type R building wire is approved for use at not over 600 volts. For the high-voltage circuit of cold-cathode lighting, 1,000-volt wire must be used.

All told, the contest between fluorescent and cold-cathode lighting promises to be a lively one; the final outcome is likely to be that for some applications the fluorescent will prove to be the better, while for other applications, the cold-cathode will be more suitable.

Benjamin Elec. Mfg. Co.
Fig. 28-5.—Typical R.L.M. type of reflector.

Direct-lighting Units.—For industrial applications the R.L.M. reflector shown in Fig. 28-5 is most commonly used. It is a very efficient device and directs the light downward so that it illuminates on the floor level an area of a diameter equivalent to the height of the reflector above the floor. Accordingly, these reflectors are spaced on the ceiling so that the distance between the reflectors is approximately the same as the mounting height above the floor. If all the work is done at table level, then the distance from the table level to the reflector is the same as the spacing between reflectors.

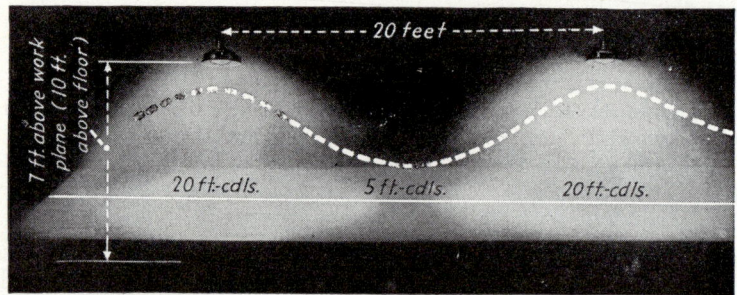

General Elec. Co.

Fig. 28-6.—Reflectors improperly spaced produce dark spots.

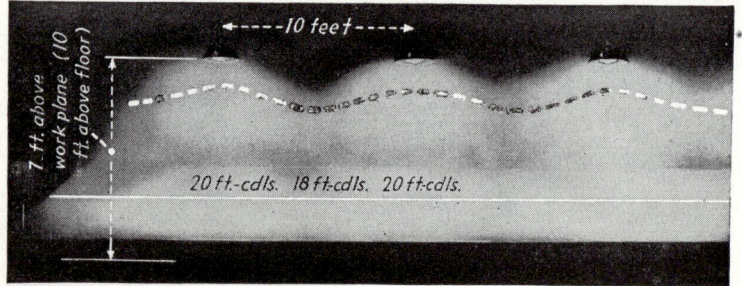

General Elec. Co.

Fig. 28-7.—Reflectors properly spaced produce even illumination.

If the reflectors are mounted too far apart, there will be areas of insufficient illumination between the units, as Fig. 28-6 will make clear. Compare this with Fig. 28-7, which shows the proper spacing.

Diffusers.—In industrial applications R.L.M. reflectors used with large bulbs have the disadvantage of causing a certain amount of glare because of the great surface brightness of the bulb. Therefore, with larger reflectors using bulbs of 300 watts and upward, it is best to use, in addition to the reflector, a diffuser or glass bowl of proper design which reduces the surface brightness. A reflector of this type complete with diffuser is shown in Fig. 28-8; it is usually known as a "Glassteel diffuser." This type of unit is recommended particularly

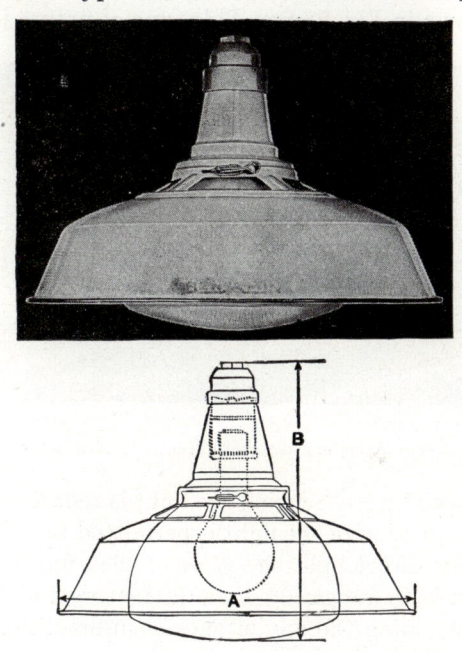

Benjamin Elec. Mfg. Co.

FIG. 28-8.—A Glassteel diffuser eliminates or at least reduces glare.

where the surfaces being illuminated are polished so that an image of the source is reflected directly into the observer's eyes.

Indirect and Semi-indirect Fixtures.—If the condition of the ceiling and walls is such that this style of lighting is practical, fixtures on the general order of those that were shown in Fig. 14-9 for residential purposes are used. Naturally, for nonresidential use, they will be larger, to accommodate the larger bulbs used. There are dozens, if not hundreds, of types of indirect and semi-indirect fixtures available to serve different and sometimes quite specialized purposes.

Combination Direct-indirect Fixtures.—Often in industrial occupancies indirect lighting may seem most desirable; yet the ceilings and walls may be of such construction as to make it impossible to use the ordinary type of indirect-lighting fixtures. For that purpose there have been developed what have come to be known as "direct-indirect" fixtures, a typical unit of which is shown in Fig. 28-9. This type of fixture incorporates

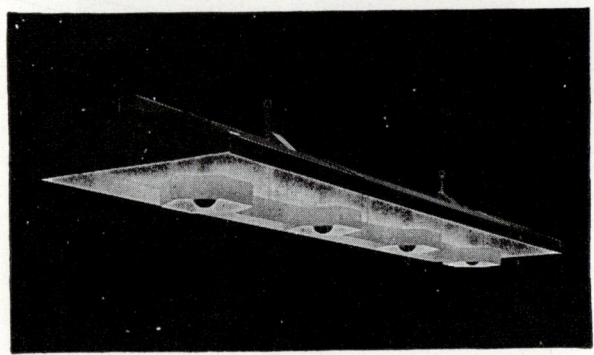

Curtis Lighting.

FIG. 28-9.—A typical direct-indirect combination fixture.

a miniature ceiling from which the light is reflected downward. Sometimes a portion of the light is permitted to escape directly downward for direct lighting. Use of such fixtures is becoming common over assembly lines in factories and in similar locations, providing the advantages of indirect lighting where it would not otherwise be possible.

Local Lighting.—In applications where the work is of a most exacting nature, it is the custom to provide, in addition to the general illumination, additional light from a local source which lights up only a small area. Care should be used that the light source provides diffused light, and the illumination in foot-candles on the small area should, generally, be not more than 10 times, at the most, that of the surrounding area. Unless this precaution is observed, the contrast will be too great, and glare will become a factor.

Lighting of Athletic Fields.—The lighting of an athletic field is a project of considerably greater proportions than most people realize. For example, to light a baseball field in a fashion that would be acceptable for major-league contests requires 750 to 1,000 kw. of power, and even for semi-professional games anything under 100 kw. would probably not be considered acceptable. It is interesting to know that the installation made in the summer of 1946, lighting the Yankee Stadium in New York City, provides 2,000 kw. of lighting power, with provision for 400 kw. more at a later date. This installation will provide about 200 foot-candles of illumination.

For football 25 kw. would be considered a minimum for a high-school game, whereas college football would require 75 to 125 kw. and more. Even a tennis court should have a minimum of $7\frac{1}{2}$ kw. for ordinary playing, and 15 kw. or more would be more nearly correct for professional or championship play.

One "trick of the trade" should be borne in mind when considering the lighting of athletic fields, or other areas where the light is needed for relatively few hours per year. As was pointed out in Chap. 14, when a lamp designed for, say, 115 volts is connected to a circuit delivering a higher voltage, the wattage consumed by the lamp increases to more than is marked on the lamp, the life of the lamp is greatly reduced, but the light output increases rapidly. In other words, when a lamp is burned at a voltage considerably higher than that for which it was designed, the light as measured in lumens *per watt* increases rapidly. Therefore, for maximum light per watt of power consumed, use lamps of a voltage considerably below the voltage of the circuit, for example, 100-volt lamps on a 115- or 120-volt circuit. Bear in mind that the capacity of the circuit must be more than the collective total of the wattages marked on the undervoltage lamps selected for the installation. True, the life of the lamps will be greatly reduced, but even if they lasted only 100 hr. (as compared with a normal life of 1,000 hr.), the extra expense of providing larger transformers, circuit breakers, and wire sizes for circuits of greater capacity might be many times that of the extra expense *per year* caused by short lamp life.

From this it should be apparent that the lighting of athletic fields in general involves problems much greater than those who are only casually interested would ever suspect.

CHAPTER 29

WIRING FOR MOTORS

Chapter 15 covered the wiring of the ordinary types and sizes of motors as used in residential and farm applications. This chapter will cover the wiring of commercial and industrial motors in considerable detail, so that the motor when installed will have proper operating characteristics, proper protection, and proper control. Only installations operating at less than 600 volts will be covered.

Sections 4301 to 4439 of the Code cover all phases of this work. This portion of the Code may at first seem decidedly complicated and involved, but it can be broken down to become relatively simple—although the wiring of motors ranging from a fraction of a horsepower to hundreds of horsepower can never be condensed to a few simple rules.

Full-load Current of Motor.—The amperage consumed by a motor while delivering rated horsepower will be found stamped on its nameplate. However, while designing an installation, that nameplate is not available. The Code in Tables 21 to 24 (see Appendix) shows the full-load current of different types of motors at various voltages. Regardless of what the nameplate of an ordinary motor shows when installed, the amperages shown in the Code tables are used in calculating feeders and branch-circuit wires, switches, overcurrent protection, and so on. However, the overcurrent device used to protect the motor against overloads will be determined by the amperage appearing on the nameplate, as will be explained later under Motor-running Overcurrent Protection.

Overcurrent Devices.—As in the Code, the term "overcurrent device" will here be generally used. Unless otherwise stated, this may be a fuse, a circuit breaker, or any other similar device described in Chap. 5.

Switches.—Various types of switches will be mentioned here as in the Code. A good understanding of these various types is essential; study the following definitions, which are quoted from the Code:

General-use Switch.—A switch intended for use as a switch in general distribution and branch circuits. It is rated in amperes and is capable of interrupting its rated current at its rated voltage.

Motor-circuit Switch.—A switch, rated in horsepower, capable of interrupting the maximum operating overload current of a motor of the same horsepower rating as the switch at the rated voltage.

Isolating Switch.—A switch intended for isolating a circuit from its source of power. It has no interrupting rating and is intended to be operated only after the circuit has been opened by some other means.

Circuit-breaker.—A device designed to open under abnormal conditions a current-carrying circuit without injury to itself. The term as used in this Code applies only to the automatic type designed to trip on a predetermined overload of current.

Motor Branch Circuit.—The elements that make up a motor branch circuit are as follows:

A. Motor branch-circuit conductors—the wires from the panelboard to the motor.

B. Motor branch-circuit overcurrent protection—to protect the wires, the controls, and the motor against overloads due to short circuits and grounds only.

C. Disconnecting means—totally to isolate the motor and its controls when necessary to work on the motor or its controls.

D. Motor-running overcurrent protection—to protect the motor, the overcurrent device itself, and the wires against damage caused by overloads other than short circuits or grounds.

E. Controller—to start and stop the motor, or reverse it, possibly control its speed, etc.

Figure 29-1 shows all the elements involved. In practice several of these elements often are combined into a single device; these cases will be considered one at a time. The

464 ACTUAL WIRING: NONRESIDENTIAL PROJECTS

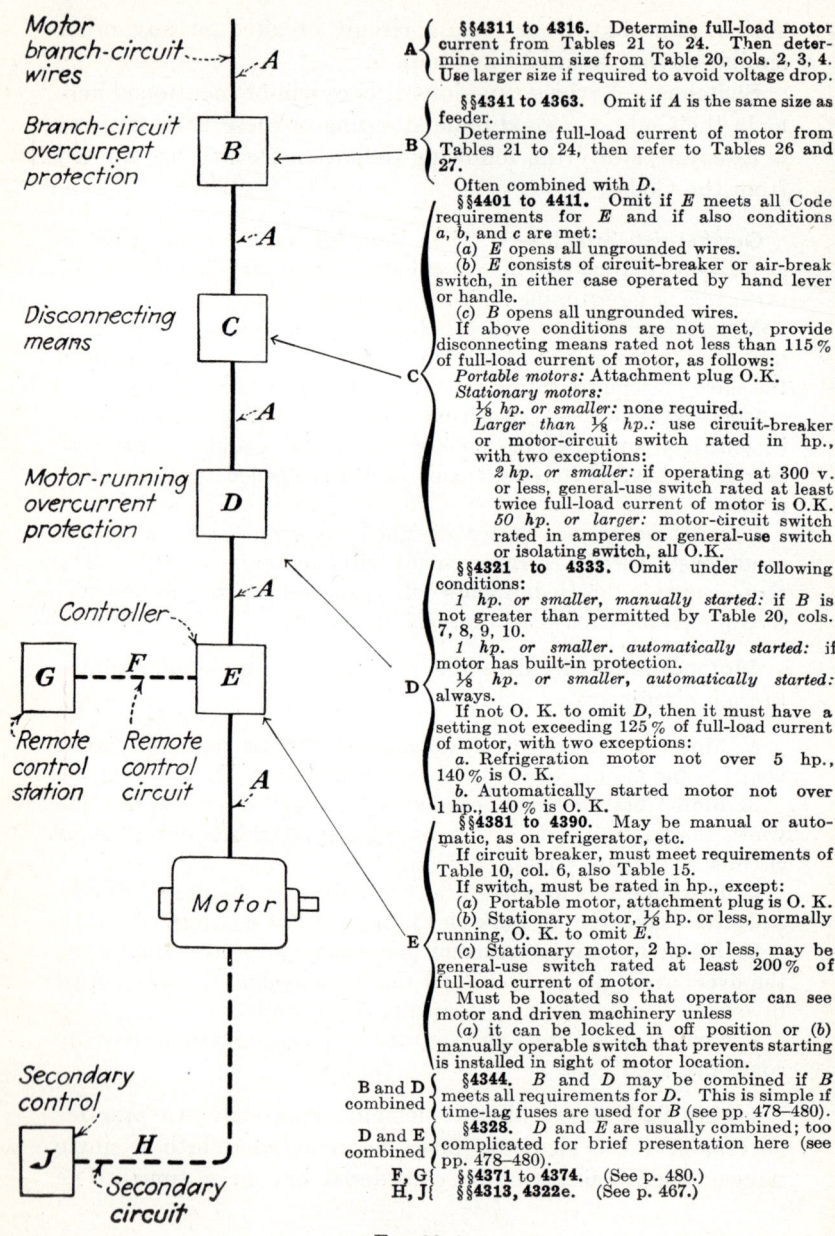

Fig. 29–1.

WIRING FOR MOTORS

first part of this chapter will cover these elements under the simplest possible conditions: one motor, and nothing except that motor, on a branch circuit. The Code in Table 20 (see Appendix) gives all the data so that relatively little figuring need be done.

PERCENTAGES OF NAMEPLATE CURRENT RATING

Classification of service	5-min. rating	15-min. rating	30- and 60-min. rating	Continuous rating
Short-time duty:				
Operating valves, raising or lowering rolls....................	110	120	150	
Intermittent duty:				
Freight and passenger elevators, shop cranes, tool heads, pumps, drawbridges, turntables, single-operator arc welders for manual welding, etc...................	85	85	90	140
Periodic duty:				
Hoists, rolls, ore- and coal-handling machines.....................	85	90	95	140
Varying duty.....................	110	120	150	200
	or lower at the discretion of the authorities enforcing the regulations			

MOTOR-BRANCH-CIRCUIT WIRES

(Code Secs. 4311 to 4316)

Must Carry 125 Per Cent of Full-load Motor Current.—The basic rule is that for all ordinary purposes the wires to the motor must have a carrying capacity, in accordance with Table 1 of the Code, equivalent to at least 125 per cent of the full-load current of the motor. Since Tables 21 to 24 show what this full-load current is for different motors, it is easy to calculate the size wire required. It is much simpler, however, merely to refer to Table 20, which gives the answers directly without calculations:

In column 2 if Type R rubber-covered wire, or Type T wire, is used.
In column 3 if Type RH rubber-covered wire is used.

Exceptions to 125 Per Cent Requirement.—There are a number of exceptions where percentages less than 125 per cent may be satisfactory, and others where a percentage greater

General Elec. Co.

FIG. 29-2.—Typical rotor of a wound-rotor motor.

than 125 per cent is required. Section 4312 of the Code covers these exceptions, which are as shown in the table on page 465.

Wound-rotor Motors.—In an ordinary polyphase motor there are no windings on the rotor or rotating part; such a motor is usually a single-speed motor. In the wound-rotor type there are windings on the rotor, the points of connection being brought out to slip rings, as shown in Fig. 29-2. Each slip ring has a brush riding on it, and through the brushes connection is made with the windings in the rotor. This type of motor has the advantage that the speed can be adjusted over a considerable range by merely connecting variable resistances between the leads to the slip rings. This control device is known as the secondary controller. Once adjusted, the speed

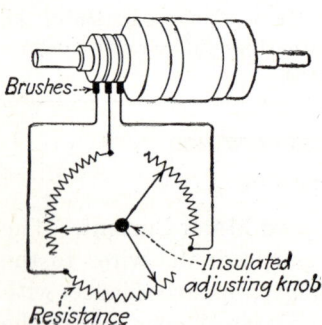

FIG. 29-3.—Diagram showing connections of the secondary controller of a wound-rotor polyphase motor.

remains practically constant. These resistances also keep the starting amperage down. The method is shown in Fig. 29-3; Fig. 29-4 shows one of the controls. The rotor is not in any way connected to the power line, but only to the resistances. Therefore the usual starter or controller is still used but is so

General Elec. Co.

FIG. 29-4.—A typical controller for a small wound-rotor polyphase motor.

interconnected with the secondary controller that operating the latter will also operate the former.

In smaller horsepowers the resistances are included in the same cabinet with the secondary controller. In the larger sizes the resistances are separate, and the Code, in Sec. 4313, requires that the wires from the controller to the resistances have a carrying capacity, in percentage of the secondary amperage which will be found on the name plate of the motor, as follows:

RESISTOR DUTY CLASSIFICATION

Light starting duty	35 per cent
Heavy starting duty	45 per cent
Extra heavy starting duty	55 per cent
Light intermittent duty	65 per cent
Medium intermittent duty	75 per cent
Heavy intermittent duty	85 per cent
Continuous duty	110 per cent

Voltage Drop.—The Code specifies only the minimum size wires that may be used in a motor circuit. It does not take into consideration the voltage drop that always occurs. Measure or figure the distance from motor back to the panelboard, measured along the wire; then calculate the voltage drop for the minimum size wire specified by Table 20 (how to do this is covered in Chap. 7), and if it exceeds $2\frac{1}{2}$ per cent of the voltage at which the motor operates, use larger wire. Remember, if the voltage drop as calculated is 5 per cent, in order to reduce it to $2\frac{1}{2}$ per cent, wire with double the cross-sectional area (twice the circular mils) must be used. It is not ordinarily considered good practice to permit voltage drop greater than $2\frac{1}{2}$ per cent, for this simply means that a substantial percentage of the power paid for is wasted, which may mean a considerable sum during the life of the motor; too great voltage drop also means that the motor will not develop full power, start as heavy loads, or accelerate so rapidly as under full voltage. Remember that there is additional voltage drop ahead of the panelboard.

MOTOR-BRANCH-CIRCUIT OVERCURRENT PROTECTION
(Code Secs. 4341 to 4363)

Starting Current Is Greater than Running Current.—The amperage consumed by a motor during the period while it is starting is considerably greater than it is after it has come up to full speed. Naturally, therefore, the circuit serving the motor must be protected by an overcurrent device of a rating large enough to carry the *starting* amperage.

This branch-circuit overcurrent protection is necessary to protect the wires of the circuit against overloads greater than the starting amperage, in other words, against short circuits and grounds. At the same time it protects the motor controller, which ordinarily is designed to handle only the amperage consumed by the motor and which would be damaged by a short circuit or ground if branch-circuit protection were not separately provided. Grounds are often practically equivalent to short circuits.

Motors ½ hp. and larger manufactured from 1940 onward are to carry on their name plates a key letter that indicates the "locked rotor current" (the current consumed by the motor while the motor is stalled), expressed in terms of kilovolt-amperes per horsepower, as follows:

Key letter	Kilovolt-amperes per horsepower with locked rotor	Key letter	Kilovolt-amperes per horsepower with locked rotor
A	Under 3.14	J	7.10 to 7.99
B	3.15 to 3.54	K	8.00 to 8.99
C	3.55 to 3.99	L	9.00 to 9.99
D	4.00 to 4.49	M	10.00 to 11.19
E	4.50 to 4.99	N	11.20 to 12.49
F	5.00 to 5.59	P	12.50 to 13.99
G	5.60 to 6.29	R	14.00 and up
H	6.30 to 7.09		

Running (Full-load) Current.—The full-load current, or current consumed by the motor while it is delivering its rated horsepower, is stamped on the nameplate of the motor. For Code calculations these full-load currents can be found for different types and sizes of motors in Tables 21 to 24 (see Appendix).

Maximum Rating of Motor-branch-circuit Overcurrent Protection.—If a fuse is to be used for this purpose, first refer to Code Tables 21 to 24 and determine the full-load current of the motor in question. Then refer to Table 20, column 7, 8, 9, or 10, which will furnish the answer directly.

If a circuit breaker is to be used, first consult Tables 21 to 24 for the full-load current of the motor under consideration. Then refer to Code Table 26 if the motor is marked with a Code letter, and to Table 27 if it is not so marked; the last column will show a percentage, which may be applied to the full-load current to determine the rating of the circuit breaker. For example, Table 24 shows a 3-phase 220-volt 10-hp. motor to have a full-load current of 27 amp. The final column of Table 27 shows that the circuit-breaker rating may be 250 per cent of full-load current. The breaker then may be rated at 2.50 × 27, or 67.5 amp. In accordance with Sec. 4349 the next higher standard rating (70 amp.) may be used. A 60-amp. breaker, however, would usually be found to be of adequate size.

Tables 26 and 27 may also be used to determine maximum permissible fuse size, but the use of Table 20 will be found more convenient.

Inspectors are authorized to increase the percentages indicated in Tables 26 and 27 to a maximum of 400 per cent if required to ensure proper operation of a specific motor.

If the motor is of a type and size which requires an overcurrent device of over 600 amp., it will be necessary to use a circuit breaker. (Fuses are not approved in sizes larger than 600 amp., and Sec. 2411 of the Code prohibits their use in parallel for motor protection.) In many other cases it will be found desirable to use a circuit breaker instead of fuses. A circuit breaker must be rated *at least* 115 per cent of the full-load motor current, and the *maximum* permissible rating can be determined from the Code, as already outlined.

All the foregoing has reference to the *maximum* setting permitted for the overcurrent device. In practice it should be set as low as possible and still carry the maximum current required by the motor while starting or running. However, Sec. 4346 requires that the fuse holder must be capable of holding the *largest* fuse permitted by Table 20. Occasionally this will necessitate using an adapter to permit, for example, 60-amp. fuses to be used in fuse holders designed for the larger 70- to 100-amp. fuses.

Since Sec. 4312 requires that the motor-branch-circuit wires must have a carrying capacity of at least 125 per cent of the motor full-load current, and since Sec. 4342 permits overcurrent protection in some cases up to 400 per cent of the motor full-load current, it is evident that the overcurrent protection may be as much as 400/125, or 320 per cent of the carrying capacity of the wire. This is contrary to general practice; hence it should be well understood that this is permitted only in the case of wires serving motors.

Under certain conditions the motor-branch-circuit overcurrent device will serve also as the *motor-running* overcurrent protection; this will be covered in a later section of this chapter.

Location of Overcurrent Device.—If the motor-branch-circuit overcurrent protection takes the form of fuses, then one fuse must be placed in each ungrounded wire; never may one be used in the grounded wire.

If the overcurrent device is anything except a fuse, it must be so designed that it will open all the ungrounded wires. It may also open the grounded wire, provided that in doing so it simultaneously opens also the ungrounded wires. In this connection remember that when circuit breakers are used, while the wires are actually opened by movable contacts, the contacts, in turn, are actuated by some type of thermal contrivance which causes them to open. The Code refers to this thermal contrivance as the "overcurrent *unit*." One such unit in one wire may actuate one or more contacts simultaneously, opening an equal number of wires, but it is still a single overcurrent *unit*.

Similarly, a *device* with contacts that will open, for example, four wires simultaneously, may be provided with two, three, or four overcurrent *units*, each in a separate wire, and, regardless of which unit operates, all wires will still be opened simultaneously.

The Code requirements as to the number of branch-circuit overcurrent units and also their location as to the several wires running up to the motor can be found in the Code, Table 28 (see Appendix). This table shows that all depends on the number of wires in the circuit, whether current is single phase or polyphase, which wires are grounded, and similar factors.

Feeder Taps in Inaccessible Locations.—At times it is necessary to tap the motor-branch-circuit wires to a feeder at a location not readily accessible. To locate the branch-circuit overcurrent protective device at such a point would render it equally inaccessible, which would be impractical. The simplest way of getting around this difficulty is to make the branch-circuit wires of the same size as the feeder, up to a convenient location, where the overcurrent device is then located. Obviously no overcurrent protection is then required at the point of the tap; beyond the overcurrent device wherever located, up to the motor, the size wire to be used is determined in the usual way.

If the distance between the tap and the location of the overcurrent device is not over 25 ft. and if the wires are protected against mechanical injury, then the Code, in Sec. 4348, permits wires to be used which are smaller than the feeder, but they must have a carrying capacity in amperes at least one-third that of the feeder; obviously they must be no smaller than the minimum required for the motor branch circuit in question.

Motor-branch-circuit Overcurrent Device Omitted.—If branch-circuit wires are the same size as the feeder, all the way up to the motor-running overcurrent device, the branch-circuit overcurrent device may be omitted entirely. Obviously the branch-circuit wires are protected by the feeder overcurrent protection. It would be more correct to say that there is no feeder and that what was considered the feeder becomes the motor branch circuit.

Motor-feeder Overcurrent Protection.—Before discussing this topic, which is covered by Secs. 4361 to 4363 of the Code, it is important to understand just what a feeder is. The Code defines feeders as "any conductors of a wiring system between the service equipment, or the generator switchboard of an isolated plant, and the branch-circuit overcurrent device." The overcurrent device used to protect the motor for *running protection*, which will be covered later in this chapter, is not the overcurrent device referred to; the feeder ends at the *branch-circuit* overcurrent device.

In large installations the requirements for power are usually such that each individual branch circuit cannot possibly be run back to a common point at the service entrance. Instead, there are feeders to panelboards at various locations, and the individual branch circuits start from these panelboards.

The feeders are subject to certain requirements as covered

in the Code. These requirements are simple. A feeder that supplies only one motor and nothing else must be provided with overcurrent protection no greater than that calculated as just outlined for the motor-branch-circuit protection.

If the feeder serves the one motor in addition to supplying power for lighting or appliances, add the amperage required for lighting or appliances to the maximum amperage permitted for the branch-circuit protection of the motor only; this is, then, the maximum setting of the feeder overcurrent device.

DISCONNECTING MEANS

(Code Secs. 4401 to 4411)

The purpose of the disconnecting means is totally to isolate the motor and its controller, for example, when it is necessary to work on either device.

Combined Disconnecting Means and Controller.—Frequently the motor controller serves the purpose of the disconnecting means as well. When this is permissible will be covered later in this chapter under the subject of Controllers.

Requirements for Disconnecting Means.—Most motors require a disconnecting means; the exceptions will be mentioned later. When required, the disconnecting means must have a capacity of at least 115 per cent of the full-load motor current. It may be a motor-circuit switch rated in horsepower, a circuit breaker, or sometimes some other device as will be described.

If a switch or circuit breaker is used, it must plainly indicate whether it is in the open or closed position. It must be located within sight[1] of the controller, unless it can be locked in the off position. It must be so arranged that it will simultaneously open all ungrounded wires (it may also open a grounded wire provided that in doing so it at the same time opens *all* wires). It may be in the same case with the controller. It must disconnect both the motor and the controller.

The disconnecting means *must* be a motor-circuit switch

[1] Any distance of more than 50 ft. is considered out of sight.

rated in horsepower, or a circuit breaker, with the following exceptions:

1. For stationary motors of ⅛ hp. or less, the branch-circuit overcurrent device is sufficient, no separate disconnecting means being required.
2. For stationary motors of 2 hp. or less and 300 volts or less, a general-use switch rated only in amperes and not in horsepower may be used, if it has an amperage rating at least twice the full-load current of the motor.
3. For stationary motors of more than 50 hp. a motor-circuit switch rated also in amperes, a general-use switch or an isolating switch may be used.
4. For portable motors the attachment plug and receptacle are sufficient.

On small motors, a very inexpensive switch such as is shown in Fig. 15-3 may be used. This switch, rated at 30 amp. and costing very little over a dollar, accommodates plug fuses up to 30 amp. and may serve as a combined disconnecting means and branch-circuit protection. Considering a single-phase motor and remembering that such a motor may require amperages while starting as high as 6 times its normal running amperage, it becomes evident from Table 22 of the Code that such a switch will be suitable on 115 volts for any motor of this type, ¼ hp. or smaller, and on 230 volts for any motor of ½ hp. or smaller. If the starting amperage of any motor under consideration does not reach 600 per cent of the full-load amperes, the switch will handle a larger motor. Moreover, if time-lag fuses described in Chap. 5 are used, the switch will handle much larger motors, limited only by its rating, which must be at least twice the full-load current of the motor.

Service Switch as Disconnecting Means.—In the rare cases when an installation consists of a single motor and nothing else, the service switch serves as the disconnecting means, provided that it is within sight of the controller and also meets the general provisions of the Code.

MOTOR-RUNNING OVERCURRENT PROTECTION
(Code Secs. 4321 to 4333)

Need for Running Protection.—A motor that requires, for example, 10 amp. while delivering its rated horsepower may require as much as 60 amp. while starting. Once the motor has come up to speed, there will probably be times when the machine which the motor drives will require more power than the rated horsepower of the motor; the motor may be entirely capable of delivering more horsepower for a nominal period of time, consuming a correspondingly greater amperage while doing so. Under overload this motor normally drawing 10 amp. may require 15 amp. If permitted to draw 15 amp. continuously, the motor will probably be damaged.

So far in this discussion only the motor-branch-circuit overcurrent device has been provided, and that may under certain conditions be as high as 400 per cent of the full-load current, or 40 amp. in this case. Obviously a 40-amp. overcurrent device will protect the motor circuit against short circuits and grounds, but it will in no way protect the motor against an overload which causes it to consume 15 amp. instead of 10 amp.

Therefore the Code requires that, in addition to the motor-branch-circuit overcurrent protection, a separate overcurrent device must be provided to protect the motor and controller against nominal overloads which cause nominal increases in amperage. Usually this overcurrent device is a component part of the controller, but it may be one of the overcurrent devices mentioned in Chap. 5.

Continuous Duty Motors.—The motor-running overcurrent device required depends on many factors, as follows:

More than 1 hp.: Whether manually started, or automatically as on refrigerators, water pumps, etc., the overcurrent device must be rated at not over 125 per cent of the full-load current of the motor *as stamped on its nameplate*, if the motor is of the ordinary type designed for a temperature rise not exceeding 40°C. If it is of a different type, the maximum rating is 115 per cent. However, if applying the 125 or 115 per cent factor results in an odd amperage rating for which there is no standard overcurrent device, the next higher standard rating may be used, provided that it is not more than 140 per cent of the full-load current of the motor.

Some motors have overcurrent devices built into them when they are made, and the Code requirements for such devices are therefore of more interest to motor builders than the general public. It is quite safe to assume that a built-in device of a reputable brand of motor will meet Code requirements.

1 hp. or less, manually started: If the motor is out of sight of the starter location (50 ft. or more is considered out of sight), it must be protected as will be covered below, for *automatically* started motors. If however it is in sight from the starter location, the branch-circuit overcurrent protection is considered adequate if it does not exceed the value shown in Table 20. However, it is permissible to operate any motor at 125 volts or less on any branch circuit protected by 20-amp. overcurrent protection.

Despite the above, which permits such motors to be very simply protected, it is wise to provide running protection for manually started motors, especially on farms where, for example, a water-pump motor may run for long periods without attention. Consider the extra cost of such protection as insurance.

1 hp. or less, automatically started: For protecting such motors, a choice of several methods is available, as follows:

a. A separate overcurrent device rated at not over 125 per cent of the full-load current. If this results in a nonstandard amperage, use the next higher standard provided that it does not exceed 140 per cent of the full-load current.

b. Inherent overcurrent protection. This is a built-in device, a component part of the motor which operates not only by the heat created by the current flowing through it but usually also by heat conducted to it from the frame and windings of the motor. If the motor is already hot from operating for a long time at full load, then the device will disconnect the motor more quickly when an overload arises than if the motor started cold and immediately overloaded to the same degree. In this respect such built-in devices as "Thermotrons" and "Thermoguards" provide better protection than separate devices.

c. "If part of an approved assembly which does not normally subject the motor to overloads and which is also equipped with other safety controls (such as the safety combustion controls of a domestic oil burner) which protect the motor against damage due to stalled-rotor current." There are very few oil burners equipped with a device which meets all these requirements.

d. Motors of the general type of clock motors are not harmed if they do not start and are considered protected by the branch-circuit overcurrent device.

Wound-rotor Motors.—Polyphase motors of this kind, usually adjustable speed, have wires running from their rotors (which are in no way connected to the line) to the control device. No overcurrent protection is required in these wires.

Intermittent and Similar Duty Motors.—Motors of this classification as defined in the table on page 465 are protected by the branch-circuit overcurrent device, which must meet the requirements set forth earlier in this chapter and covered by the Code in Tables 26 and 27 (see Appendix).

Fuses as Running Protection.—Knowing that the *running* overcurrent protection may never exceed 140 per cent of the full-load current, and is usually less, and knowing also that some types of motors require up to 600 per cent of their full-load current, *while starting*, it is evident that ordinary fuses used for running protection will usually blow during the starting period.

Therefore only time-lag fuses should be used for that purpose; in most cases they will not blow while starting, unless the motor requires unusually high starting current and is starting a machine that does not come up to speed quickly.

If the characteristics of the motor and the load are such that blowing of fuses is probable during the starting period, other kinds of protection should be used. However, fuses may be used and blowing prevented while starting by using a special type of double-throw switch, so designed that during the starting period the fuses are short-circuited and the motor is thrown directly on the line. This is permissible if the switch cannot be left in the starting position and if the motor is protected by fuses or circuit breaker somewhere in the branch circuit or feeder circuit, rated at not over 400 per cent of the full-load current of the motor.

A fused switch used as above outlined becomes a combined motor-running overcurrent protection and motor controller. The Code, in Sec. 4390, requires that under those conditions the fuse holder must be of a size to accommodate the largest size fuses permissible by Table 20, column 5, for motor-running protection. For example, this table may permit fuses of a maximum size of 70 amp. For various reasons it may be found expedient to use fuses of 60-amp. size, smaller in rating than the 70-amp. size permitted. The 60-amp. fuses, however, are too small mechanically to fit a fuse holder designed for the 70-amp. size. Accordingly, it becomes necessary to use the 60-amp. fuses in adapters which permit them to be used in holders designed for the larger 70-amp. size. The reason for this requirement is simple. With the best of intentions, it may originally appear that 60-amp. fuses are sufficient; it may later be found in practice that the 60-amp. size will blow regularly under actual working conditions; the next size, 70-amp., is too large for the 60-amp. fuse holder. If the fuse holder is capable of taking 70-amp. fuses, the size permitted by the Code, it is a simple matter to substitute the 70-amp. for the 60-amp. instead of resorting to dangerous substitutes.

When fuses are used as running protection, one must be used in each ungrounded wire.

Other Devices as Running Protection.—If devices other than fuses are used for overcurrent protection, they must be rated *at least* 115 per cent of the full-load current of the motor and the device must disconnect sufficient ungrounded wires to shut off all flow of current to the motor. The number of overcurrent units (see discussion of this in previous section of this chapter) is rather complicated. Since usually the device itself is purchased to match up with a given motor and diagrams are provided by the manufacturer for proper connection, this need not give any great concern. However, Sec. 4327 of the Code gives the requirements, as shown in the table on page 479. This table refers to running overcurrent protection and should not be confused with branch-circuit overcurrent protection, which is covered in Table 28 of the Code.

Combined Running Overcurrent Protection and Controller. The motor-running protection and the motor controller are usually combined in a single device. It is necessary only that the requirements of the foregoing table be met and that the overcurrent units be operative, in the case of direct-current motors, in both the starting and running positions; in the case of alternating-current motors they need to be operative only in the running position (Sec. 4329).

Combined Branch-circuit and Running Overcurrent Protection.—Under certain circumstances, these two separate forms of protection may be combined in a single overcurrent device. Occasionally there will be circumstances where a motor starts so readily that the starting amperes do not exceed the permissible amperage for the running overcurrent protection. In that case a single overcurrent device will serve the purpose.

Kind of motor	Supply system	Number and location of overcurrent units, such as trip coils, relays, or thermal cutouts
1-phase A.C., or D.C.	2-wire 1-phase A.C., or D.C., ungrounded	1 in either conductor
1-phase A.C., or D.C.	2-wire 1-phase A.C., or D.C., one conductor grounded	1 in ungrounded conductor
1-phase A.C., or D.C.	3-wire 1-phase A.C., or D.C., grounded-neutral	1 in either ungrounded conductor
2-phase A.C.	3-wire 2-phase A.C., ungrounded	2, one in each phase
2-phase A.C.	3-wire 2-phase A.C., one conductor grounded	2 in ungrounded conductors
2-phase A.C.	4-wire 2-phase A.C., grounded or ungrounded	2, one per phase in ungrounded conductors
2-phase A.C.	5-wire 2-phase A.C., grounded neutral or ungrounded	2, one per phase in any ungrounded phase wire
3-phase A.C.	3-wire 3-phase A.C., ungrounded	2 in any 2 conductors
3-phase A.C.	3-wire 3-phase A.C., one conductor grounded	2 in ungrounded conductors
3-phase A.C.	3-wire 3-phase A.C., grounded-neutral	2 in any 2 conductors
3-phase A.C.	4-wire 3-phase A.C., grounded-neutral or ungrounded	2 in any 2 conductors, except the neutral

In any event, as long as the branch-circuit overcurrent device is set at an amperage *no greater than is permissible for the running overcurrent protection*, then the single device, in place of two separate devices, is sufficient. It is well to remember the points brought out in Chap. 5: that, whereas an ordinary fuse blows on a normal overload beyond its rated amperage, time-lag types of fuses, as well as certain types of circuit breakers, will carry a very considerable overload for a reasonable period, but open almost instantly on a very heavy overload or a short circuit. If such a device is used for branch-circuit protection, it will permit the starting current to flow without opening the circuit, if it flows for only the normal starting period. If, however, a much smaller amperage, still in excess of normal rating of the device, flows for a long period, the circuit will be opened. Using such a device for branch-circuit protection makes it unnecessary to provide separate running overcurrent devices.

Remote-control Circuits.—Often a motor must be controlled from a point some distance from the motor. It would naturally be possible to run the branch circuit from the panelboard to the controller, then to the motor. This however in most cases would require more materials and would involve longer runs than are necessary. It is therefore more logical to use a controller of the remote-control type, consisting essentially of a relay that closes the circuit to the motor, when a very small amperage flows in the coil of the relay. The controller is then installed near the motor, the branch-circuit wires running through the controller to the motor in the shortest possible way. From the controller, small wires are run to the point from which the motor is to be controlled, at which point a push button is installed to control the motor.

The wiring from the control station to the controller proper is known as "remote-control wiring" and is covered by Code Secs. 4371 to 4374. The current in such wires is usually very small, and the wires themselves are not very large. Overcurrent protection for them is subject to the following:

1. No overcurrent protection is necessary provided that the setting of the branch-circuit overcurrent device in the circuit serving the motor in question is not over 500 per cent of the carrying capacity,

per Table 1, of the wires connecting the push-button control station with the controller proper.

2. No overcurrent protection is necessary if the controller device and the point of control (start and stop buttons, pressure switch, thermostatic switch, etc.) are both located on the same machine and the control circuit does not extend beyond the machine.

3. No overcurrent protection is necessary if the opening of the control circuit would create a hazard, as, for example, the control circuit of fire-pump motors, etc.

4. In the absence of any of the above three points, protect the wires of the control circuit with overcurrent devices rated at not over 500 per cent of their carrying capacity per Table 1. The overcurrent device, however, must not be of the time-lag type.

If damage to the remote-control circuit would constitute a hazard, the wires of the remote-control circuit must be installed in conduit or otherwise suitably protected against mechanical injury. For example, damage to the wires of the remote-control circuit of an oil burner might mean that the burner would continue in operation even after the thermostat had operated in the usual way to shut the burner off. That would lead to excessive temperatures or, in the case of a steam-heating system, dangerous pressures. Either result would be a hazard, and accordingly the control wires must be suitably protected against mechanical injury.

The control device must be so wired that it is disconnected automatically, whenever the motor is disconnected by the disconnecting means as defined in the Code, and as covered in a previous portion of this chapter.

MOTOR CONTROLLERS

(Code Secs. 4381 to 4390)

A motor controller according to Code definition is "any switch or device normally used to start and stop the motor." The controller may be a manually operable device, or it may be an automatic device as found on refrigerators, oil burners, and similar appliances.

Requirements for Controllers.—In general the controller "shall be capable of starting and stopping the motor which it controls, and for an alternating-current motor shall be capable of interrupting the stalled-rotor current of the motor." These basic requirements are of chief interest to manufacturers. Users and contractors will find that approved controllers furnished by manufacturers will automatically meet these requirements. Nevertheless it is well to be familiar with them.

The requirements for controllers are covered by Code Sec. 4383, which reads as follows:

The controller shall have a horsepower rating, which shall not be lower than the horsepower rating of the motor, except as follows:

1. Stationary motor of $\frac{1}{8}$ hp. or less: For a stationary motor rated at $\frac{1}{8}$ hp. or less, that is normally left running and is so constructed that it cannot be damaged by overload or failure to start, such as clock motors and the like, the branch-circuit overcurrent device may serve as the controller.

2. Stationary motor of 2 hp. or less: For a stationary motor rated at 2 hp. or less, and 300 v. or less, the controller may be a general-use switch having an ampere rating at least twice the full-load current rating of the motor.

3. Portable motor of $\frac{1}{4}$ hp. or less: For a portable motor rated at $\frac{1}{4}$ hp. or less, the controller may be an attachment plug and receptacle.

4. Circuit breaker as controller: A branch-circuit circuit breaker, rated in amperes only, may be used as a controller. When this circuit breaker is used for overcurrent protection also, it shall conform to the appropriate provisions of this article governing overcurrent protection.

The controller need open only enough conductors to start and stop the motor. If, however, it serves also as the disconnecting means as will be discussed shortly, then it must meet certain other requirements. In this connection note that it is permissible that the grounded wire be opened by the controller provided only that the device is so constructed that all the ungrounded wires are opened simultaneously with the grounded wire.

In general the controller must be located so that the motor and its driven machinery shall be within sight[1] of the point

[1] According to the Code, a distance of 50 ft. or more is considered out of sight.

from which the motor is controlled, unless *one* of the following points is complied with:

1. The controller or its disconnecting means is capable of being locked in the open position.

2. A manually operable switch, which shall prevent the starting of the motor, is placed within sight of the motor location. Obviously this provision is included to make it safe to work on the motor or its driven machinery without the danger of having the motor started from some remote point by some person who does not know that the motor or its machinery is being worked on. This switch may be directly in the motor circuit or it may be a very simple toggle switch such as is used for lighting purposes, in the remote-control circuit of the motor, in a wire to the push-button starting station controlling the motor.

3. Special permission is given by the inspector.

Adjustable-speed Motors.—Section 4388 of the Code provides that adjustable-speed motors, "if controlled by means of field regulation, shall be so equipped and connected that they cannot be started under weakened field, unless the motor is designed for such starting." Inasmuch as this refers to a specialized type of motor, in which the motor and the controller are usually furnished by the manufacturer on the same order, this section need not cause any great concern.

Combined Controller and Disconnecting Means.—The controller serves also as the disconnecting means if it meets *all* the following four conditions:

1. It must meet all the Code requirements for controllers when used only for controller purposes.

2. It must open all ungrounded wires to the motor.

3. It must be protected by an overcurrent device (which may be a set of fuses) which opens all ungrounded wires to the motor. This refers to the motor-branch-circuit protection.

4. It must be one of the following types:

a. A circuit breaker, or an air-break switch, operable by applying the hand to a lever or handle.

b. An oil switch of rating not more than 600 volts and 100 amp.; or exceeding 100 amp. if under expert supervision and by special permission.

Obviously, if the controller is of the automatic type such as used on oil burners, refrigerators, water systems, and similar devices, requirement 4a above is not met, and a separate disconnecting means is required. If the motor is started by means of a compensator type of controller, a separate disconnecting means is always required.

MISCELLANEOUS

Protection of Live Parts.—Most motors in common use and built today do not have exposed live parts. Some motors constructed years ago and still in use may have exposed live parts. If there are such parts, then the motor must be guarded against accidental contact by a guard rail, or some similar device.

Grounding.—Controller cases must always be grounded unless attached to portable motors. The motors themselves must be grounded if they operate at a voltage in excess of 150 volts to ground,[1] if in a hazardous location, or if in a continuously wet place. If the wires to the motor are inside armor or conduit or other metallic raceways, then the motor must also be grounded, but the armor or conduit itself serves as the ground. It is doubly necessary that all joints in the armor, or conduit, be particularly secure mechanically, to provide a good ground. Where wiring is by a different scheme, ground the motor as directed in Chap. 25.

Portable motors must be grounded if they operate at voltage in excess of 150 volts to ground. Often this is accomplished by an extra conductor in the cord serving the motor, this extra conductor in turn contacting a terminal in the receptacle to which the grounded supply wire is attached.

TWO OR MORE MOTORS ON ONE CIRCUIT

When more than one motor is served by one branch circuit, certain factors change considerably. These will be discussed

[1] In the case of a 230-volt single-phase motor connected to the outside two wires of a 3-wire system, with a grounded neutral, the voltage to ground is not 230 but 115 volts.

here in the same order in which these elements appeared in the first portion of this chapter where a single motor on a branch circuit was discussed.

Wire Sizes.—When more than one motor is involved, first determine the minimum required carrying capacity in amperes of the wires (whether branch or feeder) if only the largest motor in the group were involved. Then add the full-load current (Tables 21 to 24) for each of the other motors in the group. Finally, add amperage required for the lighting and appliance load, if any. This gives the total minimum amperage carrying capacity required, from which it is easy, with the aid of Table 1, to determine the size wire required as a minimum.

For example, consider one each 3-hp., $1\frac{1}{2}$-hp., and $\frac{1}{2}$-hp. single-phase 115-volt motors. In Table 22 the full-load currents for these three motors are, respectively, 34, 18.4, and 7.4 amp. If only the 3 hp. were connected, the minimum carrying capacity of the wires would be 125 per cent of 34 amp., or 42.5 amp. Add 18.4 and 7.4 amp., making a total of 68.3 amp. Assume a lighting load of 10 amp., which makes a grand total of 78.3 amp. Reference to Table 1 shows that, if Type R rubber-covered wire is used, No. 3 is the minimum, and good practice may demand a heavier size to prevent undue voltage drop.

If two or more motors are of the same size, consider one of them the "largest" and the others the smaller motors.

Motor-branch-circuit Overcurrent Protection.—Two or more motors of 1 hp. or less rating, and each having a full-load current of 6 amp. or less in Tables 21 to 24, may be used on a single branch circuit protected by overcurrent protection rated at 20 amp. or less at 125 volts or less, or 15 amp. at 600 volts or less. Motor-running overcurrent protection is not necessary for each motor individually, unless it is required when that motor is connected to a separate circuit of its own.

Moreover, two or more motors of any description may be used on the same branch circuit if *all* the following conditions are met:

1. Each motor must be provided with motor-running overcurrent protection, and the device must be a special type "approved for group installation."

2. Each controller must be "approved for group installation."

3. The branch circuit must be protected by *fuses* (not other overcurrent devices) having a rating as specified in Tables 26 or 27 for the largest motor, plus an additional amperage equivalent to the full-load currents of all the other motors.

4. The branch-circuit fuses must not be larger than permitted for thermal cutouts or other similar devices used for motor-running protection.

The first Code requirement is that each motor must be provided with individual *motor-running* overcurrent protection of a rating determined exactly as if the motor were alone on a circuit, but it must be a type that is approved for group installation. The ordinary devices used for motor-running overcurrent protection are not designed to be able to interrupt short circuits and would be damaged should they be subjected to short-circuit currents. Since the Code requires, in the case of a single motor on a branch circuit, that the branch-circuit overcurrent protection not exceed 400 per cent of the full-load current, the *motor-running* overcurrent device is, of course, protected against short circuits by the *branch-circuit* overcurrent device.

When, however, a *group* of motors is connected to a branch circuit, if the branch-circuit overcurrent device is of a rating heavy enough to permit all the motors to run at one time or perhaps to start at the same time, the branch-circuit overcurrent device would have to be many times greater than 400 per cent of the full-load current of the *smallest* motor in the group. The motor-running overcurrent device for that motor would not then be adequately protected by the branch-circuit overcurrent device. Consequently, the motor-running overcurrent device for each motor must be of the type approved for group installation, which tests have shown is capable of interrupting currents much heavier than merely normal motor overloads.

Such devices may be "thermal cutouts," devices something

like fuses. They are capable of interrupting quite heavy currents but not capable of opening short circuits. Such devices have stamped on them two amperages. The smaller rating is their normal rating, just as a fuse is rated in amperes. The larger rating represents the maximum permissible rating of the overcurrent device protecting the branch circuit. The rating of the branch-circuit overcurrent device must be no greater than this second or larger rating stamped on the *smallest* thermal cutout on the circuit.

Gradually becoming more common today for the purpose of motor-running overcurrent protection for motors in groups are the time-lag fuses of the types that were shown in Figs. 5-5 and 5-6. These are capable of interrupting short circuits, and therefore there is no restriction on the maximum amperage rating of the branch-circuit overcurrent device except the general rules which follow.

Assuming that *each* motor is properly protected by *motor-running* overcurrent protection of the type just discussed, the rating of the *branch-circuit* overcurrent device to protect the circuit with the group of motors is as follows:

Determine the maximum rating permitted (Table 20, column 7, 8, or 9) if only the largest motor were on the circuit. Add the full-load current (Table 21, 22, 23, or 24) for each of the other motors in question. The total adjusted upward to the next standard size of overcurrent device (if the total comes out to a nonstandard size) is the maximum rating of the branch-circuit overcurrent device, provided that fuses or other devices capable of interrupting short circuits are used for the individual *motor-running* overcurrent devices. If, however, for this purpose thermal cutouts or other devices are used, approved for group installation but still not capable of interrupting short circuits, then make sure that the rating of the branch-circuit overcurrent device, as determined above, does not exceed the maximum current-interrupting ability of the *smallest* device used on the group of motors for motor-running overcurrent protection.

Problems will arise as to the size of the wires, and protection

488 ACTUAL WIRING: NONRESIDENTIAL PROJECTS

for the wires, from the point where they branch off from the branch-circuit wires proper (see Fig. 29-5). The wire from A to B to C is the branch-circuit wire, the size of which is determined as already outlined. A is the branch-circuit overcurrent device, also determined as already outlined. From B to D, from C to E, and from C to F are the taps supplying the individual motors. If these taps are the same size as the branch-circuit wires, no overcurrent protection is required at points B and C. If the tap is the minimum size, as outlined in the first part of this chapter covering a single motor, if it

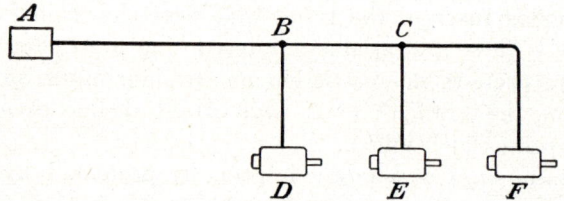

Fig. 29-5.—Problem in several motors on one circuit.

has an amperage carrying capacity at least one-third that of the branch-circuit wire A-B-C, and if it is not over 25 ft. long and is protected against mechanical injury, then no overcurrent protection is required at points B and C. Under all other conditions overcurrent protection is required at these points; determine the size just as if you were considering a single motor on a branch circuit, as outlined in the first part of this chapter.

As a matter of fact, installing overcurrent protection at the points B and C completely changes the complexion of the picture, for then the wire A-B-C is no longer a branch-circuit wire but becomes a feeder; A becomes the feeder overcurrent protection; the wires B to D and C to E, also C to F, become branch-circuit wires. The overcurrent protectors at points B and C become branch-circuit overcurrent devices, and, instead of a group of motors on a single branch circuit, we now have individual motors on individual branch circuits, fed by a common feeder A-B-C.

Motor-feeder Overcurrent Protection.—The feeder for a group of motors is to be protected by an overcurrent device of an amperage rating no greater than the *branch-circuit* overcurrent device for the largest motor served by the feeder, plus the full-load current for each of the other motors in the group. If two motors are of the same size, consider one of them as the "largest," the other as the smaller. There will be times when several motors must be started at the same time. In that case both feeder wires and feeder overcurrent may have to be increased; this is a case for consultation with the local inspector.

If a lighting or appliance load is also served by the same feeder, simply add the amperage required for this purpose to the amperage determined by the preceding paragraph.

Disconnecting Means.—Instead of a disconnecting means for each individual motor, the Code permits a group to be handled by a single disconnecting means, under one of three conditions:

1. If several motors drive different parts of a single machine, as for example metal or woodworking machines, cranes, hoists, etc.
2. If several motors are in a single room within sight of the disconnecting means.
3. If several motors are protected by a single branch-circuit overcurrent device.

The rating of such a common disconnecting means must not be smaller than would be required for a single motor of a horsepower equal to the sum of the horsepowers of all the individual motors (or a full-load amperage equal to the sum of the full-load amperages of all the individual motors).

Controllers.—A group of motors may be controlled by a single controller under the same conditions outlined for a single disconnecting means in the previous paragraph.

CHAPTER 30

WIRING SCHOOLS AND CHURCHES

Statistics show that 9 per cent of all students in the elementary grades of school have defective vision. In high schools the figure is 24 per cent, and in colleges it is 31 per cent. It is a well-established fact that, if good lighting is provided from the first grade onward, the percentages of students with defective vision are greatly reduced. Moreover it is equally well established that good lighting contributes materially toward raising the average grades of the students. Those who have been lagging behind in most cases respond quickly when proper illumination is provided; the number of failures drops. Good lighting is therefore a tremendous asset for the students themselves and likewise has been found to pay good dividends in the form of reduced over-all cost of providing education on a "per student per year" basis.

Foot-candles Required.—For class and study rooms 20 foot-candles is usually accepted as the absolute minimum. In drawing rooms 30 foot-candles is acceptable, and 50 foot-candles is not too high. Double these values would not be too high, and would be truly modern. In auditoriums 10 foot-candles is sufficient, and for corridors 5 foot-candles is ample. These are definite standards that should be met. It is safe to say that only a small percentage of schools today are lighted to a point even remotely approaching these figures; too many installations are of the type shown in Fig. 30-1. Installations made many years ago have not been changed even if woefully inadequate according to the standards of today. Here is a fertile field for modernization, and Fig. 30-2 shows what can be done. This shows the same school as in Fig. 30-1 but now equipped with modern and adequate lighting. It is safe to say that the pupils of this school will now progress further than before, with less effort.

Types of Fixtures Recommended.—Fixtures with exposed bulbs should under no circumstances be used, for they involve entirely too much glare, have too great surface brightness,

Curtis Lighting.

FIG. 30-1.—Lighting of the type shown above is not unusual in schools today. Efficient work is not possible under such conditions.

cause harsh shadows, and lead to all the other evils recounted in previous chapters. In a properly designed school installation, if incandescent bulbs are used, only fixtures of the indirect or semi-indirect type should be used. Fluorescent units are more commonly used today, furnishing an abundance of light with minimum surface brightness and relatively low wattage.

Special attention should be paid to the finish of ceilings, walls, and all reflecting surfaces. Ceilings and walls must be clean, light color to reflect well, but preferably dull finish to avoid glare, so that reflected light will be well diffused.

492 ACTUAL WIRING: NONRESIDENTIAL PROJECTS

Curtis Lighting.

FIG. 30-2.—The schoolroom shown in Fig. 30-1, but now equipped with modern lighting. Lighting of this type makes for highest pupil efficiency.

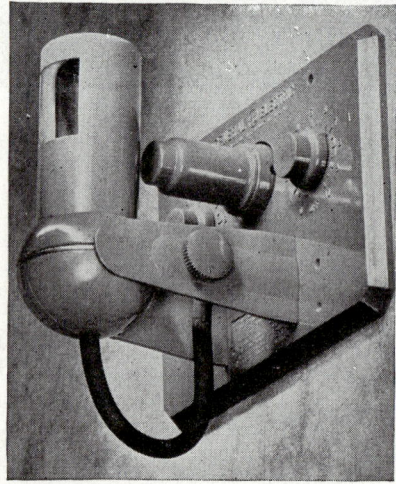

General Elec. Co.

FIG. 30-3.—This photoelectric control automatically turns lights on and off as required.

Automatic Lighting Control.—To secure "better light, better sight," it is not sufficient merely to provide an installation that is capable of producing the required illumination. The lights must be turned on and off at the right time before the most adequate installation will serve its purpose. This can be done by means of the usual switches, but the likelihood is that frequently the lights will be off when they should be on, resulting in inadequate illumination; at other times they will be on when they are not needed, resulting in wasted power. Therefore, just as it is logical to control heating equipment by thermostats, so it is logical to control lighting equipment by automatic devices. This can easily be done.

Not so many years ago the photoelectric cell was a scientific curiosity; today it is an entirely practical electrical device. A photoelectric cell is simply a device which generates an electric current so long as light falls upon it. In Fig. 30-3 is shown a complete photoelectric relay which is mounted on the wall of a room with the opening in the device aimed at the predetermined area to be lighted and shielded from the direct light that comes from the lighting fixtures. When the light that enters the opening in the device drops below a given foot-candle level, the photoelectric cell actuates a relay which turns on the lights. They stay on until the light rises to a predetermined foot-candle level, when the device turns the lights out. Both the minimum and maximum foot-candle values at which the device is to operate are adjustable. The cost of the necessary equipment for such installations is most reasonable, and automatic control of lighting is rapidly growing.

Several sets of automatic control equipment are often installed in one room, each controlling a row of lights, so that those farthest from the windows come on first, a row in the middle of the room next, and the row closest to the windows last. In a fairly large classroom with large windows the natural illumination on a clear day will be approximately 90 foot-candles at the row of desks nearest the windows. On the opposite side of the room, it will probably be not over 5 foot-candles. The need for separate control of separate groups of lights is apparent from Fig. 30-4, which shows clearly how the illumination in foot-candles varies as the distance from the windows increases.

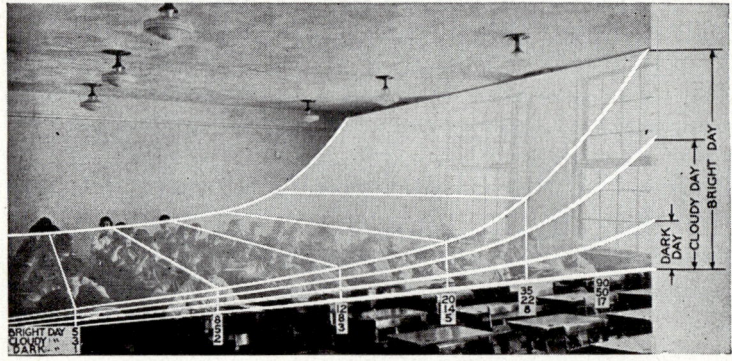

General Elec. Co.

Fig. 30-4.—The foot-candle level of illumination drops very rapidly as the distance from the windows increases.

The exact wiring diagrams for the installation of the controls are provided by the manufacturer, with the controls. Naturally, the lighting equipment in such installations can still be manually controlled by the usual switches.

Code Requirements for Schools.—For lighting purposes the Code requires 3 watts per square foot of area; on that area above 15,000 sq. ft. a demand factor of 50 per cent may be applied. Naturally the area is not the area of one floor, but the total area of all floors involved.

To the wattage determined by the area must be added the wattage for specific loads other than lighting. Take into consideration any motors that may be in operation, movie equipment, appliances in the domestic science department, special loads that may develop in laboratories, and similar loads. It is likely that a calculation based on the 3 watts per square foot required by the Code will, after application of the demand factor, result in a total wattage insufficient to provide the foot-candles suggested above for the various parts of the building.

It will be wise indeed to check the total specific lighting load that is to be connected and, if it is greater in watts than the figure reached by the first method, to take it into consideration in calculating feeders and similar factors.

Churches.—The Code requires 1 watt per square foot for churches. The demand-factor is 100 per cent regardless of the size of the installation.

Proper attention should, however, be given to what may be considered good lighting for churches. Illumination below 8 to 10 foot-candles would in most cases be considered inadequate for the church proper. To provide this level may require 4 to 7 watts per square foot, depending on a wide assortment of factors such as the reflecting ability of the ceiling and walls, the type of fixtures selected, ceiling height, and many others.

In many churches the lighting fixtures in use seem to have been designed to conform to the architectural scheme, with less thought given to the matter of proper illumination. Sometimes flame-color bulbs are used, which may nicely fit into a decorative scheme and do reduce glare, but which are very low in efficiency as compared with the usual inside-frosted bulbs. Often fixtures are selected which use a great many small bulbs, and since a dozen 25-watt bulbs consuming altogether 300 watts produce only about half the light produced by a single 300-watt bulb, the lighting suffers.

In most churches indirect lighting will be found practical. Certainly, if the walls or ceilings are decorated with paintings, no other type of lighting will suffice. Often the beauty and magnificence of a church are obscured by poor lighting. As an example, see Fig. 30-5, which shows St. Bride's Church of Chicago as it was formerly lighted, and Fig. 30-6, which shows the church after the installation of modern lighting.

Sometimes it may be found desirable to install fixtures which have substantial decorative value and which contribute toward the decorative and architectural scheme. For that purpose fixtures have been designed which outwardly seem to be the

Curtis Lighting.

FIG. 30-5.—Lighting of this type is typical of too many churches today.

Curtis Lighting.

FIG. 30-6.—The church shown in Fig. 30-5, but now equipped with modern indirect lighting. The beauty and dignity of the church have been brought out in full force.

Curtis Lighting.

FIG. 30-7.—This church is equipped with direct lighting which was installed many years ago. Note the extreme glare.

Curtis Lighting.

FIG. 30-8.—The church of Fig. 30-7 re-equipped with modern lighting. This shows what can be done when the physical structure of the building prevents an indirect lighting system from being used.

direct-lighting type; actually concealed within the fixture is the more important indirect component which provides the greater portion of the total illumination.

If the circumstances are such that indirect lighting is absolutely impossible, satisfactory results can be obtained with well-designed direct lighting equipment. Figure 30-7 shows the Bethlehem Lutheran Church of Chicago with the original lighting, and Fig. 30-8 shows this church after the installation of modern lighting.

The nave or auditorium of the church having been properly lighted, the fact that in a great majority of all churches the sanctuary and the altar constitute the focal point of the worshipers must not be overlooked. This portion of the church should be lighted to a level considerably above that of the rest of the church; levels of 20 to 30 foot-candles and above are the rule. This illumination is usually provided through the medium of spotlights, concealed from the view of the congregation. This may require a minimum of 1,500 watts upward to a much higher wattage, depending entirely on the area to be illuminated and the intensity desired. Statuary should be specially lighted. Each church will present an individual problem, and the method of lighting should be left to one well versed in the art of church lighting.

If the church has a choir loft, adequate illumination of a minimum of 20 foot-candles should be provided. The organ motor may require a special circuit. The heating plant, if it is of the oil-burning type, will require a special circuit for the motor. Throughout the church, miscellaneous loads also exist. Conveniently located receptacle outlets should not be overlooked; too often unsightly and dangerous extension cords are used to operate fans, pulpit lights, loud-speaking apparatus, and similar equipment. Outdoor receptacle outlets are most desirable for possible decorations during festival seasons.

CHAPTER 31

WIRING OFFICES

An office may consist of anything from a single room with a desk and a chair and an exposed bulb, to a well-appointed modern office with really adequate lighting, a considerable assortment of electrical devices including dictaphones, calculating machines, fans, water coolers, and similar equipment. Accordingly it is difficult to cover the subject adequately in a single chapter, and the suggestions here given must of necessity be general.

Code Requirements.—The Code requires a minimum of 2 watts per square foot for lighting purposes. In an area of more than 20,000 sq. ft., a demand factor of 70 per cent may be applied (Sec. 2203a). As usual, the specific loads such as appliances or motors must be added to the wattage so obtained.

It is not likely that the 2 watts per square foot will provide, even with the best of lighting equipment, the foot-candles of illumination today recommended for modern offices. It seldom provides as much as 15 foot-candles and usually falls lower. The minimum considered should be 20 foot-candles, and the alert office manager is beginning to discover that the extra cost of equipment that provides 40 or 50 foot-candles or more is soon offset by the increased efficiency of the personnel. The specific load which is planned, rather than the 2 watts per square foot Code minimum, will in all probability determine the total wattage.

Once the wattage and the amperage have been determined, feeder sizes and similar data can easily be determined as in other cases that have been previously discussed.

Receptacle Outlets.—Most offices have entirely too few receptacle outlets. Every individual office space, no matter how small, should have a minimum of one outlet; one such outlet for each 10 linear feet of wall space is more nearly correct. In offices larger than 400 sq. ft. there should be a minimum of four for the first 400 sq. ft. of area, and at least two additional outlets for each additional 400 sq. ft. of area.

Special outlets should be provided for fans; receptacles are available with a stud or bolt on which the fan is supported, making unsightly shelves unnecessary. There should be at least two such outlets for every 400 sq. ft. of floor area, and they should be located about 7 ft. above floor level.

Types of Fixtures.—Office work is usually of a continuous and exacting nature. Besides a sufficient quantity of light there is needed the right kind of lighting—freedom from glare, low surface brightness, avoidance of shadows. As in schools, the factors that make good lighting must be considered.

Flexibility.—If a sizable floor area is involved, which will accommodate a considerable number of people, it is not likely that the original arrangement of the individual office space will long remain unchanged. Large office space is often subdivided into many individual offices by movable partitions about 7 ft. high. These partitions are shifted as the need arises, and, as the individual office spaces change, the lighting equipment must be moved. This is frequently accomplished by originally providing flush ceiling outlet boxes on which the original lighting equipment is installed. When it becomes necessary to move this equipment, surface metal raceway of the type described in Chap. 25 is used in the way there described. Similar material is used to provide receptacle outlets for dictaphones and other equipment at the exact point needed.

Signaling Equipment.—In larger offices it will be necessary to provide a raceway, usually concealed, for low-voltage wires, for telephones, buzzer systems, call systems, and similar purposes. This raceway, which usually is conduit, must never contain wires that are part of the regular electrical system operating at the usual voltages. A review of this subject in Chap. 24 would be advisable. To bring such low-voltage wires to the individual desks in an office, surface metal raceway of the floor type which was shown in Fig. 27-14 in Chap. 27 is used.

Control Equipment.—In relatively small offices, a single panelboard or fuse cabinet with switches in the individual circuits will probably serve the purpose. In larger installations it is often necessary to install more elaborate equipment, so that an entire group of fixtures can be controlled by a single switch. Usually in such installations the individual fixtures are equipped with pull-chain or wall switches so that they can be separately controlled.

Automatic Control.—Modern offices are beginning to use photoelectric controls of the type described in the previous chapter in connection with school installations.

CHAPTER 32

WIRING STORES

Wiring in stores may vary from a most simple installation to a complicated and highly specialized one of the large department-store type. The latter type of installation is entirely beyond the scope of this book, which will cover only the small to medium type of store.

Foot-candle Recommendations.—The general illumination in the average store in neighborhood locations must be from 20 foot-candles upward, if a good selling display is to be obtained. In larger cities and in better locations 25 foot-candles is considered the minimum. The darker the color of the merchandise to be displayed, the higher the level of illumination must be. In better stores one is beginning to see many installations that well exceed the 25 foot-candle figure mentioned.

Showcases in order to display merchandise to good advantage require up to 50 foot-candles, and for special displays of merchandise 50 to 200 foot-candles is not too much.

If these levels of illumination at first seem high, remember that mediocre lighting may be sufficient to sell the customer the things that he has decided to buy before he comes into the store. No merchant, however, will be a great success if he depends only on that type of business, if he sells only the specific things his customers ask for. Good lighting draws the customer's attention to the merchandise on display emphasizes the points which lead to a wish for ownership and an urge to buy. Additional sales of customers' "wants" rather than "needs" will result, and good lighting will prove to be a good investment rather than an expense.

In show windows 50 foot-candles is usually considered a

minimum, and in larger cities 100 to 200 foot-candles is not unusual. On a dark street a window that is lighted to 50 foot-candles will appear very bright and well lighted, but if the street is itself well lighted, a window with 100 foot-candles may appear very ordinary indeed, especially if another window next door is provided with a still higher level of illumination.

In order to light a show window to the point where it will

Curtis Lighting.

FIG. 32-1.—Typical show-window reflectors designed for flush mounting.

attract attention in the daytime, it is necessary to provide sufficient light inside the window to minimize the reflections that arise from the natural outdoor light. This requires an unusual level of illumination, for 200 to 1,000 foot-candles must be provided.

Code Requirements.—For lighting purposes the Code requires a minimum of 3 watts per square foot for the store proper; naturally for warehouse space, storerooms, and similar locations this is not required. To this must be added the further load required for lighting showcases and show windows. For each linear foot measured horizontally along the base, allow 25 watts for ordinary showcases, 50 watts for wall cases, and 200 watts for show windows. Regardless of the size of the store the demand factor is always 100 per cent; in other words no deduction may be made regardless of the number of square feet involved.

As in the case of all other occupancies, specific loads such as motors, appliances, and similar equipment must be added. The demand for electricity in the average store will certainly grow rather than decrease, so it is well to leave a very generous

Curtis Lighting.

Fig. 32-2.—A battery of reflectors of the type shown in Fig. 32-1, installed in a show window.

margin for future expansion when figuring service entrance, feeders, number of spare circuits on panelboards, and all similar factors. Do not overlook probable future load for air conditioning.

Considering the suggestions regarding proper foot-candle levels of illumination, it is not likely that 3 watts per square foot, plus the special loads for showcases and show windows, will be sufficient to provide the illumination needed. Check the actual load, as determined from the foot-candle level selected, and the particular fixtures and sizes of bulbs involved to determine whether the 3-watt minimum is sufficient or not. In accordance with the very general formula shown on page 452, 6 watts per square foot is the minimum required to provide 25 foot-candles of illumination.

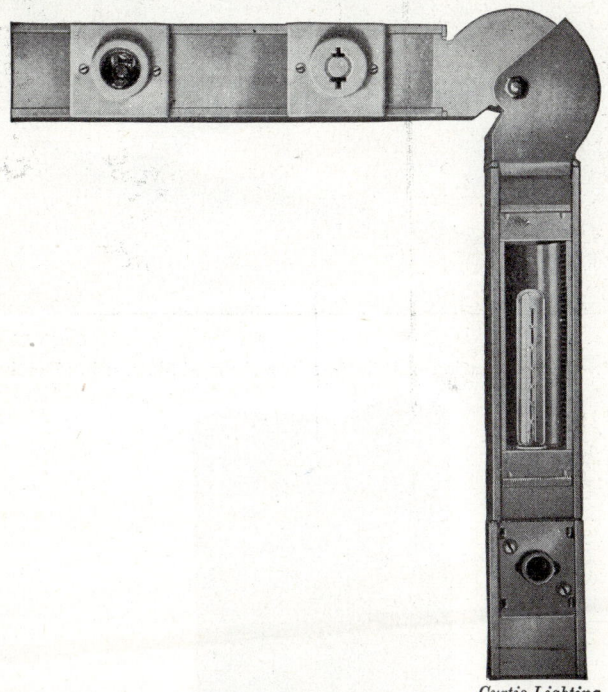

Curtis Lighting.

Fig. 32-3.—Curtistrip makes a flexible installation of reflectors and other lighting accessories simple.

Type of Lighting Equipment.—For a most modern store located in perhaps the most competitive area of a large city, there is little choice except to design the lighting system specifically to suit the exact size, structure, and layout of the building, the type of merchandise sold, the effects desired, and many other factors. Only the most general rules can be given in a book of this kind, and final selection of the equipment must be left to one competent to analyze the dozens of factors involved.

Curtis Lighting.

Fig. 32-4.—An installation of reflectors in a show window, using Curtistrip.

Sangamo Elec. Co.

Fig. 32-5.—Automatic time switches control show-window lights.

For the average store located in a smaller city or in the less competitive areas of a larger city, the choice of lighting equipment will usually lie between the indirect and the combination direct-indirect. Certainly *exposed bulbs cannot be considered;* yesterday's common fixtures consisting of bulbs merely enclosed in glass globes are today entirely unsuitable.

Show-window Lighting.—Since the Code requires 200 watts per running foot of show window, obviously a rather elaborate installation of reflectors is required. The light source must not be visible to the shopper on the street, if good display of merchandise is to be obtained. The reflectors may be the flush type shown in Fig. 32-1 in cross-section and in Fig. 32-2 in an actual installation. For the purpose of providing simple and flexible installations there is available a ready-made channel known as Curtistrip, shown in Fig. 32-3. With this material it is a simple matter to install reflectors with any required spacing. The material provides both a channel for the wires and a mechanical support for the reflectors. Figure 32-4 shows a finished installation.

A time switch, such as that shown in Fig. 32-5, is very frequently installed to control the show-window circuit, automatically turning off the show-window lighting at any desired time after closing hours.

CHAPTER 33

WIRING MISCELLANEOUS OCCUPANCIES

In determining the service entrance, feeders, panelboards, and switchboards for any type of occupancy, it is necessary only to estimate the lighting load, to which must be added the appliance load, if any, and the motor load. The Code in Sec. 2203a (see Appendix) specifies the watts per square foot that must be allowed for the lighting load. The calculation then is relatively simple.

For such factors as are not covered by Sec. 2203a, the load must be estimated from the specifications. Do not overlook future loads, including air conditioning.

Factories.—It is impossible to specify the power that will be required for lighting purposes without knowing exactly what kind of project is involved. A factory may be anything from a foundry where 5 foot-candles might be considered good lighting to a watchmaking establishment where 50 foot-candles would be considered too little. Furthermore, the complete establishment must be broken down into smaller portions. The lighting in the boiler room need not be so good as that in the office. In very few cases, however, will less than 10 foot-candles be considered ample.

The motor load can be determined from the specification of the building. The demand factor that is to be used with the motors will depend entirely upon the type of installation involved, and good common sense will be far more valuable than any number of printed pages in a book.

Theaters.—The Code in Art. 520 outlines the requirements for electrical installations in theaters, which are defined as "buildings, or parts of buildings, designed, intended or used for dramatic, operatic, motion picture or other shows." The

Code requirements are rigid and severe, but simply covered in Art. 520, which should be studied in detail by all those who intend to design or install an electrical installation in a theater. Only the simplest requirements can be here covered.

If there are over 100 seats, the wiring must be in conduit, and an emergency lighting system must be installed, as will be covered later. The projector must be approved by the Underwriters, and the circuit serving it must be No. 8, or larger if required by the specific load.

If the theater is equipped for sound, the wiring for the sound system must be considered as an entirely separate system, and its wires must not run through the raceways containing the usual wiring for light and power.

Receptacles for portable arc lamps must have a rated capacity of at least 35 amp. and must be wired with No. 6 or larger wire. Receptacles for portable incandescent lamps may be rated as little as 15 amp. but must be wired with No. 12 or heavier wire. All portable cord must be heavy-duty type such as Type S or K.

In dressing rooms, receptacle outlets or pendant lamps are not permitted. Installation of receptacles naturally leads to the use of flatirons, heaters, and similar devices, which experience has shown leads to fires. Their use should not be permitted in dressing rooms.

Emergency Lighting System.—In any theater that has more than 100 seats, an emergency lighting system is required. The emergency system includes all those lights which are normally left on during a performance, and the object is to enable the occupants of the building to be able to see their way to get out of the building in an emergency.

The Code has some definite requirements as to the method of installation of such an emergency system. These requirements apply not only in the case of theaters, where the Code definitely requires an emergency system, but also in other cases where local codes require that such a system be installed. There are a number of different ways in which the Code requirements for emergency lighting systems can be fulfilled.

The simplest is perhaps one involving two separate service entrances to the building, preferably from two separate power lines, or from two separate transformers on the same line, or even two separate service entrances from the same transformer, but entering the building as widely separated as possible. One entrance would normally carry the entire normal load, and the second would carry the emergency system.

An alternative consists of the regular service, plus a storage-battery system which must be of sufficient capacity to operate the emergency circuits not less than 30 min. at not less than 91 per cent of the full normal voltage of the circuit in question. This does not mean that, if the regular service is 115 volts, the storage battery must also be the 115-volt type. The emergency system might be equipped with 12-volt bulbs or 32-volt bulbs, and the battery need be only of sufficient capacity to maintain 91 per cent of that voltage for not less than 30 min. A popular emergency system of this kind is available incorporating a 12-volt battery with automatic charging equipment so that the batteries are maintained in a fully charged condition. The battery must be of the sealed-glass-jar type. In case the voltage of the emergency system is lower than the regular voltage, special attention must be given to the right wire size for that voltage.

The third method of providing power for emergency lighting is the usual service for the usual load, plus a gasoline-engine-driven generator for the emergency load. The generator system incorporates a low-voltage battery, usually a 12-volt automobile battery, which automatically starts the plant in case of emergency need. Such plants frequently are used, not only to operate those emergency lights required by Code or law, but also additional lights sufficient to permit carrying on the regular business of the establishment during emergencies. A typical plant of this kind is shown in Fig. 33-1. This particular plant delivers 1,000 watts of single-phase 60-cycle 115-volt alternating current. Modern plants of this type maintain correct voltage and frequency up to the rated capacity of the plant, which may be up to 35,000 watts.

WIRING MISCELLANEOUS OCCUPANCIES 511

Regardless of the system used, an automatic transfer switch must be provided so that, if for any reason power is not available from the regular source, the emergency lighting circuit is immediately thrown over to the emergency power source. Ordinarily the emergency circuit is operated from the regular service, and it is operated from the emergency source only in

D. W. Onan & Sons.

Fig. 33-1.—A typical gas-engine emergency light plant. The unit shown starts automatically upon failure of the regular service and develops 115-volt 60-cycle alternating current.

the case of actual emergency. Naturally, common sense dictates that it be frequently tested.

The requirements outlined above apply when the emergency system is required by Code. When such a system is installed but not required, the system needs to comply only with the general requirements of the Code.

Signs.—The switch that controls a sign must open all ungrounded wires to the sign and must be located within sight of the sign, unless it is a type that can be locked in the off position. Obviously this provision is intended to protect people working on the sign. All controls including flashers must be enclosed in metal cases.

All signs must be grounded, except that they may be completely insulated from the ground if "inaccessible to unauthorized persons." The maximum current permitted is 15 amp. per circuit.

The wiring in signs may be open wiring on insulators, in conduit, or in troughs formed by the construction of the sign, or armored cable. Wires must be of the lead-covered type, unless the wire is in conduit, so arranged as to be raintight and to drain in case moisture gets inside. The wiring may be no lighter than No. 14 and, in the case of those signs operating in excess of 600 volts, which includes all neon signs, must be selected with an insulation heavy enough for the voltage involved.

Signal Systems.—Ordinary installations for the operation of doorbells, door openers, buzzers, telephones, call systems, and the like are classified by the Code into four groups, as follows:

   A. Those limited to not over..... 15 volts, 5 amp.
   B. Those limited to............. 15 to 30 volts, 3 amp.
   C. Those limited to............. 30 to 60 volts, 1⅓ amp.
   D. Those operating at more than. 60 volts, 1 amp.

The usual source of power for these signal systems is a small transformer so designed that, even if the secondary is short-circuited, it will deliver not more than the amperages shown above at various voltages. In that case no fuses or other overcurrent protection is required. If, however, a source of power is used which is capable of delivering an amperage greater than specified, then overcurrent protection of a rating not heavier than the maximum amperage permitted for a signal system of the voltage involved must be used. The maximum capacity of any transformer used for the purpose is 100 volt-amp. If a primary battery (any battery other than a storage battery) is used, no fuses are required.

Class D systems, operating at a potential in excess of 60 volts, require, in addition to the 1-amp. fuse, a further current-

WIRING MISCELLANEOUS OCCUPANCIES 513

limiting device which will limit the power, in case of a fault, to 150 watts. Since such circuits usually consist of telephone systems, the manufacturer of the equipment should include what is required.

Hazardous Locations.—A location may be considered hazardous for a variety of reasons. If explosive vapors, such as those formed by gasoline, lacquers, or other similar volatile products, are present, obviously an explosion hazard exists. The same is true where explosive dusts such as coal or grain dusts are present, as also is the case where there is a considerable amount of easily ignitable fibers such as in a cotton mill.

Such materials can easily cause an explosion if ignited by electrical sparks caused by switches, motors, or pulling a plug out of a receptacle.

In such locations only conduit may be used for wiring. Ordinary outlet boxes may not be used, and special cast fittings which enclose all wires, switches, and similar devices are required. The purpose of these explosion-proof fittings is not to prevent explosive gasses from reaching the device, for that has been found impossible, but rather to enclose all such devices in fittings sufficiently sturdy so as not to be harmed by an explosion, and to confine the explosion to the interior of the fittings. In other words the small amounts of explosive vapors that do find their way into these fittings do explode occasionally, but the explosion stays inside, not getting out where it might set off a major explosion in a room filled with an explosive mixture.

Instead of outlet boxes, explosion-proof conduit fittings are required, similar to that shown in Fig. 33-2. The hubs on these fittings must engage at least five full threads of conduit. The covers are either screwed on with a sufficient number of threads engaged to make them explosion-proof or have a machined fit with a tolerance of 0.002 in. and at least $\frac{3}{8}$ in. wide, either of which experience has shown will confine the explosion. For switches, use a Type FS conduit fitting which was shown in Fig. 27-2, but of the explosion-proof type.

514 *ACTUAL WIRING: NONRESIDENTIAL PROJECTS*

Where portable devices must be used, special types of explosion-proof outlet and plug are required. Both are shown in Fig. 33-3, and the combination is so designed that with the

Killark Elec. Mfg. Co.

Fig. 33-2.—A typical explosion-proof fitting.

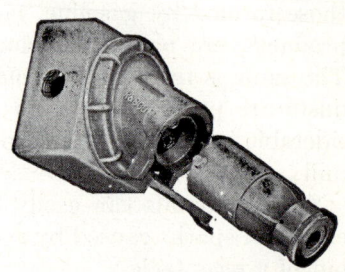

Russell & Stoll Mfg. Co.

Fig. 33-3.—For portable devices used in hazardous locations, an explosion-proof fitting of this type is used.

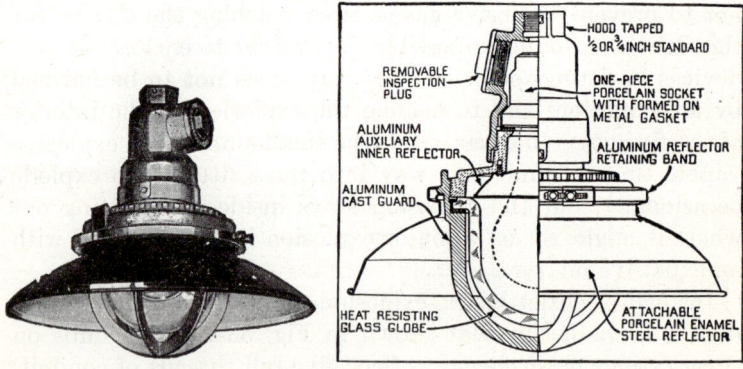

Benjamin Elec. Mfg. Co.

Fig. 33-4.—An explosion-proof fixture.

first pull the plug can be withdrawn only a part of the way. This breaks the connection, and an arc, if it forms, will explode the small amount of vapor present in the interior. This takes place during the brief period of time required to give the plug the twist that is necessary before it can be completely withdrawn.

Fixtures of the explosion-proof type are designed so that the bulb is enclosed in a sturdy glass globe. A typical unit of this type is shown in Fig. 33-4.

If such fittings are used by themselves, there will still be substantial enclosures for explosive vapor in the various lengths of conduit that connect one fitting to another. Therefore each device that is likely to cause a spark, which in turn might cause an explosion, is installed in a fitting with a pocket into which sealing compound is poured, thus effectively sealing off the device within the fitting. A separate fitting of the type shown in Fig. 33-5 may be used instead to seal off the device in question.

Killark Elec. Mfg. Co.

FIG. 33-5. By pouring sealing compound into a fitting of this kind, devices that might cause an explosion are sealed off from a run of conduit.

Code Classifications.—In its treatment of hazardous locations, the 1947 Code at first glance appears to be very complicated, but careful analysis reduces it to fairly simple proportions, perhaps easier to understand than the 1940 Code, although the subject is covered more fully. The entire subject, however, is in no sense of the word a simple one, and careful study is required to understand it.

The Code divides different kinds of explosive *atmospheres* into two *classes*, each subdivided into three or four *groups*.

The Code divides different types of *locations* into three *classes*, each subdivided into two *divisions*.

It is unfortunate that the word *class* was adopted for both *atmospheres* and *locations;* had the word *type* or a similar one been chosen for one or the other, a clear understanding might have been easier. When speaking of Class 1, be sure to indicate clearly whether a Class 1 *atmosphere* or *location* is under discussion.

Types of Hazardous Atmospheres.—The Code classifies hazardous atmospheres into classes and groups as follows:

Class 1, Group A: Atmospheres containing acetylene.

Class 1, Group B: Atmospheres containing hydrogen or gases or vapors of equivalent hazard such as manufactured gas.

Class 1, Group C: Atmospheres containing ethyl ether vapor.

Class 1, Group D: Atmospheres containing gasoline, petroleum, naptha, alcohols, acetone, lacquer solvent vapors, and natural gas.

Class 2, Group E: Atmospheres containing metal dust.

Class 2, Group F: Atmospheres containing carbon black, coal, or coke dust.

Class 2, Group G: Atmospheres containing grain dust.

Types of Hazardous Locations.—The various kinds of hazardous locations are defined in the Code as follows:

Class 1, Div. 1.—Locations in which explosive **gases** or **vapors** may be *regularly* expected (periodically, intermittently or continuously) under *normal operating conditions*. Examples: spray booths; locations with open tanks or vats of volatile inflammable liquids; drying rooms or compartments for evaporation of inflammable solvents; portions of cleaning and dyeing rooms where inflammable liquids are used; many similar locations.

Class 1, Div. 2.—Locations similar to Class 1, Div. 1, except that the explosive conditions are not present under normal operating conditions, but only under *abnormal* conditions such as exist during a period of breakdown. Details such as the amount of hazardous material that might escape in case of accident, the efficiency of the ventilating system, and similar factors will determine whether the location in question falls into Div. 1 or Div. 2. The local inspector is the judge.

Class 2, Div. 1.—Locations where combustible and explosive **dust** may be *regularly* expected (periodically, intermittently or continuously) under *normal operating conditions*. Examples: grain handling and storage plants; flour mills; starch plants.

Class 2, Div. 2.—Locations similar to Class 2, Div. 1, except that the explosive conditions are not present under normal operating conditions, but only under *abnormal* conditions such as exist during breakdown.

Class 3, Div. 1.—Locations where **ignitable fibers or combustible flyings** are handled, manufactured, or used. Examples: rayon, cotton, and similar textile mills; clothing manufacturing establishments; woodworking plants.

Class 3, Div. 2.—Locations where such materials are stored or handled.

Wiring in Hazardous Locations.—The subject of wiring in hazardous locations is a most important one, in which experience, good judgment, and "horse sense" all weigh heavily. The entire subject is much too complicated and too important

WIRING MISCELLANEOUS OCCUPANCIES

to be completely covered by the scope of this book. Therefore the discussion here given as to atmospheres and locations, and the wiring methods shown, should be considered only in very general terms, and layouts and installations involving hazardous locations should be undertaken only by those entirely conversant with the subject. The electrical inspector should be freely consulted.

Garages.—Residential garages designed to hold six cars or less are not considered hazardous locations, with the reservation that all wiring must be kept 4 ft. or more above floor level (gasoline vapors are heavier than air and tend to settle toward the ground). Therefore the wiring system for a household garage may be any system acceptable for the house proper.

With the exceptions above, certain provisions have been set up for garages, which term in addition to covering commercial garages also includes airplane hangars, gasoline service stations, and locations where service is rendered on this type of equipment.

In general, any outlet located 4 ft. or more above the floor may be wired with any wiring method otherwise acceptable, except that if the device in question is arc producing (switches, receptacles, sockets, motors, etc.) it must have all openings guarded or screened to prevent hot particles caused by the arc from falling to the floor. If the outlet or the equipment is within 4 ft. of the floor, it must be wired like a Class 2, Div. 2 location. Equipment located in a showroom or similar location, separated from the garage proper by a partition, is not included under this requirement. This includes offices, salesrooms, compressor rooms, and similar locations, provided only that they are cut off from the garage proper by a partition.

Filling Stations.—The wiring to the island on which gasoline-dispensing pumps are found must be in rigid conduit and all fittings within 4 ft. of the ground level must be of the explosion-proof type. A sealing fitting must be installed where the conduit enters the pump or other equipment on the island. If the insulation on the wires is rubber or some other type which would be affected by gasoline spilled on it, the wires must be in lead-sheathed cable. (It will be well to remember that the insulation designated as Type SN in the 1940 Code, or Type T in the 1947 Code, is in most cases not affected by gasoline. To be on the safe side, select a wire of this type which although not marked "Type T," looks just like Type T and bears an Underwriters' label marked "Approved for use in presence of oil.") All circuits feeding dispensing pumps on pump islands must be controlled by switches that disconnect every wire, including the neutral (which however does not change the requirement that there must be no fuse in the neutral wire); if a circuit breaker is used, it must break all wires simultaneously.

Motors in Hazardous Locations.—All motors for use in hazardous locations must be of the explosion-proof type. Obviously such motors can have no opening into the motor but must be totally enclosed and also constructed with extremely close tolerances on the mechanical fit of all parts.

Paint-spray Booths.—No electrical devices of any kind are permitted within the booth. Here there is danger of an explosion not only from sparks, but also by vapors present, which may explode upon contact with the relatively high temperatures found on lamp bulbs and similar devices under ordinary operating conditions.

APPENDIX

This Appendix contains tables quoted from the 1947 National Electrical Code.* A number of the tables shown in the Code are not repeated here because they refer to subjects beyond the scope of this book. Portions of certain tables have been omitted for the same reason.

On the other hand, certain sections of the Code are most important and specific, for which reason they are here included in full.

The Code usually contains some specific "examples" illustrating the application of Code requirements. Such examples were prepared for the 1947 Code but were omitted from the Code because of lack of space. They are included in this Appendix.

* Every student is urged to read the National Electrical Code. A copy may be obtained by sending 15 cts. to the National Board of Fire Underwriters, 85 John St., New York 7, N. Y., or 222 W. Adams St., Chicago 6, Ill., or Merchants Exchange Building, San Francisco 4, Calif.

TABLE 1.—ALLOWABLE CURRENT-CARRYING CAPACITIES OF CONDUCTORS IN AMPERES
Not More Than Three Conductors in Raceway or Cable
(Based on Room Temperature of 30°C., 86°F.)

Size A.W.G. M.C.M.	Rubber Type R, Type RW, Type RU (14–6) / Thermoplastic Type T (14–4/0) Type TW (14–4/0)	Rubber Type RH	Paper / Thermoplastic asbestos Type TA / Var-cam Type V / Asbestos var-cam Type AVB	Asbestos var-cam Type AVA Type AVL	Impregnated asbestos Type AI (14–8) Type AIA	Asbestos Type A (14–8) Type AA
14	15	15	25	30	30	30
12	20	20	30	35	40	40
10	30	30	40	45	50	55
8	40	45	50	60	65	70
6	55	65	70	80	85	95
4	70	85	90	105	115	120
3	80	100	105	120	130	145
2	95	115	120	135	145	165
1	110	130	140	160	170	190
0	125	150	155	190	200	225
00	145	175	185	215	230	250
000	165	200	210	245	265	285
0000	195	230	235	275	310	340
250	215	255	270	315	335	
300	240	285	300	345	380	
350	260	310	325	390	420	
400	280	335	360	420	450	
500	320	380	405	470	500	
600	355	420	455	525	545	
700	385	460	490	560	600	
750	400	475	500	580	620	
800	410	490	515	600	640	
900	435	520	555			
1,000	455	545	585	680	730	
1,250	495	590	645			
1,500	520	625	700	785		
1,750	545	650	735			
2,000	560	665	775	840		

Correction Factor for Room Temperatures over 30°C., 86°F.

°C.	°F.						
40	104	0.82	0.88	0.90	0.94	0.95	
45	113	0.71	0.82	0.85	0.90	0.92	
50	122	0.58	0.75	0.80	0.87	0.89	
55	131	0.41	0.67	0.74	0.83	0.86	
60	140	....	0.58	0.67	0.79	0.83	0.91
70	158	....	0.35	0.52	0.71	0.76	0.87
75	167	....	....	0.43	0.66	0.72	0.86
80	176	....	....	0.30	0.61	0.69	0.84
90	194	....	....	....	0.50	0.61	0.80
100	212	....	....	....	....	0.51	0.77
120	248	....	....	....	....	....	0.69
140	284	....	....	....	....	....	0.59

See notes on page 522.

APPENDIX

TABLE 2.—ALLOWABLE CURRENT-CARRYING CAPACITIES OF CONDUCTORS IN AMPERES

Single Conductor in Free Air
(Based on Room Temperature of 30°C., 86°F.)

Size A.W.G. M.C.M.	Rubber Type R, Type RW, Type RU (14-6); Thermoplastic Type T, Type TW	Rubber Type RH	Thermoplastic asbestos Type TA; Var-cam Type V; Asbestos var-cam Type AVB	Asbestos var-cam Type AVA Type AVL	Impregnated asbestos Type AI (14-8) Type AIA	Asbestos Type A (14-8) Type AA	Slow-burning Type SB; Weatherproof Type WP Type SBW
14	20	20	30	40	40	45	30
12	25	25	40	50	50	55	40
10	40	40	55	65	70	75	55
8	55	65	70	85	90	100	70
6	80	95	100	120	125	135	100
4	105	125	135	160	170	180	130
3	120	145	155	180	195	210	150
2	140	170	180	210	225	240	175
1	165	195	210	245	265	280	205
0	195	230	245	285	305	325	235
00	225	265	285	330	355	370	275
000	260	310	330	385	410	430	320
0000	300	360	385	445	475	510	370
250	340	405	425	495	530	....	410
300	375	445	480	555	590	....	460
350	420	505	530	610	655	....	510
400	455	545	575	665	710	....	555
500	515	620	660	765	815	....	630
600	575	690	740	855	910	....	710
700	630	755	815	940	1,005	....	780
750	655	785	845	980	1,045	....	810
800	680	815	880	1,020	1,085	....	845
900	730	870	940	....	....	....	905
1,000	780	935	1,000	1,165	1,240	....	965
1,250	890	1,065	1,130	....	....	....	....
1,500	980	1,175	1,260	1,450	....	....	1,215
1,750	1,070	1,280	1,370	....	....	....	....
2,000	1,155	1,385	1,470	1,715	....	....	1,405

Correction Factor for Room Temperatures over 30°C., 86°F.

°C.	°F.						
40	104	0.82	0.88	0.90	0.94	0.95	
45	113	0.71	0.82	0.85	0.90	0.92	
50	122	0.58	0.75	0.80	0.87	0.89	
55	131	0.41	0.67	0.74	0.83	0.86	
60	140	....	0.58	0.67	0.79	0.83	0.91
70	158	....	0.35	0.52	0.71	0.76	0.87
75	167	....	....	0.43	0.66	0.72	0.86
80	176	....	....	0.30	0.61	0.69	0.84
90	194	....	....	....	0.50	0.61	0.80
100	212	....	....	....	....	0.51	0.77
120	248	....	....	....	....	....	0.69
140	284	....	....	....	....	....	0.59

See notes on next page.

For explanation of Type Letters, and for recognized size of conductors for the various conductor insulations, see Code Secs. 3102 and 93101. For installation requirements, see Code Sec. 3102, and the various articles of this code.

1. Aluminum Conductors. For aluminum conductors, the allowable current-carrying capacities shall be taken as 84 per cent of those given in the table for the respective sizes of copper conductor with the same kind of insulation.

2. Bare Conductors. If bare conductors are used with insulated conductors, their allowable current-carrying capacity shall be limited to that permitted for the insulated conductor with which they are used.

3. Application of Table. For open wiring on insulators and for concealed knob-and-tube work, the allowable current-carrying capacities of Table 2 shall be used. For all other recognized wiring methods, the allowable current-carrying capacities of Table 1 shall be used, unless otherwise provided in this code.

4. More Than Three Conductors in a Raceway. Table 1 gives the allowable current-carrying capacity for not more than three conductors in a raceway or cable. If the number of conductors in a raceway or cable is from 4 to 6, the allowable current-carrying capacity of each conductor shall be reduced to 80 per cent of the values in Table 1. If the number of conductors in a raceway or cable is from 7 to 9, the allowable current-carrying capacity of each conductor shall be reduced to 70 per cent of the values in Table 1.

5. Neutral Conductor. A neutral conductor which carries only the unbalanced current from other conductors, as in the case of normally balanced circuits of three or more conductors, shall not be counted in determining current-carrying capacities as provided for in the preceding paragraph.

In a 3-wire circuit consisting of two phase wires and the neutral of a 4-wire, 3-phase system, a common conductor carries approximately the same current as the other conductors and is not therefore considered as a neutral conductor.

6. Ultimate Insulation Temperature. In no case shall conductors be associated together in such a way with respect to the kind of circuit, the wiring method employed, or the number of conductors, that the limiting temperature of the conductors will be exceeded.

7. Use of Conductors with Higher Operating Temperatures. If the room temperature is within 10 degrees C of the maximum allowable operating temperature of the insulation, it is desirable to use an insulation with a higher maximum allowable operating temperature; although insulation can be used in a room temperature approaching its maximum allowable operating temperature limit if the current is reduced in accordance with the table of correction factors for different room temperatures.

8. Voltage Drop. The allowable current-carrying capacities in Tables 1 and 2 are based on temperature alone and do not take voltage drop into consideration.

9. Overcurrent Protection. If the standard ratings and settings of overcurrent devices do not correspond with the ratings and settings allowed for conductors, the next higher standard rating and setting may be used, but not exceeding 150 per cent of the allowable carrying capacity of the conductor.

10. Deterioration of Insulation. It should be noted that even the best grades of rubber insulation will deteriorate in time, so eventually will need to be replaced.

TABLE 3.—ALLOWABLE CURRENT-CARRYING CAPACITY OF FLEXIBLE CORD AND FIXTURE WIRE IN AMPERES
(Based on Room Temperature of 30°C., 86°F.)
See Code Sec. 4008 and Table 31

Size A.W.G.	Flexible cord						Fixture wire	
	Rubber and cotton Types CT, CTJ / Rubber and asbestos Types AT, ATJ	Rubber Types PO, C, PD, P, PWP, K, E, EO / Armored Type CA	Rubber Types S, SO, SJ, SJO, SV, POSJ / Thermoplastic Types ST, SJT, SVT, POT	Types AFS, AFSJ, HC, HPD, HSJ	Types AVPO AVPD	Cotton Types CFC*, CFPO*, CFPD* / Asbestos Types AFC*, AFPO*, AFPD*	Rubber Types RF-64, RF-32, FF-64, FF-32	Thermoplastic Types TF, TFF / Cotton Type CF* / Asbestos Type AF*
27†	0.5	...	...	...	...	...	...	...
18	...	5	7	10	17	6	5	6
17	...	..	..	12	...	...	...	...
16	...	7	10	15	22	8	7	8
15	...	..	..	17	...	...	...	...
14	...	15	15	20	28	17	..	17
12	...	20	20	..	36	...	...	...
10	...	25	25	..	47	...	...	...
8	...	35						
6	...	45						
4	...	60						
2	...	80						

* These types are used almost exclusively in fixtures where they are exposed to high temperatures and ampere ratings are assigned accordingly.

† Tinsel cord.

More Than Three Conductors in a Cord. Table 3 gives the allowable current-carrying capacities for not more than three current-carrying conductors in a cord. If the number of current-carrying conductors in a cord is from four to six the allowable current-carrying capacity of each conductor shall be reduced to 80 per cent of the values in the table.

TABLE 4.—NUMBER OF CONDUCTORS IN CONDUIT OR TUBING
Rubber-covered, Types RF-32, R, RH, RW, and RU
Thermoplastic, Types TF, T, and TW
One to Nine Conductors
(For more than nine conductors see Table 9. See Code Secs. 3013, 3466, and 3486)

Size A.W.G. M.C.M.	Number of conductors in one conduit or tubing								
	1	2	3	4	5	6	7	8	9
18	½	½	½	½	½	½	½	¾	¾
16	½	½	½	½	½	½	¾	¾	¾
14	½	½	½	½	¾	¾	1	1	1
12	½	½	½	¾	¾	1	1	1	1¼
10	½	¾	¾	¾	1	1	1	1¼	1¼
8	½	¾	¾	1	1¼	1¼	1¼	1½	1½
6	½	1	1	1¼	1½	1½	2	2	2
4	½	1¼	*1¼	1½	1½	2	2	2	2½
3	¾	1¼	1¼	1½	2	2	2	2½	2½
2	¾	1¼	1¼	2	2	2	2½	2½	2½
1	¾	1½	1½	2	2½	2½	2½	3	3
0	1	1½	2	2	2½	2½	3	3	3
00	1	2	2	2½	2½	3	3	3	3½
000	1	2	2	2½	3	3	3	3½	3½
0000	1¼	2	2½	3	3	3	3½	3½	4
250,000	1¼	2½	2½	3	3	3½	4	4	4½
300,000	1¼	2½	2½	3	3½	4	4	4½	4½
350,000	1¼	3	3	3½	3½	4	4½	4½	5
400,000	1½	3	3	3½	4	4	4½	5	5
500,000	1½	3	3	3½	4	4½	5	5	6
600,000	2	3½	3½	4	4½	5	6	6	6
700,000	2	3½	3½	4½	5	5	6	6	
750,000	2	3½	3½	4½	5	6	6	6	
800,000	2	3½	4	4½	5	6	6		
900,000	2	4	4	5	6	6	6		
1,000,000	2	4	4	5	6	6			
1,250,000	2½	4½	4½	6	6				
1,500,000	3	5	5	6					
1,750,000	3	5	6	6					
2,000,000	3	6	6						

See Note 4 to Tables 1 and 2, page 522.
* Where a service run of conduit or electrical metallic tubing does not exceed 50 feet in length and does not contain more than the equivalent of two quarter bends from end to end two No. 4 insulated and one No. 4 bare conductors may be installed in 1-inch conduit or tubing.

APPENDIX

Tables 4 to 11. Tables 4 to 11 apply only to complete conduit systems, and do not apply to short sections of conduit used for the protection of exposed wiring from mechanical injury.

TABLE 5.—NUMBER OF CONDUCTORS IN CONDUIT OR TUBING
Lead-covered Types RL and RHL, 600 Volts
(See Code Secs. 3466 and 3486)

Size A.W.G. M.C.M.	Number of conductors in one conduit or tubing											
	Single-conductor cable				2-conductor cable				3-conductor cable			
	1	2	3	4	1	2	3	4	1	2	3	4
14	½	¾	¾	1	¾	1	1	1¼	¾	1¼	1½	1½
12	½	¾	¾	1	¾	1	1¼	1¼	1	1¼	1½	2
10	½	¾	1	1	¾	1¼	1¼	1½	1	1½	2	2
8	½	1	1¼	1½	1	1¼	1½	2	1	2	2	2½
6	¾	1¼	1½	1½	1¼	1½	2	2½	1¼	2½	3	3
4	¾	1¼	1½	1½	1¼	2	2½	2½	1½	3	3	3½
3	¾	1¼	1½	2	1¼	2	2½	3	1½	3	3	3½
2	1	1¼	1½	2	1¼	2	2½	3	1½	3	3½	4
1	1	1½	2	2	1½	2½	3	3½	2	3½	4	4½
0	1	2	2	2½	2	2½	3	3½	2	4	4½	5
00	1	2	2	2½	2	3	3½	4	2½	4	4½	5
000	1¼	2	2½	2½	2	3	3½	4	2½	4½	4½	6
0000	1¼	2½	2½	3	2½	3	3½	4½	3	5	6	6
250,000	1¼	2½	3	3	...	...	...	...	3	6	6	
300,000	1½	3	3	3½	...	...	...	...	3½	6	6	
350,000	1½	3	3	3½	...	...	...	...	3½	6	6	
400,000	1½	3	3	3½	...	...	...	...	3½	6	6	
500,000	1½	3	3½	4	...	...	...	...	4	6		
600,000	2	3½	4	4½								
700,000	2	4	4	5								
750,000	2	4	4	5								
800,000	2	4	4½	5								
900,000	2½	4	4½	5								
1,000,000	2½	4½	4½	6								
1,250,000	3	5	5	6								
1,500,000	3	5	6	6								
1,750,000	3	6	6									
2,000,000	3½	6	6									

The above sizes apply to straight runs or with nominal offsets equivalent to not more than two quarter-bends.

See Code Sec. 3470 for bends in conduit.

Tables 6, 7, 8. The 1947 Code does not have tables numbered 6, 7, or 8.

TABLE 9.—NUMBER OF CONDUCTORS IN CONDUIT OR TUBING
More Than Nine Conductors
Rubber-covered Types RF-32, R, RH, RW, RU,
Thermoplastic Types TF, T, and TW
When Specially Permitted by This Code*
(See Code Sec. 3012)

Size A.W.G.	Maximum number of conductors in conduit or tubing						
	¾ inch	1 inch	1¼ inch	1½ inch	2 inch	2½ inch	3 inch
18	12	20	35	49	80	115	176
16	10	17	30	41	68	97	150
14	..	10	18	25	40	59	90
12	..	..	15	21	35	50	77
10	..	..	13	17	29	41	64
8	..	..	..	10	17	25	38
6	..	..	..	..	..	15	23

* More than nine conductors are permitted in a single conduit for conductors between a motor and its controller; stage pocket and border circuits, Code Sec. 5212; sign flashers, Code Sec. 6021-d; elevator control conductors, Code Sec. 6214.

Table 10. The 1947 Code does not have a Table 10.

APPENDIX

Table 11.—Combination of Conductors
(See Code Secs. 3466 and 3486)

For groups or combinations of conductors not included in the Tables 4 to 9, it is recommended that the conduit or tubing be of such size that the sum of the cross-sectional areas of the individual conductors will not be more than the percentage of the interior cross-sectional area of the conduct or tubing than as shown in the following table:

Per Cent Area of Conduit or Tubing

	Number of conductors				
	1	2	3	4	Over 4
Conductors (not lead-covered)..............	53	31	43	40	40
Lead-covered conductors..................	55	30	40	38	35
For rewiring existing raceways for increased load where it is impracticable to increase the size of the raceway due to structural conditions............................	60	40	50	50	50

For carrying capacity of more than three conductors in a conduit or tubing, see Tables 1 and 2, Note 4.

See Note to Table 13 for size of conduit or tubing for combinations of conductors not included in Table 4.

See Tables 12 to 19 for dimensions of conductors, conduit and tubing.

Tables 12 to 17. Tables 12 to 17 give the nominal size of conductors and conduit or tubing recommended for use in computing size of conduit or tubing for various combinations of conductors. The dimensions represent average conditions only, and while variations will be found in dimensions of conductors and conduits of different manufacture, these variations will not affect the computation.

TABLE 12.—DIMENSIONS AND PER CENT AREA OF CONDUIT AND TUBING
Areas of Conduit or Tubing for the Combinations of Wires Permitted by Table 11

Trade size	Internal diameter, inches	Total 100 per cent	Area, square inches									
			Not lead-covered				Lead-covered				
			1 cond. 53 per cent	2 cond. 31 per cent	3 cond. 43 per cent	4 cond. and over 40 per cent	1 cond. 55 per cent	2 cond. 30 per cent	3 cond. 40 per cent	4 cond. 38 per cent	Over 4 cond. 35 per cent
½	0.622	0.30	0.16	0.09	0.13	0.12	0.17	0.09	0.12	0.11	0.11
¾	0.824	0.53	0.28	0.16	0.23	0.21	0.29	0.16	0.21	0.20	0.19
1	1.049	0.86	0.46	0.27	0.37	0.34	0.47	0.26	0.34	0.33	0.30
1¼	1.380	1.50	0.80	0.47	0.65	0.60	0.83	0.45	0.60	0.57	0.53
1½	1.610	2.04	1.08	0.63	0.88	0.82	1.12	0.61	0.82	0.78	0.71
2	2.067	3.36	1.78	1.04	1.44	1.34	1.85	1.01	1.34	1.28	1.18
2½	2.469	4.79	2.54	1.48	2.06	1.92	2.63	1.44	1.92	1.82	1.68
3	3.068	7.38	3.91	2.29	3.17	2.95	4.06	2.21	2.95	2.80	2.58
3½	3.548	9.90	5.25	3.07	4.26	3.96	5.44	2.97	3.96	3.76	3.47
4	4.026	12.72	6.74	3.94	5.47	5.09	7.00	3.82	5.09	4.83	4.45
4½	4.506	15.95	8.45	4.94	6.86	6.38	8.77	4.78	6.38	6.06	5.57
5	5.047	20.00	10.60	6.20	8.60	8.00	11.00	6.00	8.00	7.60	7.00
6	6.065	28.89	15.31	8.96	12.42	11.56	15.89	8.67	11.56	10.98	10.11

TABLE 13.—DIMENSIONS OF RUBBER-COVERED AND THERMOPLASTIC COVERED CONDUCTORS

Size A.W.G. M.C.M.	Types RF-32, R, RH, RW		Types TF, T, TW, RU†	
	Approx. diam., inches	Approx. area, square inches	Approx. diam., inches	Approx. area, square inches
18	0.146	0.0167	0.106	0.0088
16	0.158	0.0196	0.118	0.0109
14	³⁄₆₄ in. 0.171	0.2030	0.131	0.0135
14	³⁄₆₄ in. 0.204*	0.0327*		
12	³⁄₆₄ in. 0.188	0.0278	0.148	0.0172
12	³⁄₆₄ in. 0.221*	0.0384*		
10	0.242	0.0460	0.168	0.0224
8	0.311	0.0760	0.228	0.0408
6	0.397	0.1238	0.323	0.0819
4	0.452	0.1605	0.372	0.1087
3	0.481	0.1817	0.401	0.1263
2	0.513	0.2067	0.433	0.1473
1	0.588	0.2715	0.508	0.2027
0	0.629	0.3107	0.549	0.2367
00	0.675	0.3578	0.595	0.2781
000	0.727	0.4151	0.647	0.3288
0000	0.785	0.4840	0.705	0.3904
250,000	0.868	0.5917	0.788	0.4877
300,000	0.933	0.6837	0.843	0.5581
350,000	0.985	0.7620	0.895	0.6291
400,000	1.032	0.8365	0.942	0.6969
500,000	1.119	0.9834	1.029	0.8316
600,000	1.233	1.1940	1.143	1.0261
700,000	1.304	1.3355	1.214	1.1575
750,000	1.339	1.4082	1.249	1.2252
800,000	1.372	1.4784	1.282	1.2908
900,000	1.435	1.6173	1.345	1.4208
1,000,000	1.494	1.7531	1.404	1.5482
1,250,000	1.676	2.2062	1.577	1.9532
1,500,000	1.801	2.5475	1.702	2.2748
1,750,000	1.916	2.8895	1.817	2.5930
2,000,000	2.021	3.2079	1.922	2.9013

* The dimensions for Type RW conductors; also these dimensions to be used for new work in computing the size of conduit or tubing for combinations of conductors not shown in Table 4.

† Type RU conductors recognized in sizes No. 14 to No. 6.

No. 18 to No. 8, solid; No. 6 and larger, stranded.

Tables 14 and 15. The 1947 Code does not have tables numbered 14 or 15.

TABLE 16.—DIMENSIONS OF LEAD-COVERED CONDUCTORS
Types RL and RHL

Size A.W.G. M.C.M.	Single conductor		Two conductor		Three conductor	
	Diam., inches	Area, square inches	Diam., inches	Area, square inches	Diam., inches	Area, square inches
14	0.28	0.062	0.28 × 0.47	0.115	0.59	0.273
12	0.29	0.066	0.31 × 0.54	0.146	0.62	0.301
10	0.35	0.096	0.35 × 0.59	0.180	0.68	0.363
8	0.41	0.132	0.41 × 0.71	0.255	0.82	0.528
6	0.49	0.188	0.49 × 0.86	0.369	0.97	0.738
4	0.55	0.237	0.54 × 0.96	0.457	1.08	0.916
2	0.60	0.283	0.61 × 1.08	0.578	1.21	1.146
1	0.67	0.352	0.70 × 1.23	0.756	1.38	1.49
0	0.71	0.396	0.74 × 1.32	0.859	1.47	1.70
00	0.76	0.454	0.79 × 1.41	0.980	1.57	1.94
000	0.81	0.515	0.84 × 1.52	1.123	1.69	2.24
0000	0.87	0.593	0.90 × 1.64	1.302	1.85	2.68
250,000	0.98	0.754	....	.....	2.02	3.20
300,000	1.04	0.85	....	.....	2.15	3.62
350,000	1.10	0.95	....	.....	2.26	4.02
400,000	1.14	1.02	....	.....	2.40	4.52
500,000	1.23	1.18	....	.....	2.59	5.28

NOTE. No. 14 to No. 8, solid conductors; No. 6 and larger, stranded conductors. Data for $3/64$-in. insulation not yet computed.

TABLE 17.—DIMENSIONS OF ASBESTOS-VARNISHED-CAMBRIC INSULATED CONDUCTORS
Types AVA, AVB, and AVL

Size A.W.G. M.C.M.	Type AVA		Type AVB		Type AVL	
	Approx. diam., inches	Approx. area, square inches	Approx. diam., inches	Approx. area, square inches	Approx. diam., inches	Approx. area, square inches
14	0.245	0.047	0.205	0.033	0.320	0.080
12	0.265	0.055	0.225	0.040	0.340	0.091
10	0.285	0.064	0.245	0.047	0.360	0.102
8	0.310	0.075	0.270	0.057	0.390	0.119
6	0.395	0.122	0.345	0.094	0.430	0.145
4	0.445	0.155	0.395	0.123	0.480	0.181
2	0.505	0.200	0.460	0.166	0.570	0.255
1	0.585	0.268	0.540	0.229	0.620	0.300
0	0.625	0.307	0.580	0.264	0.660	0.341
00	0.670	0.353	0.625	0.307	0.705	0.390
000	0.720	0.406	0.675	0.358	0.755	0.447
0000	0.780	0.478	0.735	0.425	0.815	0.521
250	0.885	0.616	0.855	0.572	0.955	0.715
300	0.940	0.692	0.910	0.649	1.010	0.800
350	0.995	0.778	0.965	0.731	1.060	0.885
400	1.040	0.850	1.010	0.800	1.105	0.960
500	1.125	0.995	1.095	0.945	1.190	1.118
550	1.165	1.065	1.135	1.01	1.265	1.26
600	1.205	1.140	1.175	1.09	1.305	1.34
650	1.240	1.21	1.210	1.15	1.340	1.41
700	1.275	1.28	1.245	1.22	1.375	1.49
750	1.310	1.35	1.280	1.29	1.410	1.57
800	1.345	1.42	1.315	1.36	1.440	1.63
850	1.375	1.49	1.345	1.43	1.470	1.70
900	1.405	1.55	1.375	1.49	1.505	1.78
950	1.435	1.62	1.405	1.55	1.535	1.85
1,000	1.465	1.69	1.435	1.62	1.565	1.93

NOTE. No. 14 to No. 8, solid, No. 6 and larger, stranded; except AVL where all sizes are stranded.
For Type V, see note on page 533.

TABLE 18.—Properties of Copper Conductors

Size A.W.G.	Area, circular mils	Concentric lay stranded conductors		Bare conductors		D. C. resistance, ohms per 1,000 feet at 25°C., 77°F.	
		No. wires	Diam. each wire, inches	Diam., inches	Area,* square inches	Bare cond.	Tin'd cond.
18	1,624	Solid	0.0403	0.0403	0.0013	6.510	6.77
16	2,583	Solid	0.0508	0.0508	0.0020	4.094	4.25
14	4,107	Solid	0.0641	0.0641	0.0032	2.575	2.68
12	6,530	Solid	0.0808	0.0808	0.0051	1.619	1.69
10	10,380	Solid	0.1019	0.1019	0.0081	1.018	1.06
8	16,510	Solid	0.1285	0.1285	0.0130	0.641	0.660
6	26,250	7	0.0612	0.184	0.027	0.410	0.426
4	41,740	7	0.0772	0.232	0.042	0.259	0.269
3	52,640	7	0.0867	0.260	0.053	0.205	0.213
2	66,370	7	0.0974	0.292	0.067	0.162	0.169
1	83,690	19	0.0664	0.332	0.087	0.129	0.134
0	105,500	19	0.0745	0.373	0.109	0.102	0.106
00	133,100	19	0.0837	0.418	0.137	0.0811	0.0844
000	167,800	19	0.0940	0.470	0.173	0.0642	0.0668
0000	211,600	19	0.1055	0.528	0.219	0.0509	0.0524
	250,000	37	0.0822	0.575	0.260	0.0431	0.0444
	300,000	37	0.0900	0.630	0.312	0.0360	0.0371
	350,000	37	0.0973	0.681	0.364	0.0308	0.0318
	400,000	37	0.1040	0.728	0.416	0.0270	0.0278
	500,000	37	0.1162	0.814	0.520	0.0216	0.0225
	600,000	61	0.0992	0.893	0.626	0.0180	0.0185
	700,000	61	0.1071	0.964	0.730	0.0154	0.0159
	750,000	61	0.1109	0.998	0.782	0.0144	0.0148
	800,000	61	0.1145	1.031	0.835	0.0135	0.0139
	900,000	61	0.1215	1.093	0.938	0.0120	0.0124
	1,000,000	61	0.1280	1.152	1.042	0.0108	0.0111
	1,250,000	91	0.1172	1.289	1.305	0.00864	0.00890
	1,500,000	91	0.1284	1.412	1.566	0.00719	0.00740
	1,750,000	127	0.1174	1.526	1.829	0.00617	0.00636
	2,000,000	127	0.1255	1.631	2.089	0.00539	0.00555

* Area given is that of a circle having a diameter equal to the over-all diameter of a stranded conductor.

The values given in the table are those given in Circular 31 of the National Bureau of Standards except that those shown in the last column are those given in Specification B33 of the American Society for Testing Materials.

The resistance values given in the last two columns are applicable only to direct current.

TABLE 19.—DIMENSIONS OF CONDUIT OR TUBING

Size	Internal diam., inches	Area, square inches	Size	Internal diam., inches	Area, square inches
½	0.622	0.30	3	3.068	7.38
¾	0.824	0.53	3½	3.548	9.90
1	1.049	0.86	4	4.026	12.72
1¼	1.380	1.50	4½	4.506	15.95
1½	1.610	2.04	5	5.047	20.00
2	2.067	3.36	6	6.065	28.89
2½	2.469	4.79			

Note to Table 17, Page 531

The insulation thickness for varnished-cambric conductors, Type V, is the same as for rubber-covered conductors, Type R, except for Nos. 14 and 12 which have $3/64$-inch insulation for varnished-cambric and $2/64$-inch insulation for rubber-covered conductors and for No. 8 which has $3/64$-inch insulation for varnished-cambric, and $4/64$-inch insulation for rubber-covered conductors. See table in section 93101. Tables 4 and 5 may, therefore, be used for the number of varnished-cambric insulated conductors in a conduit or tubing.

TABLE 20.—CONDUCTOR SIZES AND OVERCURRENT PROTECTION FOR MOTORS. See Tables 26 and 27.

These values are in accordance with Code Secs. 4309, 4312, 4322, 4324, 4342, and 4349, except as follows: The current values in column 1 are to be taken from Tables 21 to 24, including footnotes, but the values shown for running protection in columns 5 and 6 must be modified if nameplate full-load current values are different, as provided in Code Sec. 4309. Conductor sizes shown in columns 2 and 3 may be smaller for certain motors as provided in Code Sec. 4312. The current values shown in columns 5 and 6 must be reduced by 8 per cent for all motors other than open-type motors marked to have a temperature rise not over 40°C. as required by Code Sec. 4322. For certain exceptions to the values in columns 7, 8, 9, and 10, see Code Secs. 4342 and 4349. See Code Sec. 4343 for values to be used for several motors on one branch circuit.

Full-load current rating of motor, amperes	Minimum size conductor in raceways For conductors in air or for other insulations see Tables 1 and 2 A.W.G. and M.C.M.		For running protection of motors*		Maximum allowable rating or setting of branch circuit protective devices			
	Type R Type T	Type RH	Maximum rating of nonadjustable protective devices, amperes	Maximum setting of adjustable protective device, amperes	**With Code Letters** Single-phase and squirrel cage and synchronous. Full voltage, resistor and reactor starting, Code letters F to R inc. **Without Code Letters** Same as above	**With Code Letters** Single-phase and squirrel cage and synchronous. Full voltage, resistor or reactor starting, Code letters B to E inc. Autotransformer starting, Code letters F to R inc. **Without Code Letters** Squirrel cage and synchronous, autotransformer starting, high reactance squirrel cage.† Both not more than 30 amperes	**With Code Letters** Squirrel cage and synchronous autotransformer starting, Code letters B to E inc. **Without Code Letters** Squirrel cage and synchronous, autotransformer starting, high reactance squirrel cage.† Both more than 30 amperes	**With Code Letters** All motors. Code letter A. **Without Code Letters** D.C. and wound-rotor motors
1	2	3	5	6	7	8	9	10
1‡	14	14	3	1.25	15	15	15	15
2‡‡	14	14	3	2.50	15	15	15	15
3‡‡	14	14	4	3.75	15	15	15	15
4‡‡	14	14	6	5.00	15	15	15	15
5‡‡	14	14	8	6.25	15	15	15	15
6‡‡	14	14	8	7.50	20	15	15	15
7	14	14	10	8.75	25	20	15	15
8	14	14	10	10.00	25	20	20	15
9	14	14	12	11.25	30	25	20	15
10	14	14	15	12.50	30	25	20	15
11	14	14	15	13.75	35	30	25	20
12	14	14	15	15.00	40	30	25	20

APPENDIX

13	12	12	20	16.25	40	35	30	20
14	12	12	20	17.50	45	35	30	25
15	12	12	20	18.75	45	40	30	25
16	12	12	20	20.00	50	40	35	25
17	10	10	25	21.25	60	45	35	30
18	10	10	25	22.50	60	45	40	30
19	10	10	25	23.75	60	50	40	30
20	10	10	25	25.00	60	50	40	30
22	10	10	30	27.50	70	60	45	35
24	10	10	30	30.00	80	60	50	40
26	8	10	35	32.50	80	60	60	40
28	8	10	35	35.00	90	70	60	45
30	8	8	40	37.50	90	70	60	45
32	8	8	40	40.00	100	80	70	50
34	6	8	45	42.50	110	90	70	60
36	6	8	45	45.00	110	90	80	60
38	6	6	50	47.50	125	100	80	60
40	6	6	50	50.00	125	100	80	60
42	6	6	50	52.50	125	110	90	70
44	6	6	60	55.00	125	110	90	70
46	4	6	60	57.50	150	125	100	70
48	4	6	60	60.00	150	125	100	80
50	4	6	60	62.50	150	125	100	80
52	4	6	70	65.00	175	150	110	80
54	4	4	70	67.50	175	150	110	90
56	4	4	70	70.00	175	150	120	90
58	3	4	70	72.50	175	150	120	90
60	3	4	80	75.00	200	150	120	90
62	3	4	80	77.50	200	175	125	100
64	3	4	80	80.00	200	175	150	100
66	2	4	80	82.50	200	175	150	100
68	2	4	90	85.00	225	175	150	110
70	2	3	90	87.50	225	175	150	110

* For running protection of motors see Code Sec. 4322.
† High-reactance squirrel-cage motors are those designed to limit the starting current by means of deep-slot secondaries or double-wound secondaries and are generally started on full voltage.
‡ For the grouping of small motors under the protection of a single set of fuses, see Code Sec. 4343.
§ For running protection of motors of 1 horsepower or less, see Code Sec. 4322.

TABLE 20.—CONDUCTOR SIZES AND OVERCURRENT PROTECTION FOR MOTORS.—(Continued)

Full-load current rating of motor, amperes	Minimum size conductor in raceways For conductors in air or for other insulations see Tables 1 and 2 A.W.G. and M.C.M.			For running protection of motors*		Maximum allowable rating or setting of branch circuit protective devices		
	Type R, Type T		Type RH	Maximum rating of nonadjustable protective devices, amperes	Maximum setting of adjustable protective device, amperes	**With Code Letters** Single-phase and squirrel cage and synchronous. Full voltage, resistor and reactor starting, Code letters F to R inc. **Without Code Letters** Same as above	**With Code Letters** Single-phase and squirrel cage and synchronous. Full voltage, resistor or reactor starting, Code letters B to E inc. Autotransformer starting, Code letters F to R inc. **Without Code Letters** Squirrel cage and synchronous, autotransformer starting, high reactance squirrel cage.† Both not more than 30 amperes	**With Code Letters** Squirrel cage and synchronous autotransformer starting, Code letters B to E inc. **Without Code Letters** Squirrel cage and synchronous, autotransformer starting, high reactance squirrel cage.† Both more than 30 amperes	**With Code Letters** All motors. Code letter A. **Without Code Letters** D.C. and wound-rotor motors
1	2		3	5	6	7	8	9	10
72	2		3	90	90.00	225	200	150	110
74	2		3	90	92.50	225	200	150	125
76	2		3	100	95.00	250	200	175	125
78	1		3	100	97.50	250	200	175	125
80	1		3	100	100.00	250	200	175	125
82	1		2	110	102.50	250	225	175	125
84	1		2	110	105.00	250	225	175	150
86	1		2	110	107.50	300	225	175	150
88	1		2	110	110.00	300	225	200	150
90	0		2	110	112.50	300	225	200	150
92	0		2	125	115.00	300	250	200	150
94	0		1	125	117.50	300	250	200	150
96	0		1	125	120.00	300	250	200	150
98	0		1	125	122.50	300	250	200	150
100	0		1	125	125.00	300	250	200	150
105	00		1	150	131.5	350	300	225	175

APPENDIX

110	00	0	150	137.5	350	300	225	175
115	00	0	150	144.0	350	300	250	175
120	000	0	150	150.0	400	300	250	200
125	000	00	175	156.5	400	350	250	200
130	000	00	175	162.5	400	350	300	200
135	0000	00	175	169.0	450	350	300	225
140	0000	00	175	175.0	450	350	300	225
145	0000	000	200	181.5	450	400	300	225
150	0000	000	200	187.5	450	400	300	225
155	0000	000	200	194.0	500	400	350	250
160	250	000	200	200.0	500	400	350	250
165	250	000	225	206.0	500	450	350	250
170	250	0000	225	213.0	500	450	350	300
175	300	0000	225	219.0	600	450	350	300
180	300	0000	250	225.0	600	450	400	300
185	300	0000	250	231.0	600	500	400	300
190	300	250	250	238.0	600	500	400	300
195	350	250	250	244.0	600	500	400	300
200	350	250	250	250.0		500	400	350
210	400	300	300	263.0		600	450	350
220	400	300	300	275.0		600	450	350
230	500	300	300	288.0			500	350
240	500	350	300	300.0			500	400
250	500	350	300	313.0			500	400
260	600	400	350	325.0			600	400
270	600	400	350	338.0			600	450
280	600	500	350	350.0			600	450
290	700	500	350	363.0			600	450
300	700	500	400	375.0			600	450
320	750	600	400	400.0				500
340	900	600	450	425.0				450
360	1000	700	450	450.0				450
380	1250	750	450	475.0				450
400	1500	900	500	500.0				500
420	1750	1000	600	525.0				600
440	2000	1250	600	550.0				600
460		1250	600	575.0				600
480		1500	600	600.0				600
500		1500		625.0				

TABLE 21.—FULL-LOAD CURRENT*
Direct-current Motors

Horsepower	115 volts	230 volts	550 volts
½	4.6	2.3	
¾	6.6	3.3	1.4
1	8.6	4.3	1.8
1½	12.6	6.3	2.6
2	16.4	8.2	3.4
3	24	12	5.0
5	40	20	8.3
7½	58	29	12.0
10	76	38	16.0
15	112	56	23.0
20	148	74	31
25	184	92	38
30	220	110	46
40	292	146	61
50	360	180	75
60	430	215	90
75	536	268	111
100	. . . . .	355	148
125	. . . . .	443	148
150	. . . . .	534	220
200	. . . . .	712	295

* These values for full-load current are average for all speeds.

APPENDIX

Table 22.—Full-load Current*
Single-phase Alternating-current Motors

Horsepower	115 volts	230 volts	440 volts
1/6	3.2	1.6	
1/4	4.6	2.3	
1/2	7.4	3.7	
3/4	10.2	5.1	
1	13.0	6.5	
1½	18.4	9.2	
2	24	12	
3	34	17	
5	56	28	
7½	80	40	21
10	100	50	26

For full-load currents of 208 and 200-volt motors, increase corresponding 230-volt motor full-load current by 10 and 15 per cent respectively.

* These values of full-load current are for motors running at speeds usual for belted motors and motors with normal torque characteristics. Motors built for especially low speeds or high torques may require more running current, in which case the nameplate current rating should be used.

TABLE 23.—FULL-LOAD CURRENT*
Two-phase Alternating-current Motors (4-wire)

Horse-power	Induction type squirrel-cage and wound-rotor, amperes					Synchronous type unity power factor,† amperes			
	110 volts	220 volts	440 volts	550 volts	2,300 volts	220 volts	440 volts	550 volts	2,300 volts
½	4	2	1	.8					
¾	4.8	2.4	1.2	1.0					
1	6.4	3.2	1.6	1.3					
1½	8.8	4.4	2.2	1.8					
2	11.2	5.6	2.8	2.2					
3	....	8	4	3.2					
5	....	13	7	6					
7½	....	19	9	8					
10	....	24	12	10					
15	....	34	17	14					
20	....	45	23	18					
25	....	55	28	22	6	47	24	19	4.7
30	....	67	34	27	7.5	56	29	23	5.7
40	....	88	44	35	9	75	37	31	7
50	....	108	54	43	11	94	47	38	9
60	....	129	65	52	13	111	56	44	11
75	....	158	79	63	16	140	70	57	13
100	....	212	106	85	21	182	93	74	17
125	....	268	134	108	26	228	114	93	22
150	....	311	155	124	31	...	137	110	26
200	....	415	208	166	41	...	182	145	35

* These values of full-load current are for motors running at speeds usual for belted motors and motors with normal torque characteristics. Motors built for especially low speeds or high torques may require more running current, in which case the nameplate current ratings should be used. Current in common conductor of 2-phase, 3-wire system will be 1.41 times value given.

† For 90 and 80 per cent P. F. the above figures should be multiplied by 1.1 and 1.25, respectively.

TABLE 24.—FULL-LOAD CURRENT*
Three-phase Alternating-current Motors

Horse-power	Induction type squirrel-cage and wound-rotor, amperes					Synchronous type unity power factor,† amperes			
	110 volts	220 volts	440 volts	550 volts	2,300 volts	220 volts	440 volts	550 volts	2,300 volts
½	4	2	1	.8					
¾	5.6	2.8	1.4	1.1					
1	7	3.5	1.8	1.4					
1½	10	5	2.5	2.0					
2	13	6.5	3.3	2.6					
3	....	9	4.5	4					
5	....	15	7.5	6					
7½	....	22	11	9					
10	....	27	14	11					
15	....	40	20	16					
20	....	52	26	21					
25	....	64	32	26	7	54	27	22	5.4
30	....	78	39	31	8.5	65	33	26	6.5
40	....	104	52	41	10.5	86	43	35	8
50	....	125	63	50	13	108	54	44	10
60	....	150	75	60	16	128	64	51	12
75	....	185	93	74	19	161	81	65	15
100	....	246	123	98	25	211	106	85	20
125	....	310	155	124	31	264	132	106	25
150	....	360	180	144	37	...	158	127	30
200	....	480	240	192	49	...	210	168	40

For full-load currents of 208 and 200 volt motors, increase the corresponding 220-volt motor full-load current by 6 and 10 per cent, respectively.

* These values of full-load current are for motors running at speeds usual for belted motors and motors with normal torque characteristics. Motors built for especially low speeds or high torques may require more running current, in which case the nameplate current rating should be used.

† For 90 and 80 per cent P. F. the above figures should be multiplied by 1.1 and 1.25, respectively.

Table 25. The 1947 Code does not have a Table 25.

Table 26.—Maximum Rating or Setting of Motor-branch-circuit Protective Devices for Motors Marked with a Code Letter Indicating Locked Rotor Kva.

	Per cent of full-load current		
Type of motor	Fuse rating (see also Table 20, columns 7, 8, 9, 10)	Circuit-breaker setting	
		Instantaneous type	Time limit type
All A.C. single-phase and polyphase squirrel-cage and synchronous motors with full-voltage, resistor or reactor starting:			
Code Letter A.............	150	...	150
Code Letter B to E........	250	...	200
Code Letter F to R........	300	...	250
All A.C. squirrel-cage and synchronous motors with autotransformer starting:			
Code Letter A.............	150	...	150
Code Letter B to E........	200	...	200
Code Letter F to R........	250	...	200

For certain exceptions to the values specified see Code Secs. 4324, 4342 and 4349. The values given in the last column also cover the ratings of non-adjustable, time-limit types of circuit-breakers which may also be modified as in Code Sec. 4342.

Synchronous motors of the low-torque, low-speed type (usually 450 r.p.m. or lower), such as are used to drive reciprocating compressors, pumps, etc., which start up unloaded, do not require a fuse rating or circuit-breaker setting in excess of 200 per cent of full-load current.

For motors not marked with a Code letter, see Table 27.

TABLE 27.—MAXIMUM RATING OR SETTING OF MOTOR-BRANCH-CIRCUIT PROTECTIVE DEVICES FOR MOTORS NOT MARKED WITH A CODE LETTER INDICATING LOCKED ROTOR KVA.

	Per cent of full-load current		
Type of motor	Fuse rating (see also Table 20, columns 7, 8, 9, 10)	Circuit-breaker setting	
		Instantaneous type	Time-limit type
Single-phase, all types..........	300	...	250
Squirrel-cage and synchronous (full-voltage, resistor and reactor starting)................	300	...	250
Squirrel-cage and synchronous (autotransformer starting)			
Not more than 30 amp.......	250	...	200
More than 30 amp...........	200	...	200
High-reactance squirrel-cage			
Not more than 30 amp.......	250	...	250
More than 30 amp...........	200	...	200
Wound-rotor.................	150	...	150
Direct-current			
Not more than 50 hp.........	150	250	150
More than 50 hp.............	150	175	150

For certain exceptions to the values specified see Code Secs. 4324, 4342 and 4349. The values given in the last column also cover the ratings of non-adjustable, time-limit types of circuit-breakers which may also be modified as in section 4342.

Synchronous motors of the low-torque low-speed type (usually 450 r.p.m. or lower) such as are used to drive reciprocating compressors, pumps, etc., which start up unloaded, do not require a fuse rating or circuit-breaker setting in excess of 200 per cent of full-load current.

For motors marked with a Code letter, see Table 26.

TABLE 28.—NUMBER OF OVERCURRENT UNITS, SUCH AS TRIP COILS OR RELAYS, FOR PROTECTION OF CIRCUITS
(See Diagrams 1 to 19)
(See Code Sec. 2405 for the overcurrent protection of conductors in general, Code Sec. 2371 for services and Code Sec. 4327 for motors.)

Systems	Number and Location of Overcurrent Units*
2-wire, single-phase A.C. or D.C., ungrounded	Two (one in each conductor. Fig. 1)
2-wire, single-phase A.C. or D.C., one wire grounded	One (in ungrounded conductor. Fig. 2)
2-wire, single-phase A.C. or D.C., mid-point grounded	Two (one in each conductor. Fig. 3)
2-wire, single-phase A.C. derived from 3-phase, with ungrounded neutral	Two (one in each conductor. Fig. 4)
2-wire, single-phase derived from 3-phase, grounded neutral system by using outside wires of 3-phase circuit	Two (one in each conductor. Fig. 5)
3-wire, single-phase A.C. or D.C., ungrounded neutral	Three (one in each conductor. Fig. 6)
3-wire, single-phase A.C., or D.C., grounded neutral	Two (one in each conductor except neutral conductor. Fig. 7)
3-wire, 2-phase, A.C., common wire ungrounded	Three (one in each conductor. Fig. 8)
3-wire, 2-phase, A.C., common wire grounded	Two (one in each conductor except common conductor. Fig. 9)
4-wire, 2-phase, ungrounded, phases separate	Four (one in each conductor. Fig. 10)
4-wire, 2-phase, grounded neutral, or 5-wire, 2-phase, grounded neutral	Four (one in each conductor except neutral conductor. Figs. 11 and 12)
3-wire, 3-phase, ungrounded	Three (one in each conductor. Fig. 13†)

* 1. An overcurrent unit may consist of a series overcurrent tripping device or the combination of a current transformer and a secondary overcurrent tripping device. Either two or three secondary overcurrent tripping devices may be used with three current transformers on a 3-phase system similar to those shown in Figs. 15 and 18.

† 2. When three current transformers are used instead of three series overcurrent tripping devices shown in Figs. 13, 15, 17, and 18, the secondary tripping devices may consist of three secondary overcurrent tripping devices or two secondary overcurrent tripping devices with a residual current tripping device of a lower range. See Fig. 16.

3. Where standard devices are not available with three or four overcurrent units as required in the table, it is permissible to substitute two overcurrent units and one fuse where three overcurrent units are called for, two overcurrent units and two fuses where four overcurrent units are called for. The fuse or fuses are to be placed in the conductors not containing an overcurrent unit. This practice, however, of substituting fuses for overcurrent units is to be discouraged for obvious reasons.

APPENDIX 545

3-wire, 3-phase, one wire grounded	Two (one in each ungrounded conductor. Fig. 14)
3-wire, 3-phase, grounded neutral	Three (one in each conductor. Fig. 15†)
3-wire, 3-phase, mid-point of one phase grounded	Three (one in each conductor. Fig. 17†)
4-wire, 3-phase, grounded neutral	Three (one in each ungrounded conductor. Fig. 18†)
4-wire, 3-phase, ungrounded neutral	Four (one in each conductor. Fig. 19)

DIAGRAMS

Diagrams 1 to 19 showing Number of Overcurrent Units such as Trip Coils or Relays for the Protection of Circuits as required by Table 28.

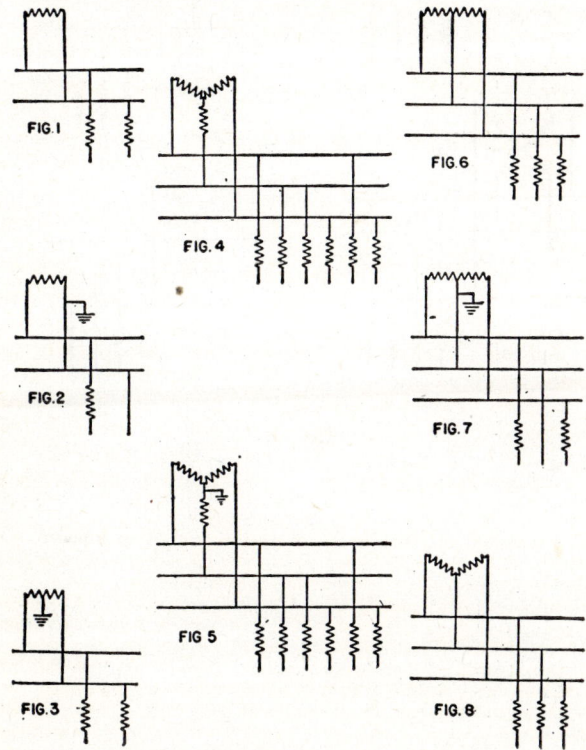

546 PRACTICAL ELECTRICAL WIRING

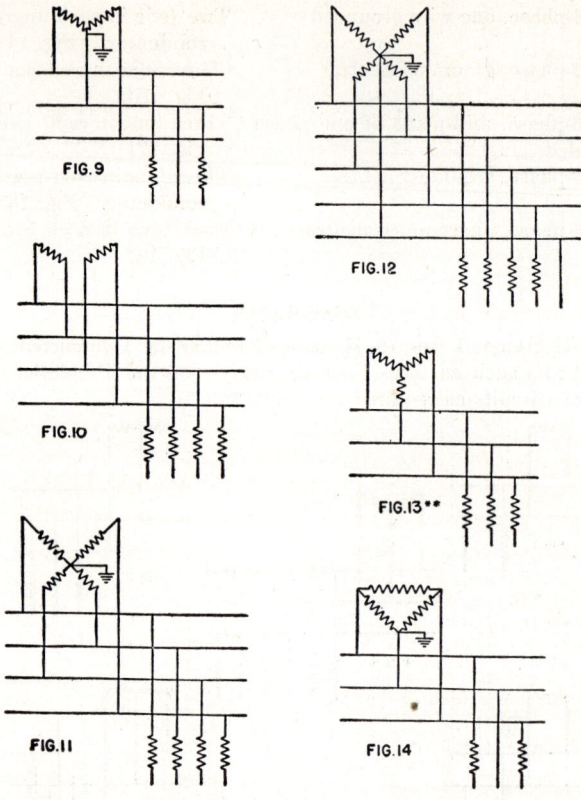

FIG. 9

FIG. 10

FIG. 11

FIG. 12

FIG. 13 **

FIG. 14

APPENDIX

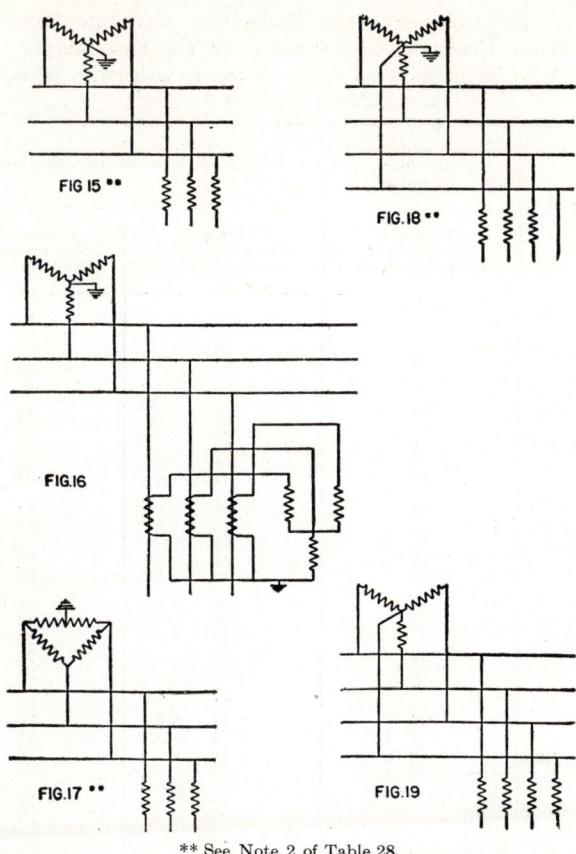

** See Note 2 of Table 28.

TABLE 29.—DEMAND LOADS FOR HOUSEHOLD ELECTRIC RANGES AND OTHER COOKING APPLIANCES OVER 1¾ KW. RATING
(Column A to be used in all cases except as otherwise permitted in Note 3 below)

Number of ranges	Maximum demand, kilowatts (see notes) Column A (Not over 12 kilowatt rating)	Demand factors, per cent (see Note 3)	
		Column B (Less than 3½ kilowatt rating)	Column C (3½ kw. to 8¾ kilowatt rating)
1	8	80	80
2	11	75	65
3	14	70	55
4	17	66	50
5	20	62	45
6	21	59	43
7	22	56	40
8	23	53	36
9	24	51	35
10	25	49	34
11	26	47	32
12	27	45	32
13	28	43	32
14	29	41	32
15	30	40	32
16	31	39	28
17	32	38	28
18	33	37	28
19	34	36	28
20	35	35	28
21	36	34	26
22	37	33	26
23	38	32	26
24	39	31	26
25	40	30	26
26–30	15 kw. plus 1 kw. for each range	30	24
31–40		30	22
41–50	25 kw. plus ¾ kw. for each range	30	20
51–60		30	18
61 and over		30	16

NOTE 1. Over 12 kw. to 21 kw. ranges. For ranges individually rated more than 12 kw. but not more than 21 kw., five per cent shall be added to the above maximum demand (column A) for each additional kw. of rating or major fraction thereof by which the individual range rating exceeds 12 kw.

NOTE 2. Over 21 kw. ranges. Ranges individually rated more than 21 kw. are not considered as household electric ranges and the demand should be determined on the basis of rating and use. Generally, the demand for commercial ranges should be based on the maximum nameplate rating.

NOTE 3. Over 1¾ kw. to 8¾ kw. In lieu of the method provided in column A, the load for ranges individually rated more than 1¾ kw. but not more than 8¾ kw. may be considered as the sum of the nameplate ratings of all the ranges, multiplied by the demand factors specified in columns B or C for the given number of ranges.

NOTE 4. Branch circuit load. Branch circuit load for one range may be computed in accordance with the above table.

TABLE 30.—CAPACITOR RATINGS FOR USE WITH OPEN-TYPE THREE-PHASE SIXTY CYCLE INDUCTION MOTORS
(See Code Sec. 4606)

Motor rating, horsepower	3,600 r.p.m.*		1,800 r.p.m.*		1,200 r.p.m.*		900 r.p.m.*		720 r.p.m.*		600 r.p.m.*	
	Max. capacitor rating, kilovolt-amperes	Reduction in line current, per cent	Max. capacitor rating, kilovolt-amperes	Reduction in line current, per cent	Max. capacitor rating, kilovolt-amperes	Reduction in line current, per cent	Max. capacitor rating, kilovolt-amperes	Reduction in line current, per cent	Max. capacitor rating, kilovolt-amperes	Reduction in line current, per cent	Max. capacitor rating, kilovolt-amperes	Reduction in line current, per cent
10	2.5	9	4	11	4	12	5	17	5	23	7.5	28
15	2.5	9	5	11	5	11	7.5	16	7.5	21	10	26
20	5	9	5	10	5	11	7.5	15	10	20	12.5	24
25	5	9	7.5	10	7.5	10	10	14	10	19	15	22
30	7.5	9	10	9	10	10	10	13	12.5	18	15	21
40	10	9	10	9	10	10	12.5	12	15	16	17.5	19
50	12.5	9	12.5	9	12.5	9	15	12	20	15	22.5	17
60	15	9	15	9	15	9	17.5	11	22.5	14	25	16
75	17.5	9	17.5	8	17.5	8	20	11	27.5	13	30	15
100	22.5	9	22.5	8	22.5	8	25	10	35	12	37.5	14
125	25	9	27.5	8	27.5	8	30	9	40	11	47.5	13
150	32.5	9	35	8	35	8	37.5	9	47.5	11	55	13
200	42.5	9	42.5	8	42.5	8	45	9	60	10	67.5	12

* Synchronous speed.
If capacitors of a lower rating than the values given in the table are used, the percentage reduction in line current given in the table shall be reduced a corresponding amount.

TABLE 31.—FLEXIBLE CORD
(See Code Sec. 4002)

Trade name	Type letter	Size A.W.G.	No. of conductors	Insulation	Braid on each conductor	Outer covering		Use	
Asbestos-covered tinsel cord	AT See Note 3	27	2 or 3	Rubber and asbestos	Cotton	None	Attached to a device	Dry places	Not hard usage
Cotton-covered tinsel cord	CT See Note 3	27	2 or 3	Rubber	None	Cotton or rayon	Attached to a device	Dry places	Not hard usage
Rubber-jacketed tinsel cord	ATJ See Note 3	27	2 or 3	Rubber and asbestos	None	Rubber	Attached to a device	Damp places	Not hard usage
	CTJ See Note 3			Rubber	Cotton				
Asbestos-covered heat-resistant cord	AFC	18, 16	2 or 3	Impregnated asbestos	Cotton or rayon	None	Pendant	Dry places	Not hard usage
	AFPO	14	2		None	Cotton, rayon, or saturated asbestos			
	AFPD		2 or 3						
Cotton-covered heat-resistant cord	CFC	18, 16	2 or 3	Impregnated cotton	Cotton or rayon	None	Pendant	Dry places	Not hard usage
	CFPO	14	2		None	Cotton or rayon			
	CFPD		2 or 3						
Parallel cord	PO-64	18	2	Rubber	Cotton	Cotton or rayon	See Note 2	Dry places	Not hard usage
	PO-32	18, 16					Pendant or port.		
	PO	14 and over							
All rubber parallel cord	POSJ-64	18	2	Rubber	None	Rubber	Pendant or portable	Damp places	Not hard usage
	POSJ-32	18, 16							

APPENDIX

	Trade name	AWG size	No. of conductors	Insulation	Braid	Outer covering	Use	Location	Usage
All-plastic parallel cord	POT-64	18	2	Thermoplastic	None	Thermoplastic	Pendant or portable	Damp places	Not hard usage
	POT-32	18, 16							
Lamp cord	C	18 and over	2 or more	Rubber	Cotton	None	Pendant or port.	Dry places	Not hard usage
Armored cord	CA	18, 16, 14	2	Rubber	Cotton	Fibrous and metal armor	Pendant or port.	Dry places	Hard usage
Twisted portable cord	PD	18 and over	2 or more	Rubber	Cotton	Cotton or rayon	Pendant or port.	Dry places	Not hard usage
Reinforced cord	P-64	18	2 or more	Rubber	Cotton	Cotton over rubber filler	Pendant or portable	Dry places	Not hard usage
	P-32	18, 16							Hard usage
	P	14 and over							
Moisture-proof reinforced cord	PWP-64	18	2 or more	Rubber	Cotton	Cotton, moisture-resistant finish over rubber filler	Pendant or portable	Damp places	Not hard usage
	PWP-32	18, 16							Hard usage
	PWP	14 and over							
Braided heavy-duty cord	K See Note 4	18 and over	2 or more	Rubber	Cotton	Two cotton, moisture-resistant finish See Note 5	Pendant or portable	Damp places	Hard usage
Vacuum cleaner cord	SV	18	2	Rubber	None	Rubber	Pendant or portable	Damp places	Hard usage
	SVT			Thermoplastic		Thermoplastic			
Junior hard-service cord	SJ	18, 16	2, 3, or 4	Rubber	None	Rubber	Pendant or portable	Damp places	Hard usage
	SJO					Oil-resist. compound			
	SJT			Thermoplastic		Thermoplastic			
Hard service cord	S See Note 6	18 to 10 incl.	2 or more	Rubber	None	Rubber	Pendant or portable	Damp places	Extra hard usage
	SO					Oil resist. compound			
	ST			Thermoplastic		Thermoplastic			

TABLE 31.—FLEXIBLE CORD.—(Continued)

Trade name	Type letter	Size A.W.G.	No. of conductors	Insulation	Braid on each conductor	Outer covering	Use	
Rubber-jacketed heat-resistant cord	AFSJ	18, 16	2 or 3	Impregnated asbestos	None	Rubber	Portable	Damp places	Portable heaters
	AFS	18, 16, 14							
Heater cord	HC	18, 17, 16 15, 14	2 or more	Rubber and asbestos	Cotton	None	Portable	Dry places	Portable heaters
	HPD				None	Cotton or rayon			
Rubber-jacketed heater cord	HSJ	18, 17, 16 15, 14	2 or more	Rubber and asbestos	None	Cotton and rubber	Portable	Damp places	Portable heaters
Heat and moisture-resistant cord	AVPO	18 to 10 incl.	2	Asbestos and var. comb.	None	Asbestos, flame-ret. moisture resist.	Pendant or portable	Damp places	Not hard usage
	AVPD		2 or 3						
Elevator cable	E See Note 7	18 and over	2 or more	Rubber	Cotton	Three cotton outer one flame-retardant and moisture resist. See Note 5	Elevator lighting and control	Non-hazardous locations	
	EO See Note 7					One cotton and a Neoprene jacket See Note 5		Hazardous locations	

NOTE 1. Except for types AFPO, CFPO, PO-64, PO-32, PO, POSJ-64, POSJ-32, and POT-64, POT-32, and AVPO individual conductors are twisted together.
NOTE 2. Type PO-64 is for use only with portable lamps, portable radio receiving appliances, portable clocks, and similar appliances which are not liable to be moved frequently and where appearance is a consideration.
NOTE 3. Types AT, CT, ATJ and CTJ are suitable for use in lengths not exceeding 8 ft. when attached directly, or by means of a special type of plug, to a portable appliance rated at 50 watts or less and of such a nature that extreme flexibility of the cord is essential. Types AT and ATJ are for use only with heating appliances.
NOTE 4. Type K is suitable for use on theater stages.
NOTE 5. Rubber-filled or varnished cambric tapes may be substituted for the inner braids.
NOTE 6. Types S, SO and ST are suitable for use on theater stages, in garages and elsewhere, where flexible cords are permitted by this code.
NOTE 7. Types E and EO may have a composite assembly of steel and copper strands in the make-up of the individual conductors or may have one or more supporting fillers of cotton or hemp rope, or of cotton-covered or rubber-covered steel wire laid up with the conductors under the outer covering of the cable. In cables containing six or more conductors the steel supporting strands shall run straight through and not be cabled with the conductors.

APPENDIX 553

Excerpts from Code. Because these particular sections are so important, they are quoted verbatim from the Code:

2115. Branch Circuits Required. Branch circuits shall be installed as follows:

a. Lighting and Appliance Circuits. For lighting, and for appliances not specifically provided for in paragraph b, branch circuits shall be provided for a computed load not less than that determined by section 2116.

The number of circuits shall be not less than that determined from the total computed load and the capacity of circuits to be used, but in every case the number shall be sufficient for the actual load to be served.

Where the load is computed on a "watts per square foot" basis, the total load, in so far as practical, shall be evenly proportioned among the branch circuits according to their capacity.

If lighting units to be installed operate at other than 100 per cent power factor, see paragraph b of section 2125 for maximum ampere load permitted on branch circuits.

For general illumination in dwelling occupancies, it is recommended that one 15-ampere branch circuit be installed for each 500 square feet (approximately 3 watts per square foot) of floor area.

See Example No. 1, Chapter 10.

b. Receptacle Circuits (Dwelling Occupancies). For the small appliance load in kitchen, laundry, pantry, dining room and breakfast room of dwelling occupancies, one or more branch circuits shall be provided for all receptacle outlets (other than outlets for clocks) in these rooms and such circuits shall have no other outlets. The conductors of such circuits shall be not smaller than No. 12.

See section 2123-c-3.

c. Other Circuits. For specific loads not otherwise provided for in paragraphs a or b, branch circuits shall be as required by other sections of the code.

2116. Calculation of Load. The branch circuit load for lighting and appliances shall be computed in accordance with the provisions of this section. Where in normal operation the maximum load of a branch circuit will continue for long periods of time, such as store lighting and similar loads, the minimum unit loads specified in this section shall be increased by 25 per cent in order that the wiring system may have sufficient branch circuit and feeder capacity to insure safe operation.

a. General Lighting. For general illumination:

1. In Listed Occupancies. In the occupancies listed in the table in section 2203, a load of not less than the unit load of Column A shall be included for each square foot of floor area.

In determining the load on the "watts per square foot" basis, the floor area shall be computed from the outside dimensions of the building, apartment or area involved, and the number of floors; not including open porches, garages in connection with dwelling occupancies, nor unfinished spaces in basements or attics of dwellings.

All receptacle outlets of 15-ampere or less rating in single-family and multi-family dwellings and in guest rooms of hotels (except those connected to the receptacle circuits specified in paragraph b of section 2115) may be considered as outlets for general illumination, and no additional load need be included for such outlets. The provisions of paragraph b of this section shall apply to all other receptacle outlets.

2. In Other Occupancies. In other occupancies, a load of not less than the unit load specified in paragraph b of this section shall be included for each outlet.

b. Other Loads. For lighting other than general illumination and for appliances other than motors, a load of not less than the unit load specified below shall be included for each outlet.

Outlets supplying specific appliances and
   other loads............................. Amp. rating of appliance
Outlets supplying heavy-duty lampholders... 5 amperes
Other outlets............................ 1½ amperes

2127. Table of Requirements. The requirements for circuits having two or more outlets (other than the receptacle circuits of paragraph b of section 2115) as specifically provided for above are summarized in the following table:

APPENDIX

Branch Circuit Requirements
(Type R, RH, RW, RU, T, and TW Conductors in Raceway or Cable)

Circuit rating	15 amp.	20 amp.	30 amp.	50 amp.
Conductors: (min. size)				
Circuit wires	14	12	10	6
Taps	14	14	14	12
Fixture wires and cords*				
Overcurrent protection	15 amp.	20 amp.	30 amp.	50 amp.
Outlet devices:				
Lampholders permitted	Any type	Heavy duty†	Heavy duty	Heavy duty
Receptacle rating	Max. 15 amp.	20 amp.‡	20 or 30 amp.	50 amp.
Maximum load	15 amp.	20 amp.	30 amp.	50 amp.
Permissible load	Sec. 2126 a	Sec. 2126 a	Sec. 2126 b	Sec. 2126 c

* See section 2121-c-3.
† See section 2123-c-2.
‡ See section 2123-c-3.

2203. Calculation of Load. The computed load of a feeder shall be not less than the sum of all branch circuit loads supplied by the feeder, as determined by section 2116, subject to the following provisions:

    a. General Lighting. The demand factors specified in this paragraph may be applied to the computed branch circuit load for general illumination.

    See paragraph c.

Unit Loads and Feeder Demand Factors

The unit values and the demand factors herein are based on minimum load conditions and 100 per cent power factor, and may not provide sufficient capacity for the installation contemplated.

In view of the trend toward higher intensity lighting systems and increased loads due to more general use of fixed and portable appliances, each installation should be considered as to the load likely to be imposed and the capacity increased to insure safe operation.

Where electric discharge lighting systems are to be installed, high power-factor type should be used or the conductor capacity may need to be increased.

Type of occupancy	Col. A Unit load per sq. ft., watts	Col. B	
		Load to which demand factor applies, watts	Demand factor, per cent
Armories and auditoriums	1	Total wattage	100
Banks	2	Total wattage	100
Barber shops and beauty parlors	3	Total wattage	100
Churches	1	Total wattage	100
Clubs	2*	Total wattage	100
Courtrooms	2	Total wattage	100
Dwellings—single-family	2*	2,500 or less Over 2,500	100 30
Dwellings—multi-family (other than hotels)	2*	3,000 or less Next 117,000 Over 120,000	100 35 25
Garages—commercial (storage)	½	Total wattage	100
Hospitals	2	50,000 or less Over 50,000	40† 20
Hotels, including apartment houses without provisions for cooking by tenants	2*	20,000 or less Next 80,000 Over 100,000	50† 40 30
Industrial commercial (loft) buildings	2	Total wattage	100
Lodge rooms	1½	Total wattage	100
Office buildings	2	20,000 or less Over 20,000	100 70
Restaurants	2	Total wattage	100
Schools	3	15,000 or less Over 15,000	100 50
Stores	3	Total wattage	100
Warehouses, storage	¼	12,500 or less Over 12,500	100 50
In any of above occupancies except single-family dwellings and individual apartments of multi-family dwellings: Assembly halls and auditoriums Halls, corridors, closets Storage spaces	1 ½ ¼	Total wattage as specified for the specific occupancy	

* See paragraph c of this section.

† For subfeeders to areas in hospitals and hotels where entire lighting is likely to be used at one time; as in operating rooms, ballrooms, dining rooms, etc., a demand factor of 100 per cent shall be used.

APPENDIX

b. Show-window Lighting. For show-window lighting, a load of not less than 200 watts shall be included for each linear foot of show-window measured horizontally along its base.

c. Small Appliances. The small appliance load specified in sub-paragraph c-1 and the computed branch circuit load for receptacle outlets in other than dwelling occupancies, for which the allowance is not more than $1\frac{1}{2}$ amperes per outlet, may be included with the general lighting load and subject to the demand factors in paragraph a of this section.

1. Dwelling Occupancies. In single-family dwellings, in individual apartments of multi-family dwellings having provisions for cooking by tenants, and in each hotel suite having a serving pantry; a feeder load of not less than 1,500 watts shall be included for small appliances (portable appliances supplied from receptacles of 15-ampere or less rating) in dining room, kitchen and laundry. If the load is subdivided through two or more feeders, the computed load for each shall include not less than 1,500 watts for small appliances.

d. Electric Ranges. The feeder load for household electric ranges and other cooking appliances, individually rated more than $1\frac{3}{4}$ kw., may be calculated in accordance with Table 29, Chapter 10.

In order to provide for possible future installation of ranges of higher ratings, it is recommended that where ranges of less than $8\frac{3}{4}$ kw. ratings are to be installed, the feeder capacity be not less than the maximum demand value specified in Column A of Table 29, Chapter 10.

Where a number of ranges are supplied by a 3-phase, 4-wire feeder, the current shall be computed on the basis of the demand of twice the maximum number of ranges connected between any two phase wires.

See Example No. 5, Chapter 10.

e. Fixed Appliances (Other than Ranges). Where four or more fixed appliances, in addition to an electric range or ranges, are connected to the same feeder in a single or multi-family dwelling, a demand factor of 75 per cent may be applied to the fixed appliance load, not including the electric ranges.

f. Motors. For motors, a load computed according to the provisions of sections 4314 and 4316 shall be included.

EXAMPLES

These examples were to appear in the 1947 Code but were dropped because of lack of space.

Selection of Conductors. In the following examples the size of conductor has been selected on the basis of the allowable current-carrying capacities of Type R rubber-covered conductors as given in Table 1. If other types of insulated conductors are used, or if the conductors are run open, or with more than three conductors in a raceway, the size of conductor may vary from those shown. Tables 1 and 2 should be consulted in selecting the size of conductor for a particular installation.

Voltage. For uniform application of the provisions of Articles 210 and 220, a nominal voltage of 115 and 230 volts shall be used in computing the ampere load on the conductor.

Fractions of an Ampere. Where the calculations result in a fraction of an ampere, such fractions may be dropped.

Ranges. For the computation of the range loads in these examples Column A of Table 29 has been used. For optional method, see Columns B and C of Table 29.

EXAMPLE NO. 1. SINGLE-FAMILY DWELLING

Dwelling having a floor area of 2,500 square feet, exclusive of unoccupied cellar, unfinished attic and open porches.

Computed Load (Section 2116):

General lighting load:

2,500 square feet at 2 watts per square foot... 5,000 watts

Minimum Number of Branch Circuits Required (Section 2115):

General lighting load: 5,000 ÷ 115 = 43 amperes, or three 15-ampere, 2-wire circuits.

Small appliance load: one 2-wire circuit of No. 12 wire. (See section 2115-b)

Minimum Size Feeders (or Service Conductors) Required (Section 2201):

Computed Load (Section 2203):

General lighting load......................	5,000 watts
Small appliance load......................	1,500 watts
Total computed load....................	6,500 watts
2,500 watts at 100%.....................	2,500 watts
4,000 watts at 30%.....................	1,200 watts
Net computed load.....................	3,700 watts

For 115-volt, 2-wire system:

3,700 ÷ 115 = 32 amperes, or No. 8.

For 115–230-volt, 3-wire system:

3,700 ÷ 230 = 16 amperes, or No. 12.

For minimum size conductor, see sections 2201 and 2304.

Minimum Number Receptacles Required (Section 2124):

Living Room: 16 feet by 22 feet; 76 feet total (gross) distance around the room. 76 feet ÷ 20 = 3.8 or 4 receptacles.

APPENDIX 559

Each Bed Room: 14 feet by 15 feet; 58 feet total (gross) distance around the room. 58 feet ÷ 20 = 2.9 or 3 receptacles.
*Dining Room: 16 feet by 16 feet; 64 feet total (gross) distance around the room. 64 feet ÷ 20 = 3.2 or 3 receptacles.
*Breakfast Room: 10 feet by 12 feet; 44 feet total (gross) distance around the room. 44 feet ÷ 20 = 2.2 or 2 receptacles.
*Kitchen: 14 feet by 14 feet; 56 feet total (gross) distance around the room. 56 feet ÷ 20 = 2.8 or 3 receptacles.

Note 1. Receptacles to be placed equal distances apart insofar as practicable.
*Note 2. Receptacles in these locations, also laundry, to be supplied by circuit or circuits of not less than No. 12 wire (section 2115).

EXAMPLE NO 2. STORE BUILDING

A store 50 feet by 60 feet, or 3,000 square feet, has 30 feet of show window.

Computed Load (Section 2116):

*General lighting load:
   3,000 square feet at 3 watts per square foot
    × 1.25.............................. 11,250 watts
**Show-window lighting load:
   30 feet at 200 watts per foot.............. 6,000 watts

Minimum Number of Branch Circuits Required (Section 2115):

General lighting load: 11,250 ÷ 230 = 49 amperes for 3-wire, 115–230 volts; or 98 amperes for 2-wire, 115 volts:

   Three 30-ampere, 2-wire, and one 15-ampere, 2-wire circuits; or
   Five 20-ampere, 2-wire, circuits; or
   Three 20-ampere, 2-wire, and three 15-ampere, 2-wire circuits; or
   Seven 15-ampere, 2-wire, circuits; or
   Three 15-ampere, 3-wire, and one 15-ampere, 2-wire circuits.

Special lighting load (show window): 6,000 ÷ 230 = 26 amperes for 3-wire, 115–230 volts; or 52 amperes for 2-wire, 115 volts:

   Four 15-ampere, 2-wire circuits; or
   Three 20-ampere, 2-wire circuits; or
   Two 15-ampere, 3-wire circuits.

* The above examples assume that the entire general lighting load is likely to be used for long periods of time and the load is therefore increased by 25 per cent in accordance with section 2116. The 25 per cent increase is not applicable to any portion of the load not used for long periods.
** If show-window load computed as per paragraph 2116-b, the unit load per outlet to be increased 25 per cent.

Minimum Size Feeders (or Service Conductors) Required (Section 2201):

For 115–230-volt, 3-wire system:
  Ampere load: 49 + 26 = 75 amperes. (Section 2203)
  Size of each feeder, No. 3.
For 115-volt system:
  Ampere load: 98 + 52 = 150 amperes. (Section 2203)
  Size of each feeder, No. 3/0.

EXAMPLE NO. 3. MULTI-FAMILY DWELLING

Multi-family dwelling having a total floor area of 32,000 square feet with 40 apartments.

Meters in two banks of 20 each and individual sub-feeders to each apartment.

One-half of the apartments are equipped with electric ranges of not exceeding 12 kw. each.

Area of each apartment is 800 square feet.

Computed Load for Each Apartment (Section 2116):

  General lighting load: 800 square feet at 2
    watts per square foot.................... 1,600 watts
  Special appliance load, electric range........ 8,000 watts

Minimum Number of Branch Circuits Required for Each Apartment (Section 2115):

  General lighting load: 1,600 ÷ 115 = 13 amperes, or one 15-ampere 2-wire circuit.
  Small appliance load: one 2-wire circuit of No. 12 wire (see section 2115-b).
  Range circuit 8,000 ÷ 230 = 34 or a circuit of two No. 8's and one No. 10, as permitted by 2121-c-1.

Minimum Size Sub-Feeder Required for Each Apartment (Section 2201):

  Computed Load (Section 2203):

    General lighting load...................... 1,600 watts
    Small appliance load....................... 1,500 watts
      Total computed load (without range)..... 3,100 watts
      3,000 watts at 100%..................... 3,000 watts
      100 watts at 35%.....................   35 watts
      Net computed load (without range)...... 3,035 watts
    Range load 8,000 watts................... 8,000 watts
      Net computed load (with range).......... 11,035 watts

APPENDIX

For 115–230-volt, 3-wire system (without range):

3,035 ÷ 230 = 13 amperes.
Size of each sub-feeder, No. 12 (see section 2115-b).

For 115–230-volt, 3-wire system (with range):

11,035 ÷ 230 = 48 amperes.
Size of each ungrounded sub-feeder No. 6.
Size of neutral sub-feeder 70 per cent of 8,000 watts—5,600 watts.

$$\begin{aligned} &3,035 \text{ watts} \\ &\underline{5,600 \text{ watts}} \end{aligned}$$

Total computed load...................... 8,635 watts
8,635 ÷ 230 = 37 amperes or a No. 8. See 2203-g.

Minimum Size Feeders Required from Service Equipment to Meter Bank (for 20 Apartments—10 with Ranges):

Total Computed Load:

Lighting and small appliance load, 20 × 3,100 watts.........................	62,000 watts
3,000 watts at 100%.....................	3,000 watts
59,000 watts at 35%.....................	20,650 watts
	23,650 watts
10 Ranges, 25,000 watts.................	25,000 watts
Net computed load....................	48,650 watts

For 115–230-volt, 3-wire system:

48,650 ÷ 230 = 211 amperes.
Net computed load 211 amperes.
Size of each ungrounded feeder to each meter bank, 250,000 c.m.
Neutral feeder 70 per cent of 25,000 = 17,500.

$$\begin{aligned} &23,650 \text{ watts} \\ &\underline{17,500 \text{ watts}} \\ &41,150 \text{ watts} \end{aligned}$$

41,150 ÷ 230 = 179 amperes, or a No. 4/0 feeder. See 2203-g.

Minimum Size Main Feeder (or Service Conductors) Required (for 40 Apartments—20 with Ranges):

Total Computed Load:

Lighting and small appliance load, 40 × 3,100 watts..........................	124,000 watts
3,000 watts at 100%...................	3,000 watts
117,000 watts at 35%...................	40,950 watts
4,000 watts at 25%...................	1,000 watts
	44,950 watts
20 ranges, 35,000 watts..................	35,000 watts
Net computed load...................	79,950 watts

For 115–230-volt, 3-wire system:

79,950 ÷ 230 = 347 amperes.
Size of each ungrounded feeder to each meter bank, 600,000 c.m.
Neutral feeder 70 per cent of 35,000 watts = 24,500.

	44,950 watts
	24,500 watts
Net computed load......................	69,450 watts

69,450 ÷ 230 = 302 amperes.

200 amperes at 100% = 200 amperes
102 amperes at 70% = 71 amperes
                       271 amperes

or 400,000 c.m. See notes 2 and 5 to Tables 1 and 2.

EXAMPLE NO. 4. CALCULATION OF NEUTRAL FEEDER
(See section 2203-g)

The following example illustrates the method of calculating size of neutral feeder for the computed load of a 5-wire, 2-phase system, where it is desired to modify the load in accordance with provisions of section 2203.

An installation consisting of a computed load of 250 amperes connected between neutral feeder and each ungrounded feeder.

Neutral feeder (maximum unbalance of load
250 amp. × 140% = 350 amperes):
200 amperes (first) at 100% = 200 amperes
150 amperes (excess) at 70% = 105 amperes
Computed load............ 305 amperes

Size of neutral feeder: 500,000 c.m.

EXAMPLE NO. 5. RANGES ON A 3-PHASE SYSTEM
(Section 2203-d)

Thirty ranges rated at 12 kw. each are supplied by a 3-phase, 4-wire, 120/208-volt feeder, 10 ranges on each phase.

APPENDIX

As there are 20 ranges connected to each ungrounded conductor, the load should be calculated on the basis of 20 ranges (or in case of unbalance, twice the maximum number between any two phase wires) since diversity applies only to the number of ranges connected to adjacent phases and not the total.

The current in any one conductor will be one-half the total watt load of two adjacent phases divided by the line-to-neutral voltage. In this case, 20 ranges, from Table 29, Chapter 10, will have total watt load of 35,000 watts for two phases; therefore, the current in the feeder conductor would be:

$$17,500 \div 120 = 146 \text{ amperes.}$$

On a three-phase basis the load would be:

$$3 \times 17,500 = 52,500 \text{ watts}$$

and the current in each feeder conductor—

$$\frac{52,500}{208 \times 1.73} = 146 \text{ amperes.}$$

EXAMPLE NO. 6. MOTORS, CONDUCTORS, AND OVERCURRENT PROTECTION

(See sections 4312, 4314, 4322 and 4342)

Determine the size of conductors, the motor-running overcurrent protection, the branch circuit protection, and the feeder protection, for one 25-h.p. squirrel-cage induction motor (full-voltage starting), and two 30-h.p. wound-rotor induction motors, on a 440-volt, 3-phase, 60-cycle supply.

Conductor Sizes

The full-load current of the 25-h.p. motor is 32 amperes (Table 24). A full-load current of 32 amperes requires a No. 8, Type R, rubber-covered conductor (Column 2, Table 20). The full-load current of the 30-h.p. motor is 39 amperes (Table 24). A full-load current of 39 amperes requires a No. 6, Type R, rubber-covered conductor (Column 2, Table 20).

The feeder conductor capacity will be 125 per cent of 39, plus 39, plus 32, or 120 amperes (section 4314). In accordance with Table 1, this would require a No. 0, Type R, rubber-covered feeder.

Note. For Type R conductors run open in air, or for conductors with insulations other than Type R, see Tables 1 and 2.

Overcurrent Protection

Running. The 25-h.p. motor, with full-load current of 32 amperes, must have running overcurrent protection of not over 40 amperes

(Columns 5 and 6, Table 20). The 30-h.p. motor with full-load current of 39 amperes must have running overcurrent protection of not over 50 amperes (Columns 5 and 6, Table 20).

Branch Circuit. The branch circuit of the 25-h.p. motor must have branch-circuit overcurrent protection of not over 100 amperes (Column 7, Table 20). The branch circuit of the 30-h.p. motor must have branch-circuit overcurrent protection of not over 60 amperes (Column 10, Table 20).

Feeder Circuit. The rating of the branch-circuit fuse for a 25-h.p. squirrel cage motor is 300 per cent of 32 amperes, or 96 amperes (Table 27); and for a 30-h.p. wound-rotor motor is 150 per cent of 39 amperes or 59 amperes (Table 27). The rating of a feeder fuse is, therefore, $96 + 39 + 39 = 174$ amperes, and a 175-ampere fuse is the maximum size which may be used. (See section 4362.)

The setting of a motor-branch-circuit circuit-breaker for a 25-h.p. squirrel cage motor is 250 per cent of 32 amperes or 80 amperes (Table 27); for a 30-h.p. wound-rotor motor is 150 per cent of 39 amperes or 59 amperes (Table 27). The maximum setting of a feeder circuit-breaker is $80 + 39 + 39 = 158$ amperes. (See section 4362.)

BIBLIOGRAPHY

ABBOTT, ARTHUR L.: "National Electrical Code Handbook," McGraw-Hill Book Company, Inc., New York.

CROFT, TERRELL: "American Electricians' Handbook," "Electrical Machinery," "Practical Electric Illumination" and "Signal Wiring," McGraw-Hill Book Company, Inc., New York.

HALL, GEORGE H.: "Motor and Control Applications," McGraw-Hill Book Company, Inc., New York.

HARRISON, WARD, and K. A. STALEY: "Fundamentals of Illumination," General Electric Co., Nela Park, Cleveland.

HARRISON, WARD, and C. E. WEIT:: "Illumination Design Data," General Electric Co., Nela Park, Cleveland.

LUCKIESH, MATTHEW, and FRANK K. MOSS: "The Science of Seeing," D. Van Nostrand Company, Inc., New York.

MOYER, JAMES A., and JOHN F. WOSTREL: "Industrial Electricity and Wiring," McGraw-Hill Book Company, Inc., New York.

VEINOTT, CYRIL G.: "Fractional Horsepower Electric Motors," McGraw-Hill Book Company, Inc., New York.

WRIGHT, FORREST B.: "Electricity in the Home and on the Farm," John Wiley & Sons, Inc., New York.

"Code of Lighting Factories, Mills and Other Work Places," Illuminating Engineering Society, New York.

"Handbook of Interior Wiring Design," Industry Committee on Interior Wiring Design, New York.

"Illuminating Engineering Nomenclature and Photometric Standards," Illuminating Engineering Society, New York.

"Industrial Control Standards," National Electrical Manufacturers Association, New York.

"Motor and Generator Standards," National Electrical Manufacturers Association, New York.

"National Electrical Code," National Board of Fire Underwriters, New York.

INDEX

A

ABC cable, 90, 160
Adequate wiring, 203
Alternating current, 31
Ampere, 15
Ampere-hour, 16, 382
Anchors, lead, 147
Annunciator wire, 100, 328
Apartments, wiring of, 385
Appliances, calculating service entrance for, 194
 "fixed," definition of, 180
 watts consumed by, 21
 wiring of, 180
Approval by the Underwriters, 4
Armored cable, 90, 160
Asbestos-covered wire, 408
Athletic-field lighting, 460
Attics, wiring of, 173
Autotransformers, 52

B

B. & S. wire gauge, 85
Bare wire (*see* Uninsulated wire)
Barn wiring, 371
Barriers, box, 326
Baseboard outlets (*see* Receptacle outlets)
Basements, wiring of, 211
Bases on bulbs, 236
Bathrooms, wiring of, 209
Batteries, storage, 381
Beam candle power, 216
Bell wire, 100, 328
Bells (*see* Low-voltage wiring)

Bills, electric, 21
Bolts, toggle, 147
Boxes, concrete, 440
 floor, 441
 junction, 145, 439
 nonmetallic, 367–370
 outlet and switch, attaching conduit and cable to, 138
 covers for, 141, 144
 depth of, 136, 347
 finish of, 137
 ganging of, 136
 installation of, 347
 material of, 137, 368
 number of wires permitted in, 138
 purpose of, 134
 supporting of, 140, 142, 347
 types of, 134, 146
 porcelain, 367
 pull, 145, 439
 round, where used, 140
Bracelet labels, 7
Branch circuits, advantages of numerous, 176
 appliance, 178
 balancing of, 181
 definition of, 176
 determining number of, 177
 motor, 418, 463, 465
 schemes for wiring, 182
 types of, 179, 415
Bulbs, bases used on, 236
 characteristics of, 236, 240, 453
 construction of, 54, 240, 453
 effects of relative voltage on, 235
 efficiency of, 239, 453

Bulbs, life of, 244, 453
  lumens produced by, per watt, 240, 244, 453
  total, 240, 453
  Lumiline, 238
  types of, 238
Bushings, conduit, 138
  fiber, for armored cable, 161
  grounding, 283
Buttons, push, 330
BX cable (*see* Cable, armored)

C

Cable, armored, construction of, 90
  use of, 160
  colors of wire in, 295
  definition of, 89
  lead-sheathed, construction of, 91
  use of, 278, 341
  nonmetallic sheathed, construction of, 90
  use of, 156
  parkway, construction of, 92
  use of, 156
  service entrance, 186, 202, 275
  thermostat, 100, 328
  type USE, 92, 278, 341
Candle power, 215
Capacitor motors, 248
Chimes, signalling, 332
Churches, wiring of, 490
Circuit, branch (*see* Branch circuits)
  definition of, 56
Circuit breakers, 79, 189
Circular mils (c.m.), 84
Clamps, cable, 140
  ground, 281
Clock outlets, 208
Closets, wiring of, 210
Code, National Electrical, 11

Coefficient of utilization, in lighting, 451
Cold-cathode lighting, 456
Color, in lighting, 233, 240, 246
  of wires, 99, 132, 295
Common neutrals, 430
Concrete boxes, 440
Conductors, 22
Conduit, flexible, 165
  rigid, 149
    bends in, 152
    cutting of, 150
    supports for, 154
  thin-wall, 154
Conduit fittings, 438
Condulets, 438
Connectors, cable, 139, 162
Controllers, motor, 481
Convenience outlets (*see* Receptacle outlets)
Cords, drop, 337
Cost of electricity, 21
Coulombs, 15
Covers, box, 141, 144
Curtistrip, 505
Cycles (frequency), 33
  in lamp cords, 99

D

Defective vision, extent of, 213
Deflection of wires, 442
Delta connections of transformers, 51
Demand charge, 42
Demand factor, in apartments, 391
  in maximum unbalance, 429
  in ranges, 195
  in service entrance, 194
Diagrams, wiring, 261
Diffused light, 224
Diffusers, light, 458
Direct current, 31
Direct lighting, 227, 457

INDEX

Disconnecting means, for motors, 473
   in outbuildings, 370
   in service entrance, 187
Door openers, 398
Door switches, 210, 333
Doorbell wiring (*see* Low-voltage wiring)
Double-locknut installations, 446
Double-pole switches, 446
Doughnut labels, 8
Drop cords, 337

E

Effects of electricity, 30
Electrical metallic tubing (EMT), 154
Electromagnets, 43
Emergency lighting, 509
EMT, 154
Engines vs. motors, 250
Entrance (*see* Service entrance)
Equipment grounds, 131
Explosion-proof fittings, 513
Explosion-proof motors, 518
Extension rings, 360

F

Factories, wiring of, 508
Farm-lighting plants, 377
Farms, wiring of, 362
Feeders, 182, 424
Feeding one building through another, 370
Festoon lighting, 341
Figuring electrical bill, 21
Fish tape, 153
Fittings, conduit, 438
"Fixed" appliances, definition of, 180
Fixture studs, 319
Fixture wire, 99

Fixtures (*see* Lighting fixtures)
Flexible conduit, 165
Flexible tubing, 168
Floor boards, lifting of, 359
Floor boxes, 441
Fluorescent lighting, 240, 455
Foot-candles, definition of, 218
   measurement of, 221
   required for, 221, 490
Formula, for lumens required for lighting, 452
   Ohm's law, 24
   power factor, 41
   pulley ratios, 256
   volt-amperes, 40
   voltage drop, 103–105
   watts, 16, 41
Four-way switches, 65
Frequency, 33
Fuses, 73, 251

G

Garages, wiring of, 338, 517
Gauge, wire, 86
Glare in lighting, 222
Greenfield (*see* Conduit, flexible)
Ground clamps, 281
Ground wire, 132, 279
Grounding bushings, 283
Grounds, artificial, 284
   continuous, 131, 279, 444
   equipment, 131, 279, 436
   method of installation of, 279, 399
   purpose of, 127
   system, 279, 435
Guard rails, knob and tube, 174
Gutters, 443

H

Hangers, for outlet box, 140, 348
Hazardous locations, 513

Heater cords (*see* Lamp cords)
Hickeys, 321
Horsepower, definition of, 17

I

Identification of approved merchandise, 10
Insulation, removing from wire, 112, 114
　rubber, 89
Insulators, definition of, 23
　types of, 165, 272
Inverse squares, law of, 213
Isolated plants, as source for emergency lighting, 511
　types and construction of, 377

J

Joints in wire (*see* Splices)
Junction boxes, 145, 439

K

Key letters on motors, 469
Kilo, 15
Kilocycles, 34
Kilovolts, 15
Kilovolt-amperes (kva.), 40
Kilowatt-hours (kw.-hr.), 19
Kilowatt-hour meter, 19
Kilowatts (kw.), 18
Knob and tube system, 165
Knockouts, 135
Knot, Underwriters', 337
Kva., 40
Kw., 18
Kw.-hr., 19

L

Labels, Underwriters', 6
Lamp cords, 95

Lampholders (*see* Sockets)
Lamps (*see* Bulbs)
Laundry outlet, 335, 399
Law, Ohm's, 20
Law of inverse squares, 217
Lead-sheathed cable, 91, 278, 341
Light meter, 221
Lighting, 213, 450
　direct, 227
　direct-indirect, 459–460
　festoon, 341
　indirect, 228
　semi-indirect, 228
Lighting fixtures, fixed, definition of, 417
　installation of, 318
　selection of, 226
Lighting plants (*see* Isolated plants)
Locknuts, conduit, 138, 445
Loom, 168
Low-voltage wiring, 100, 326, 396, 512
Lumens, definition of, 216
　formula for calculating, 452
Lumiline bulbs, 239

M

Magnets, 43
Maintenance factor in lighting, 451
Maximum unbalance, 429
Mean spherical candle power, 215
Megacycles, 34
Mercury-vapor lighting, 453
Meter poles, 365
Meters, kilowatt-hour, 18
　installation of, 270, 277
Meters, water, jumpers for, 282
Microamperes, 221
Mils, circular, 84
Motors, 248, 462
　characteristics of, 248
　key letters on, 469

INDEX

Motors, power consumed by, 196
  types of, 248, 462, 518
Multi-outlet assemblies, 336, 416

N

National Electrical Code, 11
Neutral, common, 430
Neutral feeders, 425
Neutral wire, definition of, 127, 132, 288
  fusing of, 288
  size of, 201
New work, 72, 286
Nonmetallic outlet boxes, 367
Nonmetallic sheathed cable, 90, 156

O

Offices, wiring of, 499
Ohms, 20
Ohm's law, 23
Old work, 72, 286, 344
Old-work hangers, 348, 351
Openings, cutting of, 345
Outbuildings, wiring of, 338, 370
Outdoor wiring, outlets for, 341
  switches for, 440
  wire size for, 111
  for yard lights, 375
Outlet boxes (*see* Boxes, outlet and switch)
Outlets, clock, 208
  convenience (*see* Receptacle outlets)
  definition of, 56
  installation of, 286
  outdoor, 341
  radio, 332
  range, 324
Overcurrent devices, definition of, 73, 471
  to protect motors, 253, 469, 471
  to protect wire, 80

Overcurrent devices, in service entrance, 192
Overcurrent units, 471
Overload capacity of motors, 50

P

Panelboards, 420
Parallel wiring, 59
Phase, 38
Photoelectric lighting control, 493
Pilot lights, 308
Plans, wiring, 261
Plants, isolated (*see* Isolated plants)
Plaster ears, 316
Plaster rings, 142
Plates, wall, 69, 291
Plug-in wall strip, 336, 416
Polarized systems, 133
Polyphase current, 39
Porcelain boxes, 367
Porcelain insulators, 165, 272
Poultry houses, wiring of, 374
Power factor, 40
Pry-outs, 135
Pull-boxes, 145, 439
Pulleys, motor, 256
Pulling wires into conduit, 153, 274
Push buttons, 330

R

Radio outlets, 332
Ranges, demand factor for, 195
  wiring of, 324
Receptacle outlets, clock-hanger type, 208
  Code requirements for, 204
  definition of, 62
  installation of, 291
  laundry, special type, 335
  outdoor type, 341
  range type, 324
  two-circuit type, 207, 311
  vapor-proof, 373

Reexamination service, Underwriters', 5
Reflection factors of surfaces, 232
Reflectors, 198, 372, 457
Resistance, 23
Rigid conduit, 149
Romex (*see* Cable, nonmetallic sheathed)
Room index in lighting, 450
Round boxes, 140
Rubber-covered wire, 88
Rubber insulation, 89
Running boards, 173

S

Schools, wiring of, 490
Series wiring, 58
Service drop, 185, 419
Service entrance, bare wire in, 185
    calculation for, 192, 194, 425
    definition of, 184
    for farms, 266
    installation of, 269, 419
    overcurrent protection in, 192
Service entrance cable, 186, 275
Service heads, 273
Service insulators, 272
Service switches, 187, 270, 357
Shadows in lighting, 233
Show-window lighting, 502, 507
Sign receptacles, 72
Signal systems (*see* Low-voltage wiring)
Signs, wiring of, 511
Sill plates, 277
Slow-burning wire, 408
Sockets, 55, 71, 415
Solder joints, where prohibited, 191, 271, 282
Solder lugs, 121
Solder pot, 317
Soldering, 118, 317
Solderless connectors, 113, 123

Source, 56
Spacing of wires, 167
Splices, in lamp cords, 117
    in other wires, 81, 112, 115
    in weatherproof wires, 121
Splicing compound, 120
Star connections of transformers, 51
Storage batteries, 381
Stores, wiring of, 502
Supports, vertical runs of wires, 444
Surface brightness in lighting, 225
Surface metal raceway, 447
Surface wiring, 362, 447
Switch boxes (*see* Boxes, outlet and switch)
Switch loops, color of wires in, 295
Switch plates, 69
Switchboards, 420
Switches, door, 333
    double-pole, 63, 446
    four-way, 65
    general-use, 463
    isolating, 463
    lock, 68
    motor-circuit, 463
    outdoor, 444
    push, 68
    rating of, 69
    service entrance, 187, 190, 270
    single-pole, 58
    surface, 68
    "T"-rating of, 446
    three-way, 64, 276
    time, 374, 506
    toggle, 57
Symbols, wiring, 262, 263

T

"T"-rating of switches, 446
Table, for carrying capacity of wires, 81, 95

INDEX 573

Table, conduit dimensions, 150
  cost of voltage drop, 109
  effect of voltage on bulbs, 235
  key letters on motors, 469
  lumens, total, produced by bulbs, 219
  lumens per watt in bulbs, 240
  number of wires entering boxes, 132
  overcurrent devices in motor protection, 479
  power consumed by motors, 196
  pulleys on motor and machine, 257
  reflection factors for various surfaces, 232
  types of wire, 403
  watts consumed by appliances, 21
  watts per square foot in lighting, 452
  wire size, for isolated plants, 379, 381
    for small motors, 255
    wattage-distance, 106, 107
Tape, fish, 153
  friction, 121
  rubber, 120
Taps in wire, 83, 116, 418, 471
Telephones, 331
Temperature, effect on wire, 84, 400
Temperature rise of motors, 249
Terminals, 112
Testing finished installations, 313
Theaters, wiring of, 508
Thermoplastic insulations, 408
Thermostat cable, 100
Thin-wall conduit, 154
Three-phase current, 38, 50
Three-way switches, 64, 303
Three-wire system, 28, 191
Time switches, 374, 506
Toggle bolts, 147

Transformers, 43, **327**
Trial installations, 8
Two-circuit receptacles, 207, 311
Two-phase current, 36, 49

U

Unbalance, maximum, 429
Underground wires, 91, 92, 278, 341
Underwriters' knot, **337**
Underwriters' labels, 6
Underwriters' Laboratories, Inc., 3
"Unfinished," definition of, 177n.
Uninsulated wires, 411
  in service entrance cable, 185, 202

V

Vapor-proof receptacles, 373
Varnished cambric cable, 80
Voltage, a.c., 34
  to ground, 130
Voltage drop, calculation of, 103, 468
  cost of, 108
  definition of, 25
  in motor work, 468
  practical limits of, 101
  tables of, 106, 107
  in 3-phase work, 105
Voltages, commonly used, 27
  dangerous, 25
Volt-amperes, 40
Volts, 14

W

Wall plates, 62, 317
Water heaters, 200, 325
Water-meter jumpers, 282
Watt-hours, 18
Watts, 16
  in a.c., 41
  consumed by appliances, 20

Weatherproof wire, 94
White wire, 132
Wire, bare, 411
  basic construction of, 84
  carrying capacity of, 81, 102, 400
  effect of temperature on, 84, 400
  size of, 85, 101
  spacing of, 167
  stranded, 87
  types of: annunciator, 100, 325
    bare, 185, 202, 411
    bell, 100, 325
    cable, armored, 90, 160
      lead-sheathed, 91, 278, 341
      nonmetallic sheathed, 90, 156
    parkway, 92
    service entrance, 186, 275
    thermostat, 100, 326
    U.S.E., 92, 278, 341
    fish, 153
    fixture, 99

Wire, types of: ground, 280
  lamp cord, 95
  neutral, 127
  rubber-covered, type R, 88
    type RH, 89, 402
    type RP, 89, 402
    type RU, 410
    type RW, 91
  slow-burning, 408
  synthetic (SN), 409
  table of, 403
  thermoplastic (T), 408
  varnished cambric, 406
  weatherproof, 94
  white, 132
Wires, number permitted in boxes, 138
Wound-rotor motors, 466

Y

Y connections in transformers, 51
Yard lights, 375